Jane B. Reece • Martha R. Taylor • Eric J. Simon
Jean L. Dickey • Kelly Hogan

Campbell Biology
Concepts & Connections

Custom Edition for Kirkwood Community College

Taken from:
Campbell Biology: Concepts and Connections, Eighth Edition
by Jane B. Reece, Martha R. Taylor, Eric J. Simon, Jean L. Dickey and Kelly Hogan

D1219382

Cover Art: Courtesy of Photodisc/Getty Images.

Taken from:

Campbell Biology: Concepts and Connections, Eighth Edition
by Jane B. Reece, Martha R. Taylor, Eric J. Simon, Jean L. Dickey and Kelly Hogan
Copyright © 2015, 2012, 2009 by Pearson Education, Inc.
Upper Saddle River, New Jersey 07458

This special edition published in cooperation with Pearson Learning Solutions.

All trademarks, service marks, registered trademarks, and registered service marks are the property of their respective owners and are used herein for identification purposes only.

Pearson Learning Solutions, 501 Boylston Street, Suite 900, Boston, MA 02116
A Pearson Education Company
www.pearsoned.com

Printed in the United States of America

7 8 9 10 11 V0UD 19 18 17 16 15

000200010271884324

SH

ISBN 10: 1-269-88850-1
ISBN 13: 978-1-269-88850-9

About the Authors

Jane B. Reece has worked in biology publishing since 1978, when she joined the editorial staff of Benjamin Cummings. Her education includes an A.B. in biology from Harvard University, an M.S. in microbiology from Rutgers University, and a Ph.D. in bacteriology from the University of California, Berkeley. At UC Berkeley, and later as a postdoctoral fellow in genetics at Stanford University, her research focused on genetic recombination in bacteria. Dr. Reece taught biology at Middlesex County College (New Jersey) and Queensborough Community College (New York). During her 12 years as an editor at Benjamin Cummings, she played a major role in a number of successful textbooks. She is coauthor of *Campbell Biology*, Tenth Edition, *Campbell Biology in Focus*, *Campbell Essential Biology*, and *Campbell Essential Biology with Physiology*, Fourth Edition.

Martha R. Taylor has been teaching biology for more than 35 years. She earned her B.A. in biology from Gettysburg College and her M.S. and Ph.D. in science education from Cornell University. At Cornell, she has served as assistant director of the Office of Instructional Support and has taught introductory biology for both majors and nonmajors. Most recently, she was a lecturer in the Learning Strategies Center, teaching supplemental biology courses. Her experience working with students in classrooms, in laboratories, and with tutorials has increased her commitment to helping students create their own knowledge of and appreciation for biology. She has been the author of the *Student Study Guide* for all ten editions of *Campbell Biology*.

Eric J. Simon is a professor in the Department of Biology and Health Science at New England College (Henniker, New Hampshire). He teaches introductory biology to science majors and nonscience majors, as well as upper-level courses in tropical marine biology and careers in science. Dr. Simon received a B.A. in biology and computer science and an M.A. in biology from Wesleyan University, and a Ph.D. in biochemistry from Harvard University. His research focuses on innovative ways to use technology to improve teaching and learning in the science classroom, particularly for nonscience majors. Dr. Simon is the lead author of the introductory nonmajors biology textbooks *Campbell Essential Biology*, Fifth Edition, and *Campbell Essential Biology with Physiology*, Fourth Edition, and the author of the introductory biology textbook *Biology: The Core*.

Jean L. Dickey is Professor Emerita of Biological Sciences at Clemson University (Clemson, South Carolina). After receiving her B.S. in biology from Kent State University, she went on to earn a Ph.D. in ecology and evolution from Purdue University. In 1984, Dr. Dickey joined the faculty at Clemson, where she devoted her career to teaching biology to nonscience majors in a variety of courses. In addition to creating content-based instructional materials, she developed many activities to engage lecture and laboratory students in discussion, critical thinking, and writing, and implemented an investigative laboratory curriculum in general biology. Dr. Dickey is author of *Laboratory Investigations for Biology*, Second Edition, and coauthor of *Campbell Essential Biology*, Fifth Edition, and *Campbell Essential Biology with Physiology*, Fourth Edition.

Kelly Hogan is a faculty member in the Department of Biology at the University of North Carolina at Chapel Hill, teaching introductory biology and introductory genetics to science majors. Dr. Hogan teaches hundreds of students at a time, using active-learning methods that incorporate technology such as cell phones as clickers, online homework, and peer evaluation tools. Dr. Hogan received her B.S. in biology at the College of New Jersey and her Ph.D. in pathology at the University of North Carolina, Chapel Hill. Her research interests relate to how large classes can be more inclusive through evidence-based teaching methods and technology. She provides faculty development to other instructors through peer-coaching, workshops, and mentoring. Dr. Hogan is the author of *Stem Cells and Cloning*, Second Edition, and is lead moderator of the *Instructor Exchange*, a site within MasteringBiology® for instructors to exchange classroom materials and ideas.

Neil A. Campbell (1946–2004) combined the inquiring nature of a research scientist with the soul of a caring teacher. Over his 30 years of teaching introductory biology to both science majors and nonscience majors, many thousands of students had the opportunity to learn from him and be stimulated by his enthusiasm for the study of life. While he is greatly missed by his many friends in the biology community, his coauthors remain inspired by his visionary dedication to education and are committed to searching for ever better ways to engage students in the wonders of biology.

Make important connections between biological concepts and your life

NEW! Each chapter opens with a **high-interest question** to spark your interest in the topic. Questions are revisited later in the chapter, in either a Scientific Thinking or Evolution Connection module.

CHAPTER 12

DNA Technology and Genomics

Papaya fruit, shown in the photograph below, are sweet and loaded with vitamin C. They are borne on a rapidly growing treelike plant (*Carica papaya*) that grows only in tropical climates. In Hawaii, papaya is both a dietary staple and a valuable export crop.

Although thriving today, Hawaii's papaya industry seemed doomed just a few decades ago. A deadly pathogen called the papaya ringspot virus (PRV) had spread throughout the islands and appeared poised to completely eradicate the papaya plant population. But scientists from the University of Hawaii were able to rescue the industry by creating new, genetically engineered PRV-resistant strains of papaya. Today, the papaya industry is once again vibrant—and the vast majority of Hawaii's papayas are genetically modified organisms (GMOs).

However, not everyone is happy about the circumstances surrounding the recovery of the Hawaiian papaya industry. Although genetically modified papayas are approved for consumption in the United States (as are many other GMO fruits and vegetables), some critics have raised safety concerns—for the people who eat them and for the environment. On three occasions over a three-year

Are genetically modified organisms safe?

span, thousands of papaya tre[...] down under the cover of dar[...] GMO crops. Although few w[...] should we in fact be concern[...] question continues to foster [...]

In addition to GMOs in [...] in many other ways: Gene c[...] dustrial products, DNA pro[...] ence, new technologies pro[...] and DNA can even be used [...] chapter, we'll discuss each [...] specific techniques used, h[...] legal, and ethical issues tha[...]

230

MasteringBiology®

◁ ABC News Videos and Current Events articles from The *New York Times* connect what you learn in biology class to fascinating stories in the news.

Big Ideas help you connect the overarching concepts that are explored in the chapter.

Gene Cloning
(12.1–12.5)

A variety of laboratory techniques can be used to copy and combine DNA molecules.

Genetically Modified Organisms
(12.6–12.10)

Transgenic cells, plants, and animals are used in agriculture and medicine.

DNA Profiling
(12.11–12.16)

Genetic markers can be used to definitively match a DNA sample to an individual.

Genomics
(12.17–12.21)

The study of complete DNA sets helps us learn about evolutionary history.

sland of Hawaii were hacked
bly as a protest against
such criminal behavior,
afety of GMO crops? This
ebate and disagreement.
echnologies affect our lives
o produce medical and in-
ged the field of forensic sci-
ata for biological research,
historical questions. In this
tions. We'll also consider the
plied, and some of the social,
the new technologies.

231

CONNECTION

Connection modules in every chapter relate biology to your life and the world outside the classroom.

16.5 Biofilms are complex associations of microbes

CONNECTION

In many natural environments, prokaryotes attach to surfaces in highly organized colonies called **biofilms**. A biofilm may consist of one or several species of prokaryotes, and it may include protists and fungi as well. Biofilms can form on almost any support, including rocks, soil, organic material (including living tissue), metal, and plastic. You have a biofilm on your teeth—dental plaque is a biofilm that can cause tooth decay. Biofilms can even form without a solid foundation, for example, on the surface of stagnant water.

Biofilm formation begins when prokaryotes secrete signaling molecules that attract nearby cells into a cluster. Once the cluster becomes sufficiently large, the cells produce a gooey coating that glues them to the support and to each other, making the biofilm extremely difficult to dislodge. For example, if you don't scrub your shower, you could find a biofilm growing around the drain—running water alone is not strong enough to wash it away. As the biofilm gets larger and more complex, it becomes a "city" of microbes. Communicating by chemical signals, members of the community coordinate the division of labor, defense against invaders, and other activities. Channels in the biofilm allow nutrients to reach cells in the interior and allow wastes to leave, and a variety of environments develop within it.

Biofilms are common among bacteria that cause disease in humans. For instance, ear infections and urinary tract infections are often the result of biofilm-forming bacteria. Cystic fibrosis patients are vulnerable to pneumonia caused by bacteria their lungs. Biofilms of harmful

bacteria can also form on implanted medical devices such as catheters, replacement joints, or pacemakers. The complexity of biofilms makes these infections especially difficult to defeat. Antibiotics may not be able to penetrate beyond the outer layer of cells, leaving much of the community intact. For example, some biofilm bacteria produce an enzyme that breaks down penicillin faster than it can diffuse inward.

Biofilms that form in the environment can be difficult to eradicate, too. A variety of industries spend billions of dollars every year trying to get rid of biofilms that clog and corrode pipes, gum up filters and drains, and coat the hulls of ships (Figure 16.5). Biofilms in water distribution pipes may survive chlorination, the most common method of ensuring that drinking water does not contain any harmful microorganisms. For example, biofilms of *Vibrio cholera*, the bacterium that causes cholera, found in water pipes were capable of withstanding levels of chlorine 10 to 20 times higher than the concentrations routinely used to chlorinate drinking water.

▲ Figure 16.5 A biofilm fouling the insides of a pipe

? Why are biofilms difficult to eradicate?

the biofilm sticks to the surface it resides on, and the cells biofilm stick to each other; the outer layer of cells may prevent antimicrobial substances from penetrating into the interior of the biofilm.

EVOLUTION CONNECTION

Evolution Connection modules present concrete examples of the evidence for evolution within each chapter, providing you with a coherent theme for the study of life.

10.19 Emerging viruses threaten human health

EVOLUTION CONNECTION

Emerging viruses are ones that seem to burst on to the scene, becoming apparent to the medical community quite suddenly. There are many familiar examples, such as the 2009 H1N1 influenza virus (discussed in the chapter introduction). Another example is **HIV** (human immunodeficiency virus), the virus that causes **AIDS** (acquired immunodeficiency syndrome). HIV appeared in New York and California in the early 1980s, seemingly out of nowhere. Yet another example is the deadly Ebola virus, recognized initially in 1976 in central Africa; it is one of several emerging viruses that cause hemorrhagic fever, an often fatal syndrome characterized by fever, vomiting, massive bleeding, and circulatory system collapse. A number of other dangerous newly recognized viruses cause encephalitis, inflammation of the brain. One example is the West Nile virus, which appeared in North America in 1999 and has since spread to all 48 contiguous U.S. states. West Nile virus is spread primarily by mosquitoes, which carry the virus in blood sucked from one victim and can transfer it to another victim. West Nile virus cases surged in 2012, especially in Texas. Severe acute respiratory syndrome (SARS) first appeared in China in 2002. Within eight months, about 8,000
and 10% died. Researchers quickly

Why are viral diseases such a constant threat?

▼ Figure 10.19 A Hong Kong health-care worker prepares to cull a chicken to help prevent the spread of the avian flu virus (shown in the inset)

Colorized TEM 180,000×

To the Student: How to use this book and MasteringBiology®

Stay focused on the key concepts

Central concepts summarize the key topic of each module, helping you stay focused as you study.

Checkpoint questions at the end of each module help you stay on track.

NEW and revised art provides clear visuals to help you understand key topics. Selected figures include numbered steps that are keyed to explanations in the text.

4.9 The Golgi apparatus modifies, sorts, and ships cell products

After leaving the ER, many transport vesicles travel to the **Golgi apparatus**. Using a light microscope and a staining technique he developed, Italian scientist Camillo Golgi discovered this membranous organelle in 1898. The electron microscope confirmed his discovery more than 50 years later, revealing a stack of flattened sacs, looking much like a pile of pita bread. A cell may contain many, even hundreds, of these stacks. The number of Golgi stacks correlates with how active the cell is in secreting proteins—a multistep process that, as you have just seen, is initiated in the rough ER.

The Golgi apparatus serves as a molecular warehouse and processing station for products manufactured by the ER. You can follow these activities in Figure 4.9. Note that the flattened Golgi sacs are not connected, as are ER sacs. ❶ One side of a Golgi stack serves as a receiving dock for transport vesicles produced by the ER. ❷ A vesicle fuses with a Golgi sac, adding its membrane and contents to the "receiving" side. ❸ Products of the ER are modified as a Golgi sac progresses through the stack. ❹ The "shipping" side of the Golgi

functions as a depot, dispatching its products in vesicles that bud off and travel to other sites.

How might ER products be processed during their transit through the Golgi? Various Golgi enzymes modify the carbohydrate portions of the glycoproteins made in the ER, removing some sugars and substituting others. Molecular identification tags, such as phosphate groups, may be added that help the Golgi sort molecules into different batches for different destinations.

Finished secretory products, packaged in transport vesicles, move to the plasma membrane for export from the cell. Alternatively, finished products may become part of the plasma membrane itself or part of another organelle, such as a lysosome, which we discuss next.

? What is the relationship of the Golgi apparatus to the ER in a protein-secreting cell?

● The Golgi receives transport vesicles budded from the ER that contain proteins synthesized by bound ribosomes. The Golgi finishes processing the proteins and dispatches transport vesicles to the plasma membrane, where the proteins are secreted.

"Receiving" side of Golgi apparatus

Transport vesicle from the ER

Golgi apparatus

Colorized, TEM 145,000×

Transport vesicle from the Golgi

"Shipping" side of Golgi apparatus

▲ Figure 4.9   The Golgi apparatus receiving, processing, and shipping products

MasteringBiology®

◁ **Connecting the Concepts** activities link one biological concept to another.

Learn how to to think like a scientist

▷ **New Scientific Thinking** modules explore how scientists use the processes of science for discovery. Each module concludes with a question that challenges you to think like a scientist.

SCIENTIFIC THINKING

▷ **New Scientific Thinking** topics include:

▸ **Module 2.15** — Scientists study the effects of rising atmospheric CO_2 on coral reef ecosystems

▸ **Module 8.10** — Tailoring treatment to each patient may improve cancer therapy

▸ **Module 25.3** — Coordinated waves of movement in huddles help penguins thermoregulate

▸ **Module 26.3** — A widely used weed killer demasculinizes male frogs

▸ **Module 29.2** — The model for magnetic sensory reception is incomplete

---

12.9 Genetically modified organisms raise health concerns

SCIENTIFIC THINKING

As soon as scientists realized the power of DNA technology, they began to worry about potential dangers. Early concerns focused on the possibility that recombinant DNA technology might create new pathogens. To guard against rogue microbes, scientists developed a set of guidelines including strict laboratory safety and containment procedures, the genetic crippling of transgenic organisms to ensure that they cannot survive outside the laboratory, and a prohibition on certain dangerous experiments. Today, most public concern centers on GMOs used for food.

Are genetically modified organisms safe?

Human Safety Genetically modified organisms are used in crop production because they are more nutritious or because they are cheaper to produce. But do these advantages come at a cost to the health of people consuming GMOs? When investigating complex questions like this one, scientists often use multiple experimental methods. A 2012 animal study involved 104 pigs that were divided into two groups: The first was fed a diet containing 39% GMO corn and the other a closely related non-GMO corn. The health of the pigs was measured over the short term (31 days), the medium term (110 days), and the normal generational life span. The researchers reported no significant differences between the two groups and no traces of foreign DNA in the slaughtered pigs.

Although pigs are a good model organism for human digestion, critics argue that human data are required to draw conclusions about the safety of dietary GMOs for people. The results of one human study, conducted jointly by Chinese and [American] were published in 2012. Sixty-eight Chi[nese children] (ages 6–8) were fed Golden Rice, spinach [containing b]eta-carotene), or a capsule containing [... O]ver 21 days, blood samples were drawn [... whi]ch vitamin A the body produced from [... The] data show that the beta-carotene in [... an]d the capsules was converted to vitamin [A with si]milar efficiency, while the beta-carotene [... sign]ificantly less vitamin A (Figure 12.9). [... researc]hers to conclude that GMO rice can [... in p]reventing vitamin A deficiency.

[... Th]ese findings, this study caused an uproar. [... ca]lled the study an unethical "scandal." [... scientists had used Chinese schoolchil[dren as sub]jects. The project leaders countered [that approval] and consent had been obtained in [both China and the U]nited States. The controversy highlights [the difficulties i]n conducting research on human [... stud]ies are of limited value, but human [... cruci]al. To date, no study has documented [... harm] from GMO foods, and there is gen[eral agreement among] scientists that the GMO foods on the [market are safe. Howev]er, it is not yet possible to measure the [long-term safet]y) of GMOs on human health.

[Environmental Concerns] Advocates of a cautious approach [... fear] that transgenic plants might pass [... Biol]ogy and Genomics

their new genes to related species in nearby wild areas, disturbing the composition of the natural ecosystem. Critics of GMO crops can point to several studies that do indeed show unintended gene transfer from engineered crops to nearby wild relatives. But GMO advocates counter that no lasting or detrimental effects from such transfers have been demonstrated, and that some GMOs (such as bacteria engineered to break down oil spills) can actively help the environment.

Labeling Although the majority of several staple crops grown in the United States—including corn and soybeans—are genetically modified, products made from GMOs are not required to be labeled in any way. Chances are you ate a food containing GMOs today, but the lack of labeling means you probably can't say for certain. Labeling of foods containing more than trace amounts of GMOs is required in Europe, Japan, Australia, China, Russia, and other countries. Labeling advocates point out that the information would allow consumers to decide for themselves whether they wish to be exposed to GMO foods. Some biotechnology advocates, however, respond that similar demands were not made when "transgenic" crop plants produced by traditional breeding techniques were put on the market. For example, triticale (a crop used primarily in animal feed but also in some human foods) was created decades ago by combining the genomes of wheat and rye—two plants that do not interbreed in nature. Triticale is now sold worldwide without any special labeling.

Scientists and the public need to weigh the possible benefits versus risks on a case-by-case basis. The best scenario would be to proceed with caution, basing our decisions on sound scientific information rather than on either irrational fear or blind optimism.

? Why might crop plants engineered to be resistant to weed killer pose a danger to the environment?

● The genes for herbicide resistance could transfer to closely related weeds, which could themselves then become resistant.

▲ Figure 12.9 Vitamin A production after consumption of different sources of beta-carotene

Data from G. Tang et al., Beta-carotene in Golden Rice is as good as beta-carotene in oil at providing vitamin A to children, *American Journal of Clinical Nutrition* 96(3): 658–64 (2012).

Scientific Thinking

Signed in as Libby Reiser, Instructor | Help | Close

What Roles Do Diet and the Microbial ... | Scientific Thinking: What Roles Do Diet and the Microbial Community In the In...

Item Type: Coaching Activities | **Difficulty:** -- | **Time:** -- | Contact the Publisher **Manage this Item:** Standard View

Scientific Thinking: What Roles Do Diet and the Microbial Community in the Intestines Play in Obesity?

Fast foods, cookies and ice cream, sodas and energy drinks–Americans eat a lot of processed foods high in fats and simple sugars. Not surprisingly, this type of diet can lead to weight gain and is one of the main culprits in the obesity epidemic in this country. But, is there more to this story?

The foods you eat serve as food for the community of microorganisms that inhabit your digestive tract. Those microbes have their own food "preferences," metabolizing different types of food molecules and releasing their byproducts, which your body then absorbs.

Scientists have hypothesized that a high-fat, high sugar diet actually alters the composition of the microbial community that inhabits the beginning of the large intestine, which contributes to obesity. Because of the difficulties of carrying out experiments on humans, scientists have used mice as an animal model in which to test this hypothesis.

Part A - Designing a controlled experiment

In one experiment, scientists raised mice in germ-free conditions (who therefore lacked intestinal microbes). The mice were fed a low-fat diet rich in the complex plant polysaccharides often called fiber.

When the mice were 12 weeks old, the scientists transplanted the microbial community from the intestine of a single "donor" mouse into all of the germ-free mice. Then they divided the mice randomly into two groups and fed each group a different diet.

- Group 1 (the control group) continued to eat a low-fat, high-fiber diet.
- Group 2 (the experimental group) ate a high-fat, high-sugar diet.

"Donor" mouse
Group 1: Control group — Low-fat, high-fiber diet
Germ-free mice
Group 2: Experimental group — High-fat, high-sugar diet

MasteringBiology®

◁ **NEW! Scientific Thinking activities** teach you how to practice important scientific skills like understanding variables and making predictions. Specific wrong-answer feedback coaches you to the correct response.

To the Student: How to use this book and MasteringBiology®

Maximize your learning and success

▷ **New Visualizing the Concept** modules walk you through challenging concepts and complex processes.

▷ The brief narrative works together with the artwork to help you visualize and understand the topic.

Hints embedded within the module emulate the guidance that you might receive during instructor office hours or in a tutoring session. These hints provide additional information to deepen your understanding of the topic.

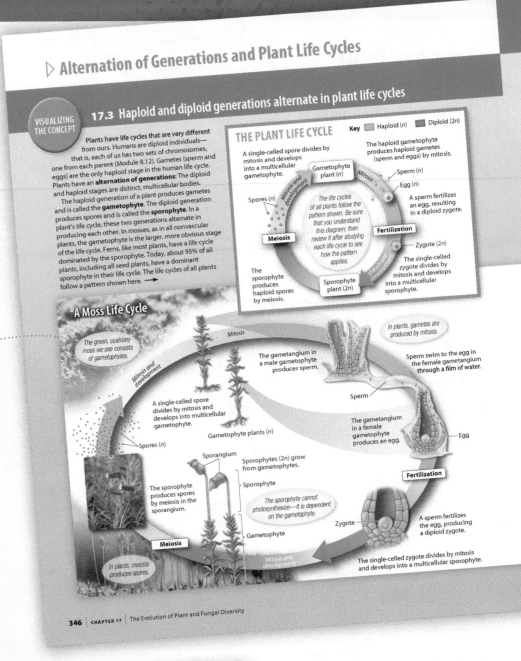

MasteringBiology®

▷ **NEW! Visualizing the Concept Activities** include interactive videos that were created and narrated by the authors of the text.

Life Cycle

Gametophyte plant (n)

A single-celled spore divides by mitosis and develops into a multicellular gametophyte.

Mitosis

Mitosis and development

Spores

Underside of gametophyte: actual size 0.5 cm across

The male gametangium produces sperm.

Sperm

Sperm swim to the egg in the female gametangium through a film of water.

The female gametangium produces an egg.

Egg

Although eggs and sperm are usually produced in separate locations on the same gametophyte, a variety of mechanisms promote cross-fertilization between gametophytes.

Fertilization

The sporophyte produces spores by meiosis in sporangia.

Meiosis

Mature sporophyte

Zygote

The new sporophyte grows from the gametophyte.

Mitosis and development

Clusters of sporangia on this fern look like brown dots.

The single-celled zygote divides by mitosis and develops into a multicellular sporophyte.

The tiny gametophyte soon disintegrates, and the sporophyte grows independently.

The ferns we see are sporophytes.

? What is the major difference between the moss and fern life cycles?

In mosses, the dominant plant body is the gametophyte; in ferns, the sporophyte is dominant and independent of the gametophyte.

Colorized TEM 9,375×

▲ **Figure 4.1C** Transmission electron micrograph of *Toxoplasma* (This parasite of cats can be transmitted to humans, causing the disease toxoplasmosis.)

Try This Describe a major difference between the *Paramecium* in Figure 4.1B and the protist in this figure. (*Hint:* Compare the notations along the right sides of the micrographs.)

△ **New! Try This** activities help you actively engage with the figures and develop positive study habits.

MasteringBiology®

Save & Return   Help

First Group

Total Questions: 22

REVIEW ANSWERS One of Your Answers Was Correct

The DNA structures of prokaryotes and eukaryotes are different in several ways, but one way in which they are the same is that _____.

Correct Answer:

both have a sugar-phosphate backbone

Your answers: One of your answers was correct

both have a sugar-phosphate backbone

histones are present in the nucleosomes

Click the arrow to the right to see the explanation

MasteringBiology®

◁ **New Dynamic Study Modules** enable you to study effectively on your own and more quickly learn the information. These modules can be accessed on smartphones, tablets, and computers.

To the Instructor: Implement active learning in your classroom

Resources save you hours of time preparing for class

▷ **NEW! Learning Catalytics™** is a "bring your own device" student engagement, assessment, and classroom intelligence system. This technology has grown out of twenty years of cutting-edge research, innovation, and implementation of interactive teaching and peer instruction.

Connect your lectures to current topics

◁ **Campbell Current Topics PowerPoint** slides help you prepare a high-impact lecture developed around current issues. Topics include cancer, global climate change, athletic cheating, nutrition, and more.

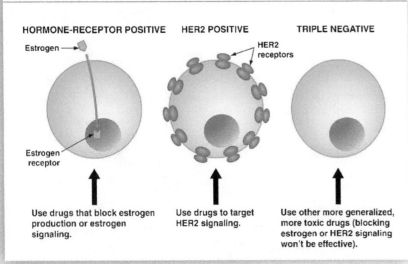

Three classes of breast cancer tumors lead to more personalized therapy

HORMONE-RECEPTOR POSITIVE   HER2 POSITIVE   TRIPLE NEGATIVE

Estrogen

HER2 receptors

Estrogen receptor

Use drugs that block estrogen production or estrogen signaling.

Use drugs to target HER2 signaling.

Use other more generalized, more toxic drugs (blocking estrogen or HER2 signaling won't be effective).

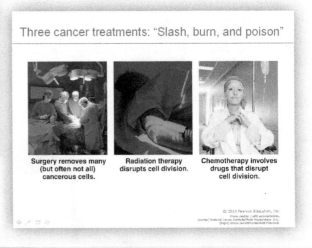

Three cancer treatments: "Slash, burn, and poison"

Surgery removes many (but often not all) cancerous cells.

Radiation therapy disrupts cell division.

Chemotherapy involves drugs that disrupt cell division.

MasteringBiology®

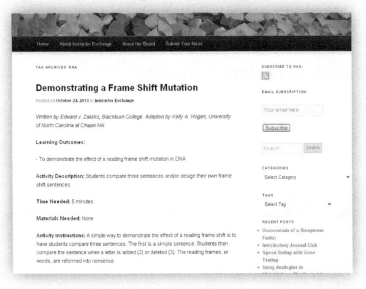

◁ **Instructor Exchange,** moderated by co-author Kelly Hogan, offers a library of active learning strategies contributed by instructors from across the country.

▽ **BioFlix activities** offer students 3-D animations to help them visualize and learn challenging topics.

Assign tutorials to help students prepare for class

▽ **Video Tutor Sessions and MP3 Tutor Sessions,** hosted by co-author Eric Simon, provide on-the-go tutorials focused on key concepts and vocabulary.

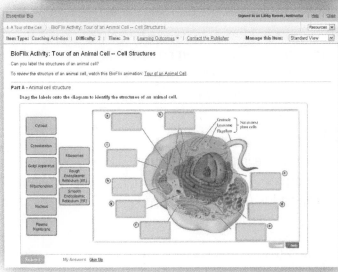

To the Instructor: How to use MasteringBiology®

MasteringBiology® is an online assessment and tutorial system designed to help you teach more efficiently. It offers a variety of interactive activities to engage students and help them to succeed in the course.

Access students' results with easy-to-interpret student performance data

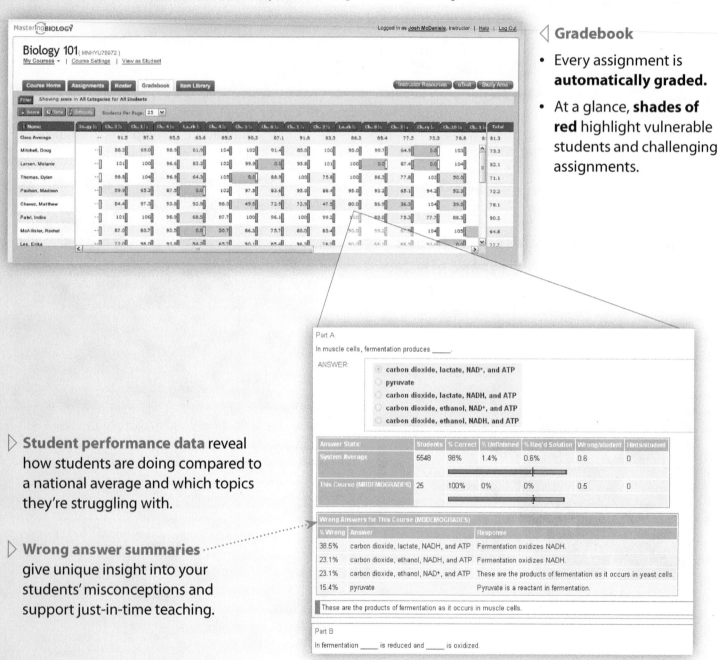

Gradebook

- Every assignment is **automatically graded.**

- At a glance, **shades of red** highlight vulnerable students and challenging assignments.

▷ **Student performance data** reveal how students are doing compared to a national average and which topics they're struggling with.

▷ **Wrong answer summaries** give unique insight into your students' misconceptions and support just-in-time teaching.

Gain insight into student progress at a glance

▷ **Get daily diagnostics.**

Gradebook Diagnostics provide unique insight into class performance. With a single click, see a summary of how your students are struggling or progressing.

MasteringBiology® is easy for you and your students to use

◁ **The Mastering platform** is the most effective and widely used online tutorial, homework, and assessment system for the sciences.

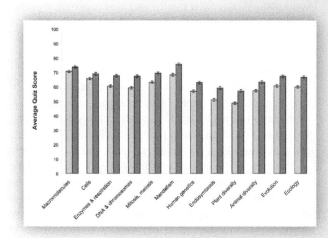

△ **Efficacy studies**

Go to the **"Proven Results"** tab at www.masteringbiology.com to see efficacy studies.

With MasteringBiology®, you can:

- **Assign** publisher-created pre-built assignments to get started quickly.
- **Easily edit** any of our questions or answers to match the precise language you use.
- **Import your own questions** and begin compiling meaningful data on student performance.
- **Easily export grades** to Microsoft® Excel or other course-management systems.

Preface

Inspired by the thousands of students in our own classes over the years and by enthusiastic feedback from the many instructors who have used our book, we are delighted to present this new, Eighth Edition. We authors have worked together closely to ensure that both the book and the supplementary material online reflect the changing needs of today's courses and students, as well as current progress in biology. Titled *Campbell Biology: Concepts & Connections* to honor Neil Campbell's founding role and his many contributions to biology education, this book continues to have a dual purpose: to engage students from a wide variety of majors in the wonders of the living world and to show them how biology relates to their own existence and the world they inhabit. Most of these students will not become biologists themselves, but their lives will be touched by biology every day. Understanding the concepts of biology and their connections to our lives is more important than ever. Whether we're concerned with our own health or the health of our planet, a familiarity with biology is essential. This basic knowledge and an appreciation for how science works have become elements of good citizenship in an era when informed evaluations of health issues, environmental problems, and applications of new technology are critical.

Concepts and Connections

Concepts   Biology is a vast subject that gets bigger every year, but an introductory biology course is still only one or two semesters long. This book was the first introductory biology textbook to use concept modules to help students recognize and focus on the main ideas of each chapter. The heading of each module is a carefully crafted statement of a key concept. For example, "A nerve signal begins as a change in the membrane potential" announces a key concept about the generation of an action potential (Module 28.4). Such a concept heading serves as a focal point, and the module's text and illustrations converge on that concept with explanation and, often, analogies. The module text walks the student through the illustrations, just as an instructor might do in class. And in teaching a sequential process, such as the one diagrammed in Figure 28.4, we number the steps in the text to correspond to numbered steps in the figure. The synergy between a module's narrative and graphic components transforms the concept heading into an idea with meaning to the student. The checkpoint question at the end of each module encourages students to test their understanding as they proceed through a chapter. Finally, in the Chapter Review, all the key concept statements are listed and briefly summarized under the overarching section titles, explicitly reminding students of what they've learned.

Connections   Students are more motivated to study biology when they can connect it to their own lives and interests—for example, when they are able to relate science to health

issues, economic problems, environmental quality, ethical controversies, and social responsibility. In this edition, blue Connection icons mark the numerous application modules that go beyond the core biological concepts. For example, the new Connection Module 26.12 describes the potential role oxytocin plays in human–dog bonding. In addition, our Evolution Connection modules, identified by green icons, connect the content of each chapter to the grand unifying theme of evolution, without which the study of life has no coherence. Explicit connections are also made between the chapter introduction and either the Evolution Connection module or the new Scientific Thinking module in each chapter; new high-interest questions introduce each chapter, drawing students into the topic and encouraging a curiosity to explore the question further when it appears again later in the chapter.

New to This Edition

New Scientific Thinking Modules   In this edition we placed greater emphasis on the process of scientific inquiry through the addition to each chapter of a new type of module called Scientific Thinking, which is called out with a purple icon. These modules cover recent scientific research as well as underscore the spirit of inquiry in historical discoveries. All Scientific Thinking modules strive to demonstrate to students what scientists do. Each of these modules identifies key attributes of scientific inquiry, from the forming and testing of hypotheses to the analysis of data to the evaluation and communication of scientific results among scientists and with society as a whole. For example, the new Module 2.15 describes how scientists use both controlled experiments and observational field studies to document the effects of rising atmospheric CO_2 on coral reef ecosystems. Module 13.3 describes the scientific search for the common ancestor of whales, using different lines of inquiry from early fossil clues, molecular comparisons, and a series of transitional fossils that link whales to cloven-hoofed mammals, animals that live on land. And to prepare students for the renewed focus in the book on how biological concepts emerge from the process of science, we have significantly revised the introduction in Chapter 1, Biology: Exploring Life. These changes will better equip students to think like scientists and emphasize the connections between discovery and the concepts explored throughout the course.

New Visualizing the Concept Modules   Also new to this edition are modules that raise our hallmark art–text integration to a new level. These Visualizing the Concept modules take challenging concepts or processes and walk students through them in a highly visual manner, using engaging, attractive art; clear and concise labels; and instructor "hints" called out in light blue bubbles. These short hints emulate the one-on-one coaching an instructor might provide to a students during office hours and help students make key connections within the figure. Examples of this new feature include Module 9.8, which demonstrates to students the process of reading and analyzing a family pedigree; Module 17.3, which introduces the concept of plant life cycles through a combination of photographs and detailed life cycle art displayed across an impressive two-page layout; and Module 26.8, which walks students through the concept of homeostatic controls in blood glucose levels.

New "Try This" Tips   One theme of the revision for the Eighth Edition is to help all students learn positive study habits they can take with them throughout their college careers and, in particular, to encourage them to be active in their reading and studying. To foster good study habits, several figures in each chapter feature a new "Try This" study tip. These action-oriented statements or questions direct students to study a figure more closely and explain, interpret, or extend what the figure presents. For example, in Figure 3.13B, students are asked to "Point out the bonds and functional groups that make the R groups of these three amino acids either hydrophobic or hydrophilic." Figure 6.10B is a new figure illustrating the molecular rotary motor ATP synthase, and the accompanying Try This tip asks students to "Identify the power source that runs this motor. Explain where this 'power' comes from." Figure 36.7, on the effect of predation on the life history traits of guppies, offers the following Try This tip: "Use the figure to explain how the hypothesis was tested."

Improvements to End-of-Chapter Section   The Testing Your Knowledge questions are now arranged to reflect Bloom's Taxonomy of cognitive domains. Questions and activities are grouped into Level 1: Knowledge/Comprehension, Level 2: Application/Analysis, and Level 3: Synthesis/Evaluation. In addition, a new Scientific Thinking question has been added to each chapter that connects to and extends the topic of the Scientific Thinking module. Throughout the Chapter Review, new questions have been added that will help students better engage with the chapter topic and practice higher-level problem solving.

New Design and Improved Art   The fresh new design used throughout the chapters and the extensive reconceptualization of many figures make the book even more appealing and accessible to visual learners. The cellular art in Chapter 4, A Tour of the Cell, for example, has been completely reimagined for more depth perspective and richer color. The new big-picture diagrams of the animal and plant cells are vibrant and better demonstrate the spatial relationships among the cellular structures with an almost three-dimensional style. The illustrations of cellular organelles elsewhere in Chapter 4 include electron micrographs overlaid on diagrams to emphasize the connection between the realistic micrograph depiction and the artwork. Figure 4.9, for example, shows a micrograph of an actual Golgi apparatus paired with an illustration; an accompanying orientation diagram—a hallmark of *Concepts and Connections*—continues to act as a roadmap that reminds students of how an organelle fits within the overall cell structure. Finally, throughout the book we have

introduced new molecular art; for example, see Figure 10.11B for a new representation of a molecule of tRNA binding to an enzyme molecule.

The Latest Science   Biology is a dynamic field of study, and we take pride in our book's currency and scientific accuracy. For this edition, as in previous editions, we have integrated the results of the latest scientific research throughout the book. We have done this carefully and thoughtfully, recognizing that research advances can lead to new ways of looking at biological topics; such changes in perspective can necessitate organizational changes in our textbook to better reflect the current state of a field. You will find a unit-by-unit account of new content and organizational improvements in the "New Content" section on pp. xvii–xviii following this Preface.

New MasteringBiology®   A specially developed version of MasteringBiology, the most widely used online tutorial and assessment program for biology, continues to accompany *Campbell Biology: Concepts & Connections*. In addition to 170 author-created activities that help students learn vocabulary, extend the book's emphasis on visual learning, demonstrate the connections among key concepts (helping students grasp the big ideas), and coach students on how to interpret data, the Eighth Edition features two additional new activity types. New Scientific Thinking activities encourage students to practice the basic science skills explored in the in-text Scientific Thinking feature, allowing students to try out thinking like a scientist and allowing instructors to assess this understanding; new Visualizing the Concept activities take students on an animated and narrated tour of select Visualizing the Concept modules from the text, offering students the chance to review key concepts in a digital learning modality. MasteringBiology® for *Campbell Biology: Concepts & Connections*, Eighth Edition, will help students to see strong connections through their print textbook, and the additional practice available online allows instructors to capture powerful data on student performance, thereby making the most of class time.

This Book's Flexibility

Although a biology textbook's table of contents is by design linear, biology itself is more like a web of related concepts without a single starting point or prescribed path. Courses can navigate this network by starting with molecules, with ecology, or somewhere in between, and courses can omit topics. *Campbell Biology: Concepts & Connections* is uniquely suited to offer flexibility and thus serve a variety of courses. The seven units of the book are largely self-contained, and in a number of the units, chapters can be assigned in a different order without much loss of coherence. The use of numbered modules makes it easy to skip topics or reorder the presentation of material.

■ ■ ■

For many students, introductory biology is the only science course that they will take during their college years. Long after today's students have forgotten most of the specific content of their biology course, they will be left with general impressions and attitudes about science and scientists. We hope that this new edition of *Campbell Biology: Concepts & Connections* helps make those impressions positive and supports instructors' goals for sharing the fun of biology. In our continuing efforts to improve the book and its supporting materials, we benefit tremendously from instructor and student feedback, not only in formal reviews but also via informal communication. Please let us know how we are doing and how we can improve the next edition of the book.

Jane Reece, janereece@cal.berkeley.edu

Martha Taylor (Chapter 1 and Unit I), mrt2@cornell.edu

Eric Simon (Units II and VI and Chapters 21 and 27), esimon@nec.edu

Jean Dickey (Units III, IV, and VII and Chapters 22, 23, and 30), dickeyj@clemson.edu

Kelly Hogan (Chapters 20, 24–26, 28, and 29), leek@email.unc.edu

New Content

Below are some important highlights of new content and organizational improvements in *Campbell Biology: Concepts & Connections*, Eighth Edition.

Chapter 1, Biology: Exploring Life   The snowy owl, our cover organism for the Eighth Edition, is featured in the chapter introduction. The discussion of the evolutionary adaptations of these owls to life on the arctic tundra links to a new Scientific Thinking module on testing the hypothesis that camouflage coloration protects some animals from predation. An expanded module on evolution as the core theme of biology now includes a phylogenetic tree of elephants to enhance the discussion of the unity and diversity of life.

Unit I, The Life of the Cell   Throughout the Eighth Edition, the themes introduced in new chapter introductions are expanded and further explored in either Scientific Thinking or Evolution Connection modules. For instance, in this unit, Chapter 5, The Working Cell, begins with the question "How can water flow through a membrane?" and an essay that describes the role these water channels play in kidney function; the essay is illustrated with a computer model of aquaporins spanning a membrane. Module 5.7, a Scientific Thinking module, then details the serendipitous discovery of aquaporins and presents data from a study that helped identify their function. Chapter 7, Photosynthesis: Using Light to Make Food, begins with the question "Will global climate change make you itch?" and uses the example of proliferation of poison ivy to introduce this chapter on photosynthesis. Then, Module 7.13, another Scientific Thinking module, explores various ways that scientists test the effects of rising atmospheric CO_2 levels on plant growth and presents results from a study on poison ivy growth. The Scientific Thinking question at the end of the chapter continues this theme, with data from a study on pollen production by ragweed under varying CO_2 concentrations, beginning with the question "Will global climate change make you sneeze as well as itch?" This unit also has three of the new Visualizing the Concept modules: Module 3.14: A protein's functional shape results from four levels of structure; Module 5.1: Membranes are fluid mosaics of lipids and proteins with many functions; and Module 7.9: The light reactions take place within the thylakoid membranes. These modules use both new and highly revised art to guide students through these challenging topics in a visual, highly intuitive manner. Chapter 6, How Cells Harvest Chemical Energy, now includes a new figure and expanded explanation of the amazing molecular motor, ATP synthase. The art program in Chapter 4, A Tour of the Cell, has been completely reimagined and revised. The beautiful new diagrams of animal and plant cells and their component parts are designed to help students appreciate the complexities of cell structure and explore the relationship between structure and function.

Unit II, Cellular Reproduction and Genetics   The purpose of this unit is to help students understand the relationship between DNA, chromosomes, and organisms and to help them see that genetics is not purely hypothetical but connects in many important and interesting ways to their lives, human society, and other life on Earth. In preparing this edition, we worked to clarify difficult concepts, enhancing text and illustrations and providing timely new applications of genetic principles. The content is reinforced with updated discussions of relevant topics, such as personalized cancer therapy, the H1N1 and H5N1 influenza viruses, umbilical cord blood banking, and the science and controversy surrounding genetically modified foods. This edition includes discussion of many recent advances in the field. Some new topics concern our basic understanding of genetics and the cell cycle, such as how sister chromatids are physically attached during meiosis, how chemical modifications such as methylation and acetylation affect inheritance, and the roles of activators and enhancers in controlling gene expression. Other topics include recent advances in our understanding of genetics, such as the analysis of recent human evolution of high-altitude-dwelling Sherpas, expanded roles for microRNAs in the control of genetic information, and our improved understanding of the cellular basis of health problems in cloned animals. In some cases, sections within chapters have been reorganized to present a more logical flow of materials. Examples of new organization include the discussion of human karyotypes and the diagnosis of chromosomal abnormalities (Modules 8.18–8.20) and the processes of reproductive and therapeutic cloning (Modules 11.12–11.14). Material throughout the unit has been updated to reflect recent data, such as the latest cancer statistics and results from whole-genome sequencing.

Unit III, Concepts of Evolution   This unit presents the basic principles of evolution and natural selection, the overwhelming evidence that supports these theories, and their relevance to all of biology—and to the lives of students. A new chapter introduction in Chapter 13, How Populations Evolve, highlights the role that evolution plays in thwarting human attempts to eradicate disease. The chapter has been reorganized so that the opening module on Darwin's development of the theory of evolution is followed immediately by evidence for evolution, including a Scientific Thinking module on fossils of transitional forms. Another new module (13.4) assembles evidence from homologies, including an example of "pseudogenes." New material in this unit also supports our goal of directly addressing student misconceptions about evolution. For example, a new chapter introduction and Scientific Thinking module in Chapter 14, The Origin of Species, tackle the question "Can we observe speciation occurring?" and a new chapter introduction in Chapter 15, Tracing Evolutionary History, poses the question (answered in Module 15.12) "How do brand-new structures arise by evolution?"

Unit IV, The Evolution of Biological Diversity   The diversity unit surveys all life on Earth in less than a hundred pages! Consequently, descriptions and illustrations of the unifying characteristics of each major group of organisms, along with a small sample of its diversity, make up the bulk of the content. Two recurring elements are interwoven with these descriptions: evolutionary history and examples of relevance to our everyday lives and society at large. For the Eighth Edition, we have improved and updated those two elements. For example, Chapter 16, Microbial Life: Prokaryotes and Protists, opens with a new introduction on human microbiota and the question "Are antibiotics making us fat?" The related Scientific Thinking module (16.11) updates the story of Marshall's discovery of the role of *Helicobacter pylori* in ulcers with a new hypothesis about a possible connection between *H. pylori* and obesity. A new chapter introduction and Scientific Thinking module in Chapter 17, The Evolution of Plant and Fungal Diversity, highlight the interdependence of plants and fungi. The alternation of generations and the life cycle in mosses and ferns are presented in an attractive two-page Visualizing the Concept module (17.3), while details of the pine life cycle have been replaced with a new Module 17.5 that emphasizes pollen and seeds as key adaptations for terrestrial life. The animal diversity chapters (18, The Evolution of Invertebrate Diversity; and 19, The Evolution of Vertebrate Diversity) also have new opening essays. A Visualizing the Concept module (18.3) beautifully illustrates features of the animal body plan. A new Module 18.16 calls attention to the value of invertebrate diversity. Chapter 19 includes a Visualizing the Concept module (19.9) on primate diversity and also updates the story of hominin evolution, including the recently described *Australopithecus sediba*.

Unit V, Animals: Form and Function   This unit combines a comparative approach with an exploration of human anatomy and physiology. Many chapters begin with an overview of a general problem that animals face and a comparative discussion of how different animals address this problem, all framed within an evolutionary context. For example, the introduction to Chapter 20, Unifying Concepts of Animal Structure and Function, begins with the question "Does evolution lead to the perfect animal form?" Module 20.1 is a new Evolution Connection that discusses the long, looped laryngeal nerve in vertebrates (using the giraffe as an example) to illustrate that a structure in an ancestral organism can become adapted to function in a descendant organism without being "perfected," thereby combating common student misconceptions about evolution. The main portion of every chapter is devoted to detailed presentations of human body systems, frequently illuminated by discussion of the health consequences of disorders in those systems. For example, Chapter 28, Nervous Systems, includes new material describing a genetic risk for developing Alzheimer's disease, the long-term consequences of traumatic brain injury, and how some antidepressants may not be as effective at combating depression as once thought. In many areas, content has been updated to reflect

newer issues in biology. The chapter introduction and new Scientific Thinking module in Chapter 26, Hormones and the Endocrine System, discuss the consequences of endocrine disruptors in the environment. The Scientific Thinking module in Chapter 23 describes large clinical trials investigating the hypothesis that heart attacks are caused by the body's inflammatory response. Chapter 27, Reproduction and Embryonic Development, has a new chapter introduction on viral STDs, improved figures presenting embryonic development, as well as a Visualizing the Concept module on human pregnancy. Improvements to this unit also include a significant revision to the presentation of nutrition in Modules 21.14 to 21.21 and a reorganization of text and art in Modules 25.6 and 25.7 to guide students through the anatomy and physiology of the kidneys.

Unit VI, Plants: Form and Function   To help students gain an appreciation of the importance of plants, this unit presents the anatomy and physiology of angiosperms with frequent connections to the importance of plants to society. New Connections in this edition include an increased discussion of the importance of agriculture to human civilization (including presentation of genomic data investigating this question) in Chapter 31, issues surrounding organic farming (including presentation of data on the nutritional value of organic versus conventionally grown produce) in Chapter 32, an expanded discussion of phytoestrogens, as well as a new discussion on the production of seedless vegetables in Chapter 33. Throughout the unit, the text has been revised with the goal of making the material more engaging and accessible to students. For example, the difficult topic of transpiration is now presented in an entirely new, visual style within a Visualizing the Concept module (Module 32.3), and streamlined and simplified discussions were written for such topics as the auxin hormones and phytochromes. All of these changes are meant to make the point that human society is inexorably connected to the health of plants.

Unit VII, Ecology   In this unit, students learn the fundamental principles of ecology and how these principles apply to environmental problems. Along with a new introduction in each chapter, the Eighth Edition features many new photos and two Visualizing the Concept modules (35.7 and 37.9)—one focuses on whether animal movement is a response to stimuli or requires spatial learning and the other explores the interconnection of food chains and food webs. Scientific Thinking modules sample the variety of approaches to studying ecology, including the classic field study that led to the concept of keystone species (37.11); the "natural experiment" of returning gray wolves to the Yellowstone ecosystem (38.11); and the combination of historical records, long-term experimentation, and modern technology to investigate the snowshoe hare–lynx population cycle (36.6). The pioneering work of Rachel Carson (34.2) and Jane Goodall (35.22) is also described in Scientific Thinking modules. Modules that present data on human population (36.3, 36.9–36.11), declining biodiversity (38.1), and global climate change (38.3, 38.4) have all been updated.

Acknowledgments

This Eighth Edition of *Campbell Biology: Concepts & Connections* is a result of the combined efforts of many talented and hardworking people, and the authors wish to extend heartfelt thanks to all those who contributed to this and previous editions. Our work on this edition was shaped by input from the biologists acknowledged in the reviewer list on pages xx–xxii, who shared with us their experiences teaching introductory biology and provided specific suggestions for improving the book. Feedback from the authors of this edition's supplements and the unsolicited comments and suggestions we received from many biologists and biology students were also extremely helpful. In addition, this book has benefited in countless ways from the stimulating contacts we have had with the coauthors of *Campbell Biology*, Tenth Edition.

We wish to offer special thanks to the students and faculty at our teaching institutions. Marty Taylor thanks her students at Cornell University for their valuable feedback on the book. Eric Simon thanks his colleagues and friends at New England College, especially within the collegium of Natural Sciences and Mathematics, for their continued support and assistance. Jean Dickey thanks her colleagues at Clemson University for their expertise and support. And Kelly Hogan thanks her students for their enthusiasm and thanks her colleagues at the University of North Carolina, Chapel Hill, for their continued support.

We thank Paul Corey, president, Science, Business, and Technology, Pearson Higher Education. In addition, the superb publishing team for this edition was headed up by acquisitions editor Alison Rodal, with the invaluable support of editor-in-chief Beth Wilbur. We cannot thank them enough for their unstinting efforts on behalf of the book and for their commitment to excellence in biology education. We are fortunate to have had once again the contributions of executive director of development Deborah Gale and executive editorial manager Ginnie Simione Jutson. We are similarly grateful to the members of the editorial development team—Debbie Hardin, who also served as the day-to-day editorial project manager, and Susan Teahan—for their steadfast commitment to quality. We thank them for their thoroughness, hard work, and good humor; the book is far better than it would have been without their efforts. Thanks also to senior supplements project editor Susan Berge for her oversight of the supplements program and to editorial assistants Rachel Brickner, Katherine Harrison-Adcock, and Libby Reiser for the efficient and enthusiastic support they provided.

This book and all the other components of the teaching package are both attractive and pedagogically effective in large part because of the hard work and creativity of the production professionals on our team. We wish to thank managing editor Mike Early and production project manager Lori Newman. We also acknowledge copyeditor Joanna Dinsmore, proofreader Pete Shanks, and indexer Lynn Armstrong. We again thank senior photo editor Donna Kalal and photo researcher Kristin Piljay for their contributions, as well as project manager for text permissions Alison Bruckner. S4Carlisle Publishing Services was responsible for composition, headed by senior project editor Emily Bush, with help from paging specialist Donna Healy; and Precision Graphics, headed by project manager Amanda Bickel, was responsible for rendering new and revised illustrations. We also thank manufacturing buyer Jeffrey Sargent.

We thank Gary Hespenheide for creating a beautiful and functional interior design and a stunning cover, and we are again indebted to design manager Marilyn Perry for her oversight and design leadership. The new Visualizing the Concept modules benefited from her vision, as well as from the early input of art editor Elisheva Marcus and the continuing contributions of artist Andrew Recher of Precision Graphics. Art editor Kelly Murphy envisioned the beautiful new cell art throughout the book.

The value of *Campbell Biology: Concepts & Connections* as a learning tool is greatly enhanced by the hard work and creativity of the authors of the supplements that accompany this book: Ed Zalisko (*Instructor's Guide* and *PowerPoint® Lecture Presentations*); Jean DeSaix, Tanya Smutka, Kristen Miller, and Justin Shaffer (*Test Bank*); Dana Kurpius (*Active Reading Guide*); Robert Iwan and Amaya Garcia (*Reading Quizzes* and media correlations); and Shannon Datwyler (*Clicker Questions* and *Quiz Shows*). In addition to senior supplements project editor Susan Berge, the editorial and production staff for the supplements program included supplements production project manager Jane Brundage, *PowerPoint® Lecture Presentations* editor Joanna Dinsmore, and project manager Sylvia Rebert of Progressive Publishing Alternatives. And the superlative MasteringBiology® program for this book would not exist without Lauren Fogel, Stacy Treco, Tania Mlawer, Katie Foley, Sarah Jensen, Juliana Tringali, Daniel Ross, Dario Wong, Taylor Merck, Caroline Power, and David Kokorowski and his team. And a special thanks to Sarah Young-Dualan for her thoughtful work on the Visualizing the Concepts interactive videos.

For their important roles in marketing the book, we are very grateful to senior marketing manager Amee Mosley, executive marketing manager Lauren Harp, and vice president of marketing Christy Lesko. We also appreciate the work of the executive marketing manager for MasteringBiology®, Scott Dustan. The members of the Pearson Science sales team have continued to help us connect with biology instructors and their teaching needs, and we thank them.

Finally, we are deeply grateful to our families and friends for their support, encouragement, and patience throughout this project. Our special thanks to Paul, Dan, Maria, Armelle, and Sean (J.B.R.); Josie, Jason, Marnie, Alice, Jack, David, Paul, Ava, and Daniel (M.R.T.); Amanda, Reed, Forest, and dear friends Jamey, Nick, Jim, and Bethany (E.J.S.); Jessie and Katherine (J.L.D.); and Tracey, Vivian, Carolyn, Brian, Jake, and Lexi (K.H.)

Jane Reece, Martha Taylor, Eric Simon, Jean Dickey, and Kelly Hogan

Reviewers

Visualizing the Concept Review Panel, Eighth Edition

Erica Kipp, *Pace University*
David Loring, *Johnson County Community College*
Sheryl Love, *Temple University*
Sukanya Subramanian, *Collin County Community College*
Jennifer J. Yeh, *San Francisco, California*

Reviewers of the Eighth Edition

Steven Armstrong, *Tarrant County College*
Michael Battaglia, *Greenville Technical College*
Lisa Bonneau, *Metropolitan Community College*
Stephen T. Brown, *Los Angeles Mission College*
Nancy Buschhaus, *University of Tennessee at Martin*
Glenn Cohen, *Troy University*
Nora Espinoza, *Clemson University*
Karen E. Francl, *Radford University*
Jennifer Greenwood, *University of Tennessee at Martin*
Joel Hagen, *Radford University*
Chris Haynes, *Shelton State Community College*
Duane A. Hinton, *Washburn University*
Amy Hollingsworth, *The University of Akron*
Erica Kipp, *Pace University*
Cindy Klevickis, *James Madison University*
Dubear Kroening, *University of Wisconsin, Fox Valley*
Dana Kurpius, *Elgin Community College*
Dale Lambert, *Tarrant County College*
David Loring, *Johnson County Community College*
Mark Meade, *Jacksonville State University*
John Mersfelder, *Sinclair Community College*
Andrew Miller, *Thomas University*
Zia Nisani, *Antelope Valley College*
Camellia M. Okpodu, *Norfolk State University*
James Rayburn, *Jacksonville State University*
Ashley Rhodes, *Kansas State University*
Lori B. Robinson, *Georgia College & State University*
Ursula Roese, *University of New England*
Doreen J. Schroeder, *University of St. Thomas*
Justin Shaffer, *North Carolina A&T State University*
Marilyn Shopper, *Johnson County Community College*
Ayesha Siddiqui, *Schoolcraft College*
Ashley Spring, *Brevard Community College*
Thaxton Springfield, *St. Petersburg College*
Linda Brooke Stabler, *University of Central Oklahoma*
Patrick Stokley, *East Central Community College*
Lori Tolley-Jordan, *Jacksonville State University*
Jimmy Triplett, *Jacksonville State University*
Lisa Weasel, *Portland State University*
Martin Zahn, *Thomas Nelson Community College*

Reviewers of Previous Editions

Michael Abbott, *Westminster College*
Tanveer Abidi, *Kean University*
Daryl Adams, *Mankato State University*

Dawn Adrian Adams, *Baylor University*
Olushola Adeyeye, *Duquesne University*
Shylaja Akkaraju, *Bronx Community College*
Felix Akojie, *Paducah Community College*
Dan Alex, *Chabot College*
John Aliff, *Georgia Perimeter College*
Sylvester Allred, *Northern Arizona University*
Jane Aloi-Horlings, *Saddleback College*
Loren Ammerman, *University of Texas at Arlington*
Dennis Anderson, *Oklahoma City Community College*
Marjay Anderson, *Howard University*
Bert Atsma, *Union County College*
Yael Avissar, *Rhode Island College*
Gail Baker, *LaGuardia Community College*
Caroline Ballard, *Rock Valley College*
Andrei Barkovskii, *Georgia College and State University*
Mark Barnby, *Ohlone College*
Chris Barnhart, *University of San Diego*
Stephen Barnhart, *Santa Rosa Junior College*
William Barstow, *University of Georgia*
Kirk A. Bartholomew, *Central Connecticut State University*
Michael Battaglia, *Greenville Technical College*
Gail Baughman, *Mira Costa College*
Jane Beiswenger, *University of Wyoming*
Tania Beliz, *College of San Mateo*
Lisa Bellows, *North Central Texas College*
Ernest Benfield, *Virginia Polytechnic Institute*
Rudi Berkelhamer, *University of California, Irvine*
Harry Bernheim, *Tufts University*
Richard Bliss, *Yuba College*
Lawrence Blumer, *Morehouse College*
Dennis Bogyo, *Valdosta State University*
Lisa K. Bonneau, *Metropolitan Community College, Blue River*
Mehdi Borhan, *Johnson County Community College*
Kathleen Bossy, *Bryant College*
William Bowen, *University of Arkansas at Little Rock*
Robert Boyd, *Auburn University*
Bradford Boyer, *State University of New York, Suffolk County Community College*
Paul Boyer, *University of Wisconsin*
William Bradshaw, *Brigham Young University*
Agnello Braganza, *Chabot College*
James Bray, *Blackburn College*
Peggy Brickman, *University of Georgia*
Chris Brinegar, *San Jose State University*
Chad Brommer, *Emory University*
Charles Brown, *Santa Rosa Junior College*
Carole Browne, *Wake Forest University*
Becky Brown-Watson, *Santa Rosa Junior College*
Delia Brownson, *University of Texas at Austin and Austin Community College*
Michael Bucher, *College of San Mateo*
Virginia Buckner, *Johnson County Community College*
Joseph C. Bundy, Jr., *University of North Carolina at Greensboro*
Ray Burton, *Germanna Community College*

Warren Buss, *University of Northern Colorado*
Linda Butler, *University of Texas at Austin*
Jerry Button, *Portland Community College*
Carolee Caffrey, *University of California, Los Angeles*
George Cain, *University of Iowa*
Beth Campbell, *Itawamba Community College*
John Campbell, *Northern Oklahoma College*
John Capeheart, *University of Houston, Downtown*
James Cappuccino, *Rockland Community College*
M. Carabelli, *Broward Community College*
Jocelyn Cash, *Central Piedmont Community College*
Cathryn Cates, *Tyler Junior College*
Russell Centanni, *Boise State University*
David Chambers, *Northeastern University*
Ruth Chesnut, *Eastern Illinois University*
Vic Chow, *San Francisco City College*
Van Christman, *Ricks College*
Craig Clifford, *Northeastern State University, Tahlequah*
Richard Cobb, *South Maine Community College*
Mary Colavito, *Santa Monica College*
Jennifer Cooper, *Itawamba Community College*
Bob Cowling, *Ouachita Technical College*
Don Cox, *Miami University*
Robert Creek, *Western Kentucky University*
Hillary Cressey, *George Mason University*
Norma Criley, *Illinois Wesleyan University*
Jessica Crowe, *South Georgia College*
Mitch Cruzan, *Portland State University*
Judy Daniels, *Monroe Community College*
Michael Davis, *Central Connecticut State University*
Pat Davis, *East Central Community College*
Lewis Deaton, *University of Louisiana*
Lawrence DeFilippi, *Lurleen B. Wallace College*
James Dekloe, *Solano Community College*
Veronique Delesalle, *Gettysburg College*
Loren Denney, *Southwest Missouri State University*
Jean DeSaix, *University of North Carolina at Chapel Hill*
Mary Dettman, *Seminole Community College of Florida*
Kathleen Diamond, *College of San Mateo*
Alfred Diboll, *Macon College*
Jean Dickey, *Clemson University*
Stephen Dina, *St. Louis University*
Robert P. Donaldson, *George Washington University*
Gary Donnermeyer, *Iowa Central Community College*
Charles Duggins, *University of South Carolina*
Susan Dunford, *University of Cincinnati*
Lee Edwards, *Greenville Technical College*
Betty Eidemiller, *Lamar University*
Jamin Eisenbach, *Eastern Michigan University*
Norman Ellstrand, *University of California, Riverside*
Thomas Emmel, *University of Florida*
Cindy Erwin, *City College of San Francisco*
Gerald Esch, *Wake Forest University*
David Essar, *Winona State University*

Cory Etchberger, *Longview Community College*
Nancy Eyster-Smith, *Bentley College*
William Ezell, *University of North Carolina at Pembroke*
Laurie Faber, *Grand Rapids Community College*
Terence Farrell, *Stetson University*
Shannon Kuchel Fehlberg, *Colorado Christian University*
Jerry Feldman, *University of California, Santa Cruz*
Eugene Fenster, *Longview Community College*
Dino Fiabane, *Community College of Philadelphia*
Kathleen Fisher, *San Diego State University*
Edward Fliss, *St. Louis Community College, Florissant Valley*
Linda Flora, *Montgomery County Community College*
Dennis Forsythe, *The Citadel Military College of South Carolina*
Robert Frankis, *College of Charleston*
James French, *Rutgers University*
Bernard Frye, *University of Texas at Arlington*
Anne Galbraith, *University of Wisconsin*
Robert Galbraith, *Crafton Hills College*
Rosa Gambier, *State University of New York, Suffolk County Community College*
George Garcia, *University of Texas at Austin*
Linda Gardner, *San Diego Mesa College*
Sandi Gardner, *Triton College*
Gail Gasparich, *Towson University*
Janet Gaston, *Troy University*
Shelley Gaudia, *Lane Community College*
Douglas Gayou, *University of Missouri at Columbia*
Robert Gendron, *Indiana University of Pennsylvania*
Bagie George, *Georgia Gwinnett College*
Rebecca German, *University of Cincinnati*
Grant Gerrish, *University of Hawaii*
Julie Gibbs, *College of DuPage*
Frank Gilliam, *Marshall University*
Patricia Glas, *The Citadel Military College of South Carolina*
David Glenn-Lewin, *Wichita State University*
Robert Grammer, *Belmont University*
Laura Grayson-Roselli, *Burlington County College*
Peggy Green, *Broward Community College*
Miriam L. Greenberg, *Wayne State University*
Sylvia Greer, *City University of New York*
Eileen Gregory, *Rollins College*
Dana Griffin, *University of Florida*
Richard Groover, *J. Sargeant Reynolds Community College*
Peggy Guthrie, *University of Central Oklahoma*
Maggie Haag, *University of Alberta*
Richard Haas, *California State University, Fresno*
Martin Hahn, *William Paterson College*
Leah Haimo, *University of California, Riverside*
James Hampton, *Salt Lake Community College*
Blanche Haning, *North Carolina State University*
Richard Hanke, *Rose State College*
Laszlo Hanzely, *Northern Illinois University*
David Harbster, *Paradise Valley Community College*
Sig Harden, *Troy University Montgomery*
Reba Harrell, *Hinds Community College*
Jim Harris, *Utah Valley Community College*
Mary Harris, *Louisiana State University*
Chris Haynes, *Shelton State Community College*

Janet Haynes, *Long Island University*
Jean Helgeson, *Collin County Community College*
Ira Herskowitz, *University of California, San Francisco*
Paul Hertz, *Barnard College*
Margaret Hicks, *David Lipscomb University*
Jean Higgins-Fonda, *Prince George's Community College*
Phyllis Hirsch, *East Los Angeles College*
William Hixon, *St. Ambrose University*
Carl Hoagstrom, *Ohio Northern University*
Kim Hodgson, *Longwood College*
Jon Hoekstra, *Gainesville State College*
Kelly Hogan, *University of North Carolina at Chapel Hill*
John Holt, *Michigan State University*
Laura Hoopes, *Occidental College*
Lauren Howard, *Norwich University*
Robert Howe, *Suffolk University*
Michael Hudecki, *State University of New York, Buffalo*
George Hudock, *Indiana University*
Kris Hueftle, *Pensacola Junior College*
Barbara Hunnicutt, *Seminole Community College*
Brenda Hunzinger, *Lake Land College*
Catherine Hurlbut, *Florida Community College*
Charles Ide, *Tulane University*
Mark Ikeda, *San Bernardino Valley College*
Georgia Ineichen, *Hinds Community College*
Robert Iwan, *Inver Hills Community College*
Mark E. Jackson, *Central Connecticut State University*
Charles Jacobs, *Henry Ford Community College*
Fred James, *Presbyterian College*
Ursula Jander, *Washburn University*
Alan Jaworski, *University of Georgia*
R. Jensen, *Saint Mary's College*
Robert Johnson, *Pierce College, Lakewood Campus*
Roishene Johnson, *Bossier Parish Community College*
Russell Johnson, *Ricks College*
John C. Jones, *Calhoun Community College*
Florence Juillerat, *Indiana University at Indianapolis*
Tracy Kahn, *University of California, Riverside*
Hinrich Kaiser, *Victor Valley College*
Klaus Kalthoff, *University of Texas at Austin*
Tom Kantz, *California State University, Sacramento*
Jennifer Katcher, *Pima Community College*
Judy Kaufman, *Monroe Community College*
Marlene Kayne, *The College of New Jersey*
Mahlon Kelly, *University of Virginia*
Kenneth Kerrick, *University of Pittsburgh at Johnstown*
Joyce Kille-Marino, *College of Charleston*
Joanne Kilpatrick, *Auburn University, Montgomery*
Stephen Kilpatrick, *University of Pittsburgh at Johnstown*
Lee Kirkpatrick, *Glendale Community College*
Peter Kish, *Southwestern Oklahoma State University*
Cindy Klevickis, *James Madison University*
Robert Koch, *California State University, Fullerton*
Eliot Krause, *Seton Hall University*
Dubear Kroening, *University of Wisconsin, Fox Valley*
Kevin Krown, *San Diego State University*

Margaret Maile Lam, *Kapiolani Community College*
MaryLynne LaMantia, *Golden West College*
Mary Rose Lamb, *University of Puget Sound*
Dale Lambert, *Tarrant County College, Northeast*
Thomas Lammers, *University of Wisconsin, Oshkosh*
Carmine Lanciani, *University of Florida*
Vic Landrum, *Washburn University*
Deborah Langsam, *University of North Carolina at Charlotte*
Geneen Lannom, *University of Central Oklahoma*
Brenda Latham, *Merced College*
Liz Lawrence, *Miles Community College*
Steven Lebsack, *Linn-Benton Community College*
Karen Lee, *University of Pittsburgh at Johnstown*
Tom Lehman, *Morgan Community College*
William Lemon, *Southwestern Oregon Community College*
Laurie M. Len, *El Camino College*
Peggy Lepley, *Cincinnati State University*
Richard Liebaert, *Linn-Benton Community College*
Kevin Lien, *Portland Community College*
Harvey Liftin, *Broward Community College*
Ivo Lindauer, *University of Northern Colorado*
William Lindsay, *Monterey Peninsula College*
Kirsten Lindstrom, *Santa Rosa Junior College*
Melanie Loo, *California State University, Sacramento*
David Loring, *Johnson County Community College*
Eric Lovely, *Arkansas Tech University*
Paul Lurquin, *Washington State University*
James Mack, *Monmouth University*
David Magrane, *Morehead State University*
Joan Maloof, *Salisbury State University*
Joseph Marshall, *West Virginia University*
Presley Martin, *Drexel University*
William McComas, *University of Iowa*
Steven McCullagh, *Kennesaw State College*
Mitchell McGinnis, *North Seattle Community College*
James McGivern, *Gannon University*
Colleen McNamara, *Albuquerque TVI Community College*
Caroline McNutt, *Schoolcraft College*
Scott Meissner, *Cornell University*
Joseph Mendelson, *Utah State University*
Timothy Metz, *Campbell University*
Iain Miller, *University of Cincinnati*
Robert Miller, *University of Dubuque*
V. Christine Minor, *Clemson University*
Brad Mogen, *University of Wisconsin, River Falls*
James Moné, *Millersville University*
Jamie Moon, *University of North Florida*
Juan Morata, *Miami Dade College*
Richard Mortensen, *Albion College*
Henry Mulcahy, *Suffolk University*
Christopher Murphy, *James Madison University*
Kathryn Nette, *Cuyamaca College*
James Newcomb, *New England College*
Zia Nisani, *Antelope Valley College*
James Nivison, *Mid Michigan Community College*
Peter Nordloh, *Southeastern Community College*
Stephen Novak, *Boise State University*
Bette Nybakken, *Hartnell College*
Michael O'Donnell, *Trinity College*
Steven Oliver, *Worcester State College*
Karen Olmstead, *University of South Dakota*

Steven O'Neal, *Southwestern Oklahoma State University*
Lowell Orr, *Kent State University*
William Outlaw, *Florida State University*
Phillip Pack, *Woodbury University*
Kevin Padian, *University of California, Berkeley*
Kay Pauling, *Foothill College*
Mark Paulissen, *Northeastern State University, Tahlequah*
Debra Pearce, *Northern Kentucky University*
David Pearson, *Bucknell University*
Patricia Pearson, *Western Kentucky University*
Kathleen Pelkki, *Saginaw Valley State University*
Andrew Penniman, *Georgia Perimeter College*
John Peters, *College of Charleston*
Gary Peterson, *South Dakota State University*
Margaret Peterson, *Concordia Lutheran College*
Russell L. Peterson, *Indiana University of Pennsylvania*
Paula Piehl, *Potomac State College*
Ben Pierce, *Baylor University*
Jack Plaggemeyer, *Little Big Horn College*
Barbara Pleasants, *Iowa State University*
Kathryn Podwall, *Nassau Community College*
Judith Pottmeyer, *Columbia Basin College*
Donald Potts, *University of California, Santa Cruz*
Nirmala Prabhu, *Edison Community College*
Elena Pravosudova, *University of Nevada, Reno*
James Pru, *Belleville Area College*
Rongsun Pu, *Kean University*
Charles Pumpuni, *Northern Virginia Community College*
Kimberly Puvalowski, *Old Bridge High School*
Rebecca Pyles, *East Tennessee State University*
Shanmugavel Rajendran, *Baltimore City Community College*
Bob Ratterman, *Jamestown Community College*
Jill Raymond, *Rock Valley College*
Michael Read, *Germanna Community College*
Brian Reeder, *Morehead State University*
Bruce Reid, *Kean College*
David Reid, *Blackburn College*
Stephen Reinbold, *Longview Community College*
Erin Rempala, *San Diego Mesa College*
Michael Renfroe, *James Madison University*
Tim Revell, *Mt. San Antonio College*
Douglas Reynolds, *Central Washington University*
Fred Rhoades, *Western Washington University*
John Rinehart, *Eastern Oregon University*
Laura Ritt, *Burlington County College*
Lynn Rivers, *Henry Ford Community College*
Bruce Robart, *University of Pittsburgh at Johnstown*
Jennifer Roberts, *Lewis University*
Laurel Roberts, *University of Pittsburgh*
Luis A. Rodriguez, *San Antonio Colleges*
Duane Rohlfing, *University of South Carolina*
Jeanette Rollinger, *College of the Sequoias*

Steven Roof, *Fairmont State College*
Jim Rosowski, *University of Nebraska*
Stephen Rothstein, *University of California, Santa Barbara*
Donald Roush, *University of North Alabama*
Lynette Rushton, *South Puget Sound Community College*
Connie Rye, *East Mississippi Community College*
Linda Sabatino, *State University of New York, Suffolk County Community College*
Douglas Schamel, *University of Alaska, Fairbanks*
Douglas Schelhaas, *University of Mary*
Beverly Schieltz, *Wright State University*
Fred Schindler, *Indian Hills Community College*
Robert Schoch, *Boston University*
Brian Scholtens, *College of Charleston*
John Richard Schrock, *Emporia State University*
Julie Schroer, *Bismarck State College*
Fayla Schwartz, *Everett Community College*
Judy Shea, *Kutztown University of Pennsylvania*
Daniela Shebitz, *Kean University*
Thomas Shellberg, *Henry Ford Community College*
Cara Shillington, *Eastern Michigan University*
Lisa Shimeld, *Crafton Hills College*
Brian Shmaefsky, *Kingwood College*
Mark Shotwell, *Slippery Rock University*
Jane Shoup, *Purdue University*
Michele Shuster, *New Mexico State University*
Linda Simpson, *University of North Carolina at Charlotte*
Gary Smith, *Tarrant County Junior College*
Marc Smith, *Sinclair Community College*
Michael Smith, *Western Kentucky University*
Phil Snider, *University of Houston*
Sam C. Sochet, *Thomas Edison Career and Technical Education High School*
Gary Sojka, *Bucknell University*
Ralph Sorensen, *Gettysburg College*
Ruth Sporer, *Rutgers University*
Linda Brooke Stabler, *University of Central Oklahoma*
David Stanton, *Saginaw Valley State University*
Amanda Starnes, *Emory University*
John Stolz, *Duquesne University*
Ross Strayer, *Washtenaw Community College*
Donald Streuble, *Idaho State University*
Megan Stringer, *Jones County Junior College*
Mark Sugalski, *New England College*
Gerald Summers, *University of Missouri*
Marshall Sundberg, *Louisiana State University*
Christopher Tabit, *University of West Georgia*
David Tauck, *Santa Clara University*
Hilda Taylor, *Acadia University*
Franklin Te, *Miami Dade College*
Gene Thomas, *Solano Community College*
Kenneth Thomas, *Northern Essex Community College*

Kathy Thompson, *Louisiana State University*
Laura Thurlow, *Jackson Community College*
Anne Tokazewski, *Burlington County College*
John Tolli, *Southwestern College*
Bruce Tomlinson, *State University of New York, Fredonia*
Nancy Tress, *University of Pittsburgh at Titusville*
Donald Trisel, *Fairmont State College*
Kimberly Turk, *Mitchell Community College*
Virginia Turner, *Harper College*
Mike Tveten, *Pima College*
Michael Twaddle, *University of Toledo*
Rani Vajravelu, *University of Central Florida*
Leslie VanderMolen, *Humboldt State University*
Cinnamon VanPutte, *Southwestern Illinois College*
Sarah VanVickle-Chavez, *Washington University*
John Vaughan, *Georgetown College*
Martin Vaughan, *Indiana University*
Mark Venable, *Appalachian State University*
Ann Vernon, *St. Charles County Community College*
Rukmani Viswanath, *Laredo Community College*
Frederick W. Vogt, *Elgin Community College*
Mary Beth Voltura, *State University of New York, Cortland*
Jerry Waldvogel, *Clemson University*
Robert Wallace, *Ripon College*
Dennis Walsh, *MassBay Community College*
Patricia Walsh, *University of Delaware*
Lisa Weasel, *Portland State University*
James Wee, *Loyola University*
Harrington Wells, *University of Tulsa*
Jennifer Wiatrowski, *Pasco-Hernando Community College*
Larry Williams, *University of Houston*
Ray S. Williams, *Appalachian State University*
Lura Williamson, *University of New Orleans*
Sandra Winicur, *Indiana University, South Bend*
Robert R. Wise, *University of Wisconsin Oshkosh*
Mary E. Wisgirda, *San Jacinto College*
Mary Jo Witz, *Monroe Community College*
Neil Woffinden, *University of Pittsburgh at Johnstown*
Michael Womack, *Macon State University*
Patrick Woolley, *East Central College*
Maury Wrightson, *Germanna Community College*
Tumen Wuliji, *University of Nevada, Reno*
Mark Wygoda, *McNeese State University*
Tony Yates, *Seminole State College*
William Yurkiewicz, *Millersville University of Pennsylvania*
Gregory Zagursky, *Radford University*
Martin Zahn, *Thomas Nelson Community College*
Edward J. Zalisko, *Blackburn College*
David Zeigler, *University of North Carolina at Pembroke*
Uko Zylstra, *Calvin College*

Detailed Contents

Biology: *Exploring Life*

Snowy owls (*Bubo scandiacus*), such as the one on the cover of this textbook and pictured below, are strikingly beautiful owls with bright orange eyes and wingspans as wide as five feet. These swift and silent predators exhibit remarkable adaptations for life in their frozen, barren habitat. The layers of fine feathers on their face, body, legs, and even their feet provide insulation in subzero weather. They breed on the Arctic tundra, nesting on open ground. The female broods the eggs and young, while the male provides a steady supply of food. His keen vision and acute hearing help him locate small mammals such as voles and lemmings, which he then snatches in mid-flight with his sharp talons.

? *Why do so many animals match their surroundings?*

The majority of owl species are nocturnal. But during the endless days of arctic summers, snowy owls hunt in daylight. Projecting upper eyelids help shield their eyes from bright sun. As with all owls, the overlapping fields of vision of their forward-facing eyes provide superior depth perception. These large eyes cannot move, so an owl must turn its whole head to follow a moving object. This is not a problem for an owl, as you can see in the photo below, because adaptations of its neck

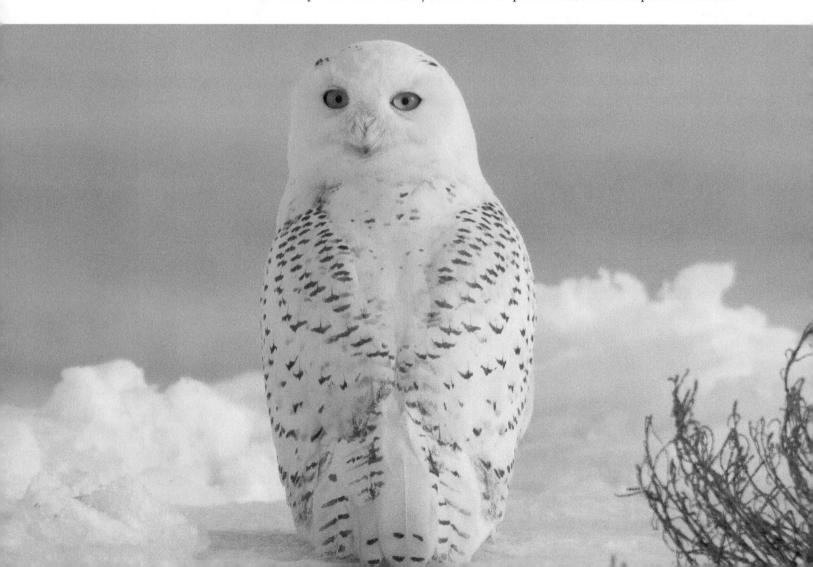

vertebrae enable it to rotate its head a full 270 degrees. Imagine being able to look over your left shoulder by turning your head to the right!

You may think of owls in general in shades of brown, nesting in tree cavities and blending in with their surroundings. And with snowy owls, you may think of Harry Potter's white-feathered companion. In real life, these owls also blend in with their wintry habitat. Later in this chapter, you will read about an experiment that tests the hypothesis that camouflage coloration protects animals from predators.

The amazing adaptations of snowy owls are the result of evolution, the process that has transformed life from its earliest beginnings to the astounding array of organisms living today. In this chapter, we begin our exploration of biology—the scientific study of life.

Themes in the Study of Biology
(1.1–1.4)

Common themes help to organize the study of life.

Evolution, the Core Theme of Biology
(1.5–1.7)

Evolution accounts for the unity and diversity of life and the evolutionary adaptations of organisms to their environment.

The Process of Science
(1.8–1.9)

In studying nature, scientists make observations, form hypotheses, and test predictions.

Biology and Everyday Life
(1.10–1.11)

Learning about biology helps us understand many issues involving science, technology, and society.

▷ Themes in the Study of Biology

1.1 All forms of life share common properties

Defining **biology** as the scientific study of life raises the obvious question: What is *life*? Even a small child realizes that a bug or a flower is alive, whereas a rock or a car is not. But the phenomenon we call life defies a simple, one-sentence definition. We recognize life mainly by what living things do. **Figure 1.1** highlights seven of the properties and processes that we associate with life.

1. *Order.* This sunflower illustrates the ordered structure that typifies life. Living cells make up this complex organization.

2. *Reproduction.* Organisms reproduce their own kind. Here a baby African elephant walks beneath its mother.

3. *Growth and development.* Inherited information in the form of DNA controls the pattern of growth and development of all organisms, including this hatching crocodile.

4. *Energy processing.* This caterpillar will use the chemical energy stored in the plant it is eating to power its own activities and chemical reactions.

5. *Regulation.* Many types of mechanisms regulate an organism's internal environment, keeping it within limits that sustain life. Pictured here is a lizard "sunbathing"—which helps raise its body temperature on cool mornings.

6. *Response to the environment.* All organisms respond to environmental stimuli. This Venus flytrap closed its trap rapidly in response to the stimulus of a damselfly landing on it.

7. *Evolutionary adaptation.* A snowy owl's sharp talons facilitate prey capture and its feathered feet keep it warm in its cold habitat. Such adaptations evolve over many generations as individuals with traits best suited to their environment have greater reproductive success and pass their traits to offspring.

Figure 1.1 reminds us that the living world is wondrously varied. How do biologists make sense of this diversity and complexity, and how can you? Indeed, biology is a subject of enormous scope that gets bigger all the time. One of the ways to help you organize this information is to connect what you learn to a set of themes that you will encounter throughout your study of life. The next few modules introduce several important themes: novel properties emerging at each level of biological organization, the correlation of structure and function, and the exchange of matter and energy as organisms interact with the environment. We then focus on the core theme of biology—evolution, the theme that makes sense of both the unity and diversity of life.

Let's begin our journey with a tour through the levels of the biological hierarchy.

? **How would you define life?**

● Life can be defined by a set of common properties such as those described in this module.

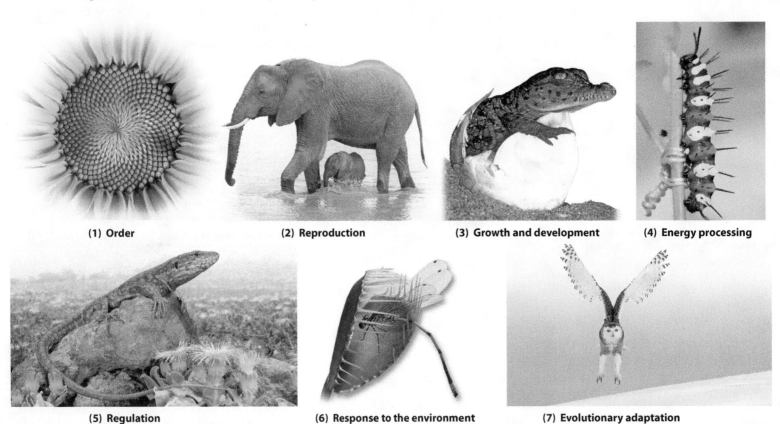

(1) Order   **(2) Reproduction**   **(3) Growth and development**   **(4) Energy processing**

(5) Regulation   **(6) Response to the environment**   **(7) Evolutionary adaptation**

▲ **Figure 1.1**   Some important properties of life

1.2 In life's hierarchy of organization, new properties emerge at each level

As **Figure 1.2** illustrates, the study of life extends from the global scale of the biosphere to the microscopic level of molecules. At the upper left we take a distant view of the **biosphere**, all of the environments on Earth that support life.

These include most regions of land, bodies of water, and the lower atmosphere. A closer look at one of these environments brings us to the level of an **ecosystem**, which consists of all the organisms living in a particular area, as well as the physical components with which the organisms interact, such as air, soil, water, and sunlight.

The entire array of organisms in an ecosystem is called a **community**. In this community, we find alligators and snakes, herons and egrets, myriad insects, trees and other plants, fungi, and enormous numbers of microorganisms. Each unique form of life is called a species.

A **population** includes all the individuals of a particular species living in an area. Next in the hierarchy is the **organism**, an individual living thing, such as an alligator.

Within a complex organism, life's hierarchy continues to unfold. An **organ system**, such as the circulatory system or nervous system, consists of several organs that cooperate in a specific function. For instance, the organs of the nervous system are the brain, the spinal cord, and the nerves. An alligator's nervous system controls all its actions.

An **organ** is made up of several different **tissues**, each in turn made up of a group of similar cells that perform a specific function. A **cell** is the fundamental unit of life. In the nerve cell shown here, you can see several organelles, such as the nucleus. An **organelle** is a membrane-enclosed structure that performs a specific function within a cell.

Finally, we reach the level of molecules in the hierarchy. A **molecule** is a cluster of small chemical units called atoms held together by chemical bonds. Our example in Figure 1.2 is a computer graphic of a section of DNA (deoxyribonucleic acid)—the molecule of inheritance.

Now let's work our way in the opposite direction in Figure 1.2, moving up life's hierarchy from molecules to the biosphere. At each higher level, there are novel properties that arise, properties that were not present at the preceding level. For example, life emerges at the level of the cell—a test tube full of organelles is not alive. Such **emergent properties** represent an important theme of biology. The familiar saying that "the whole is greater than the sum of its parts" captures this idea. The emergent properties of each level result from the specific arrangement and interactions of its parts.

> **?** Which of these levels of biological organization includes all others in the list: cell, molecule, organ, tissue?
>
> Organ

- **Biosphere** — Florida
- **Ecosystem** Florida Everglades
- **Community** All organisms in this wetland ecosystem
- **Population** All alligators living in the wetlands
- **Organism** an American alligator
- **Organ system** Nervous system — Nerve, Spinal cord, Brain
- **Organ** Brain
- **Tissue** Nervous tissue
- **Cell** Nerve cell — Nucleus
- **Organelle** Nucleus
- **Molecule** DNA — Atom

▲ **Figure 1.2** Life's hierarchy of organization

1.3 Cells are the structural and functional units of life

The cell has a special place in the hierarchy of biological organization. It is the level at which the properties of life emerge—the lowest level of structure that can perform all activities required for life. A cell can regulate its internal environment, take in and use energy, respond to its environment, and build and maintain its complex organization. The ability of cells to give rise to new cells is the basis for all reproduction and also for the growth and repair of multicellular organisms.

All organisms are composed of cells. They occur singly as a great variety of unicellular (single-celled) organisms, such as amoebas and most bacteria. And cells are the subunits that make up multicellular organisms, such as owls and trees. Your body consists of trillions of cells of many different kinds.

All cells share certain characteristics. For example, every cell is enclosed by a membrane that regulates the passage of materials between the cell and its surroundings. And every cell uses DNA as its genetic information. However, we can distinguish between two main forms of cells. **Prokaryotic cells** were the first to evolve and were Earth's sole inhabitants for more than 1.5 billion years. Fossil evidence indicates that **eukaryotic cells** evolved from prokaryotic ancestral cells about 1.8 billion years ago.

Figure 1.3 shows these two types of cells as artificially colored photographs taken with an electron microscope. A prokaryotic cell is much simpler and usually much smaller than a eukaryotic cell. The cells of the microorganisms we call bacteria are prokaryotic. Plants, animals, fungi, and protists (mostly unicellular organisms) are all composed of eukaryotic cells. As you can see in Figure 1.3, a eukaryotic cell is subdivided by membranes into various functional compartments, or organelles. These include a nucleus, which houses the cell's DNA.

The properties of life emerge from the ordered arrangement and interactions of the structures of a cell. Such a combination of components forms a more complex organization that we can call a *system*. Systems and their emergent properties are not unique to life. Consider a box of bicycle parts. When all of the individual parts are properly assembled, the result is a mechanical system you can use for exercise or transportation.

The emergent properties of life, however, are particularly challenging to study because of the unrivaled complexity of biological systems. Biologists today often use an approach called **systems biology**—the study of a biological system and the modeling of its dynamic behavior by analyzing the interactions among its parts. Biological systems can range from the functioning of the biosphere to the molecular machinery of an organelle.

Cells illustrate another theme of biology: the correlation of structure and function. Experience shows you that form

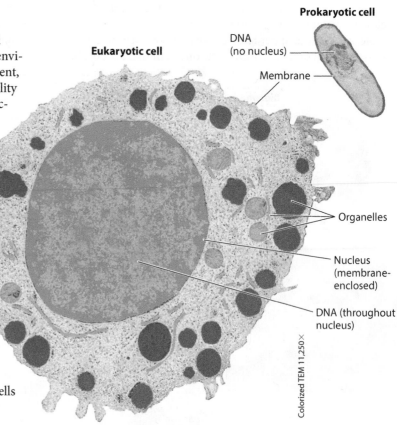

Eukaryotic cell

Prokaryotic cell

DNA (no nucleus)

Membrane

Organelles

Nucleus (membrane-enclosed)

DNA (throughout nucleus)

Colorized TEM 11,250×

▲ **Figure 1.3** Contrasting the size and complexity of prokaryotic and eukaryotic cells (shown here approximately 11,250 times their real size)

generally fits function. A screwdriver tightens or loosens screws, a hammer pounds nails. Because of their form, these tools can't do each other's jobs. Applied to biology, this theme of form fitting function is a guide to the structure of life at all its organizational levels. For example, the long extension of the nerve cell shown in Figure 1.2 enables it to transmit impulses across long distances in the body. Often, analyzing a biological structure gives us clues about what it does and how it works.

The activities of organisms are all based on cells. For example, your every thought is based on the actions of nerve cells, and your movements depend on muscle cells. Even a global process such as the cycling of carbon is the result of cellular activities, including the photosynthesis of plant cells and the cellular respiration of nearly all cells, a process that uses oxygen to break down sugar for energy and releases carbon dioxide. In the next module, we explore these processes and how they relate to the theme of organisms interacting with their environments.

? **Why are cells considered the basic units of life?**

● They are the lowest level in the hierarchy of biological organization at which the properties of life emerge.

1.4 Organisms interact with their environment, exchanging matter and energy

An organism interacts with its environment, and that environment includes other organisms as well as physical factors. Figure 1.4 is a simplified diagram of such interactions taking place in a forest in Canada. Plants are the producers that provide the food for a typical ecosystem. A tree, for example, absorbs water (H_2O) and minerals from the soil through its roots, and its leaves take in carbon dioxide (CO_2) from the air. In photosynthesis, a tree's leaves use energy from sunlight to convert CO_2 and H_2O to sugar and oxygen (O_2). The leaves release O_2 to the air, and the roots help form soil by breaking up rocks. Thus, both organism and environment are affected by the interactions between them.

The consumers of a ecosystem eat plants and other animals. The moose in Figure 1.4 eats the grasses and tender shoots and leaves of trees in a forest ecosystem in Canada. To release the energy in food, animals (as well as plants and most other organisms) take in O_2 from the air and release CO_2. An animal's wastes return other chemicals to the environment.

Another vital part of the ecosystem includes the small animals, fungi, and bacteria in the soil that decompose wastes and the remains of dead organisms. These decomposers act as recyclers, changing complex matter into simpler chemicals that plants can absorb and use.

The dynamics of ecosystems include two major processes—the recycling of chemicals and the flow of energy. These processes are illustrated in Figure 1.4. The most basic chemicals necessary for life—carbon dioxide, oxygen, water, and various minerals—cycle within an ecosystem from the air and soil to plants, to animals and decomposers, and back to the air and soil (shown with blue arrows in the figure).

By contrast, an ecosystem gains and loses energy constantly. Energy flows into the ecosystem when plants and other photosynthesizers absorb light energy from the sun (yellow arrow) and convert it to the chemical energy of sugars and other complex molecules. Chemical energy (orange arrow) is then passed through a series of consumers and, eventually, to decomposers, powering each organism in turn. In the process of these energy conversions between and within organisms, some energy is converted to heat, which is then lost from the system (red arrow). In contrast to chemicals, which recycle within an ecosystem, energy flows through an ecosystem, entering as light and exiting as heat.

In this first section, we have touched on several themes of biology, from emergent properties in the biological hierarchy of organization, to cells as the structural and functional units of life, to the exchange of matter and energy as organisms interact with their environment. In the next section, we begin our exploration of evolution, the core theme of biology.

? **Explain how the photosynthesis of plants functions in both the cycling of chemicals and the flow of energy in an ecosystem.**

Photosynthesis uses light energy to convert carbon dioxide and water to energy-rich food, making it the pathway by which both chemicals and energy become available to most organisms.

▲ Figure 1.4   The cycling of chemicals and flow of energy in an ecosystem

1.5 The unity of life is based on DNA and a common genetic code

All cells have DNA, and the continuity of life depends on this universal genetic material. DNA is the chemical substance of **genes**, the units of inheritance that transmit information from parents to offspring. Genes, which are grouped into very long DNA molecules called chromosomes, also control all the activities of a cell.

How does the molecular structure of DNA account for its ability to encode and transmit information? Each DNA molecule is made up of two long chains, called strands, coiled together into a double helix. The strands are made up of four kinds of chemical building blocks. **Figure 1.5** (left side) illustrates these four building blocks, called nucleotides, with different colors and letter abbreviations of their names. The right side of the figure shows a short section of a DNA double helix.

Each time a cell divides, its DNA is first replicated, or copied—the double helix unzips and new complementary strands assemble along the separated strands. Thus, each new cell inherits a complete set of DNA, identical to that of the parent cell. You began as a single cell stocked with DNA inherited from your two parents. The replication of that DNA during each round of cell division transmitted copies of the DNA to what eventually became the trillions of cells of your body.

The way DNA encodes a cell's information is analogous to the way we arrange letters of the alphabet into precise sequences with specific meanings. The word *rat*, for example, conjures up an image of a rodent; *tar* and *art*, which contain the same letters, mean very different things. We can think of the four building blocks as the alphabet of inheritance. Specific sequential arrangements of these four chemical letters encode precise information in genes, which are typically hundreds or thousands of "letters" long.

The DNA of genes provides the blueprints for making proteins, and proteins serve as the tools that actually build and maintain the cell and carry out its activities. A bacterial gene may direct the cell to "Make a yellow pigment." A particular human gene may mean "Make the hormone insulin." All

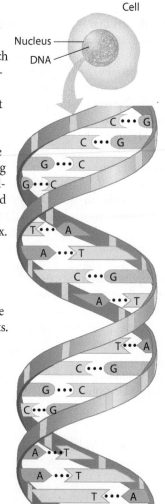

▲ **Figure 1.5** The four building blocks of DNA (left); part of a DNA double helix (right)

forms of life use essentially the same genetic code to translate the information stored in DNA into proteins. This makes it possible to engineer cells to produce proteins normally found only in some other organism. Thus, bacteria can be used to produce insulin for the treatment of diabetes by inserting a gene for human insulin into bacterial cells.

The diversity of life arises from differences in DNA sequences—in other words, from variations on the common theme of storing genetic information in DNA. Bacteria and humans are different because they have different genes. But both sets of instructions are written in the same language.

The entire "library" of genetic instructions that an organism inherits is called its **genome**. A typical human cell has two similar sets of chromosomes, and each set contains about 3 billion nucleotide pairs. In recent years, scientists have determined the entire sequence of nucleotides in the human genome, as well as the genomes of thousands of other species. More species continue to be added to the list of species whose genomes have been sequenced as the rate at which sequencing can be done has accelerated rapidly in recent years. To deal with the resulting deluge of data, scientists are applying a systems biology approach at the molecular level. In an emerging field known as genomics, researchers now study whole sets of genes in a species and then compare genes across multiple species. The benefits from such an approach range from identifying genes that may be implicated in human cancers to revealing the evolutionary relationships among diverse organisms based on similarities in their genomes. Genomics affirms the unity of life based on the universal genetic material—DNA.

In the next module, we see how biologists attempt to organize the diversity of life.

? **What are the two main functions of DNA?**

● DNA is the genetic material that is passed from parents to offspring, and it codes for proteins that control the activity of cells.

1.6 The diversity of life can be arranged into three domains

We can think of biology's enormous scope as having two dimensions. The "vertical" dimension, which we examined in Module 1.2, is the size scale that stretches from molecules to

the biosphere. But biology also has a "horizontal" dimension, spanning across the great diversity of organisms existing now and over the long history of life on Earth.

Diversity is a hallmark of life. Biologists have so far identified and named about 1.8 million species. Estimates of the total number of species range from 10 million to more than 100 million.

There seems to be a human tendency to group things, such as owls or butterflies, although we recognize that each group includes many different species. And then we cluster groups into broader categories, such as birds and insects. Taxonomy, the branch of biology that names and classifies species, arranges species into a hierarchy of broader and broader groups: genus, family, order, class, phylum, and kingdom.

Historically, biologists divided all of life into five kingdoms. But new methods for assessing evolutionary relationships, such as comparisons of DNA sequences, have led to an ongoing reevaluation of the number and boundaries of kingdoms. Although the debate on such divisions continues, there is consensus among biologists that life can be organized into three higher levels called **domains**. Figure 1.6 shows representatives of domains Bacteria, Archaea, and Eukarya.

Domains **Bacteria** and **Archaea** both consist of prokaryotes, organisms with prokaryotic cells. Bacteria are the most diverse and widespread prokaryotes. Many of the prokaryotes known as archaea live in Earth's extreme environments, such as salty lakes and boiling hot springs. Each rod-shaped or round structure in the photos of the prokaryotes in Figure 1.6 is a single cell. These photos were made with an electron microscope, and the number along the side indicates the magnification of the image.

All the eukaryotes, organisms with eukaryotic cells, are grouped in domain **Eukarya**. Protists are a diverse collection of mostly single-celled organisms. Pictured in Figure 1.6 is an assortment of protists in a drop of pond water. Biologists are currently assessing how to group the protists to reflect their evolutionary relationships.

The three remaining groups within Eukarya are distinguished partly by their modes of nutrition. Kingdom Plantae consists of plants, which produce their own food by photosynthesis. The plant pictured in Figure 1.6 is a tropical bromeliad, a plant native to the Americas.

Kingdom Fungi, represented by the mushrooms in Figure 1.6, is a diverse group whose members mostly decompose the remains of dead organisms and organic wastes and absorb the nutrients into their cells.

Animals obtain food by eating other organisms. The sloth in Figure 1.6 resides in South American rain forests. There are actually members of two other groups in the sloth photo. The sloth is clinging to a tree (kingdom Plantae), and the greenish tinge in its hair is a luxuriant growth of photosynthetic prokaryotes (domain Bacteria). This photograph exemplifies a theme reflected in our book's title: connections between living things. The sloth depends on trees for food and

Domain Bacteria

Colorized SEM 7,500×

Bacteria

Domain Archaea

Colorized SEM 10,000×

Archaea

Domain Eukarya

LM 340×

Protists (multiple kingdoms)

Kingdom Plantae

Kingdom Fungi

Kingdom Animalia

▲ Figure 1.6   The three domains of life

shelter; the tree uses nutrients from the decomposition of the sloth's feces; the prokaryotes gain access to the sunlight necessary for photosynthesis by living on the sloth; and the sloth is camouflaged from predators by its green coat.

The diversity of life and its interconnectedness are evident almost everywhere. Earlier we looked at life's unity in its shared properties and common genetic code. In the next module, we explore how evolution explains both the unity and the diversity of life.

? **To which of the three domains of life do we belong?**

Eukarya

1.7 Evolution explains the unity and diversity of life

Evolution can be defined as the process of change that has transformed life on Earth from its earliest beginnings to the diversity of organisms living today. The fossil record documents the fact that life has been evolving on Earth for billions of years, and patterns of ancestry can be traced through this record. For example, the mammoth being excavated in **Figure 1.7A** is clearly related to present-day elephants. We can explain the shared traits of mammoths and elephants with the premise that they descended from a common ancestor in the distant past. Their differences reflect the evolutionary changes that occurred within their separate lineages during the history of their existence on Earth. Thus, evolution accounts for life's dual nature of kinship and diversity.

This evolutionary view of life came into sharp focus in November 1859, when Charles Darwin (**Figure 1.7B**) published one of the most important and influential books ever written. Entitled *On the Origin of Species by Means of Natural Selection*, Darwin's book was an immediate bestseller and soon made his name synonymous with the concept of evolution.

As a young man, Darwin made key observations that greatly influenced his thinking. During a five-year, around-the-world voyage, he collected and documented plants and animals in widely varying locations—from the isolated Galápagos Islands off the coast of Ecuador to the heights of the Andes mountains to the jungles of Brazil. He was particularly struck by the adaptations of these varied organisms that fit them to their diverse habitats. After returning to England, Darwin spent more than two decades continuing his observations, performing experiments, corresponding with other scientists, and refining his thinking before he finally published his work.

The first of two main points that Darwin presented in *The Origin of Species* was that species living today arose from a successor of ancestors that differed from them. Darwin called this process "descent with modification." It was an insightful phrase, because it captured both the unity of life (descent from a common ancestor) and the diversity of life (modifications that evolved as species diverged from their ancestors). **Figure 1.7C** illustrates this unity and diversity among birds. These three birds all have a common "bird" body plan of wings, beak, feet, and feathers, but these features are highly specialized for each bird's unique lifestyle.

Darwin's second point was to propose a mechanism for evolution, which he called **natural selection**. Darwin started with two observations, from which he drew two inferences.

OBSERVATION #1: Individual variation. Individuals in a population vary in their traits, many of which are inherited from parents to offspring.

OBSERVATION #2: Overproduction of offspring. All species can produce far more offspring than the environment can support. Competition for resources is thus inevitable, and many of these offspring fail to survive and reproduce.

INFERENCE #1: Unequal reproductive success. Individuals with heritable traits best suited to the local environment are more likely to survive and reproduce than are less well-suited individuals.

INFERENCE #2: Accumulation of favorable traits over time. As a result of this unequal reproductive success over many generations, a higher and higher proportion of individuals in the population will have the advantageous traits.

▲ Figure 1.7A Excavation of 26,000-year-old fossilized mammoth bones from a site in South Dakota

▲ Figure 1.7B Charles Darwin in 1859

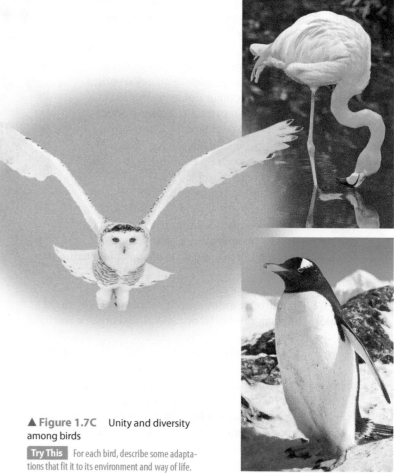

▲ Figure 1.7C Unity and diversity among birds

Try This For each bird, describe some adaptations that fit it to its environment and way of life.

① Population with varied inherited traits.

② Elimination of individuals with certain traits and reproduction of survivors.

③ Increasing frequency of traits that enhance survival and reproductive success.

▲ **Figure 1.7D** An example of natural selection in action

Try This Describe what might happen if some of these beetles colonized a sand dune habitat.

Figure 1.7D uses a simple example to show how natural selection works. ① An imaginary beetle population has colonized an area where the soil has been blackened by a recent brush fire. Initially, the population varies extensively in the inherited coloration of individuals, from very light gray to charcoal. ② A bird eats the beetles it sees most easily, the light-colored ones. This selective predation reduces the number of light-colored beetles and favors the survival and reproductive success of the darker beetles, which pass on the genes for dark coloration to their offspring. ③ After several generations, the population is quite different from the original one. As a result of natural selection, the frequency of the darker-colored beetles in the population has increased.

Darwin realized that numerous small changes in populations as a result of natural selection could eventually lead to major alterations of species. He proposed that new species could evolve as a result of the gradual accumulation of changes over long periods of time. This could occur, for example, if one population fragmented into subpopulations isolated in different environments. In these separate arenas of natural selection, one species could gradually divide into multiple species as isolated populations adapted over many generations to different sets of environmental factors.

The fossil record provides evidence of such diversification of species from ancestral species. **Figure 1.7E** traces an evolutionary tree of elephants and some of their relatives. (Biologists' diagrams of evolutionary relationships generally take the form of branching trees, usually turned sideways and read from left to right.) You can see that the three living species of elephants are very similar because they shared a recent common ancestor (dating to about 3 million years ago, which is relatively recent in an evolutionary timeframe). Notice that all the other close relatives of elephants are extinct—their branches do not extend to the present. (The mammoth being excavated in Figure 1.7A belonged to the genus *Mammuthus*, whose members became extinct less than 10,000 years ago.) If we were to trace this family tree back to about 60 million years ago, however, you would find a common ancestor that connects elephants to their closest living relatives—the manatees and hyraxes. The fossil record, along with other evidence such as comparisons of DNA, allows scientists to trace the evolutionary history of life back through time.

All of life is connected, and the basis for this kinship is evolution—the core theme that makes sense of everything we

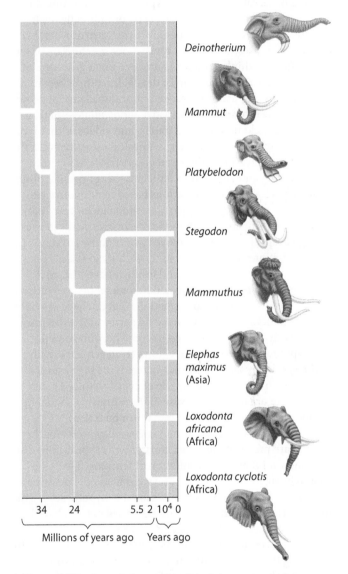

▲ **Figure 1.7E** An evolutionary tree of elephants

Try This Use this tree to determine when mastodons (in the genus *Mammut*) last shared a common ancestor with African elephants.

know and learn about life. In the next module, we introduce scientific inquiry, the process we use to study the natural world.

? **Explain the cause and effect of unequal reproductive success.**

● Those individuals with heritable traits best suited to the local environment produce the greatest number of offspring. Over many generations, the frequency of those adaptive traits increases in the population.

▷ The Process of Science

1.8 In studying nature, scientists make observations and form and test hypotheses

Science is a way of knowing—an approach to understanding the natural world. It stems from our curiosity about ourselves and the world around us. At the heart of science is the process of inquiry, the search for information and explanations of natural phenomena. Scientific inquiry usually involves making observations, forming hypotheses, and testing them.

Observations may be made directly or indirectly, such as with the help of microscopes and other instruments that extend our senses. Recorded observations are the data of science. You may think of data as numbers, but a great deal of scientific data are in the form of detailed, carefully recorded observations. For example, much of our knowledge of snowy owl behavior is based on descriptive, or *qualitative*, data, documented in field notes, photographs, and videos. Other types of data are *quantitative*, such as numerical measurements that may be organized into tables and graphs.

Collecting and analyzing a large number of specific observations can lead to generalizations based on inductive reasoning. For example, "All organisms are made of cells" is an inductive conclusion based on the discovery of cells in every biological specimen observed over two centuries of time.

Observations often prompt us to ask questions and seek answers through the forming and testing of hypotheses. A **hypothesis** is a proposed explanation for a set of observations. A good hypothesis leads to predictions that can be tested by making additional observations or by performing experiments.

Deductive reasoning is used to come up with ways to test hypotheses. Here, the logic flows from general premises to the specific results we should expect if the premises are correct. *If* all organisms are made of cells (premise 1), *and* humans are organisms (premise 2), *then* humans should be composed of cells (a prediction that can be tested).

We all use hypotheses in solving everyday problems. Let's say you are preparing for a big storm that is approaching your area and find that your flashlight isn't working. That your flashlight isn't working is an observation, and the question is obvious: Why doesn't it work? Reasonable hypotheses are that the batteries are dead or the bulb is burned out. Each of these hypotheses leads to predictions you can test with experiments. For example, the dead-battery hypothesis predicts that replacing the batteries with new ones will fix the problem. Figure 1.8 diagrams the results of testing these hypotheses.

An important point about scientific inquiry is that we can never *prove* that a hypothesis is true. As shown in Figure 1.8, the burned-out bulb hypothesis is the more likely explanation in our hypothetical scenario. But perhaps the old bulb was simply loose and the new bulb was inserted correctly. We could test this hypothesis by trying another experiment—carefully reinstalling the original bulb. If the flashlight still doesn't work, the burned-out bulb hypothesis is supported by another line of evidence. Testing a hypothesis in various ways provides additional support for a hypothesis and increases our confidence in it.

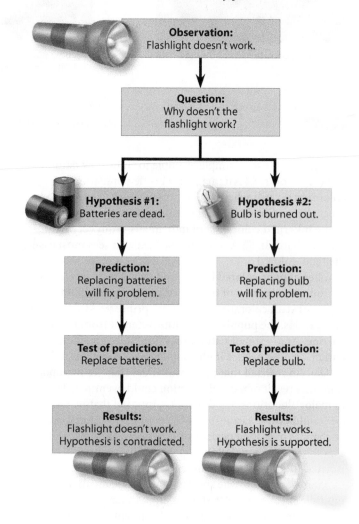

▲ Figure 1.8   An everyday example of forming and testing hypotheses

A scientific **theory** is much broader in scope than a hypothesis and is supported by a large and usually growing body of evidence. For example, the theory of evolution explains a great diversity of observations and is supported by multiple lines of evidence. In addition, the theory of evolution has not been contradicted by any scientific data.

Another important aspect of science is that it is necessarily repetitive: In testing a hypothesis, researchers may make observations that call for rejecting the hypothesis or at least revising and further testing it. This process allows biologists to circle closer and closer to their best estimation of how nature works. As in all quests, science includes elements of challenge, adventure, and luck, along with careful planning, reasoning, creativity, cooperation, competition, and persistence.

Science is a social activity, with most scientists working in teams, which often include graduate and undergraduate students. Scientists share information through peer-reviewed publications, seminars, meetings, and personal communication. Scientists build on what has been learned from earlier research and often check each other's claims by attempting to confirm observations or repeat experiments.

To help you better understand what scientists do, we include a Scientific Thinking module in each chapter. These discussions will encompass several broad activities of science: the forming and testing of hypotheses using various research methods; the analysis and evaluation of data; the use of tools and technologies that have built and continue to expand scientific knowledge; and the communication of the results of scientific studies and the evaluation of their implications for society as a whole.

? What is the main criterion for a scientific hypothesis?

It must generate predictions that can be tested.

1.9 Hypotheses can be tested using controlled field studies

SCIENTIFIC THINKING

You have undoubtedly observed that many animals match their environment: white snowy owls in their arctic habitat, toads the color of dead leaves, flounders that blend in with the sandy sea floor. From these observations, you might hypothesize that such color patterns have evolved as adaptations that protect animals from predation. Can scientists test this camouflage hypothesis? Let's consider an experiment with two populations of mice that belong to the same species (*Peromyscus polionotus*) but live in different environments.

The beach mouse lives along the Florida seashore, a habitat of white sand dunes with sparse clumps of beach grass. The inland mouse lives on darker soil farther inland. As you can see in **Figure 1.9**, there is a striking match between mouse coloration and habitat. In 2010, biologist Hopi Hoekstra of Harvard University and a group of her students headed to Florida to test the camouflage hypothesis. They reasoned that *if* camouflage coloration protects mice from predators, *then* mice with coloration that did not match their habitat would be preyed on more heavily than the native mice that were well-matched to their environment.

The researchers built 250 plastic models of mice and painted them to resemble either beach or inland mice. Equal numbers of models were placed randomly in both habitats. The models resembling the native mice in each habitat were

TABLE 1.9 | RESULTS FROM CAMOUFLAGE EXPERIMENT

| Habitat | Number of Attacks | | % Attacks on Non-camouflaged Models |
	On Camouflaged Models	On Non-camouflaged Models	
Beach (light habitat)	2	5	71%
Inland (dark habitat)	5	16	76%

Data from S. N. Vignieri et al., The selective advantage of crypsis in mice, *Evolution* 64: 2153–2158 (2010).

the control group, and the mice with the non-native coloration were the experimental group. Signs of predation were recorded for three days. Judging by the bite marks and surrounding tracks, the researchers determined the predators were likely foxes, coyotes, owls, herons, and hawks.

As you can see by the results presented in **Table 1.9**, the noncamouflaged models had a much higher percentage of predation attacks in both the beach and inland habitats. The data thus fit the key prediction of the camouflage hypothesis.

Why do so many animals match their surroundings?

This study is an example of a **controlled experiment**, one that is designed to compare an experimental group (the noncamouflaged mice models) with a control group (the camouflaged models that matched the mice native in each area). Ideally, in a controlled experiment the two groups differ only in the one factor the experiment is designed to test—in this case, coat color and its effect on the success of predators. The experimental design left coloration as the only factor that could account for the higher predation rate on the noncamouflaged mice in both the beach and the inland habitats. This study is also an example of a field study, one not done in a laboratory but out in nature. Researchers tested their hypothesis using the natural habitat of the mice and their predators.

? These two populations of mice belong to the same species, yet they have very different coloration. How does natural selection explain these differences?

Camouflaged mice are more likely to survive and reproduce, passing their protective coloration to their offspring.

Beach population Beach mice living on sparsely vegetated sand dunes along the coast have light tan, dappled coats.

Inland population Members of the same species living about 30 km inland are darker in color.

▲ **Figure 1.9** Beach mouse and inland mouse with their native habitat

1.10 Evolution is connected to our everyday lives

EVOLUTION CONNECTION

To emphasize evolution as the core theme of biology, we include an Evolution Connection module in each chapter in this text. But how is evolution connected to your everyday life?

You just learned that natural selection is the primary mechanism of evolution, in which the environment "selects" for adaptive traits when organisms with such traits are better able to survive and reproduce. Through the selective breeding of plants and animals, humans are also an agent of evolution. As a result of **artificial selection**, our crops, livestock, and pets bear little resemblance to their wild ancestors. Humans have been modifying species for millennia, and recent advances in biotechnology have increased our capabilities. Plant biologists using genomics can identify beneficial genes in relatives of our crop plants, enabling the breeding or genetic engineering of enhanced crops. Genes from totally unrelated species have also been inserted into plants. For example, genes for such traits as drought or flood tolerance, improved growth, and increased nutrition have been engineered into rice plants **(Figure 1.10)**.

But humans also affect evolution unintentionally. The impact of habitat loss and global climate change can be seen in the loss of species. Indeed, scientists estimate that the current rate of extinction is 100 to 1,000 times the typical rate seen in the fossil record. Our actions are also driving evolutionary changes in species. For example, our widespread use of antibiotics and pesticides has led to the evolution of antibiotic resistance in bacteria and pesticide resistance in insects.

How can evolutionary theory help address such worldwide problems? Understanding evolution can help us develop strategies for conservation efforts and prompt us to be more judicious in our use of antibiotics and pesticides. It can also help us create flu vaccines and HIV drugs by tracking the rapid evolution of these viruses. Identifying shared genes and studying their actions in closely related organisms may produce new knowledge about cancer or other diseases and lead to new medical treatments. New sources of drugs may be found by tracing the evolutionary history of medicinal plants and identifying beneficial compounds in their relatives. Our understanding of evolution can yield many beneficial results.

▲ **Figure 1.10**　Researcher working with transgenic rice

? **How might an understanding of evolution contribute to the development of new drugs?**

● As one example, we can test the actions of potential drugs in organisms that share our genes and similar cellular processes.

1.11 Biology, technology, and society are connected in important ways

CONNECTION

Many of the current issues facing society are related to biology, and they often involve our expanding technology. What are the differences between science and technology? The goal of science is to understand natural phenomena. In contrast, the goal of **technology** is to apply scientific knowledge for some specific purpose. Scientists usually speak of "discoveries," whereas engineers more often speak of "inventions." These two fields, however, are interdependent. Scientists use new technology in their research, and scientific discoveries often lead to the development of new technologies.

The potent combination of science and technology can have dramatic effects on society. For example, the discovery of the structure of DNA by Watson and Crick 60 years ago and subsequent advances in DNA science led to the technologies of DNA manipulation that today are transforming applied fields such as medicine, agriculture, and forensics.

Technology has improved our standard of living in many ways, but not without consequences. Technology has helped Earth's population to grow tenfold in the past three centuries and more than double to 7 billion in just the past 40 years. Global climate change, toxic wastes, deforestation, and nuclear accidents are just some of the repercussions of more and more people wielding more and more technology. Science can help identify problems and provide insight into how to slow down or prevent further damage. But solutions to these problems have as much to do with politics, economics, and cultural values as with science and technology. Every citizen has a responsibility to develop a reasonable amount of scientific literacy to be able to participate in the debates regarding science and technology. The crucial science-technology-society relationship is a theme we will return to throughout this text.

We hope this book will help you develop an appreciation for biology and help you apply your new knowledge to evaluating issues ranging from your personal health to the well-being of the whole world.

? **How do science and technology interact?**

● New scientific discoveries may lead to new technologies; new technologies may increase the ability of scientists to discover new knowledge.

For practice quizzes, BioFlix animations, MP3 tutorials, video tutors, and more study tools designed for this textbook, go to

MasteringBiology®

Reviewing the Concepts

Themes in the Study of Biology (1.1–1.4)

1.1 All forms of life share common properties. Biology is the scientific study of life. Properties of life include order, reproduction, growth and development, energy processing, regulation, response to the environment, and evolutionary adaptation.

1.2 In life's hierarchy of organization, new properties emerge at each level. Biological organization unfolds as follows: biosphere > ecosystem > community > population > organism > organ system > organ > tissue > cell > organelle > molecule. Emergent properties result from the interactions among component parts.

1.3 Cells are the structural and functional units of life. Eukaryotic cells contain membrane-enclosed organelles, including a nucleus. Prokaryotic cells lack such organelles. Structure is related to function at all levels of organization. Systems biology models the complex behavior of biological systems.

1.4 Organisms interact with their environment, exchanging matter and energy. Ecosystems are characterized by the cycling of chemicals from the atmosphere and soil through producers, consumers, decomposers, and back to the environment. Energy flows one way through an ecosystem—entering as sunlight, converted to chemical energy by producers, passed on to consumers, and exiting as heat.

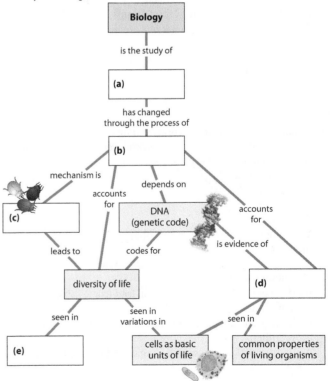

ENERGY FLOW
CHEMICAL CYCLING
Light
Heat
Producers
Consumer
Chemical energy

Evolution, the Core Theme of Biology (1.5–1.7)

1.5 The unity of life is based on DNA and a common genetic code. DNA is responsible for heredity and for programming the activities of a cell. A species' genes are coded in the sequences of the four building blocks making up DNA's double helix. Genomics is the analysis and comparison of genomes.

1.6 The diversity of life can be arranged into three domains. Taxonomists name species and classify them into a system of broader groups. Domains Bacteria and Archaea consist of prokaryotes. The eukaryotic domain, Eukarya, includes various protists and the kingdoms Fungi, Plantae, and Animalia.

1.7 Evolution explains the unity and diversity of life. Darwin synthesized the theory of evolution by natural selection.

Observations

Heritable variations

Overproduction of offspring

Inferences

Natural selection: Unequal reproductive success leads to evolution of adaptations in populations.

The Process of Science (1.8–1.9)

1.8 In studying nature, scientists make observations and form and test hypotheses. Scientists use inductive reasoning to draw general conclusions from many observations. They form hypotheses and use deductive reasoning to make predictions, which can be tested with experiments or additional observations. Data may be qualitative or quantitative. A scientific theory is broad in scope and is supported by a large body of evidence.

1.9 Hypotheses can be tested using controlled field studies. Researchers found that mice models that did not match their habitat had higher predation rates than camouflaged models. In a controlled experiment, the use of control and experimental groups can demonstrate the effect of a single variable.

Biology and Everyday Life (1.10–1.11)

1.10 Evolution is connected to our everyday lives. Evolutionary theory is useful in medicine, agriculture, forensics, and conservation. Human-caused environmental changes are powerful selective forces that affect the evolution of many species.

1.11 Biology, technology, and society are connected in important ways. Technological advances stem from scientific research, and research benefits from new technologies.

Connecting the Concepts

1. Complete the following map organizing some of biology's major concepts.

Biology

is the study of

(a)

has changed through the process of

(b)

mechanism is

accounts for

depends on

(c)

DNA (genetic code)

accounts for

leads to

codes for

is evidence of

diversity of life

(d)

seen in

seen in variations in

seen in

(e)

cells as basic units of life

common properties of living organisms

Testing Your Knowledge

Level 1: Knowledge/Comprehension

2. All the organisms on your campus make up
   a. an ecosystem.
   b. a community.
   c. a population.
   d. the domain Eukarya.

3. Single-celled amoebas and bacteria are grouped into different domains because
   a. amoebas eat bacteria.
   b. bacteria are not made of cells.
   c. bacterial cells lack a membrane-enclosed nucleus.
   d. amoebas are motile; bacteria are not.

4. Which of the following statements best distinguishes hypotheses from theories in science?
   a. Theories are hypotheses that have been proved.
   b. Hypotheses usually are narrow in scope; theories have broad explanatory power.
   c. Hypotheses are tentative guesses; theories are correct answers to questions about nature.
   d. Hypotheses and theories are different terms for essentially the same thing in science.

5. Which of the following best demonstrates the unity among all living organisms?
   a. descent with modification
   b. DNA and a common genetic code
   c. emergent properties
   d. natural selection

6. A controlled experiment is one that
   a. proceeds slowly enough that a scientist can make careful records of the results.
   b. keeps all variables constant.
   c. is repeated many times to make sure the results are accurate.
   d. tests experimental and control groups in parallel.

7. The core idea that makes sense of all of biology is
   a. evolution.
   b. the correlation of function with structure.
   c. systems biology.
   d. the process of science.

Level 2: Application/Analysis

8. A biologist studying interactions among the protists in an ecosystem could *not* be working at which level in life's hierarchy? (*Choose carefully and explain your answer.*)
   a. the population level
   b. the molecular level
   c. the organism level
   d. the organ level

9. Which of the following best describes the logic of scientific inquiry?
   a. If I generate a testable hypothesis, tests and observations will support it.
   b. If my prediction is correct, it will lead to a testable hypothesis.
   c. If my observations are accurate, they will support my hypothesis.
   d. If my hypothesis is correct, I can expect certain test results.

10. In an ecosystem, how is the movement of energy similar to that of chemicals, and how is it different?

11. Explain the role of heritable variations in Darwin's theory of natural selection.

12. Describe the process of scientific inquiry and explain why it is not a rigid method.

13. Contrast technology with science. Give an example of each to illustrate the difference.

14. Biology can be described as having both a vertical scale and a horizontal scale. Explain what that means.

Level 3: Synthesis/Evaluation

15. Explain what is meant by this statement: Natural selection is an editing mechanism rather than a creative process.

16. The graph below shows the results of an experiment in which mice learned to run through a maze.

   a. State the hypothesis and prediction that you think this experiment tested.
   b. Which was the control group and which the experimental? Why was a control group needed?
   c. List some variables that must have been controlled so as not to affect the results.
   d. Do the data support the hypothesis? Explain.

17. **SCIENTIFIC THINKING** Suppose that in an experiment similar to the camouflage experiment described in Module 1.9, a researcher observed and recorded more total predator attacks on dark-model mice in the inland habitat than on dark models in the beach habitat. From comparing these two pieces of data, the researcher concluded that the camouflage hypothesis is false. Do you think this conclusion is justified? Why or why not?

18. The fruits of wild species of tomato are tiny compared to the giant beefsteak tomatoes available today. This difference in fruit size is almost entirely due to the larger number of cells in the domesticated fruits. Plant biologists have recently discovered genes that are responsible for controlling cell division in tomatoes. Why would such a discovery be important to producers of other kinds of fruits and vegetables? To the study of human development and disease? To our basic understanding of biology?

19. The news media and popular magazines frequently report stories that are connected to biology. In the next 24 hours, record the ones you hear or read about in three different sources and briefly describe the biological connections in each story.

Answers to all questions can be found in Appendix 4.

The Life of the Cell

2

The Chemical Basis of Life

Coral reefs are among the most diverse ecosystems on Earth. They are formed from the gradual buildup of the calcium carbonate skeletons of small coral animals. As you can see in the photo below, these structurally diverse habitats provide havens for a huge diversity of fish and other marine organisms. But in recent years, something in the air is threatening coral reefs. How might a chemical compound in the air harm such a vibrant ecosystem? The answer is chemistry. When carbon dioxide dissolves in water, it reacts with water to form an acid, which then makes the water more acidic. Later in the chapter we will see how scientists are exploring the effects of this ocean acidification on coral reefs.

Will rising atmospheric CO_2 harm coral reefs?

Why do we begin our study of biology with a chapter on chemistry? Well, chemistry is the basis of life—it explains how elements combine into the compounds that make up your body and the bodies of all other living organisms and how chemical reactions underlie the functions of all cells.

Life and its chemistry are tied to water. Life began in water and evolved there for 3 billion years before spreading onto land. And all life, even land-dwelling life, is still dependent on water. Your cells are about 75% water, and that is where the chemical reactions of your body take place. What properties of the simple water molecule make it so indispensable to life on Earth? You'll find out in this chapter.

This chapter will also make connections to one of the main themes in biology—the organization of life into a hierarchy of structural levels, with new properties emerging at each successive level (see Chapter 1). You will see that emergent properties are apparent even at the lowest levels of biological organization—the ordering of atoms into molecules and the interactions of those molecules. Thus we begin our study of biology with some basic concepts of chemistry that will apply throughout our study of life.

BIG IDEAS

Elements, Atoms, and Compounds
(2.1–2.4)

Living organisms are made of atoms of certain elements, mostly combined into compounds.

Chemical Bonds
(2.5–2.9)

The structure of an atom determines what types of bonds it can form with other atoms.

Water's Life-Supporting Properties
(2.10–2.16)

The unique properties of water derive from the polarity and hydrogen bonding of water molecules.

▷ Elements, Atoms, and Compounds

2.1 Organisms are composed of elements, in combinations called compounds

You and all things around you are made of matter—the physical "stuff" of the universe. **Matter** is defined as anything that occupies space and has mass. (In everyday language, we can think of mass as an object's weight.) Matter is found on Earth in three physical states: solid, liquid, and gas. Water is a rare example of matter that exists in the natural environment in all three physical forms: as ice, liquid water, and water vapor.

Types of matter as diverse as water, rocks, air, and biology students are all composed of chemical elements. An **element** is a substance that cannot be broken down to other substances by ordinary chemical means. Today, chemists recognize 92 elements that occur in nature; gold, copper, carbon, and oxygen are some examples. Chemists have also made a few dozen synthetic elements. Each element has a symbol, the first letter or two of its English, Latin, or German name. For example, the symbol for sodium, Na, is from the Latin word *natrium*; the symbol O comes from the English word *oxygen*.

A **compound** is a substance consisting of two or more different elements combined in a fixed ratio. Compounds are much more common than pure elements. In fact, few elements exist in a pure state in nature.

Many compounds consist of only two elements; for instance, table salt (sodium chloride, NaCl) has equal parts of the elements sodium (Na) and chlorine (Cl). Pure sodium is a metal and pure chlorine is a poisonous gas. Chemically combined, however, they form an edible compound (**Figure 2.1**). Hydrogen (H) and oxygen (O) are elements that typically exist as gases. Chemically combined in a ratio of 2:1, however, they form the most abundant compound on the surface of Earth—water (H_2O). These are simple examples of organized matter having emergent properties: A compound has characteristics different from those of its elements.

Most of the compounds in living organisms contain at least three or four elements. Sugar, for example, is formed of carbon (C), hydrogen, and oxygen. Proteins are compounds containing carbon, hydrogen, oxygen, nitrogen (N), and a small amount of sulfur (S). Different arrangements of the atoms of these elements give rise to the unique properties of each compound.

How many of the 92 natural elements are essential for life? The requirements are similar among organisms, but there is some variation. For example, humans need 25 elements, but plants need only 17. Four elements—oxygen, carbon, hydrogen, and nitrogen—make up about 96% of all living matter. These elements are the main ingredients of biological molecules. As you can see in **Table 2.1**, which lists the 25 elements found in humans, calcium (Ca), phosphorus Ⓟ, potassium (K), sulfur, sodium, chlorine, and magnesium (Mg) account for most of the remaining 4% of your body. These elements are involved in such important functions as bone formation

TABLE 2.1 | ELEMENTS IN THE HUMAN BODY

Element	Symbol	Percentage of Body Weight (Including Water)	
Oxygen	O	65.0	
Carbon	C	18.5	96.3%
Hydrogen	H	9.5	
Nitrogen	N	3.3	
Calcium	Ca	1.5	
Phosphorus	P	1.0	
Potassium	K	0.4	
Sulfur	S	0.3	3.7%
Sodium	Na	0.2	
Chlorine	Cl	0.2	
Magnesium	Mg	0.1	

Trace elements, less than 0.01% of human body weight: Boron (B), chromium (Cr), cobalt (Co), copper (Cu), fluorine (F), iodine (I), iron (Fe), manganese (Mn), molybdenum (Mo), selenium (Se), silicon (Si), tin (Sn), vanadium (V), zinc (Zn)

(calcium and phosphorus) and nerve signaling (potassium, sodium, calcium, and chlorine).

The **trace elements** listed at the bottom of the table are essential for humans, but only in minute quantities. Some trace elements, such as iron (Fe), are needed by all forms of life. Iron makes up only about 0.004% of your body weight but is vital for energy processing and for transporting oxygen in your blood. Other trace elements are required only by certain species. For example, iodine is an essential element only for vertebrates—animal with backbones, which, of course, includes you. We explore the importance of trace elements to your health next.

? **Explain how table salt illustrates the theme of emergent properties.**

● The elements that make up the edible crystals of table salt, sodium and chlorine, are in pure form a metal and a poisonous gas.

| Sodium (Na) | + | Chlorine (Cl) | → | Sodium chloride (NaCl) |

▲ **Figure 2.1** The emergent properties of the edible compound sodium chloride

2.2 Trace elements are common additives to food and water

CONNECTION

Trace elements are required in very small quantities, but, in some cases, even those small requirements are difficult to fulfill.

Iodine is an essential ingredient of a hormone produced by the thyroid gland, which is located in your neck. You need to ingest only a tiny speck of iodine each day, about 0.15 milligram (mg). An iodine deficiency in the diet causes the thyroid gland to grow to abnormal size, a condition called goiter (**Figure 2.2A**). The most serious effects of iodine deficiency take place during fetal development and childhood, leading to miscarriages, poor growth, and mental impairment. A global strategy to eliminate iodine deficiency involves universal iodization of all salt used for human and animal consumption. Unfortunately, about 30% of global households still do not have access to iodized salt, and an estimated 2 billion people are still at risk of iodine deficiency. Seafood, kelp, dairy products, and dark, leafy greens are good natural sources. Thus, deficiencies are often found in inland regions, especially in areas where the soil is lacking in iodine. Although most common in developing nations, iodine deficiencies may also result from excessive consumption of highly processed foods (which often use non-iodized salt) and low-salt diets intended to lower the risk of cardiovascular disease.

▲ **Figure 2.2A** Goiter, a symptom of iodine deficiency, in a Burmese woman

Iodine is just one example of a trace element added to food or water to improve health. For more than 60 years, the American Dental Association has supported fluoridation of community drinking water as a public health measure. Fluoride is a form of fluorine (F), an element in Earth's crust that is found in small amounts in all water sources. In many communities, fluoride is added during the municipal water treatment process to raise levels to a concentration that can reduce tooth decay. If you mostly drink bottled water, however, your fluoride intake may be reduced, although some bottled water now contains added fluoride. Fluoride is also frequently added to dental products, such as toothpaste and mouthwash (**Figure 2.2B**).

Chemicals are added to food to help preserve it, make it more nutritious, or simply make it look better. Read the nutrition facts label from the side of the cereal box in **Figure 2.2C** to see a familiar example of how foods are fortified with mineral elements. Iron, for example, is commonly added to foods. (You can actually see that iron has been added to a fortified cereal by crushing the cereal and then stirring a magnet through it.) Also note that the nutrition facts label lists numerous vitamins that are added to improve the nutritional value of the cereal. For instance, the cereal in this example supplies 10%

◄ **Figure 2.2B**
Mouthwash and toothpaste with added fluoride

of the recommended daily value for vitamin A. Vitamins consist of more than one element and are examples of compounds.

In the next module, we explore the chemical properties of elements and how the structure of an atom—the smallest unit of an element—determines those properties.

? In addition to iron, what other trace elements are found in the cereal in Figure 2.2C? Does one serving provide the total daily amount needed of these elements?

● Zinc and copper: one serving provides 100% of the zinc but only 4% of the copper needed in a day.

Nutrition Facts
Serving Size ¾ cup (30g)
Servings Per Container about 17

Amount Per Serving	Whole Grain Cereal	with ½ cup skim milk
Calories	100	140
Calories from Fat	5	10
		% Daily Value**
Total Fat 0.5g*	1%	1%
Saturated Fat 0g	0%	0%
Trans Fat 0g		
Polyunsaturated Fat 0g		
Monounsaturated Fat 0g		
Cholesterol 0mg	0%	1%
Sodium 135mg	6%	9%
Potassium 125mg	4%	10%
Total Carbohydrate 23g	8%	10%
Dietary Fiber 3g	10%	10%
Sugars 5g		
Other Carbohydrate 15g		
Protein 2g		
Vitamin A	10%	15%
Vitamin C	100%	100%
Calcium	100%	110%
Iron	100%	100%
Vitamin D	10%	25%
Vitamin E	100%	100%
Thiamin	100%	100%
Riboflavin	100%	110%
Niacin	100%	100%
Vitamin B$_6$	100%	100%
Folic Acid	100%	100%
Vitamin B$_{12}$	100%	110%
Pantothenic Acid	100%	100%
Phosphorus	8%	20%
Magnesium	6%	10%
Zinc	100%	100%
Copper	4%	4%

* Amount in cereal. A serving of cereal plus skim milk provides 1g total fat, less than 5mg cholesterol, 260mg sodium, 290mg potassium, 29g total carbohydrate (11g sugars) and 7g protein.
** Percent Daily Values are based on a 2,000 calorie diet. Your daily values may be higher or lower depending on your calorie needs:

	Calories	2,000	2,500
Total Fat	Less than	65g	80g
Sat Fat	Less than	20g	25g
Cholesterol	Less than	300mg	300mg
Sodium	Less than	2,400mg	2,400mg
Potassium		3,500mg	3,500mg
Total Carbohydrate		300g	375g
Dietary Fiber		25g	30g

▲ **Figure 2.2C** Nutrition facts from a fortified cereal

2.3 Atoms consist of protons, neutrons, and electrons

Each element has its own type of atom, which is different from the atoms of other elements. An **atom**, named from a Greek word meaning "indivisible," is the smallest unit of matter that still retains the properties of an element. Atoms are so small that it would take about a million of them to stretch across the period printed at the end of this sentence.

Subatomic Particles   Physicists have split the atom into more than a hundred types of subatomic particles. However, only three kinds of particles are relevant here. A **proton** is a subatomic particle with a single positive electrical charge (+). An **electron** is a subatomic particle with a single negative charge (−). A **neutron**, as its name implies, is electrically neutral (has no charge).

Figure 2.3 shows two very simple models of an atom of the element helium (He), the "lighter-than-air" gas that makes balloons rise. Notice that two protons (+) and two neutrons (●) are tightly packed in the atom's central core, or **nucleus**. Two electrons (⊖) form a sort of cloud of negative charge around the nucleus. The attraction between the negatively charged electrons and the positively charged protons holds the electrons near the nucleus. The left-hand model shows the two electrons on a circle around the nucleus. The right-hand model, slightly more realistic, shows a spherical cloud of negative charge created by the two rapidly moving electrons. Neither model is drawn to scale. In real atoms, the electrons are very much smaller than the protons and neutrons, and the electron cloud is very much bigger compared to the nucleus. Imagine that this atom was the size of a baseball stadium: The nucleus would be the size of a pea in center field, and the electrons would be like two tiny gnats buzzing around the stadium.

Atomic Number and Mass Number   So what makes the atoms of different elements different? All atoms of a particular element have the same unique number of protons. This number is the element's **atomic number**. Thus, an atom of helium, with 2 protons, has an atomic number of 2. Unless otherwise indicated, an atom has an equal number of protons and electrons, and thus its net electrical charge is 0 (zero).

What other numbers are associated with an atom? An atom's **mass number** is the sum of the number of protons and neutrons in its nucleus. For helium, the mass number is 4. The mass of a proton and the mass of a neutron are almost identical and are expressed in a unit of measurement called the dalton. Protons and neutrons each have masses close to 1 dalton. An electron has only about 1/2,000 the mass of a proton, so it contributes very little to an atom's mass. Thus, an atom's **atomic mass** (or weight) is approximately equal to its mass number—the sum of its protons and neutrons—in daltons.

Isotopes   All atoms of an element have the same atomic number, but some atoms of that element may differ in mass number. The different **isotopes** of an element have the same number of protons and behave identically in chemical reactions, but they have different numbers of neutrons. **Table 2.3** shows the numbers of subatomic particles in the three isotopes of carbon. Note that carbon's atomic number is 6—all of its atoms have 6 protons. Carbon-12 (named for its mass number), with 6 neutrons, accounts for about 99% of naturally occurring carbon. Most of the remaining 1% consists of carbon-13, with a mass number of 13 and thus 7 neutrons. A third isotope, carbon-14, with 8 neutrons, occurs in minute quantities. Of course, all three isotopes have 6 protons—otherwise, they would not be carbon.

Both carbon-12 and carbon-13 are stable isotopes, meaning that their nuclei remain intact more or less forever. The isotope carbon-14, on the other hand, is unstable, or radioactive. A **radioactive isotope** is one in which the nucleus decays spontaneously, giving off particles and energy. Radiation from decaying isotopes can damage cellular molecules and thus can pose serious risks to living organisms. But radioactive isotopes can be helpful, as in their use in dating fossils (see Module 15.5). They are also used in biological research and medicine, as we see next.

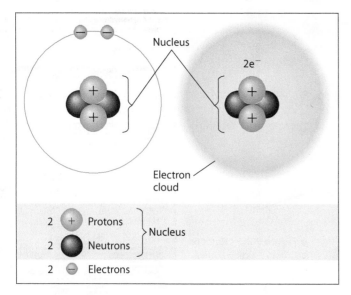

▲ **Figure 2.3**   Two models of a helium atom. (Note that these models are not to scale; they greatly overestimate the size of the nucleus in relation to the electron cloud.)

TABLE 2.3 | ISOTOPES OF CARBON

	Carbon-12		Carbon-13		Carbon-14	
Protons	6	Mass number 12	6	Mass number 13	6	Mass number 14
Neutrons	6		7		8	
Electrons	6		6		6	

? A nitrogen atom has 7 protons, and its most common isotope has 7 neutrons. A radioactive isotope of nitrogen has 9 neutrons. What is the atomic number and mass number of this radioactive nitrogen?

Atomic number = 7; mass number = 16

2.4 Radioactive isotopes can help or harm us

CONNECTION

Living cells cannot readily distinguish between isotopes of the same element. Consequently, organisms take up and use compounds containing radioactive isotopes in the usual way. Because radioactivity is easily detected and measured by instruments, radioactive isotopes are useful as tracers—biological spies, in effect—for monitoring the fate of atoms in living organisms.

Basic Research   Biologists often use radioactive tracers to follow molecules as they undergo chemical changes in an organism. For example, researchers have used carbon dioxide (CO_2) containing the radioactive isotope carbon-14 to study photosynthesis. Using sunlight to power the conversion, plants take in CO_2 from the air and use it to make sugar molecules. Radioactively labeled CO_2 has enabled researchers to trace the sequence of molecules made by plants in the chemical route from CO_2 to sugar.

Medical Diagnosis and Treatment   Radioactive isotopes may also be used to tag chemicals that accumulate in specific areas of the body, such as phosphorus in bones. After injection of such a tracer, a special camera produces an image of where the radiation collects. In most diagnostic uses, the patient receives only a tiny amount of an isotope.

Sometimes radioactive isotopes are used for treatment. As you learned in Module 2.2, the body uses iodine to make a thyroid hormone. Because radioactive iodine accumulates in the thyroid, it can be used to kill cancer cells there.

Substances that the body metabolizes, such as glucose or oxygen, may also be labeled with a radioactive isotope. **Figure 2.4A** shows a patient being examined by a PET (positron-emission tomography) scanner, which can produce three-dimensional images of areas of the body with high metabolic activity. PET is useful for diagnosing certain heart disorders and cancers and for basic research on the brain.

The early detection of Alzheimer's disease may be a new use for such techniques. This devastating illness gradually destroys a person's memory and ability to think. As the disease progresses, the brain becomes riddled with deposits (plaques) of a protein called beta-amyloid. Researchers have identified

▲ **Figure 2.4B**   PET images of brains of a healthy person (left) and a person with Alzheimer's disease (right). Red and yellow colors indicate high levels of PIB bound to beta-amyloid plaques.

a protein molecule called PIB that binds to beta-amyloid. PIB contains a radioactive isotope that can be detected on a PET scan. **Figure 2.4B** shows PET images of the brains of a healthy person (left) and a person with Alzheimer's (right) injected with PIB. Notice that the brain of the Alzheimer's patient has high levels of PIB (red and yellow areas), whereas the unaffected person's brain has lower levels (blue). New therapies are focused on limiting the production of beta-amyloid or clearing it from the brain. A diagnostic test using PIB would allow researchers to monitor the effectiveness of new drugs in people living with the disease.

Dangers   Although radioactive isotopes have many beneficial uses, uncontrolled exposure to them can harm living organisms by damaging molecules, especially DNA. The particles and energy thrown off by radioactive atoms can break chemical bonds and also cause abnormal bonds to form. The explosion of a nuclear reactor in Chernobyl, Ukraine, in 1986 released large amounts of radioactive isotopes into the environment, which drifted over large areas of Russia, Belarus, and Europe. A few dozen people died from acute radiation poisoning, and more than 100,000 people were evacuated from the immediate area. Increased rates of thyroid cancer in children exposed to the radiation have been reported. Likewise, scientists will carefully monitor the long-term health consequences of the 2011 post-tsunami Fukushima nuclear disaster in Japan.

Natural sources of radiation can also pose a threat. Radon, a radioactive gas, may be a cause of lung cancer. Radon can contaminate buildings in regions where underlying rocks naturally contain uranium, a radioactive element. Homeowners can buy a radon detector or hire a company to test their home to ensure that radon levels are safe. If levels are found to be unsafe, technology exists to remove radon from homes.

?   **Why are radioactive isotopes useful as tracers on the chemistry of life?**

Organisms incorporate radioactive isotopes of an element into their molecules, and researchers can use special scanning devices to detect the presence of these isotopes in biological pathways or locations in the body.

▲ **Figure 2.4A**   Technician monitoring the output of a PET scanner

▷ Chemical Bonds

2.5 The distribution of electrons determines an atom's chemical properties

To understand how atoms interact with each other, we need to explore atomic structure further. Of the three subatomic particles—protons, neutrons, and electrons—only electrons are directly involved in the chemical activity of an atom.

If you glance back to the model of the helium atom in Figure 2.3, you see that its 2 electrons are shown together on a circle around the nucleus. But where should the electrons be shown in an atom with more than 2 electrons—say, in carbon, whose atomic number is 6? As you see in **Figure 2.5A**, 2 electrons are still shown on an inner circle, but the next 4 are placed on a larger outside circle. It turns out that electrons can be located in different **electron shells**, each with a characteristic distance from the nucleus. Depending on an element's atomic number, an atom may have one, two, or more electron shells.

▲ **Figure 2.5A** An electron distribution model of carbon

Figure 2.5B is an abbreviated version of the periodic table of the elements (see Appendix 2 for the complete table). The figure shows the distribution of electrons for the first 18 elements, arranged in rows according to the number of electron shells (one, two, or three). Within each shell, electrons travel in different *orbitals*, which are discrete volumes of space in which electrons are most likely to be found. Each orbital can hold a maximum of 2 electrons. The first electron shell has only one orbital and can hold only 2 electrons. Thus, hydrogen and helium are the only elements in the first row. For the second and third rows, the outer shell has four orbitals and can hold up to 8 electrons (four pairs).

It is the number of electrons present in the outermost shell, called the valence shell, that determines the chemical properties of an atom. Atoms whose outer shells are not full tend to interact with other atoms in ways that enable them to complete or fill their valence shells.

Look at the electron shells of the atoms of the four elements that are the main components of biological molecules (highlighted in green in Figure 2.5B). Because their outer shells are incomplete, all these atoms react readily with other atoms. The hydrogen atom has only 1 electron in its single electron shell, which can accommodate 2 electrons. Atoms of carbon, nitrogen, and oxygen also have unpaired electrons and incomplete shells. In contrast, the helium atom has a first-level shell that is full with 2 electrons. Neon and argon also have full outer shells. As a result, these elements are chemically inert (unreactive).

How do chemical interactions between atoms enable them to fill their outer electron shells? When two atoms with incomplete outer shells react, each atom will share, donate, or receive electrons, so that both partners end up with completed outer shells. These interactions usually result in atoms staying close together, held by attractions known as **chemical bonds**. In the next two modules, we look at two important types of chemical bonds.

> **?** How many electrons and electron shells does a sodium atom have? How many electrons are in its valence shell?

● 11 electrons; 3 electron shells; 1 electron in the outer shell

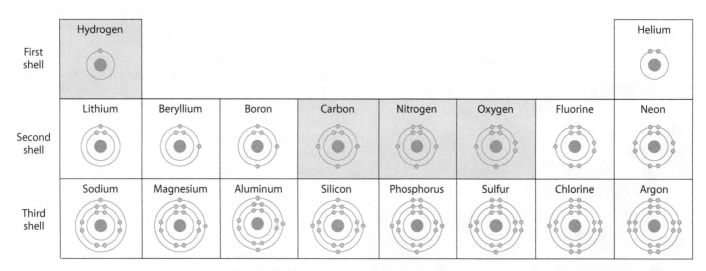

▲ **Figure 2.5B** The electron distribution diagrams of the first 18 elements in the periodic table

Try This As you read from left to right across each row, describe how the number of electrons changes. Note that the electrons don't pair up until all orbitals have at least one electron.

2.6 Covalent bonds join atoms into molecules through electron sharing

In a **covalent bond**, two atoms, each with an unpaired electron in its outer shell, actually *share* a pair of electrons. Sharing one or more pairs of electrons enables atoms to complete their outer shells. Atoms held together by covalent bonds form a **molecule**. For example, a covalent bond connects two hydrogen atoms in a molecule of the gas H_2, and a covalent bond connects each of two hydrogen atoms to an oxygen atom in a molecule of water (H_2O).

How many covalent bonds can an atom form? It depends on the number of additional electrons needed to fill its valence shell. This number is called the valence, or bonding capacity, of an atom. Look back at the electron distribution diagrams in Figure 2.5B and see if you can determine how many covalent bonds hydrogen, oxygen, nitrogen, and carbon can form.

Figure 2.6 shows how molecules can be represented in several different ways. Let's see what we can learn from this figure. As you will notice in the electron distribution diagram, the hydrogen atoms in H_2 are held together by a pair of shared electrons. But two atoms can share more than just one pair of electrons. In an oxygen molecule (O_2), for example, the two oxygen atoms share two pairs of electrons, forming a double bond. A double bond is indicated in a structural formula by a pair of lines.

H_2 and O_2 are molecules composed of only one element. Methane (CH_4) and water (H_2O) are compounds. Methane is a major component of natural gas. As shown in Figure 2.6, it takes four hydrogen atoms to satisfy carbon's valence of 4.

Atoms in a molecule are in a constant tug-of-war for the shared electrons of their covalent bonds. An atom's attraction for shared electrons is called its **electronegativity**. The more electronegative an atom, the more strongly it pulls shared electrons toward its nucleus. In molecules of only one element, such as H_2 and O_2, the two identical atoms exert an equal pull on the electrons. The bonds in such molecules are said to be **nonpolar covalent bonds** because the electrons are shared equally between the atoms. Compounds such as methane also have nonpolar bonds, because the atoms of carbon and hydrogen are not substantially different in electronegativity.

Water, on the other hand, is composed of atoms with quite different electronegativities. Oxygen is one of the most electronegative of the elements. As indicated by the arrows in the blowup of a water molecule in Figure 2.6, oxygen attracts the shared electrons in H_2O much more strongly than does hydrogen, so that the electrons spend more time near the oxygen atom than near the hydrogen atoms. This unequal sharing of electrons produces a **polar covalent bond**. In a polar covalent bond, the pulling of shared, negatively charged electrons closer to the more electronegative atom makes that atom partially negative and the other atom partially positive. Thus, in H_2O, the oxygen atom actually has a slight negative charge and each hydrogen atom a slight positive charge.

Molecular Formula: tells types and numbers of atoms	**Electron Distribution Diagram:** shows how each atom completes outer shell by sharing electrons	**Structural Formula:** represents each covalent bond with a line	**Space-Filling Model:** uses color-coded balls to show shape of a molecule
H_2 Hydrogen		H—H Single bond (a pair of shared electrons)	
O_2 Oxygen		O=O Double bond (two pairs of shared electrons)	
CH_4 Methane		Nonpolar covalent bonds (electrons shared equally)	
H_2O Water		Polar covalent bonds (electrons not shared equally)	

(slightly −)

Shared electrons are pulled closer to electronegative oxygen, making oxygen slightly negative and hydrogens slightly positive

(slightly +)   (slightly +)

Polar covalent bonds in a water molecule (Polarity refers to a separation of charges—think of the positive and negative poles or ends of a battery.)

▲ **Figure 2.6** Alternative ways to represent four common molecules

In some cases, two atoms are so unequal in their attraction for electrons that the more electronegative atom strips an electron completely away from its partner, as we see next.

? What is chemically nonsensical about this structure?

$$H—C≡C—H$$

● Each C has only three bonds instead of the four required by its valence.

2.7 Ionic bonds are attractions between ions of opposite charge

Table salt is an example of how the transfer of electrons can bond atoms together. **Figure 2.7A** shows how a sodium atom (Na) and a chlorine atom (Cl) can form the compound sodium chloride (NaCl). Notice that sodium has only 1 electron in its outer shell, whereas chlorine has 7. When these atoms interact, the sodium atom transfers its single outer electron to chlorine. Sodium now has only two shells, the second shell having a full set of 8 electrons. When chlorine strips away sodium's electron, its own outer shell is now full with 8 electrons.

But how does this electron transfer result in an ionic bond between sodium and chlorine? Remember that electrons are negatively charged particles. The transfer of an electron moves one unit of negative charge from one atom to the other. Sodium, with 11 protons but now only 10 electrons, has a net electrical charge of 1+. Chlorine, having gained an extra electron, now has 18 electrons but only 17 protons, giving it a net electrical charge of 1−. In each case, an atom has become an **ion**—an atom or molecule with an electrical charge resulting from a gain or loss of one or more electrons. (Note that the names of negatively charged ions often end in *-ide*, such as *chloride*.) Two ions with opposite charges attract each other. When the attraction holds them together, it

is called an **ionic bond**. The resulting compound, in this case NaCl, is electrically neutral.

Sodium chloride is a familiar type of **salt**, a synonym for an ionic compound. Salts often exist as crystals in nature. **Figure 2.7B** shows the ions Na^+ and Cl^- in a crystal of sodium chloride. An NaCl crystal can be of any size (there is no fixed number of ions), but sodium and chloride ions are always present in a 1:1 ratio. The ratio of ions can differ in the various kinds of salts.

The environment affects the strength of ionic bonds. In a dry salt crystal, the bonds are so strong that it takes a hammer and chisel to break enough of them to crack the crystal. If the same salt crystal is placed in water, however, the ionic bonds break when the ions interact with water molecules and the salt dissolves, as we'll discuss in Module 2.13. Most drugs are manufactured as salts because they are quite stable when dry but can dissolve easily in water.

? Explain what holds together the ions in a crystal of table salt (NaCl).

● Opposite charges attract. The positively charged sodium ions (Na⁺) and the negatively charged chloride ions (Cl⁻) are held together by ionic bonds, attractions between oppositely charged ions.

The lone outer electron of a sodium atom is transferred to join the 7 valence electrons of a chlorine atom.

Each resulting ion has a completed valence shell. The attraction between the ions—an ionic bond—holds them together.

Na
Sodium atom

Cl
Chlorine atom

Na⁺
Sodium ion

Cl⁻
Chloride ion

Sodium chloride (NaCl)

▲ **Figure 2.7A** Formation of an ionic bond, producing sodium chloride

Cl⁻
Na⁺

▲ **Figure 2.7B** A crystal of sodium chloride

2.8 Hydrogen bonds are weak bonds important in the chemistry of life

In living organisms, most of the strong chemical bonds are covalent, linking atoms to form a cell's molecules. But crucial to the functioning of a cell are weaker bonds within and between molecules, such as the ionic bonds we just discussed. One of the most important types of weak bonds is the **hydrogen bond**, which is best illustrated with water molecules.

As you saw in Figure 2.6, the hydrogen atoms of a water molecule are attached to oxygen by polar covalent bonds. Because of these polar bonds and the wide V shape of the

molecule, water is a **polar molecule**—that is, it has an unequal distribution of charges. It is slightly negative at the oxygen end of the molecule (the point of the V) and slightly positive at each of the two hydrogen ends. This partial positive charge allows each hydrogen to be attracted to—in a sense, to "flirt" with—a nearby atom (often an oxygen or nitrogen) that has a partial negative charge.

Figure 2.8, on the next page, illustrates how these weak bonds form between water molecules. They are called

▶ Figure 2.8 Hydrogen bonds between water molecules

Hydrogen bond
Polar covalent bonds

Try This Describe polar covalent bonds and hydrogen bonds and explain how they are related.

hydrogen bonds because the positively charged atom in this type of attraction is always a hydrogen atom. As Figure 2.8 shows, each hydrogen atom of a water molecule can form a hydrogen bond (depicted by dotted lines) with a nearby partially negative oxygen atom of another water molecule. And the negative (oxygen) pole of a water molecule can form hydrogen bonds to two hydrogen atoms. Thus, each water molecule can hydrogen-bond to as many as four partners.

You will learn later how hydrogen bonds help to create a protein's shape (and thus its function) and hold the two strands of a DNA molecule together (see Chapter 3). Later in this chapter, we explore how water's polarity and hydrogen bonds give it unique, life-supporting properties. But first we discuss how the making and breaking of bonds change the composition of matter.

? What enables neighboring water molecules to hydrogen-bond to one another?

⦿ The molecules are polar, with each positive end (hydrogen end) of one molecule attracted to the negative (oxygen end) of another molecule.

2.9 Chemical reactions make and break chemical bonds

Your cells are constantly rearranging molecules in **chemical reactions**—breaking existing chemical bonds and forming new ones. A simple example of a chemical reaction is the reaction between hydrogen gas and oxygen gas that forms water (this is an explosive reaction, which, fortunately, does not occur in your cells):

$$2\,H_2 + O_2 \rightarrow 2\,H_2O$$

In this case, two molecules of hydrogen ($2\,H_2$) react with one molecule of oxygen (O_2) to produce two molecules of water ($2\,H_2O$). The arrow in the equation indicates the conversion of the starting materials, called the **reactants**, to the **product**, the material resulting from the chemical reaction. Notice that the same *numbers* of hydrogen and oxygen atoms appear on the left and right sides of the arrow, although they are grouped differently. Chemical reactions do not create or destroy matter; they only rearrange it in various ways. As shown in **Figure 2.9**, the covalent bonds (represented here as white "sticks" between atoms) holding hydrogen atoms together in H_2 and holding oxygen atoms together in O_2 are broken, and new bonds are formed to yield the H_2O product molecules.

Organisms cannot make water from H_2 and O_2, but they do carry out a great number of chemical reactions that rearrange matter in significant ways. Let's examine a chemical reaction that is essential to life on Earth: photosynthesis. The raw materials of photosynthesis are carbon dioxide (CO_2), which is taken from the air, and water (H_2O), which plants absorb from the soil. Within green plant cells, sunlight powers the conversion of these reactants to the sugar product glucose ($C_6H_{12}O_6$) and oxygen (O_2), a by-product that the plant releases into the air. The following chemical shorthand summarizes the process:

$$6\,CO_2 + 6\,H_2O \rightarrow C_6H_{12}O_6 + 6\,O_2$$

Although photosynthesis is actually a sequence of many chemical reactions, we see that we end up with the same number and kinds of atoms we started with. Matter has simply been rearranged, with an input of energy provided by sunlight.

Your body routinely carries out thousands of chemical reactions. These reactions take place in the watery environment of your cells. We look at the life-supporting properties of water next.

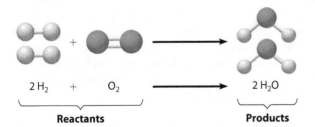

$2\,H_2$ + O_2 → $2\,H_2O$

Reactants   **Products**

▲ Figure 2.9 Breaking and making of bonds in a chemical reaction

? Fill in the blanks with the correct numbers in the following chemical process:

$$C_6H_{12}O_6 + \underline{}O_2 \rightarrow \underline{}CO_2 + \underline{}H_2O$$

What process do you think this reaction represents? (*Hint:* Think about how your cells use these reactants to produce energy.)

⦿ $C_6H_{12}O_6 + 6\,O_2 \rightarrow 6\,CO_2 + 6\,H_2O$; the breakdown of sugar in the presence of oxygen to carbon dioxide and water, with the release of energy that the cell can use

▷ Water's Life-Supporting Properties

2.10 Hydrogen bonds make liquid water cohesive

We can trace water's life-supporting properties to the structure and interactions of its molecules—their polarity and resulting hydrogen bonding between molecules (review Figure 2.8).

Hydrogen bonds between molecules of liquid water last for only a few trillionths of a second, yet at any instant, many molecules are hydrogen-bonded to others. This tendency of molecules of the same kind to stick together, called **cohesion**, is much stronger for water than for most other liquids. The cohesion of water is important in the living world. Trees, for example, depend on cohesion to help transport water and nutrients from their roots to their leaves. The evaporation of water from a leaf exerts a pulling force on water within the veins of the leaf. Because of cohesion, the force is relayed all the way down to the roots. **Adhesion**, the clinging of one substance to another, also plays a role. The adhesion of water to the cell walls of a plant's thin veins helps counter the downward pull of gravity.

Related to cohesion is **surface tension**, a measure of how difficult it is to stretch or break the surface of a liquid. Hydrogen

▼ **Figure 2.10**   Surface tension allowing a water strider to walk on water

bonds give water unusually high surface tension, making it behave as though it were coated with an invisible film. You can observe the surface tension of water by slightly overfilling a glass; the water will stand above the rim. The water strider in **Figure 2.10** takes advantage of the high surface tension of water to "stride" across ponds without breaking the surface.

> **?**   After a hard workout, you may notice "beads" of sweat on your face. Can you explain what holds the sweat in droplet form?

● The cohesion of water molecules and its high surface tension hold water in droplets. The adhesion of water to your skin helps hold the beads in place.

2.11 Water's hydrogen bonds moderate temperature

Thermal energy is the energy associated with the random movement of atoms and molecules. Thermal energy in transfer from a warmer to a cooler body of matter is defined as **heat**. **Temperature** measures the intensity of heat—that is, the *average* speed of molecules in a body of matter. If you have ever burned your finger on a metal pot while waiting for the water in it to boil, you know that water heats up much more slowly than metal. In fact, because of hydrogen bonding, water has a stronger resistance to temperature change than most other substances.

Heat must be absorbed to break hydrogen bonds, and heat is released when hydrogen bonds form. To raise the temperature of water, hydrogen bonds between water molecules must be broken before the molecules can move faster. Thus, water absorbs a large amount of heat (much of it used to disrupt hydrogen bonds) while warming up only a few degrees. Conversely, when water cools, water molecules slow down and more hydrogen bonds form, releasing a considerable amount of heat.

Earth's giant water supply moderates temperatures, helping to keep temperatures within limits that permit life. Oceans, lakes, and rivers store a huge amount of heat from the sun during warm periods. Heat given off from gradually cooling

▲ **Figure 2.11**   Sweating as a mechanism of evaporative cooling

water warms the air. That's why coastal areas generally have milder climates than inland regions. Water's resistance to temperature change also stabilizes ocean temperatures, creating a favorable environment for marine life. Because water accounts for approximately 66% of your body weight, it also helps moderate your temperature.

When a substance evaporates (changes physical state from a liquid to a gas), the surface of the liquid that remains behind cools down. This **evaporative cooling** occurs because the molecules with the greatest energy (the "hottest" ones) leave. It's as if the 10 fastest runners on the track team left school, lowering the average speed of the remaining team. Evaporative cooling helps prevent some land-dwelling organisms from overheating. Evaporation from a plant's leaves keeps them from becoming too warm in the sun, just as sweating helps dissipate our excess body heat (**Figure 2.11**). On a much larger scale, the evaporation of surface waters cools tropical seas.

> **?**   Explain the popular adage "It's not the heat, it's the humidity."

● High humidity hampers cooling by slowing the evaporation of sweat.

2.12 Ice floats because it is less dense than liquid water

Water exists on Earth in three forms: gas (water vapor), liquid, and solid. Unlike most substances, water is less dense as a solid than as a liquid. As you might guess, this unusual property is due to hydrogen bonds.

As water freezes, each molecule forms stable hydrogen bonds with its neighbors, holding them at "arm's length" and creating a three-dimensional crystal. In **Figure 2.12**, compare the spaciously arranged molecules in the ice crystal with the more tightly packed molecules in the liquid water. The ice crystal has fewer molecules than an equal volume of liquid water. Therefore, ice is less dense and floats on top of liquid water.

If ice sank, then eventually ponds, lakes, and even oceans would freeze solid. Instead, when a body of water cools, the floating ice insulates the water below from colder air above. This "blanket" of ice prevents the water from freezing and allows fish and other aquatic forms of life to survive under the frozen surface.

In the Arctic, this frozen surface serves as the winter hunting ground for polar bears (Figure 2.12). The shrinking of this ice cover as a result of global climate change may doom these bears.

Ice
Hydrogen bonds are stable.

Hydrogen bond

Liquid water
Hydrogen bonds constantly break and re-form.

> **?** Explain how freezing water can crack boulders.

Water in the crevices of a boulder expands as it freezes because the water molecules become spaced farther apart in forming ice crystals, which can crack the rock.

▲ **Figure 2.12** Hydrogen bonds between water molecules in ice and water

---

2.13 Water is the solvent of life

If you add a teaspoon of table salt to a glass of water, the salt will eventually dissolve, forming a solution. A **solution** is a liquid consisting of a uniform mixture of two or more substances. The dissolving agent (in our example, water) is the **solvent**, and a substance that is dissolved (in this case, salt) is a **solute**. An **aqueous solution** (from the Latin *aqua*, water) is one in which water is the solvent.

Water's versatility as a solvent results from the polarity of its molecules. **Figure 2.13** shows how a teaspoon of salt dissolves in water. At the surface of each grain, or crystal, the sodium and chloride ions are exposed to water. These ions and the water molecules are attracted to each other due to their opposite charges. The oxygen ends of the water molecules have a partial negative charge and cling to the positive sodium ions (Na⁺). The hydrogen ends of the water molecules, with their partial positive charge,

Positive hydrogen ends of water molecules attracted to negative chloride ion

Negative oxygen ends of water molecules attracted to positive sodium ion

Salt crystal

▲ **Figure 2.13** A crystal of salt (NaCl) dissolving in water

are attracted to the negative chloride ions (Cl⁻). Working inward from the surface of each salt crystal, water molecules eventually surround and separate all the ions. Water dissolves other ionic compounds as well. Seawater, for instance, contains a great variety of dissolved ions, as do your cells.

A compound doesn't need to be ionic to dissolve in water. A spoonful of sugar will also dissolve in a glass of water. Polar molecules such as sugar dissolve as water molecules surround them and form hydrogen bonds with their polar regions. Even large molecules, such as proteins, can dissolve if they have ionic or polar regions on their surface. As the solvent inside all cells, in blood, and in plant sap, water dissolves an enormous variety of solutes necessary for life.

> **?** Why are blood and most other biological fluids classified as aqueous solutions?

The solvent in these fluids is water.

2.14 The chemistry of life is sensitive to acidic and basic conditions

In liquid water, a small percentage of the water molecules dissociate or break apart into hydrogen ions (H⁺) and hydroxide ions (OH⁻). These ions are very reactive, and changes in their concentrations can drastically affect a cell's proteins and other complex molecules.

Some chemical compounds contribute additional H⁺ to an aqueous solution, whereas others remove H⁺ from it. A substance that donates hydrogen ions to solutions is called an **acid**. An example of a strong acid is hydrochloric acid (HCl), the acid in the gastric juice in your stomach. An acidic solution has a higher concentration of H⁺ than OH⁻.

A **base** is a substance that reduces the hydrogen ion concentration of a solution. Some bases, such as sodium hydroxide (NaOH), do this by donating OH⁻; the OH⁻ combines with H⁺ to form H₂O, thus reducing the H⁺ concentration. Sodium hydroxide is a common ingredient in oven cleaners. Other bases accept H⁺ ions from solution, resulting in a higher OH⁻ concentration.

We use the **pH scale** to describe how acidic or basic a solution is (pH stands for potential of hydrogen). As shown in **Figure 2.14**, the scale ranges from 0 (most acidic) to 14 (most basic). Each pH unit represents a 10-fold change in the concentration of H⁺ in a solution. For example, lemon juice at pH 2 has 10 times more H⁺ than an equal amount of a cola at pH 3 and 100 times more H⁺ than tomato juice at pH 4.

Pure water and aqueous solutions that are neither acidic nor basic are said to be neutral; they have a pH of 7, and the concentrations of H⁺ and OH⁻ are equal. The pH inside most cells is close to 7.

The pH of human blood plasma (the fluid portion of the blood) is very close to 7.4. A person cannot survive for more than a few minutes if the blood pH drops to 7.0 or rises to 7.8. How can your body maintain a relatively constant pH in your cells and blood? Biological fluids contain **buffers**, substances that minimize changes in pH. They do so by accepting H⁺ when it is in excess and donating H⁺ when it is depleted.

▲ **Figure 2.14**   The pH scale, which reflects the relative concentrations of H⁺ and OH⁻

? Compared to a basic solution at pH 9, the same volume of an acidic solution at pH 4 has _____ times more H⁺.

100,000

2.15 Scientists study the effects of rising atmospheric CO₂ on coral reef ecosystems

SCIENTIFIC THINKING

Carbon dioxide is the main product of fossil fuel combustion, and its steadily increasing release into the atmosphere is linked to global climate change (see Module 38.4). About 25% of this CO₂ is absorbed by the oceans—and this naturally occurring remedy to excess CO₂ would seem to be a good thing. However, as CO₂ levels on the planet continue to rise, the increasing absorption of CO₂ is expected to change ocean chemistry and harm marine life and ecosystems.

In **ocean acidification**, CO₂ dissolving in seawater lowers the pH of the ocean. Recent studies estimate that the pH of the oceans is 0.1 pH unit lower now than at any time in the past

Will rising atmospheric CO₂ harm coral reefs?

420,000 years and may drop from the current level of 8.1 to 7.8 by the end of this century. How will this affect marine organisms?

Several studies investigating the impact of a lower pH on coral reef ecosystems have looked at the process called calcification, in which coral animals combine calcium and carbonate ions to form their calcium carbonate skeletons. As seawater acidifies, the extra hydrogen ions (H⁺) combine with carbonate ions (CO₃²⁻) to form bicarbonate ions (HCO₃⁻). This reaction reduces the carbonate ion concentration available to corals and other shell-building animals. Scientists predict that ocean acidification will cause the carbonate ion concentration to decrease by 40% by the year 2100.

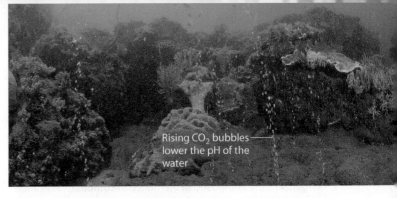

Rising CO_2 bubbles lower the pH of the water

▲ **Figure 2.15B** A "champagne" reef with bubbles of CO_2 rising from a volcanic seep

Source: Adaptation of figure 5 from "Effect of Calcium Carbonate Saturation State on the Calcification Rate of an Experimental Coral Reef" by C. Langdon, et al., from *Global Biogeochemical Cycles*, June 2000, Volume 14(2). Copyright © 2000 by American Geophysical Union. Reprinted with permission of Wiley Inc.

▲ **Figure 2.15A** The effect of carbonate ion concentration on calcification rate in an artificial coral reef system. (The independent variable shown on the *x* axis is the concentration of carbonate ions, which the researchers manipulated. The dependent variable—the calcification rate, shown on the *y* axis—is what was measured in the experiment and was predicted to "depend on" or respond to the experimental treatment.)

In a controlled experiment, scientists looked at the effect of decreasing carbonate ion concentration on the rate of calcium deposition by reef organisms. The Biosphere 2 aquarium in Arizona contains a large coral reef system that behaves like a natural reef. Researchers measured how the calcification rate changed with differing amounts of dissolved carbonate ions. **Figure 2.15A** presents the results of one set of experiments, in which pH, temperature, and concentration of calcium ions were held constant while the carbonate ion concentration of the seawater was varied. As you can see from the graph, the lower the concentration of carbonate ions, the lower the rate of calcification, and the slower the growth of coral animals.

Controlled studies such as this one have provided evidence that ocean acidification and the resulting reduction in carbonate ion concentration will negatively affect coral reefs. But

scientists have also looked to natural habitats to study how ocean acidification affects coral reef ecosystems. A 2011 study looked at three volcanic seeps in Papua New Guinea. As you can see in **Figure 2.15B**, bubbles of CO_2 released from underwater volcanoes around such "champagne reefs" lower the pH of the water. Researchers surveyed three study sites in which the pH naturally varied from 8.1 to 7.8. They found reductions in coral diversity and the recruitment of juvenile coral as the pH of the sites declined, both of which undermine the resiliency of a reef community. Researchers also found a shift to less structurally complex and slower growing corals. The structural complexity of coral reef ecosystems makes them havens for a great diversity of organisms.

Scientists often synthesize their conclusions using multiple lines of evidence. The results from both controlled experimental studies and observational field studies of sites where pH naturally varies have dire implications for the health of coral reefs and the diversity of organisms they support.

 What is the relationship between fossil fuel consumption and coral reefs?

● Some of the increased CO_2 released by burning fossil fuels dissolves in and lowers the pH of the oceans. A lower pH reduces levels of carbonate ions, which then lowers the rate of calcification by coral animals. A lower pH also changes the composition and resiliency of coral reefs.

2.16 The search for extraterrestrial life centers on the search for water

EVOLUTION CONNECTION

When astrobiologists search for signs of extraterrestrial life on distant planets, they look for evidence of water. Why? As we've seen in this chapter, the emergent properties of water support life on Earth in many ways. Is it possible that some form of life has evolved on other planets that have water in their environment? Scientists with the National Aeronautics and Space Administration (NASA) are looking into this possibility.

Like Earth, Mars has an ice cap at both poles, and scientists have found signs that water may exist elsewhere on the planet. In 2008, the robotic spacecraft *Phoenix* landed on Mars and sent back images showing that ice is present just under Mars's surface. Then, in 2011, high-resolution images sent to Earth from the Mars Reconnaissance Orbiter showed

evidence for liquid water beneath the surface. Distinctive streaks form along steep slopes during the Mars spring and summer, which then vanish during the winter. Careful study of these images over time has led scientists to conclude that these streaks are most likely seasonal streams of flowing water resulting when subsurface ice melts during the warm season. This exciting finding has reinvigorated the search for signs of life, past or present, on Mars and other planets. If any life-forms or fossils are found, their study will shed light on the process of evolution from an entirely new perspective.

? **Why is the presence of water important in the search for extraterrestrial life?**

● Water plays important roles in life as we know it, from moderating temperatures on the planet to functioning as the solvent of life.

CHAPTER 2 REVIEW

For practice quizzes, BioFlix animations, MP3 tutorials, video tutors, and more study tools designed for this textbook, go to

MasteringBiology®

Reviewing the Concepts

Elements, Atoms, and Compounds (2.1–2.4)

2.1 Organisms are composed of elements, in combinations called compounds. Oxygen, carbon, hydrogen, and nitrogen make up about 96% of living matter.

2.2 Trace elements are common additives to food and water.

2.3 Atoms consist of protons, neutrons, and electrons.

Protons (+ charge) determine element

Nucleus

Electrons (+ charge) form negative cloud and determine chemical behavior

Neutrons (no charge) determine isotope

Atom

2.4 Radioactive isotopes can help or harm us. Radioactive isotopes are valuable in basic research and medicine.

Chemical Bonds (2.5–2.9)

2.5 The distribution of electrons determines an atom's chemical properties. An atom whose outer electron shell is not full tends to interact with other atoms and share, gain, or lose electrons, resulting in attractions called chemical bonds.

2.6 Covalent bonds join atoms into molecules through electron sharing. In a nonpolar covalent bond, electrons are shared equally. In polar covalent bonds, such as those found in water, electrons are pulled closer to the more electronegative atom.

2.7 Ionic bonds are attractions between ions of opposite charge. Electron gain and loss create charged atoms, called ions.

2.8 Hydrogen bonds are weak bonds important in the chemistry of life. The slightly positively charged H atoms in one polar molecule may be attracted to the partial negative charge of an oxygen or nitrogen atom in a neighboring molecule.

2.9 Chemical reactions make and break chemical bonds. The composition of matter is changed as bonds are broken and formed to convert reactants to products.

Water's Life-Supporting Properties (2.10–2.16)

2.10 Hydrogen bonds make liquid water cohesive. Cohesion creates surface tension and allows water to move from plant roots to leaves.

2.11 Water's hydrogen bonds moderate temperature. Heat is absorbed when hydrogen bonds break and released when hydrogen bonds form. This helps keep temperatures relatively steady. As the most energetic water molecules evaporate, the surface of a substance cools.

2.12 Ice floats because it is less dense than liquid water. Floating ice protects lakes and oceans from freezing solid, which in turn protects aquatic life.

Liquid water: Hydrogen bonds constantly break and re-form

Ice: Stable hydrogen bonds hold molecules apart

2.13 Water is the solvent of life. Polar or charged solutes dissolve when water molecules surround them, forming aqueous solutions.

2.14 The chemistry of life is sensitive to acidic and basic conditions. A compound that releases H^+ in solution is an acid, and one that accepts H^+ is a base. The pH scale ranges from 0 (most acidic) to 14 (most basic). The pH of most cells is close to 7 (neutral) and is kept that way by buffers.

2.15 Scientists study the effects of rising atmospheric CO_2 on coral reef ecosystems. The acidification of the ocean threatens coral reefs and other marine organisms.

2.16 The search for extraterrestrial life centers on the search for water. The emergent properties of water support life on Earth and may contribute to the potential for life to have evolved on other planets.

Connecting the Concepts

1. Fill in the blanks in this concept map to help you tie together the key concepts concerning elements, atoms, and molecules.

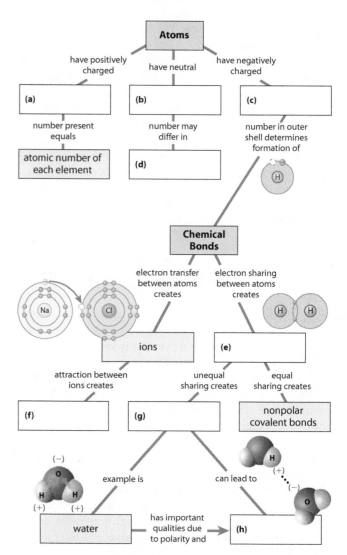

2. Create a concept map to organize your understanding of the life-supporting properties of water. A sample map is in the answer section, but the value of this exercise is in the thinking and integrating you must do to create your own map.

Testing Your Knowledge

Level 1: Knowledge/Comprehension

3. Changing the _____ would change it into an atom of a different element.
   a. number of electrons surrounding the nucleus of an atom
   b. number of protons in the nucleus of an atom
   c. electrical charge of an atom
   d. number of neutrons in the nucleus of an atom

4. A solution at pH 6 contains _____ H^+ than the same amount of a solution at pH 8.
   a. 20 times more
   b. 100 times more
   c. 2 times less
   d. 100 times less

5. Most of the unique properties of water result from the fact that water molecules
   a. are the most abundant molecules on Earth's surface.
   b. are held together by covalent bonds.
   c. are constantly in motion.
   d. are polar and form hydrogen bonds.

6. A can of cola consists mostly of sugar dissolved in water, with some carbon dioxide gas that makes it fizzy and makes the pH less than 7. In chemical terms, you could say that cola is an aqueous solution where water is the _____, sugar is a _____, and carbon dioxide makes the solution _____.
   a. solvent . . . solute . . . basic
   b. solute . . . solvent . . . basic
   c. solvent . . . solute . . . acidic
   d. solute . . . solvent . . . acidic

Level 2: Application/Analysis

7. The atomic number of sulfur (S) is 16. Sulfur combines with hydrogen by covalent bonding to form a compound, hydrogen sulfide. Based on the number of valence electrons in a sulfur atom, predict the molecular formula of the compound. (*Explain your answer.*)
   a. HS
   b. H_2S
   c. H_4S_2
   d. H_4S

8. In what way does the need for iodine or iron in your diet differ from your need for calcium or phosphorus?

9. Use carbon-12, the most common isotope of carbon, to define these terms: atomic number, mass number, valence. Which of these numbers is most related to the chemical behavior of an atom? Explain.

10. In terms of electron sharing between atoms, compare nonpolar covalent bonds, polar covalent bonds, and ions.

11. The diagram below shows the arrangement of electrons around the nucleus of a fluorine and a potassium atom. What kind of bond do you think would form between these two atoms?

Fluorine atom   Potassium atom

Level 3: Synthesis/Evaluation

12. Look back at the abbreviated periodic table of the elements in Figure 2.5B. If two elements are in the same row, what do they have in common? If two elements are in the same column, what do they have in common? Would you predict that elements in the same row or the same column will have similar chemical properties? Explain.

13. **SCIENTIFIC THINKING** A recent experimental study looked at the combined effects of ocean acidification (see Module 2.15) and increased ocean temperatures, both aspects of global climate change, on the growth of polyps, juvenile coral animals. Researchers reported the average polyp biomass (in μg/polyp) after 42 days of growth under four treatments: a control with pH and temperature maintained close to normal reef conditions, a pH lowered by 0.2 units, a temperature raised by 1°C, and a combined lower pH and higher temperature. The results showed that polyp biomass was reduced somewhat in both the low-pH and high-temperature treatments, but the combined treatment resulted in a reduction in growth by almost a third—a statistically significant result. Experiments often look at the effects of changing one variable at a time, while keeping all other variables constant. Explain why this experiment considered two variables—both a higher temperature and a lower pH—at the same time.

14. In agricultural areas, farmers pay close attention to the weather forecast. Right before a predicted overnight freeze, farmers spray water on crops to protect the plants. Use the properties of water to explain how this method works. Be sure to mention why hydrogen bonds are responsible for this phenomenon.

15. This chapter explains how the emergent properties of water contribute to the suitability of the environment for life. Until fairly recently, scientists assumed that other physical requirements for life included a moderate range of temperature, pH, and atmospheric pressure. That view has changed with the discovery of organisms known as extremophiles, which have been found flourishing in hot, acidic sulfur springs and around hydrothermal vents deep in the ocean. What does the existence of life in such environments say about the possibility of life on other planets?

Answers to all questions can be found in Appendix 4.

The Molecules of Cells

? *What does evolution have to do with drinking milk?*

Is a big glass of milk a way to a healthy diet—or an upset stomach? Quite often, the answer is the latter. Most of the world's adult populations cannot easily digest milk-based foods. Such people suffer from lactose intolerance, the inability to properly break down lactose, the main sugar found in milk. Almost all infants are able to drink breast milk or other dairy products, benefiting from the proteins, fats, and sugars in this nutritious food. But as they grow older, many people find that drinking milk comes with a heavy dose of digestive discomfort.

The young man in the photograph below can enjoy drinking milk because his body continues to produce lactase—the enzyme that speeds the digestion of lactose into smaller sugars that his digestive system can absorb. In most human populations, the production of this enzyme begins to decline after the age of 2. In the United States, as many as 80% of African Americans and Native Americans and 90% of Asian Americans are lactase-deficient once they reach their teenage years. Americans of northern European descent make up one of the few groups in which lactase production continues into adulthood. Why are some people lactose tolerant while others are not? As you'll find out later in this chapter, the answer has to do with evolution and the inheritance of a genetic mutation that occurred in the ancestors of certain groups.

In people who easily digest milk, lactose (a sugar) is broken down by lactase (a protein), which is coded for by a gene made of DNA (a nucleic acid). Such molecular interactions, repeated in countless variations, drive all biological processes. In this chapter, we explore the structure and function of sugars, proteins, fats, and nucleic acids—the biological molecules that are essential to life. We begin with a look at carbon, the versatile atom at the center of life's molecules.

BIG IDEAS

Introduction to Organic Compounds
(3.1–3.3)

Carbon-containing compounds are the chemical building blocks of life.

Carbohydrates
(3.4–3.7)

Carbohydrates serve as a cell's fuel and building material.

Lipids
(3.8–3.11)

Lipids are hydrophobic molecules with diverse functions.

Proteins
(3.12–3.14)

Proteins are essential to the structures and functions of life.

Nucleic Acids
(3.15–3.17)

Nucleic acids store, transmit, and help express hereditary information.

▷ Introduction to Organic Compounds

3.1 Life's molecular diversity is based on the properties of carbon

When it comes to making molecules, carbon usually takes center stage. Almost all the molecules a cell makes are composed of carbon atoms bonded to one another and to atoms of other elements. Carbon is unparalleled in its ability to form large and complex molecules, which build the structures and carry out the functions required for life. Carbon-based molecules are called **organic compounds**, and they usually contain hydrogen atoms in addition to carbon.

Why are carbon atoms the lead players in the chemistry of life? Remember that the number of electrons in the outermost shell determines an atom's chemical properties. A carbon atom has 4 electrons in a valence shell that holds 8. Carbon completes its outer shell by sharing electrons with other atoms in four covalent bonds (see Module 2.6).

Figure 3.1A presents a ball-and-stick model of methane (CH_4), one of the simplest organic molecules. It shows that carbon's four bonds (the white "sticks") angle out toward the corners of an imaginary tetrahedron (an object with four triangular sides, as illustrated in red to the right of the model). This shape occurs wherever a carbon atom participates in four single bonds. In molecules with more than one carbon, each carbon atom is a connecting point from which a molecule can branch in up to four directions. In addition, different shapes occur when carbon atoms form double bonds. Thanks to the geometry of carbon's single and double bonds, large organic molecules can have very elaborate shapes. And as you will see repeatedly, a molecule's shape usually determines its function.

Carbon chains form the backbone of most organic molecules. **Figure 3.1B** illustrates four ways in which such "carbon skeletons" (shaded in gray in the figure) can vary. They may differ in length and can be straight, branched, or arranged in rings. Carbon skeletons may also include double bonds, which can vary in number and location.

Notice that the two compounds on the bottom left of Figure 3.1B, butane and isobutane, have the same molecular formula, C_4H_{10}. They differ, however, in the arrangement of their carbon skeleton. The two molecules on the top right

The four single bonds of carbon point to the corners of a tetrahedron.

▲ **Figure 3.1A** A model of methane (CH_4) and the tetrahedral shape of a molecule in which a carbon atom forms four single bonds to other atoms

also have the same numbers of atoms (C_4H_8), but they have different three-dimensional shapes because of the location of the double bond. Compounds with the same formula but different structural arrangements are called **isomers**. The different shapes of isomers result in unique properties and add greatly to the diversity of organic molecules.

Isomers can also result from the different spatial arrangements that can occur when four different partners are bonded to a carbon atom. This type of isomer is important in the pharmaceutical industry, because the two isomers of a drug may not be equally effective or may have different (and sometimes harmful) effects.

Methane (Figure 3.1A) and the compounds illustrated in Figure 3.1B are composed of only carbon and hydrogen—they are called **hydrocarbons**. The majority of naturally occurring hydrocarbons are found in crude oil and natural gas and provide most of the world's energy. Hydrocarbons are rare in living organisms, but hydrocarbon chains are found in regions of some molecules. For instance, fats contain hydrocarbon chains that provide fuel to your body.

In the next module, we see how attaching atoms other than just hydrogen to carbon skeletons produces a huge diversity of biological molecules.

> ? One isomer of methamphetamine is the addictive illegal drug known as "crank." The other is a medicine for sinus congestion. How can you explain the differing effects of the two isomers?

● Isomers have different structures, or shapes, and the shape of a molecule usually helps determine the way it functions in the body.

Length: Carbon skeletons vary in length.

Double bond

1-Butene   2-Butene

Double bonds: Carbon skeletons may have double bonds, which can vary in location.

Butane   Isobutane

Branching: Carbon skeletons may be unbranched or branched.

Cyclohexane   Benzene

Rings: Carbon skeletons may be arranged in rings. (In the abbreviated ring structures, each corner represents a carbon and its attached hydrogens.)

▲ **Figure 3.1B**   Four ways in which carbon skeletons can vary

3.2 A few chemical groups are key to the functioning of biological molecules

The unique properties of an organic compound depend not only on the size and shape of its carbon skeleton but also on the groups of atoms that are attached to that skeleton.

Figure 3.2 shows what a difference chemical groups can make. The hormones testosterone and estradiol (a type of estrogen) differ only in the groups of atoms highlighted here with colored boxes. These subtle differences affect the functioning of these molecules, helping to produce male and female features in lions, humans, and other vertebrates.

Table 3.2 illustrates six important chemical groups. The first five are called **functional groups**. They affect a molecule's function by participating in chemical reactions. These groups are polar, which tends to make compounds containing them **hydrophilic** (water-loving) and therefore soluble in water—a necessary condition for their roles in water-based life. The sixth group, a methyl group, is nonpolar and not reactive, but it affects molecular shape and thus function.

A **hydroxyl group** consists of a hydrogen atom bonded to an oxygen atom, which in turn is bonded to the carbon skeleton. Ethanol, shown in the table, and other organic compounds containing hydroxyl groups are called alcohols.

In a **carbonyl group**, a carbon atom is linked by a double bond to an oxygen atom. If the carbonyl group is at the end of a carbon skeleton, the compound is called an aldehyde; if it is within the chain, the compound is called a ketone. Simple sugars contain a carbonyl group and several hydroxyl groups.

A **carboxyl group** consists of a carbon double-bonded to an oxygen atom and also bonded to a hydroxyl group. The carboxyl group acts as an acid by contributing an H^+ to a solution (see Module 2.14) and thus becoming ionized. Compounds with carboxyl groups are called carboxylic acids.

An **amino group** has a nitrogen bonded to two hydrogens and the carbon skeleton. It acts as a base by picking up an H^+ from a solution. Organic compounds with an amino group are called amines. The building blocks of proteins—amino acids—contain an amino and a carboxyl group.

Testosterone   **Estradiol**

▲ Figure 3.2   Differences in the chemical groups of sex hormones

TABLE 3.2 | IMPORTANT CHEMICAL GROUPS OF ORGANIC COMPOUNDS

Chemical Group	Examples
Hydroxyl group —OH	Alcohol
Carbonyl group C=O	Aldehyde Ketone
Carboxyl group —COOH	Carboxylic acid Ionized
Amino group —NH₂	Amine Ionized
Phosphate group —OPO₃²⁻	Adenosine ... Organic phosphate
Methyl group —CH₃	Methylated compound

A **phosphate group** consists of a phosphorus atom bonded to four oxygen atoms. It is usually ionized and attached to the carbon skeleton by one of its oxygen atoms. Compounds with phosphate groups are called organic phosphates and are often involved in energy transfers, as is the energy-rich compound ATP, shown in the table.

A **methyl group** consists of a carbon bonded to three hydrogen atoms. The methylated compound in the table—a component of DNA—affects the expression of genes.

You will meet these chemical groups again as you learn about the four major classes of organic molecules. But first, let's see how your cells make large molecules out of smaller ones.

? Identify the chemical groups that do *not* contain carbon.

The hydroxyl, amino, and phosphate groups

3.3 Cells make large molecules from a limited set of small molecules

Given the rich complexity of life on Earth, we might expect there to be an enormous diversity of types of molecules. Remarkably, however, the important molecules of all living things—from bacteria to elephants—fall into just four main classes: carbohydrates, lipids, proteins, and nucleic acids. On a molecular scale, molecules of three of these classes—carbohydrates, proteins, and nucleic acids—can be gigantic; in fact, biologists call them **macromolecules**. For example, a protein may consist of thousands of atoms. How does a cell make such a huge molecule?

Cells make most of their macromolecules by joining smaller molecules into chains called **polymers** (from the Greek *polys*, many, and *meros*, part). A polymer is a long molecule consisting of many identical or similar building blocks strung together, much as a train consists of a chain of cars. The building blocks of polymers are called **monomers**.

Making Polymers Cells link monomers together to form polymers by a **dehydration reaction**, a reaction that removes a molecule of water as two molecules become bonded together. Each monomer contributes part of the water molecule that is released during the reaction. As you can see on the left side of Figure 3.3, one monomer (the one at the right end of the short polymer in this example) loses a hydroxyl group and the other monomer loses a hydrogen atom to form H_2O. As this occurs, a new covalent bond forms, linking the two monomers. Dehydration reactions are the same regardless of the specific monomers and the type of polymer the cell is producing.

Breaking Polymers Cells not only make macromolecules but also have to break them down. For example, most of the organic molecules in your food are in the form of polymers that are much too large to enter your cells. You must digest these polymers to make their monomers available to your cells. This digestion process is called **hydrolysis**. Essentially the reverse of a dehydration reaction, hydrolysis means to break (*lyse*) with water (*hydro-*). As the right side of Figure 3.3 shows, the bond between monomers is broken by the addition of a water molecule, with the hydroxyl group from the water attaching to one monomer and a hydrogen attaching to the adjacent monomer.

The lactose-intolerant individuals you learned about in the chapter introduction are unable to hydrolyze such a bond in the sugar lactose because they lack the enzyme lactase. Both dehydration reactions and hydrolysis require the help of enzymes to make and break bonds. **Enzymes** are specialized macromolecules that speed up chemical reactions in cells.

The Diversity of Polymers The diversity of macromolecules in the living world is vast. Surprisingly, a cell makes all its thousands of different macromolecules from a small list of ingredients—about 40 to 50 common components and a few others that are rare. Proteins, for example, are built from only 20 kinds of amino acids. Your DNA is built from just four kinds of monomers called nucleotides. The key to the great diversity of polymers is arrangement—variation in the sequence in which monomers are strung together.

The variety in polymers accounts for the uniqueness of each organism. The monomers themselves, however, are essentially universal. Your proteins and those of a tree or an ant are assembled from the same 20 amino acids. Life has a simple yet elegant molecular logic: Small molecules common to all organisms are ordered into large molecules, which vary from species to species and even from individual to individual in the same species.

In the remainder of the chapter, we explore each of the four classes of large biological molecules. Like water and simple organic molecules, large biological molecules have unique emergent properties arising from the orderly arrangement of their atoms. As you will see, for these molecules of life, structure and function are inseparable.

> **?** Suppose you eat some cheese. What reactions must occur for the protein of the cheese to be broken down into its amino acid monomers and then for these monomers to be converted to proteins in your body?

● In digestion, the proteins are broken down into amino acids by hydrolysis. New proteins are formed in your body cells from these monomers in dehydration reactions.

▲ **Figure 3.3** Dehydration reaction building a polymer (left); Hydrolysis breaking down a polymer (right)

▷ Carbohydrates

3.4 Monosaccharides are the simplest carbohydrates

Let's start our survey of large biological molecules with **carbohydrates**, the class of molecules that range from small sugar molecules, such as those dissolved in soft drinks, to large polysaccharides, such as the starch molecules we consume in pasta and potatoes.

Simple sugars, or **monosaccharides** (from the Greek *monos*, single, and *sacchar*, sugar), are the monomers of carbohydrates. The honey shown in **Figure 3.4A** consists mainly of monosaccharides called glucose and fructose. These and other single-unit sugars can be hooked together by dehydration reactions to form more complex sugars and polysaccharides.

Monosaccharides generally have molecular formulas that are some multiple of CH_2O. For example, the formula for **glucose**, a common monosaccharide of central importance in the chemistry of life, is $C_6H_{12}O_6$. **Figure 3.4B** illustrates the molecular structure of glucose, with its carbons numbered 1 to 6. This structure also shows the two trademarks of a sugar: a number of hydroxyl groups (—OH) and a carbonyl group ($>C=O$, highlighted in blue). The hydroxyl groups make a sugar an alcohol, and the carbonyl group, depending on its location, makes it either an aldehyde sugar (glucose) or a ketone sugar (fructose).

If you count the numbers of different atoms in the fructose molecule in Figure 3.4B, you will find that its molecular formula is $C_6H_{12}O_6$, identical to that of glucose. Thus, glucose and fructose are isomers; they differ only in the arrangement of their atoms (in this case, the positions of the carbonyl groups). Because the shape of molecules is so important, seemingly minor differences like this give isomers different properties, such as how they react with other molecules. These differences also make fructose taste considerably sweeter than glucose.

The carbon skeletons of both glucose and fructose are six carbon atoms long. Other monosaccharides may have three to seven carbons. Five-carbon sugars, called pentoses, and six-carbon sugars, called hexoses, are among the most common. (Note that most names for sugars end in *-ose*. Also, as you saw with the enzyme lactase, which digests the sugar lactose, the names for most enzymes end in *-ase*.)

It is convenient to draw sugars as if their carbon skeletons were linear, but in aqueous solutions, most five- and six-carbon sugars form rings, as shown for glucose in **Figure 3.4C**. To form the glucose ring, carbon 1 bonds to the oxygen attached to carbon 5. As shown in the middle representation, the ring diagram of glucose and other sugars may be abbreviated by not showing the carbon atoms at the corners of the ring. Also, the bonds in the ring are often drawn with varied thickness, indicating that the ring is a relatively flat structure with attached atoms extending above and below it. The simplified ring symbol on the right is often used in this book to represent glucose.

Monosaccharides, particularly glucose, are the main fuel molecules for cellular work. Because cells release energy from glucose when they break it down, an aqueous solution of glucose (often called dextrose) may be injected into the bloodstream of sick or injured patients; the glucose provides an immediate energy source to tissues in need of repair. Cells also use the carbon skeletons of monosaccharides as raw material for making other kinds of organic molecules, such as amino acids and fatty acids. Sugars not used in these ways may be incorporated into disaccharides and polysaccharides, as we see next.

> **?** Write the formula for a monosaccharide that has three carbons.
>
> ● $C_3H_6O_3$

◀ **Figure 3.4B** Structures of glucose and fructose

Try This Identify the two functional groups that are characteristic of a monosaccharide.

▲ **Figure 3.4A** Bees with honey, a mixture of two monosaccharides

Structural formula · Abbreviated structure · Simplified structure

▲ **Figure 3.4C** Three representations of the ring form of glucose

3.5 Two monosaccharides are linked to form a disaccharide

Cells construct a **disaccharide** from two monosaccharide monomers by a dehydration reaction. **Figure 3.5** shows how maltose, also called malt sugar, is formed from two glucose monomers. One monomer gives up a hydroxyl group and the other gives up a hydrogen atom. As H_2O is released, an oxygen atom is left, linking the two monomers. Malt sugar, which is common in germinating seeds, is used in making beer, malt whiskey, and malted milk candy.

Sucrose is the most common disaccharide. It is made of a glucose monomer linked to a fructose monomer. Transported in plant sap, sucrose provides a source of energy and raw materials to all the parts of the plant. We extract it from the stems of sugarcane or the roots of sugar beets to use as table sugar.

> **?** Lactose, as you read in the chapter introduction, is the disaccharide sugar in milk. It is formed from glucose and galactose. The formula for both these monosaccharides is $C_6H_{12}O_6$. What is the formula for lactose?
>
> ● $C_{12}H_{22}O_{11}$

▲ **Figure 3.5** Disaccharide formation by a dehydration reaction

3.6 What is high-fructose corn syrup, and is it to blame for obesity?

CONNECTION

If you want to sweeten your coffee or tea, you probably reach for sugar—the disaccharide sucrose. But if you drink sodas, you're probably consuming the monosaccharides of sucrose in the form of high-fructose corn syrup. In fact, if you look at the label of almost any processed food, you will see high-fructose corn syrup listed as one of the ingredients (Figure 3.6).

What is high-fructose corn syrup (HFCS)? Let's start with the corn syrup part. The main carbohydrate in corn is starch, a polysaccharide built from glucose monomers. Industrial processing hydrolyzes starch into these monomers, producing corn syrup. Glucose, however, does not taste as sweet to us as sucrose. Fructose, on the other hand, tastes much sweeter than both glucose and sucrose. When a new process was developed in the 1970s that used an enzyme to rearrange the atoms of glucose into the sweeter isomer, fructose (see Figure 3.4B), the high-fructose corn syrup industry was born. (High-fructose corn syrup is a bit of a misnomer, because the fructose is combined with regular corn syrup to produce a mixture of about 55% fructose and 45% glucose, not much different from the proportions in sucrose.)

The resulting clear, goopy liquid is cheaper than sucrose and easier to mix into drinks and processed food. And it contains the same monosaccharides as sucrose, the disaccharide it is replacing. So is there a problem with HFCS? Some point to circumstantial evidence. From 1980 to 2000, the incidence of obesity doubled in the United States. In that same time period, the consumption of HFCS more than tripled, whereas the consumption of refined cane and beet sugar decreased 21%.

▲ **Figure 3.6** High-fructose corn syrup, a main ingredient of soft drinks and processed foods

Is high-fructose corn syrup to blame for the current "obesity epidemic" with its attendant increases in type 2 diabetes, high blood pressure, and other chronic diseases associated with increased weight? Does this *correlation* between increased HFCS consumption and increased obesity indicate *causation*? In spite of alarming claims in the popular press, most scientific studies have not shown health consequences associated with replacing sucrose with HFCS. Data also show that some countries with high obesity rates consume little high-fructose corn syrup. And although HFCS consumption has declined somewhat in recent years, obesity rates continue to rise, with almost 36% of U.S. adults now considered obese. Alternative hypotheses for our increasing obesity abound, including the fact that, from 1980 to 2000, the U.S. per capita daily caloric intake increased 23%.

It does not appear that high-fructose corn syrup is the "smoking gun" responsible for the obesity crisis. There is solid evidence, however, that overconsumption of sugar and/or HFCS along with dietary fat and decreased physical activity contribute to weight gain. In addition, high sugar consumption tends to replace eating more varied and nutritious foods. For good health, you require proteins, fats, vitamins, and minerals, as well as complex carbohydrates, the topic of the next module.

> **?** How is high-fructose corn syrup made from corn?
>
> ● Corn starch is hydrolyzed to glucose; then enzymes convert glucose to fructose. This fructose is combined with corn syrup to produce HFCS.

3.7 Polysaccharides are long chains of sugar units

Polysaccharides are macromolecules, polymers of hundreds to thousands of monosaccharides linked together by dehydration reactions. Polysaccharides may function as storage molecules or as structural compounds. **Figure 3.7** illustrates three common types: starch, glycogen, and cellulose.

Starch, a storage polysaccharide in plants, consists of long chains of glucose monomers. Starch molecules coil into a helical shape and may be unbranched (as shown in the figure) or branched. Starch granules serve as carbohydrate "banks" from which plant cells can withdraw glucose for energy or building materials. Humans and most other animals have enzymes that can hydrolyze plant starch to glucose. Potatoes and grains, such as wheat, corn, and rice, are the major sources of starch in the human diet.

Animals store glucose in a polysaccharide called **glycogen**. Glycogen is more highly branched than starch, as shown in the figure. Most of your glycogen is stored as granules in your liver and muscle cells, which hydrolyze the glycogen to release glucose when it is needed.

Cellulose, the most abundant organic compound on Earth, is a major component of the tough walls that enclose plant cells. Cellulose is also a polymer of glucose, but its monomers are linked together in a different orientation. (Carefully compare the oxygen "bridges" highlighted in yellow in the figure between glucose monomers in starch, glycogen, and cellulose.) Arranged parallel to each other, cellulose molecules are joined by hydrogen bonds, forming cable-like microfibrils. Layers of microfibrils combine with other polymers, producing strong support for trees and the structures we build with lumber.

Animals do not have enzymes that can hydrolyze the glucose linkages in cellulose. Therefore, cellulose is not a nutrient for humans, although it does contribute to digestive health. The cellulose that passes unchanged through your digestive tract is referred to as "insoluble fiber." Fresh fruits, vegetables, and whole grains are rich in fiber.

Some microorganisms do have enzymes that can hydrolyze cellulose. Cows and termites house such microorganisms in their digestive tracts and are thus able to derive energy from cellulose. Decomposing fungi also digest cellulose, helping to recycle its chemical elements within ecosystems.

Chitin is a structural polysaccharide used by insects and crustaceans to build their exoskeleton, the hard case enclosing the animal. Chitin is also found in the cell walls of fungi.

Almost all carbohydrates are hydrophilic owing to the many hydroxyl groups attached to their sugar monomers (see Figure 3.4B). Thus, cotton bath towels, which are mostly cellulose, are quite water absorbent due to the water-loving nature of cellulose. As you'll see next, not all biological molecules "love water."

> **?** Compare and contrast starch and cellulose, two plant polysaccharides.
>
> ● Both are polymers of glucose, but the bonds between glucose monomers have different shapes. Starch functions mainly for sugar storage. Cellulose is a structural polysaccharide that is the main material of plant cell walls.

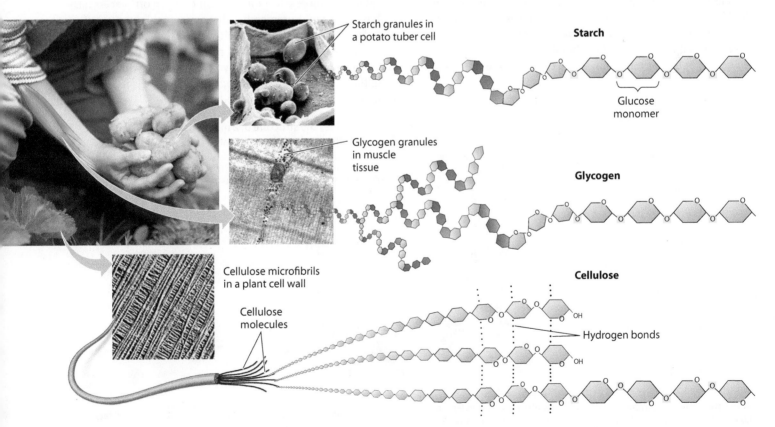

Starch granules in a potato tuber cell

Starch

Glucose monomer

Glycogen granules in muscle tissue

Glycogen

Cellulose microfibrils in a plant cell wall

Cellulose molecules

Cellulose

Hydrogen bonds

▲ **Figure 3.7** Polysaccharides of plants and animals

3.8 Fats are lipids that are mostly energy-storage molecules

Lipids are a diverse group of molecules that are classified together because they share one trait: They do not mix well with water. In contrast to carbohydrates and most other biological molecules, lipids are **hydrophobic** (water-fearing). You can see this chemical behavior in an unshaken bottle of salad dressing. The oil (a type of lipid) separates from the vinegar (which is mostly water).

Lipids also differ from carbohydrates, proteins, and nucleic acids in that they are neither huge macromolecules nor polymers built from similar monomers. In this and the next few modules, we consider the structures and functions of three important types of lipids: fats, phospholipids, and steroids.

A **fat** is a large lipid made from two kinds of smaller molecules: glycerol and fatty acids. Shown at the top in **Figure 3.8A**, glycerol consists of three carbons, each bearing a hydroxyl group (—OH). A fatty acid consists of a carboxyl group (the functional group that gives these molecules the name fatty *acid*, —COOH) and a hydrocarbon chain, usually 16 or 18 carbon atoms in length. The nonpolar C—H bonds in the hydrocarbon chains are the reason fats are hydrophobic.

Figure 3.8A shows how one fatty acid molecule can link to a glycerol molecule by a dehydration reaction. Linking three fatty acids to glycerol produces a fat, as illustrated in **Figure 3.8B**. A synonym for fat is *triglyceride*, a term you may see on food labels or on medical tests for fat in the blood.

A fatty acid whose hydrocarbon chain contains one or more double bonds is called an **unsaturated fatty acid**. Each carbon atom connected by a double bond has one fewer hydrogen atom attached to it. These double bonds usually cause kinks (or bends) in the carbon chain, as you can see in the third fatty

acid in Figure 3.8B. A fatty acid that has no double bonds in its hydrocarbon chain has the maximum number of hydrogen atoms attached to each carbon atom (its carbons are "saturated" with hydrogen) and is called a **saturated fatty acid**.

Most animal fats are saturated: Their hydrocarbon chains—the "tails" of their fatty acids—lack double bonds and thus pack closely together, making them solid at room temperature (**Figure 3.8C**). In contrast, the fats of plants and fishes generally contain unsaturated fatty acids. The kinks in their unsaturated fatty acid tails prevent them from packing tightly together. Thus, unsaturated fats are usually liquid at room temperature and are referred to as oils. When you see "hydrogenated vegetable oils" on a margarine label, it means that unsaturated fats have been converted to saturated fats by adding hydrogen. Unfortunately, the process of hydrogenation also creates **trans fats**, a form of fat that recent research associates with health risks. We will discuss some of that research in Module 3.9.

The main function of fats is long-term energy storage. A gram of fat stores more than twice as much energy as a gram of polysaccharide. For immobile plants, the bulky energy storage form of starch is not a problem. (Vegetable oils are generally obtained from seeds, where more compact energy storage is a benefit.) Mobile animals, such as humans, can get around much more easily carrying their energy stores in the form of fat. Of course, the downside of this energy-packed storage form is that it takes more effort for a person to "burn off" excess fat.

It is important to remember that a reasonable amount of body fat is both normal and healthy. You stock these long-term fuel reserves in specialized reservoirs called adipose cells, which swell and shrink as you deposit and withdraw fat from them. In addition to storing energy, fatty tissue cushions vital organs and insulates the body.

? **How does the structure of a monounsaturated fat differ from a polyunsaturated fat?**

● A monounsaturated fat has a fatty acid with a single double bond in its carbon chain. A polyunsaturated fat contains a fatty acid with more than one double bond.

▲ **Figure 3.8A** A dehydration reaction that will link a fatty acid to glycerol

▲ **Figure 3.8B** A fat molecule (triglyceride) consisting of three fatty acids linked to glycerol

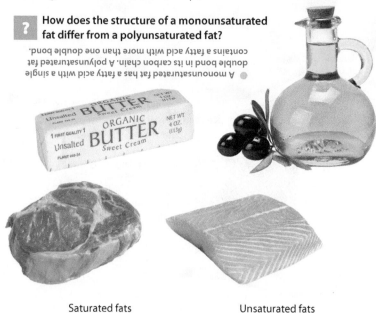

Saturated fats

Unsaturated fats

▲ **Figure 3.8C** Types of fats

3.9 Scientific studies document the health risks of trans fats

In the previous module, you learned about the difference between vegetable oils and animal fats and their unsaturated versus saturated fatty acids. In the 1890s, a process was invented that added hydrogen atoms to the double-bonded carbon atoms of unsaturated fats, producing partially hydrogenated vegetable oils. These new fats had several desirable traits: They didn't spoil as quickly as oils and could withstand repeated reheating for frying. In addition, in the 1950s and 1960s, scientific studies began to associate saturated fats with an increased risk of heart disease, leading to a public health campaign to reduce consumption of animal fats (such as butter) and replace them with unsaturated oils and the supposedly healthier partially hydrogenated vegetable oils (such as margarine).

Jump ahead to the 1990s, and partially hydrogenated oils were found in myriad foods—cookies, crackers, snacks, baked goods, and fried foods. But new research began to show that the trans fats produced in the process of hydrogenation were an even greater health risk than were saturated fats. One study estimated that eliminating trans fats from the food supply could prevent up to one in five heart attacks! In 2006, the U.S. Food and Drug Administration required the listing of trans fat on food labels. Because foods sold in restaurants and schools do not come with labels, many cities and states since have passed laws to eliminate trans fats in these foods. And an increasing number of countries have banned trans fats.

The scientific studies establishing the risks of trans fats were of two types: experimental and observational. In experimental controlled feeding trials, the diets of participants contained different proportions of saturated, unsaturated, and partially hydrogenated fats. The hypothesis of these studies was that trans fats adversely affect cardiovascular health; the prediction was that the more trans fats in the diet, the greater the risk. But how does one measure risk? Should the study proceed until participants start having heart attacks? For both ethical and practical reasons, controlled feeding trials are usually fairly short in duration, involve only limited dietary changes, generally use healthy individuals, and measure intermediary risk factors, such as changes in cholesterol levels, rather than actual disease outcomes.

Many scientific studies on dietary health effects are observational. The advantages of such studies are that they can extend over a longer time period, use a more representative population, and measure disease outcomes as well as risk factors. Observational studies may be retrospective (looking backward): Present health status is documented, and participants report their prior eating habits. Two difficulties with retrospective studies are that people may not accurately remember and report their dietary histories, and anyone who has already died, say, of a heart attack, is not included in the study. Prospective studies, on the other hand, look forward. Researchers conducting such studies enlist a study group, quantify participants' health attributes, and then collect data on the group over many years. Diet, lifestyle habits, risk factors, and disease outcomes can all be recorded and then analyzed.

TABLE 3.9 | RISK OF HEART DISEASE ASSOCIATED WITH INCREASES IN SPECIFIC TYPES OF FAT CONSUMED

Variable	Relative Risk*
Saturated fat (each increase of 5% of energy)	1.17
Monounsaturated fat (each increase of 5% of energy)	0.81
Polyunsaturated fat (each increase of 5% of energy)	0.62
Trans fat (each increase of 2% of energy	1.93

* A relative risk (RR) of 1 means that there is no difference in risk of coronary heart disease when compared to an equivalent intake of carbohydrate; RR of less than 1 means there is a decreased risk; RR greater than 1, there is a greater risk.

Data from F. B. Hu et al. Dietary fat intake and the risk of coronary heart disease in women, *New England Journal of Medicine* 337: 1491–9 (1997).

A landmark example of a prospective study is the Nurses' Health Study, begun in 1976 with more than 120,000 female nurses. In a portion of the study that looked at dietary fat intake, 80,082 women were followed from 1980 to 1994. The researchers estimated the relative risk of coronary heart disease associated with the intake of different types of fats. As you can see in Table 3.9, for each 5% increase in energy consumed in the form of saturated fat, as compared to an equivalent energy intake from carbohydrates, the relative risk rises to 1.17—or a 17% increase in the risk of heart disease. For each 2% increase in the amount of energy consumed in the form of trans fat, however, there is a 93% increase in risk. Trans fats are indeed a greater health risk than saturated fats.

Based on an accumulation of scientific evidence from many studies, U.S. governmental agencies have revised their policies—from promoting partially hydrogenated vegetable oils as a healthful alternative to saturated fats in the middle of the 20th century to today regulating and increasingly banning the trans fats that are produced when such oils are hydrogenated. Such changes in policy reflect changes in our understanding based on current research. Scientific knowledge both expands and is revised as new questions are asked, new studies are done, and new evidence accumulates.

In the next module, we consider two other important types of lipids: phospholipids and steroids.

Data from D. Mozaffarian et al., Trans fatty acids and cardiovascular disease, *The New England Journal of Medicine* 354: 1601–13 (2006).

? How does the relative risk of coronary heart disease change with a 5% increase in polyunsaturated fat in the diet?

● The relative risk drops to 0.62. In other words, there is a 38% decrease in risk.

3.10 Phospholipids and steroids are important lipids with a variety of functions

Cells could not exist without **phospholipids**, the major component of cell membranes. Phospholipids are structurally similar to fats, except that they contain only two fatty acids attached to glycerol instead of three. As shown in Figure 3.10A, a negatively charged phosphate group (shown as a yellow circle in the figure and linked to another small molecule) is attached to glycerol's third carbon.

▲ **Figure 3.10A** Chemical structure of a phospholipid molecule

Try This Explain why the gray region of this phospholipid is hydrophilic and why the yellow tails are hydrophobic.

The structure of phospholipids provides a classic example of how form fits function. The two ends of a phospholipid have different relationships with water, resulting in the aggregation of multiple phospholipid molecules into a membrane (Figure 3.10B). The hydrophobic tails of the fatty acids cluster together in the center, excluded from water, and the hydrophilic phosphate heads face the watery environment on either side of the membrane. Each gray-headed, yellow-tailed structure in the membrane shown here represents a phospholipid; this visual representation is used throughout this book. (We will explore the structure and function of biological membranes in more detail in Chapter 5.)

Steroids are lipids in which the carbon skeleton contains four fused rings, as shown in the structural formula of cholesterol in Figure 3.10C. (The diagram omits the carbons making up the rings and most of the chain and also their attached hydrogen atoms.) **Cholesterol** is a common component in animal cell membranes and is also the precursor for making other steroids, including sex hormones. Different steroids vary in the chemical groups attached to the rings, as you saw in Figure 3.2. Too much cholesterol in the blood may contribute to atherosclerosis.

❓ **Compare the structure of a phospholipid with that of a fat (triglyceride).**

● A phospholipid has two fatty acids and a phosphate group attached to glycerol. Three fatty acids are attached to the glycerol of a fat molecule.

▲ **Figure 3.10C** Cholesterol, a steroid

3.11 Anabolic steroids pose health risks

CONNECTION

Anabolic steroids are synthetic variants of the male hormone testosterone. Testosterone causes a general buildup of muscle and bone mass in males during puberty and maintains masculine traits throughout life. Because anabolic steroids structurally resemble testosterone, they also mimic some of its effects. (The word *anabolic* comes from *anabolism*, the building of substances by the body.)

Anabolic steroids are used to treat general anemia and diseases that destroy body muscle. Some athletes use these drugs to build up their muscles quickly and enhance their performance. But at what cost? Steroid abuse may cause violent mood swings ("roid rage"), depression, liver damage or cancer, and high cholesterol levels and blood pressure. Use of these drugs often makes the body reduce its output of natural male sex hormones, which

can cause shrunken testicles, reduced sex drive, infertility, and breast enlargement in men. Use in women has been linked to menstrual cycle disruption and development of masculine characteristics. An effect in teens is that bones may stop growing.

Despite the risks, some athletes continue to abuse synthetic steroids, and unscrupulous chemists, trainers, and coaches try to find ways to avoid their detection. Meanwhile, the U.S. Congress, professional sports authorities, and high school and college athletic programs ban the use of anabolic steroids, implement drug testing, and penalize violators in an effort to keep the competition fair and protect the health of athletes.

❓ **Explain why fats and steroids, which are structurally very different, are both classed as lipids?**

● Fats and steroids are hydrophobic molecules, the key characteristic of lipids.

▷ Proteins

3.12 Proteins have a wide range of functions and structures

Nearly every dynamic function in your body depends on proteins. A **protein** is a polymer of small building blocks called amino acids. Of all of life's molecules, proteins are structurally and functionally the most elaborate and varied.

You have tens of thousands of different proteins in your body. What do they all do? Probably their most important role is as enzymes, the chemical catalysts that speed and regulate virtually all chemical reactions in your cells. Lactase, which you read about in the chapter introduction, is just one example of an enzyme.

Other types of proteins include transport proteins that are embedded in cell membranes and move sugar molecules and other nutrients into your cells. Moving through your blood stream are defensive proteins, such as the antibodies of the immune system, and signal proteins, such as many of the hormones and other chemical messengers that help coordinate your body's activities. Receptor proteins built into cell membranes receive and transmit such signals into your cells.

Muscle cells are packed with contractile proteins, and structural proteins are found in the fibers that make up your tendons and ligaments. Indeed, the structural protein collagen, which forms the long, strong fibers of connective tissues, accounts for 40% of the protein in your body.

Some proteins are storage proteins, which supply amino acids to developing embryos. The proteins found in eggs and seeds are examples.

The functions of all of these different types of proteins depend on their individual shapes. **Figure 3.12A** shows a ribbon model of lysozyme, an enzyme found in your sweat, tears, and saliva. Lysozyme consists of one long polymer of amino acids, represented by the purple ribbon. Lysozyme's general shape is called globular. This overall shape is more apparent in **Figure 3.12B**, a space-filling model of lysozyme. In that model, the colors represent the different atoms of carbon, oxygen, nitrogen, and hydrogen. The barely visible yellow balls represent sulfur atoms that form the stabilizing bonds shown as yellow lines in the ribbon model. Most enzymes and many other proteins are globular. Structural proteins, such as those making up hair, tendons, and ligaments, are typically long and thin and are called fibrous proteins. **Figure 3.12C** shows a spider's web, made up of fibrous silk proteins. The structural arrangement within these proteins makes each silk fiber stronger than a steel strand of the same weight.

Descriptions such as *globular* and *fibrous* refer to a protein's general shape. Each protein also has a much more specific shape. The coils and twists of lysozyme's ribbon in Figure 3.12A may appear haphazard, but they represent the molecule's specific, three-dimensional

shape. Nearly all proteins must recognize and bind to some other molecule to function. Lysozyme can destroy bacterial cells, but first it must bind to molecules on the bacterial cell surface. Lysozyme's specific shape enables it to recognize and attach to its molecular target, which fits into the groove you see on the right in the figures.

The dependence of protein function on a protein's shape becomes clear when a protein is altered. In a process called **denaturation**, a protein unravels, losing its specific shape and, as a result, its function. Excessive heat can denature many proteins. For example, visualize what happens when you fry an egg. Heat quickly denatures the clear proteins surrounding the yolk, making them solid, white, and opaque.

Given the proper cellular environment, a newly synthesized amino acid chain spontaneously folds into its functional shape. What happens if a protein doesn't fold correctly? Many diseases, such as Alzheimer's and Parkinson's, involve an accumulation of misfolded proteins. Prions are infectious misshapen proteins that are associated with serious degenerative brain diseases such as mad cow disease (see Module 10.21). Such diseases reinforce the theme that structure fits function: A protein's unique three-dimensional shape

▲ **Figure 3.12C** Fibrous silk proteins of a spider's web

determines its proper functioning. In the next two modules, we'll learn how a protein's structure takes shape.

? **Why does a denatured protein no longer function normally?**

● The function of each protein is a consequence of its specific shape, which is lost when a protein denatures.

▲ **Figure 3.12A** Ribbon model of the protein lysozyme

Groove

Groove

▲ **Figure 3.12B** Space-filling model of the protein lysozyme

3.13 Proteins are made from amino acids linked by peptide bonds

Now let's see what the monomers of proteins look like. **Amino acids** all have an amino group and a carboxyl group (which makes it an acid, hence the name amino *acid*). As you can see in the general structure shown in **Figure 3.13A**, both of these functional groups are covalently bonded to a central carbon atom. Also bonded to this carbon is a hydrogen atom. The fourth bond of the central carbon is to a variable chemical group symbolized by the letter R. In the simplest amino acid (glycine), the R group is just a hydrogen atom. In all others, the R group consists of one or more carbon atoms with various functional groups attached.

▲ **Figure 3.13A** General structure of an amino acid

All 20 amino acids are included in Appendix 3, grouped according to whether their R groups are hydrophobic or hydrophilic. **Figure 3.13B** shows representatives of these two main types. Hydrophobic amino acids have nonpolar R groups—note the nonpolar C—H bonds in the R group of leucine (abbreviated Leu) shown in the figure. The R groups of hydrophilic amino acids may be polar or charged. R groups that contain acidic or basic groups are charged at the pH of a cell. Indeed, the amino and carboxyl groups attached to the central carbon of all amino acids are also usually ionized at cellular pH (see ionized forms in Table 3.2).

Now that we have examined amino acids, let's see how they are linked to form polymers. Can you guess? Cells join amino acids together in a dehydration reaction that links the carboxyl group of one amino acid to the amino group of the next amino acid as a water molecule is removed **(Figure 3.13C)**. The resulting covalent linkage is called a **peptide bond**. The product of the reaction shown in the figure is called a *di*peptide, because it was made from *two* amino acids. Additional amino acids can be added by the same process to form a chain of amino acids, a **polypeptide**.

How is it possible to make thousands of different kinds of proteins from just 20 amino acids? The answer has to do with sequence. You know that thousands of English words can be made by varying the sequence of letters and word length. Although the protein "alphabet" is slightly smaller (just 20 "letters," rather than 26), the "words" are much longer. Most polypeptides are at least 100 amino acids in length; some are 1,000 or more. Each polypeptide has a unique sequence of amino acids.

But a long polypeptide chain of specific sequence is not the same as a protein, any more than a long strand of yarn is the same as a sweater that can be knit from that yarn. What are the stitches that coil and fold a polypeptide chain into a unique three-dimensional shape? This is where the R groups of the constituent amino acids play their role in influencing protein structure. Hydrophobic amino acids may cluster together in the center of a globular protein, while hydrophilic amino acids face the outside, helping proteins dissolve in the aqueous solution of a cell. Hydrogen bonds and ionic bonds between hydrophilic R groups help determine a protein's shape, as do covalent bonds called disulfide bridges between sulfur atoms in some R groups. (Look back at the yellow lines in Figure 3.12A.) The unique sequence of the various types of amino acids in a polypeptide determines how a protein takes shape. Let's visualize this process in the next module.

? By what process do you digest the proteins you eat into their individual amino acids?

● By hydrolysis, adding a molecule of water back to break each peptide bond

Hydrophobic	Hydrophilic	
Leucine (Leu)	Serine (Ser)	Aspartic acid (Asp)

▲ **Figure 3.13B** Examples of amino acids with hydrophobic and hydrophilic R groups

Try This Point out the bonds and functional groups that make the R groups of these three amino acids either hydrophobic or hydrophilic.

Carboxyl group   Amino group   Dehydration reaction   Peptide bond

Amino acid + Amino acid → H_2O → Dipeptide

▲ **Figure 3.13C** Peptide bond formation

3.14 A protein's functional shape results from four levels of structure

The **primary structure** of a protein is the precise sequence of amino acids in the polypeptide chain. Segments of the chain then coil or fold into local patterns called **secondary structure**. The overall three-dimensional shape of a protein is called **tertiary structure**. Proteins with more than one polypeptide chain have **quaternary structure.**

To help you visualize how these structural levels are super-imposed on each other to form a functional protein, let's look at transthyretin, an important transport protein found in your blood. Its specific shape enables it to transport vitamin A and one of the thyroid hormones throughout your body.

PRIMARY STRUCTURE

^+H_3N Amino end

Peptide bonds connect the 127 amino acids of a transthyretin polypeptide. Part of the polypeptide is shown.

Amino acids

Each amino acid has a specific R group.

The three-letter abbreviations represent specific amino acids.

Two types of **SECONDARY STRUCTURES**

Alpha helix

Secondary structures are maintained by hydrogen bonds between atoms of the polypeptide backbone, shown here as dotted lines.

Beta pleated sheet

The flat arrow points toward the carboxyl end of the polypeptide chain.

TERTIARY STRUCTURE

A transthyretin polypeptide has one alpha helix region and several beta pleated sheets, which are compacted into a globular shape.

Tertiary structure is stabilized by interactions between R groups, such as the clustering of hydrophobic R groups in the center of the molecule, and hydrogen bonds, ionic bonds, and disulfide bridges between hydrophilic R groups.

QUARTERNARY STRUCTURE

Interactions similar to those involved in tertiary structures hold these subunits together.

The four identical polypeptides, or subunits, of transthyretin are precisely associated into a functional protein.

? **If a genetic mutation changes the primary structure of a protein, how might this destroy the protein's function?**

Primary structure determines the secondary and tertiary structure due to the chemical nature of the polypeptide backbone and R groups of the amino acids positioned along the chain. Even a slight change may affect a protein's shape and thus its function.

▷ Nucleic Acids

3.15 DNA and RNA are the two types of nucleic acids

As we just saw, the primary structure of a polypeptide determines the shape of a protein. But what determines the primary structure? The amino acid sequence of a polypeptide is programmed by a discrete unit of inheritance known as a **gene**. Genes consist of **DNA** (**d**eoxyribo**nucleic a**cid), one of the two types of polymers called **nucleic acids**. The name *nucleic* comes from their location in the nuclei of eukaryotic cells. The genetic material that humans and other organisms inherit from their parents consists of DNA. Unique among molecules, DNA provides directions for its own replication. Thus, as a cell divides, its genetic instructions are passed to each daughter cell. These instructions program all of a cell's activities by directing the synthesis of proteins.

The genes present in DNA do not build proteins directly. They work through an intermediary—the second type of nucleic acid, known as **ribonucleic acid (RNA)**. **Figure 3.15** illustrates the main roles of these two types of nucleic acids in the production of proteins. In the nucleus of a eukaryotic cell, a gene directs the synthesis of an RNA molecule. We say that DNA is transcribed into RNA. The RNA molecule moves out of the nucleus and interacts with the protein-building machinery of the cell. There, the gene's instructions, written in "nucleic acid language," are translated into "protein language," the amino acid sequence of a polypeptide. (In prokaryotic

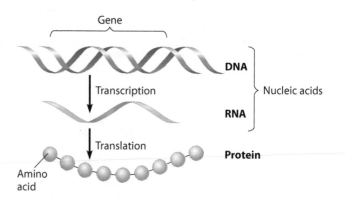

▲ **Figure 3.15**   The flow of genetic information in the building of a protein

cells, which lack nuclei, both transcription and translation take place within the cytoplasm of the cell.)

Recent research has found previously unknown types of RNA molecules that play many other roles in the cell. (We return to the functions of DNA and RNA later in the book.)

?   **How are the two types of nucleic acids functionally related?**

● The hereditary material of DNA contains the instructions for the primary structure of polypeptides. RNA is the intermediary that conveys those instructions to the protein-making machinery that assembles amino acids in the designated order.

3.16 Nucleic acids are polymers of nucleotides

The monomers that make up nucleic acids are **nucleotides**. As indicated in **Figure 3.16A**, each nucleotide contains three parts. At the center of a nucleotide is a five-carbon sugar (blue); the sugar in DNA is deoxyribose, whereas RNA has a slightly different sugar called ribose. Linked to one side of the sugar in both types of nucleotides is a negatively charged phosphate group (yellow). Linked to the sugar's other side is a nitrogenous base (green), a molecular structure containing nitrogen and carbon. (The nitrogen atoms tend to take up H^+ in aqueous solutions, which explains why it is called a nitrogenous *base*.) Each DNA nucleotide has one of four different nitrogenous bases: adenine (A), thymine (T), cytosine (C), and guanine (G). Thus, all genetic information is written in a four-letter alphabet. RNA nucleotides also contain the bases A, C, and G; but the base uracil (U) is found instead of thymine.

Like polysaccharides and polypeptides, a nucleic acid polymer—a polynucleotide—is built from its monomers by dehydration reactions. In this process, the sugar of one nucleotide bonds to the phosphate group of the next monomer. The result is a repeating sugar-phosphate backbone in the polymer, as represented by the blue and yellow ribbon in **Figure 3.16B**. (Note that the nitrogenous bases are not part of the backbone.)

RNA usually consists of a single polynucleotide strand, but DNA is a **double helix**, in which two polynucleotides wrap around each other (**Figure 3.16C**). The nitrogenous bases protrude from the two sugar-phosphate backbones and pair in the center of the helix. As shown by their diagrammatic shapes in the figure, A always pairs with T, and C always pairs with G. The two DNA chains are held together by hydrogen bonds (indicated by the dotted lines) between their paired bases. These bonds are individually weak, but

Phosphate group

Nitrogenous base (adenine)

Sugar

▲ **Figure 3.16A**   A nucleotide

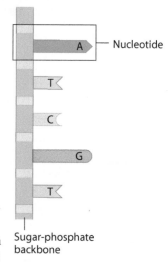

Nucleotide

Sugar-phosphate backbone

▲ **Figure 3.16B**   Part of a polynucleotide

collectively they zip the two strands together into a very stable double helix. Most DNA molecules have thousands or even millions of base pairs.

Because of the base-pairing rules, the two strands of the double helix are said to be *complementary*, each a predictable counterpart of the other. Thus, if a stretch of nucleotides on one strand has the base sequence –AGCACT–, then the same stretch on the other strand must be –TCGTGA–. Complementary base pairing is the key to how a cell makes two identical copies of each of its DNA molecules every time it divides. Thus, the structure of DNA accounts for its function of transmitting genetic information whenever a cell reproduces. The same base-pairing rules (with the exception that U nucleotides of RNA pair with A nucleotides of DNA) also

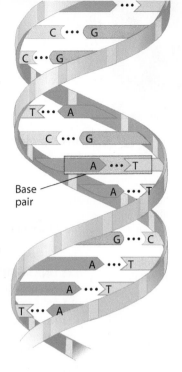

Base pair

account for the precise transcription of information from DNA to RNA. (The details of gene transcription and translation are covered in detail in Chapter 10.)

An organism's genes determine the proteins and thus the structures and functions of its body. Let's return to the subject of the chapter introduction—lactose intolerance—to conclude our study of biological molecules. (In the next chapter, we move up in the biological hierarchy to the level of the cell.)

? **What roles do complementary base pairing play in the functioning of nucleic acids?**

● Complementary base pairing makes possible the precise replication of DNA, ensuring that genetic information is faithfully transmitted every time a cell divides. It also ensures that RNA molecules carry accurate instructions for the synthesis of proteins.

▲ Figure 3.16C   DNA double helix

3.17 Lactose tolerance is a recent event in human evolution

EVOLUTION CONNECTION

As you'll recall from the chapter introduction, the majority of people stop producing the enzyme lactase in early childhood and thus do not easily digest the milk sugar lactose. Researchers were curious about the genetic and evolutionary basis for the regional distribution of lactose tolerance and intolerance.

What does evolution have to do with drinking milk?

In 2002, a group of scientists completed a study of the genes of 196 lactose-intolerant adults of African, Asian, and European descent. They determined that lactose intolerance is actually the human norm. It is "lactose tolerance" that represents a relatively recent mutation in the human genome.

The ability to make lactase into adulthood is concentrated in people of northern European descent, and the researchers speculated that lactose tolerance became widespread among this group because it offered a survival advantage. In northern Europe's relatively cold climate, only one harvest a year is possible. Therefore, animals were a main source of food for early humans in that region. Cattle were first domesticated in northern Europe about 9,000 years ago (**Figure 3.17**). With milk and other dairy products at hand year-round, natural selection would have favored anyone with a mutation that kept the lactase gene switched on into adulthood.

Researchers wondered whether the lactose tolerance mutation found in Europeans might be present in other cultures that kept dairy herds. Indeed, a 2006 study compared the genetic makeup and lactose tolerance of 43 ethnic groups in East Africa. The researchers identified three mutations, all different from each other and from the European mutation, that keep the lactase gene permanently turned on. The

▲ Figure 3.17   A prehistoric European cave painting of cattle

mutations appear to have occurred beginning around 7,000 years ago, around the time that archaeological evidence shows the domestication of cattle in these African regions.

Mutations that conferred a selective advantage, such as surviving cold winters or withstanding drought by drinking milk, spread rapidly in these early pastoral peoples. Their evolutionary and cultural history is thus recorded in their genes and in their continuing ability to digest milk.

Data from S. A. Tishkoff et al., Convergent adaptation of human lactase persistence in Africa and Europe, *Nature Genetics* 39: 31–40 (2006).

? **Explain how lactose tolerance involves three of the four major classes of biological macromolecules.**

● Lactose, milk sugar, is a carbohydrate that is hydrolyzed by the enzyme lactase, a protein. The ability to make this enzyme and the regulation of when it is made is coded for in DNA, a nucleic acid.

CHAPTER 3 REVIEW

For practice quizzes, BioFlix animations, MP3 tutorials, video tutors, and more study tools designed for this textbook, go to

MasteringBiology®

Reviewing the Concepts

Introduction to Organic Compounds (3.1–3.3)

3.1 Life's molecular diversity is based on the properties of carbon. Carbon's ability to bond with four other atoms is the basis for building large and diverse organic compounds. Hydrocarbons are composed of only carbon and hydrogen. Isomers have the same molecular formula but different structures.

3.2 A few chemical groups are key to the functioning of biological molecules. Hydrophilic functional groups give organic molecules specific chemical properties.

3.3 Cells make large molecules from a limited set of small molecules.

Carbohydrates (3.4–3.7)

3.4 Monosaccharides are the simplest carbohydrates. A monosaccharide has a formula that is a multiple of CH_2O and contains hydroxyl groups and a carbonyl group.

3.5 Two monosaccharides are linked to form a disaccharide.

3.6 What is high-fructose corn syrup, and is it to blame for obesity? HFCS, a mixture of glucose and fructose derived from corn, is commonly added to drinks and processed foods.

3.7 Polysaccharides are long chains of sugar units. Starch and glycogen are storage polysaccharides; cellulose is structural, found in plant cell walls. Chitin is a component of insect exoskeletons and fungal cell walls.

Lipids (3.8–3.11)

3.8 Fats are lipids that are mostly energy-storage molecules. Lipids are diverse, hydrophobic compounds composed largely of carbon and hydrogen. Fats (triglycerides) consist of glycerol linked to three fatty acids. Saturated fatty acids are found in animal fats; unsaturated fatty acids are typical of plant oils.

3.9 Scientific studies document the health risks of trans fats.

3.10 Phospholipids and steroids are important lipids with a variety of functions. Phospholipids are components of cell membranes. Steroids include cholesterol and some hormones.

3.11 Anabolic steroids pose health risks.

Proteins (3.12–3.14)

3.12 Proteins have a wide range of functions and structures. Proteins are involved in almost all of a cell's activities; as enzymes, they regulate chemical reactions.

3.13 Proteins are made from amino acids linked by peptide bonds. Protein diversity is based on different sequences of amino acids, monomers that contain an amino group, a carboxyl group, an H atom, and an R group, all attached to a central carbon. The R groups distinguish 20 amino acids, each with specific properties.

3.14 A protein's functional shape results from four levels of structure. A protein's primary structure is the sequence of amino acids in its polypeptide chain. Its secondary structure is the coiling or folding of the chain, stabilized by hydrogen bonds. The tertiary structure is the overall three-dimensional shape of a polypeptide, resulting from interactions among R groups. Proteins made of more than one polypeptide have quaternary structure.

Nucleic Acids (3.15–3.17)

3.15 DNA and RNA are the two types of nucleic acids. DNA and RNA serve as the blueprints for proteins and thus control the life of a cell. DNA is the molecule of inheritance.

3.16 Nucleic acids are polymers of nucleotides. Nucleotides are composed of a sugar, a phosphate group, and a nitrogenous base. DNA is a double helix; RNA is a single polynucleotide chain.

3.17 Lactose tolerance is a recent event in human evolution. Mutations in DNA have led to lactose tolerance in several human groups whose ancestors raised dairy cattle.

Connecting the Concepts

1. Complete the table to help review the structures and functions of the four classes of organic molecules.

Classes of Molecules and Their Components		Functions	Examples
Carbohydrates Monosaccharide		Energy for cell, raw material	a. _____
		b. _____	Starch, glycogen
		Plant cell support	c. _____
Lipids (don't form polymers) Glycerol Fatty acid Components of a fat molecule		Energy storage	d. _____
		e. _____	Phospholipids
		Hormones	f. _____
Proteins g. _____ h. _____ i. _____ Amino acid		j. _____	Lactase
		k. _____	Hair, tendons
		l. _____	Muscle proteins
		Transport	m. _____
		Communication	Signal proteins
		n. _____	Antibodies
		Storage	Proteins in seeds
		Receive signals	Receptor protein
Nucleic Acids o. _____ p. _____ q. _____ Nucleotide		Heredity	r. _____
		s. _____	DNA and RNA

Testing Your Knowledge

Level 1: Knowledge/Comprehension

2. A glucose molecule is to starch as (*Explain your answer.*)
   a. a steroid is to a lipid.
   b. a protein is to an amino acid.
   c. a nucleic acid is to a polypeptide.
   d. a nucleotide is to a nucleic acid.

3. What makes a fatty acid an acid?
   a. It does not dissolve in water.
   b. It is capable of bonding with other molecules to form a fat.
   c. It has a carboxyl group that can donate an H^+ to a solution.
   d. It contains only two oxygen atoms.

4. Cows can derive nutrients from cellulose because
   a. they produce enzymes that recognize the shape of the glucose-glucose bonds and hydrolyze them.
   b. they re-chew their cud to break down cellulose fibers.
   c. their digestive tract contains prokaryotes that can hydrolyze the bonds of cellulose.
   d. they convert cellulose to starch and can digest starch.

5. Of the following functional groups, which is/are polar, tending to make organic compounds hydrophilic?
   a. carbonyl
   b. amino
   c. hydroxyl
   d. all of the above

6. Unsaturated fats
   a. have double bonds in their fatty acid chains.
   b. have fewer fatty acid molecules per fat molecule.
   c. are associated with greater health risks than are saturated fats.
   d. are more common in animals than in plants.

Level 2: Application/Analysis

7. A shortage of phosphorus in the soil would make it especially difficult for a plant to manufacture
   a. DNA.
   b. proteins.
   c. cellulose.
   d. sucrose.

8. Which of the following substances is a major component of the cell membrane of a fungus?
   a. cellulose
   b. chitin
   c. cholesterol
   d. phospholipids

9. Which structural level of a protein would be *least* affected by a disruption in hydrogen bonding?
   a. primary structure
   b. secondary structure
   c. tertiary structure
   d. quaternary structure

10. Circle and name the functional groups in this organic molecule. What type of compound is this? For which class of macromolecules is it a monomer?

11. Most proteins are soluble in the aqueous environment of a cell. Knowing that, where in the overall three-dimensional shape of a protein would you expect to find amino acids with hydrophobic R groups?

12. Sucrose is broken down in your intestine to the monosaccharides glucose and fructose, which are then absorbed into your blood. What is the name of this type of reaction? Using this diagram of sucrose, show how this would occur.

Sucrose

Level 3: Synthesis/Evaluation

13. The diversity of life is staggering. Yet the molecular logic of life is simple and elegant: Small molecules common to all organisms are ordered into unique macromolecules. Explain why carbon is central to this diversity of organic molecules. How do carbon skeletons, chemical groups, monomers, and polymers relate to this molecular logic of life?

14. How can a cell make many different kinds of proteins out of only 20 amino acids? Of the myriad possibilities, how does the cell "know" which proteins to make?

15. Given that the function of egg yolk is to nourish and support the developing chick, explain why egg yolks are so high in fat, protein, and cholesterol.

16. Enzymes usually function best at an optimal pH and temperature. The following graph shows the effectiveness of two enzymes at various temperatures.

    a. At which temperature does enzyme A perform best? Enzyme B?
    b. One of these enzymes is found in humans and the other in thermophilic (heat-loving) bacteria. Which enzyme would you predict comes from which organism?
    c. From what you know about enzyme structure, explain why the rate of the reaction catalyzed by enzyme A slows down at temperatures above 40°C (140°F).

17. **SCIENTIFIC THINKING** Another aspect of the Nurses' Health Study introduced in Module 3.9 looked at the percentage of change in the risk of coronary heart disease associated with substituting one dietary component for another. These results estimated that replacement of 5% of energy from saturated fat in the diet with unsaturated fats would reduce the risk by 42%, and that the replacement of 2% of energy from trans fat with unsaturated fats would reduce the risk by 53%. Explain what these numbers mean.

Answers to all questions can be found in Appendix 4.

A Tour of the Cell

How has our knowledge of cells grown?

You can probably identify the blue blobs in this beautiful micrograph as the nuclei of the cells it depicts. But did you know that the brightly colored strands you also see form a cell's skeleton? These structures are part of a system of protein fibers called the cytoskeleton. Much like the way your skeleton provides support and also enables you to move, the cytoskeleton provides structural support to a cell and allows some cells to crawl and others to swim. But even stationary cells have movement: Many of their internal parts bustle about, often traveling on cytoskeletal "roads." Later in the chapter you will learn more about the cytoskeleton and how our knowledge of its structures and functions has grown. As you will see, our understanding of nature often goes hand in hand with the invention and refinement of instruments that extend our senses. This certainly applies to how cells were first discovered.

In 1665, Robert Hooke used a crude microscope to examine a piece of cork. Hooke compared the structures he saw to "little rooms"—*cellulae* in Latin—and the term *cell* stuck. His contemporary, Antoni van Leeuwenhoek, working with more refined lenses, examined numerous subjects, from

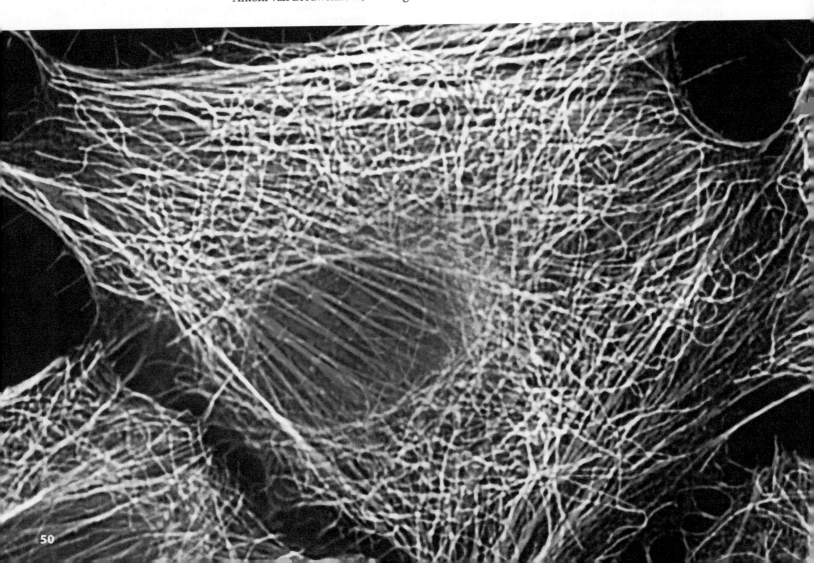

blood and sperm to pond water. He produced drawings and enthusiastic descriptions of his discoveries, such as the tiny "animalcules, very prettily a-moving" he found in the scrapings from his teeth.

Since the days of Hooke and Leeuwenhoek, improved microscopes and techniques have vastly expanded our view of the cell. For example, fluorescently colored stains reveal the cytoskeleton in the cells pictured below. In this chapter, you will see many micrographs using such techniques, and they will often be paired with drawings that help emphasize specific details.

Neither drawings nor micrographs allow you to see the dynamic nature of living cells. For that, you need to look through a microscope or view videos. As you study the images in this chapter, keep in mind that the parts of a cell are moving and interacting. Indeed, the phenomenon we call life emerges from the interactions of the many components of a cell.

BIG IDEAS

Introduction to the Cell
(4.1–4.4)

Microscopes reveal the structures of cells—the fundamental units of life.

The Nucleus and Ribosomes
(4.5–4.6)

A cell's genetic instructions are housed in the nucleus and carried out by ribosomes.

The Endomembrane System
(4.7–4.12)

The endomembrane system participates in the manufacture, distribution, and breakdown of materials.

Energy-Converting Organelles
(4.13–4.15)

Mitochondria in all eukaryotic cells and chloroplasts in plant cells function in energy processing.

The Cytoskeleton and Cell Surfaces
(4.16–4.22)

The cytoskeleton and extracellular components provide support, motility, and functional connections.

▷ Introduction to the Cell

4.1 Microscopes reveal the world of the cell

Before microscopes were first used in the 1600s, no one knew that living organisms were composed of the tiny units we call cells. The first microscopes were light microscopes, like the ones you may use in a biology laboratory. In a **light microscope (LM)**, visible light is passed through a specimen, such as a microorganism or a thin slice of animal or plant tissue, and then through glass lenses. The lenses bend the light in such a way that the image of the specimen is magnified as it is projected into your eye or a camera.

Magnification is the increase in an object's image size compared with its actual size. **Figure 4.1A** shows a micrograph of a single-celled organism called *Paramecium*. The notation "LM 230✕" printed along the right edge tells you that this photograph was taken through a light microscope and that the image is 230 times the actual size of the organism. This *Paramecium* is about 0.33 millimeter in length. **Table 4.1** shows the most common units of length that biologists use.

An important factor in microscopy is resolution, a measure of the clarity of an image. Resolution is the ability to distinguish two nearby objects as separate. For example, what you see as a single star in the sky may be resolved as twin stars with a telescope. Each optical instrument—be it an eye, a telescope, or a microscope—has a limit to its resolution. The human eye can distinguish points as close together as 0.1 millimeter (mm), about the size of a very fine grain of sand. A typical light microscope cannot resolve detail finer than about 0.2 micrometer (µm), about the size of the smallest bacterium. No matter how many times the image of such a small cell is magnified, the light microscope cannot resolve the details of its structure. Indeed, light microscopes can effectively magnify objects only about 1,000 times.

From the time that Hooke discovered cells in 1665 until the middle of the 1900s, biologists had only light microscopes for viewing cells. With these microscopes and various staining techniques to increase contrast between parts of cells, these early biologists discovered microorganisms, animal and plant cells, and even some structures within cells. By the mid-1800s, this accumulation of evidence led to the **cell theory**, which states that all living things are composed of cells and that all cells come from other cells.

Our knowledge of cell structure took a giant leap forward as biologists began using the electron microscope in the 1950s. Instead of using light, an **electron microscope (EM)** focuses a beam of electrons through a specimen or onto its

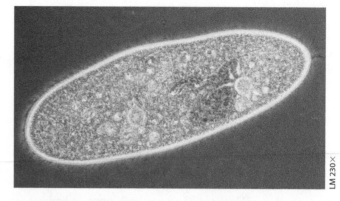

▲ **Figure 4.1A**   Light micrograph of a unicellular organism, *Paramecium*

▲ **Figure 4.1B**   Scanning electron micrograph of *Paramecium*

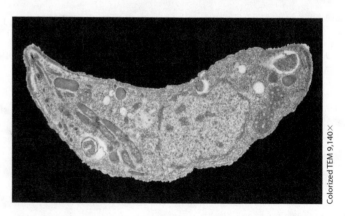

▲ **Figure 4.1C**   Transmission electron micrograph of *Toxoplasma* (This parasite of cats can be transmitted to humans, causing the disease toxoplasmosis.)

Try This   Describe a major difference between the *Paramecium* in Figure 4.1B and the protist in this figure. (*Hint*: Compare the notations along the right sides of the micrographs.)

surface. Electron microscopes can distinguish biological structures as small as about 2 nanometers (nm), a 100-fold improvement over the light microscope. This high resolution has enabled biologists to explore cell ultrastructure, the complex internal anatomy of a cell. **Figures 4.1B** and **4.1C** show images produced by two kinds of electron microscopes.

TABLE 4.1 | METRIC MEASUREMENT EQUIVALENTS

1 meter (m) = 100 cm = 1,000 mm = 39.4 inches

1 centimeter (cm) = 10^{-2} (1/100) m = 0.4 inch

1 millimeter (mm) = 10^{-3} (1/1,000) m = 10^{-1} (1/10) cm

1 micrometer (µm) = 10^{-6} m = 10^{-3} mm

1 nanometer (nm) = 10^{-9} m = 10^{-3} µm

Biologists use the **scanning electron microscope (SEM)** to study the detailed architecture of cell surfaces. The SEM uses an electron beam to scan the surface of a cell or other sample, which is usually coated with a thin film of gold. The beam excites electrons on the surface, and these electrons are then detected by a device that translates their pattern into an image projected onto a video screen. The scanning electron micrograph in Figure 4.1B highlights the numerous cilia on *Paramecium*, projections it uses for movement. Notice the indentation, called the oral groove, through which food enters the cell. As you can see, the SEM produces images that look three-dimensional.

The **transmission electron microscope (TEM)** is used to study the details of internal cell structure. The TEM aims an electron beam through a very thin section of a specimen, just as a light microscope aims a beam of light through a specimen. The section is stained with atoms of heavy metals, which attach to certain cellular structures more than others. Electrons are scattered by these more dense parts, and the image is created by the pattern of transmitted electrons. Instead of using glass lenses, both the SEM and TEM use electromagnets as lenses to bend the paths of the electrons, magnifying and focusing the image onto a monitor. The transmission electron micrograph in Figure 4.1C shows internal details of a protist called *Toxoplasma*. SEMs and TEMs are initially black and white but are often artificially colorized, as they are in these figures, to highlight or clarify structural features.

Electron microscopes have truly revolutionized the study of cells and their structures. Nonetheless, they have not replaced the light microscope: Electron microscopes cannot be used to study living specimens because the methods used to prepare the specimen kill the cells. For a biologist studying a living process, such as the movement of *Paramecium*, a light microscope equipped with a video camera is more suitable than either an SEM or a TEM.

There are different types of light microscopy, and major technical advances in the past several decades have greatly expanded our ability to visualize cells. **Figure 4.1D** shows *Paramecium* as seen using differential interference contrast microscopy. This optical technique amplifies differences in density so that the structures in living cells appear almost three-dimensional. Other techniques use fluorescent stains that selectively bind to various cellular molecules (see the chapter introduction).

You will see many beautiful and illuminating examples of microscopy in this textbook. But even with the magnification shown beside each micrograph, it is often hard to imagine just how small cells are. **Figure 4.1E** shows the size range of cells compared with objects both larger and smaller and the optical instrument that allows us to view them. Notice that the scale along the left side of the figure is logarithmic to accommodate the range of sizes shown. Starting at the top with 10 meters (m), each reference measurement marks a 10-fold decrease in length. Most cells are between 1 and 100 μm in diameter (yellow region of the figure) and are therefore visible only with a microscope. Certain bacteria are as small as 0.2 μm and can barely be seen with a light microscope, whereas bird eggs are large enough to be seen with the unaided eye. A single nerve cell running from the base of your spinal cord to your big toe may be 1 m in length, although it is so thin you would still need a microscope to see it. In the next module, we explore why cells are so small.

? Which type of microscope would you use to study (a) the changes in shape of a living human white blood cell; (b) the finest details of surface texture of a human hair; (c) the detailed structure of an organelle in a liver cell?

⊙ (a) Light microscope; (b) scanning electron microscope; (c) transmission electron microscope

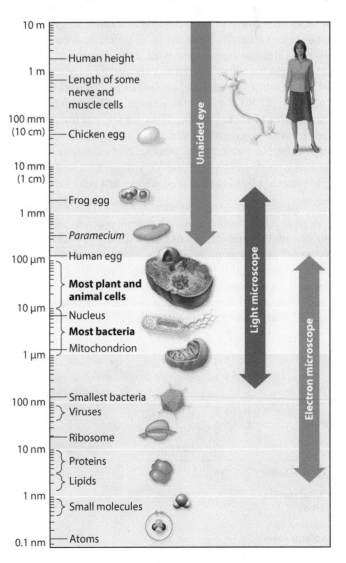

▲ **Figure 4.1E** The size range of cells and related objects

LM 380×

▲ **Figure 4.1D** Differential interference contrast micrograph of *Paramecium*

4.2 The small size of cells relates to the need to exchange materials across the plasma membrane

As you saw in Figure 4.1E, most cells are microscopic. Are there advantages to being so small? The logistics of carrying out a cell's functions appear to set both lower and upper limits on cell size. At minimum, a cell must be large enough to house enough DNA, protein molecules, and structures to survive and reproduce. But why aren't most cells as large as chicken eggs? The maximum size of a cell is influenced by geometry—the need to have a surface area large enough to service the volume of a cell. Active cells have a huge amount of traffic across their outer surface. A chicken egg cell isn't very active, but once a chick embryo starts to develop, the egg is divided into many microscopic cells, each bounded by a membrane that allows the essential flow of oxygen, nutrients, and wastes across its surface.

Surface-to-Volume Ratio Large cells have more surface area than small cells, but they have a much smaller surface area relative to their volume than small cells. **Figure 4.2A** illustrates this by comparing one large cube to 27 small ones. Using arbitrary units of measurement, the total volume is the same in both cases: 27 units^3 (height $\times$ width $\times$ length). The total surface areas, however, are quite different. A cube has six sides; thus, its surface area is six times the area of each side (height $\times$ width). The surface area of the large cube is 54 units^2, while the total surface area of all 27 cubes is 162 units^2 ($27 \times 6 \times 1 \times 1$), three times greater than the surface area of the large cube. Thus, we see that the smaller cubes have a much greater surface-to-volume ratio than the large cube. How about those neurons that extend from the base of your spine to your toes? Very thin, elongated shapes also provide a large surface area relative to a cell's volume.

The Plasma Membrane So what is a cell's surface like? And how does it control the traffic of molecules across it? The **plasma membrane** forms a flexible boundary between the living cell and its surroundings. For a structure that separates life from nonlife, this membrane is amazingly thin. It would take a stack of more than 8,000 plasma membranes to equal the thickness of this page. And, as you have come to expect with all things biological, the structure of the plasma membrane correlates with its function.

Total volume	27 units^3	27 units^3
Total surface area	54 units^2	162 units^2
Surface-to-volume ratio	2	6

▲ **Figure 4.2A** Effect of cell size on surface area

© Pearson Education Inc.

▲ **Figure 4.2B** A plasma membrane: a phospholipid bilayer with associated proteins

The structure of phospholipid molecules is well suited to their role as a major constituent of biological membranes. Each phospholipid is composed of two distinct regions—a head with a negatively charged phosphate group and two nonpolar fatty acid tails (see Module 3.10). Phospholipids group together to form a two-layer sheet called a phospholipid bilayer. As you can see in **Figure 4.2B**, the phospholipids' hydrophilic (water-loving) heads face outward, exposed to the aqueous solutions on both sides of a membrane. Their hydrophobic (water-fearing) tails point inward, mingling together and shielded from water. Embedded in this lipid bilayer are diverse proteins, floating like icebergs in a phospholipid sea. The regions of the proteins within the center of the membrane are hydrophobic; the exterior sections exposed to water are hydrophilic.

Now let's see how the properties of the phospholipid bilayer and the proteins suspended in it relate to the plasma membrane's job as a traffic cop, regulating the flow of material into and out of the cell. Nonpolar molecules, such as O_2 and CO_2, can easily move across the membrane's hydrophobic interior. Some of the membrane's proteins form channels (tunnels) that shield ions and polar molecules as they pass through the hydrophobic center of the membrane. Still other proteins serve as pumps, using energy to actively transport molecules into or out of the cell.

We will return to the structure and function of biological membranes later (see Chapter 5). In the next module, we consider other features common to all cells and take a closer look at the prokaryotic cells of domains Bacteria and Archaea.

> **?** To convince yourself that a small cell has a greater surface area relative to volume than a large cell, compare the surface-to-volume ratios of the large cube and one of the small cubes in Figure 4.2A.

● Large cube: 54/27 = 2; small cube: 6/1 = 6 (surface area is 1 × 1 × 6 sides = 6 units^2; volume is 1 × 1 × 1 unit^3)

4.3 Prokaryotic cells are structurally simpler than eukaryotic cells

Cells are of two distinct types: prokaryotic and eukaryotic. The microorganisms placed in domains Bacteria and Archaea consist of **prokaryotic cells**. These organisms are known as prokaryotes. All other forms of life (protists, fungi, plants, and animals) are placed in domain Eukarya and are composed of **eukaryotic cells**. They are referred to as eukaryotes.

Eukaryotic cells are distinguished by having a membrane-enclosed nucleus, which houses most of their DNA, and many membrane-enclosed organelles that perform specific functions. Prokaryotic cells are smaller and simpler in structure.

Both types of cells, however, share certain basic features. In addition to being bounded by a plasma membrane, the interior of all cells is filled with a thick, jellylike fluid called **cytosol**, in which cellular components are suspended. All cells have one or more **chromosomes**, which carry genes made of DNA. They also contain **ribosomes**, tiny structures that make proteins according to instructions from the genes. The inside of both types of cells is called the **cytoplasm**. However, in eukaryotic cells, this term refers only to the region between the nucleus and the plasma membrane.

Figure 4.3 explores the structure of a generalized prokaryotic cell. Notice that the DNA is coiled into a region called the **nucleoid** ("nucleus-like"), but no membrane surrounds the DNA. The ribosomes of prokaryotes (shown here in brown) are smaller and differ somewhat from those of eukaryotes. These molecular differences are the basis for the action of some antibiotics, such as tetracycline and streptomycin, which target prokaryotic ribosomes. Thus, protein synthesis can be blocked for the bacterium that's invaded you, but not for you, the eukaryote who is taking the drug.

Outside the plasma membrane (shown here in gray) of most prokaryotes is a fairly rigid, chemically complex cell wall (orange). The wall protects the cell and helps maintain its shape. Some antibiotics, such as penicillin, prevent the formation of these protective walls. Again, because your cells don't have such walls, these antibiotics can kill invading bacteria without harming your cells. Certain prokaryotes have a sticky outer coat called a capsule (yellow) around the cell wall, helping to glue the cells to surfaces or to other cells in a colony. In addition to capsules, some prokaryotes have surface projections. Short projections help attach prokaryotes to each other or their substrate. Longer projections called **flagella** (singular, *flagellum*) propel a prokaryotic cell through its liquid environment.

It takes an electron microscope to see the internal details of any cell, and this is especially true of prokaryotic cells. Notice that the TEM of the bacterium in Figure 4.3 has a magnification of 4,700✕. Most prokaryotic cells are about one-tenth the size of a typical eukaryotic cell (see Figure 1.3). (Prokaryotes will be described in more detail later; see Chapter 16.) Eukaryotic cells are the main focus of this chapter, so we turn to these next.

? **List three features that are common to prokaryotic and eukaryotic cells. List three features that differ.**

● **Both types of cells have plasma membranes, chromosomes containing DNA, and ribosomes. Prokaryotic cells are smaller, do not have a nucleus that houses their DNA or other membrane-enclosed organelles, and have smaller, somewhat different ribosomes.**

Fimbriae: attachment structures on the surface of some prokaryotes

Ribosomes: structures that synthesize proteins

Nucleoid: region where the cell's DNA is located (not enclosed by a membrane)

Plasma membrane: membrane enclosing the cytoplasm

Cell wall: rigid structure outside the plasma membrane

Capsule: jellylike outer coating of many prokaryotes

Bacterial chromosome

A typical rod-shaped bacterium

Flagella: locomotion organelles of some bacteria

TEM 65,000✕

A colorized TEM of the bacterium *Escherichia coli. (E. coli* is a normal inhabitant of the human intestine.)

▲ **Figure 4.3** A diagram (left) and electron micrograph (right) of a typical prokaryotic cell

4.4 Eukaryotic cells are partitioned into functional compartments

All eukaryotic cells—whether from animals, plants, protists, or fungi—are fundamentally similar to one another and profoundly different from prokaryotic cells. Let's look at an animal cell and a plant cell as representatives of the eukaryotes.

Figure 4.4A is a diagram of a generalized animal cell, and Figure 4.4B shows a generalized plant cell. We color-code the various organelles and other structures in the diagrams for easier identification, and you will see miniature versions of these cells to orient you during our in-depth tour in the rest of the chapter. But no cells would look exactly like these. For one thing, cells have multiple copies of all of these structures (except for the nucleus). Your cells have hundreds of mitochondria and millions of ribosomes. A plant cell may have 30 chloroplasts packed inside. Cells also have different shapes and relative proportions of cell parts, depending on their specialized functions.

The nucleus is the most obvious difference between a prokaryotic and eukaryotic cell. A eukaryotic cell also contains various other **organelles** ("little organs"), which perform specific functions in the cell. Just as the cell itself is wrapped in a membrane made of phospholipids and proteins that perform various functions, each organelle is bounded by a membrane with a lipid and protein composition that suits its function.

The organelles and other structures of eukaryotic cells can be organized into four basic functional groups: (1) The nucleus and ribosomes carry out the genetic control of the cell. (2) Organelles involved in the manufacture, distribution, and breakdown of molecules include the endoplasmic reticulum, Golgi apparatus, lysosomes, vacuoles, and peroxisomes. (3) Mitochondria in all cells and chloroplasts in plant cells function in energy processing. (4) Structural support, movement, and communication between cells are the functions of the cytoskeleton, plasma membrane, and plant cell wall. The cellular components identified in these two figures will be examined in detail in the modules that follow.

In essence, the internal membranes of a eukaryotic cell partition it into compartments. Many of the chemical

NUCLEUS
Nuclear envelope
Nucleolus
Chromatin
Rough endoplasmic reticulum
Smooth endoplasmic reticulum
Ribosomes
Golgi apparatus
Peroxisome
Centrosome with pair of centrioles
Mitochondrion
Lysosome
Plasma membrane
CYTOSKELETON
Intermediate filament
Microfilament
Microtubule

▼ Figure 4.4A   A generalized animal cell

activities of cells—collectively, **cellular metabolism**—occur within organelles. In fact, many enzymes essential for metabolic processes are built into the membranes of organelles. The fluid-filled spaces within organelles are important as sites where specific chemical conditions are maintained. These conditions vary among organelles and favor the metabolic processes occurring in each. For example, while a part of the endoplasmic reticulum is engaged in making hormones, neighboring peroxisomes may be detoxifying harmful compounds and making hydrogen peroxide (H_2O_2) as a poisonous by-product of their activities. But because the H_2O_2 is confined within the peroxisomes, where it is converted to H_2O by resident enzymes, the rest of the cell is protected.

Except for lysosomes and centrosomes, the organelles and other structures of animal cells are found in plant cells. Also, although some animal cells have flagella or cilia (not shown in Figure 4.4A), among plants, only the sperm cells of a few species have flagella.

A plant cell (Figure 4.4B) also has some structures that an animal cell lacks. For example, a plant cell has a rigid, rather thick cell wall. Cell walls protect cells and help maintain their shape. Chemically different from prokaryotic cell walls, plant cell walls contain the polysaccharide cellulose. Plasmodesmata (singular, plasmodesma) are cytoplasmic channels through cell walls that connect adjacent cells. An important organelle found in plant cells is the chloroplast, where photosynthesis occurs. Unique to plant cells is a large central vacuole, a compartment that stores water and a variety of chemicals.

Eukaryotic cells contain nonmembranous structures as well. The cytoskeleton, which you were introduced to in the chapter introduction, is composed of different types of protein fibers that extend throughout the cell. These networks provide for support and movement. And ribosomes occur throughout the cytosol, as they do in prokaryotic cells. In addition, eukaryotic cells have many ribosomes attached to membranes.

After you preview these cell diagrams, let's move to the first stop on our detailed tour of the eukaryotic cell—the nucleus.

> ? Identify the structures in the plant cell that are not present in the animal cell.

Chloroplasts, central vacuole, cell wall, and plasmodesmata

▼ **Figure 4.4B** A generalized plant cell

NUCLEUS
Nuclear envelope
Nucleolus
Chromatin

Rough endoplasmic reticulum

Smooth endoplasmic reticulum

Mitochondrion

CYTOSKELETON
Microfilament
Microtubule

Ribosomes

Central vacuole

Chloroplast

Peroxisome

Golgi apparatus

Cell wall

Plasmodesma

Cell wall of adjacent cell

Plasma membrane

▷ The Nucleus and Ribosomes

4.5 The nucleus contains the cell's genetic instructions

You just saw a preview of the many intricate structures that can be found in a eukaryotic cell. A cell must build and maintain these structures and also process energy to support its work of transport, movement, and communication. But who is in charge of this bustling factory? Who stores the master plans, gives the orders, changes course in response to environmental input, and, when called on, makes another factory just like itself? The cell's nucleus functions as this command center.

The **nucleus** contains the cell's genetic instructions encoded in DNA. These master plans control the cell's activities by directing protein synthesis. The DNA is associated with many proteins and organized into structures called chromosomes. The proteins help coil these long DNA molecules. Indeed, the DNA of the 46 chromosomes in one of your cells laid end to end would stretch to a length of more than 2 m, but it must coil up to fit into a nucleus only 5 μm in diameter. When a cell is not dividing, this complex of proteins and DNA, called **chromatin**, appears as a diffuse mass within the nucleus, as shown in the TEM (right half) and diagram (left half) of a nucleus in Figure 4.5.

As a cell prepares to divide, the DNA is copied so that each daughter cell can later receive an identical set of genetic instructions. Just prior to cell division, the thin chromatin fibers coil up further, becoming thick enough to be visible with a light microscope as the familiar separate structures you would probably recognize as chromosomes.

Enclosing the nucleus is a double membrane called the **nuclear envelope**. Each of the two membranes is a separate phospholipid bilayer with associated proteins. Similar in function to the plasma membrane, the nuclear envelope controls the flow of materials into and out of the nucleus. As you can see in the diagram of a nucleus in Figure 4.5, the nuclear envelope is perforated with protein-lined pores. These pores regulate the entry and exit of large molecules and also connect with the cell's network of membranes called the endoplasmic reticulum.

The **nucleolus**, a prominent structure in the nucleus, is the site where a special type of RNA called ribosomal RNA(rRNA) is synthesized according to instructions in the DNA. Proteins brought in from the cytoplasm are assembled with this rRNA to form the subunits of ribosomes. These subunits then exit to the cytoplasm, where they will join to form functional ribosomes.

Another type of RNA, messenger RNA (mRNA), directs protein synthesis. Essentially, mRNA is a transcription of protein-synthesizing instructions written in a gene's DNA (see Figure 10.7). The mRNA moves into the cytoplasm, where ribosomes translate it into the amino acid sequences of proteins. Let's look at ribosomes next.

? **Describe the processes that occur in the nucleus.**

● DNA is copied and passed on to daughter cells in cell division; rRNA is made and ribosomal subunits assembled; protein-making instructions in DNA are transcribed into mRNA.

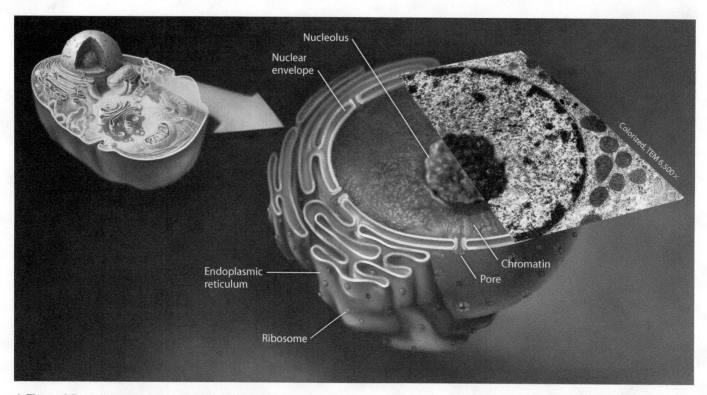

▲ Figure 4.5   A diagram with a superimposed TEM of the nucleus

4.6 Ribosomes make proteins for use in the cell and for export

If the nucleus is the cell's command center, then ribosomes are the machines that carry out those commands. Ribosomes are the cellular components that use instructions from the nucleus, written in mRNA, to build proteins. Cells that make a lot of proteins have a large number of ribosomes. For example, a cell in your pancreas that produces digestive enzymes may contain a few million ribosomes. What other structure would you expect to be prominent in cells that are active in protein synthesis? Remember that the nucleolus in the nucleus is the site where the subunits of ribosomes are assembled.

As shown in **Figure 4.6**, ribosomes are found in two locations in the cell. Free ribosomes are suspended in the cytosol, while bound ribosomes are attached to the outside of the endoplasmic reticulum or nuclear envelope. Free and bound ribosomes are structurally identical, and they can move about and function in either location.

Most of the proteins made on free ribosomes function within the cytosol; examples are enzymes that catalyze the first steps of sugar breakdown for cellular respiration. In Module 4.8, you will see how bound ribosomes make proteins that will be inserted into membranes, packaged in certain organelles, or exported from the cell.

At the bottom right in Figure 4.6, you see how ribosomes interact with messenger RNA (carrying the instructions from a gene) to build a protein. The nucleotide sequence of an mRNA molecule is translated into the amino acid sequence of a polypeptide. (Protein synthesis is explored in more detail in Chapter 10.) Next let's look at more of the manufacturing equipment of the cell.

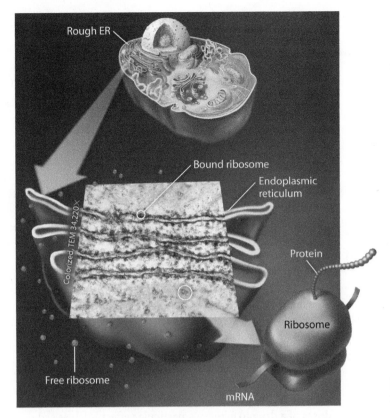

▲ **Figure 4.6**   The locations and structure of ribosomes

? **What role do ribosomes play in carrying out the genetic instructions of a cell?**

● Ribosomes synthesize proteins according to the instructions of messenger RNA, which was transcribed from DNA in the nucleus.

▷ The Endomembrane System

4.7 Many organelles are connected in the endomembrane system

Ribosomes may be a cell's protein-making machines, but running a factory as complex as a cell requires infrastructure and many different departments that perform separate but related functions. Internal membranes, a distinguishing feature of eukaryotic cells, are involved in most of a cell's functions. Many of the membranes of the eukaryotic cell are part of an **endomembrane system**. Some of these membranes are physically connected and others are linked when tiny **vesicles** (sacs made of membrane) transfer membrane segments between them.

The endomembrane system includes the nuclear envelope, endoplasmic reticulum, Golgi apparatus, lysosomes, vacuoles, and the plasma membrane. (The plasma membrane is not exactly an *endo* membrane in physical location, but it is related to the other membranes by the transfer of vesicles). Many of these organelles interact in the synthesis, distribution, storage, and export of molecules.

The largest component of the endomembrane system is the **endoplasmic reticulum (ER)**, an extensive network of flattened sacs and tubules. (The term *endoplasmic* means "within the cytoplasm," and *reticulum* is Latin for "little net.") The ER is a prime example of the direct and indirect interrelatedness of parts of the endomembrane system. As shown in Figure 4.5 on the facing page, membranes of the ER are continuous with the nuclear envelope. And when vesicles bud from the ER, they travel to many other components of the endomembrane system.

The tubules and sacs of the ER enclose a space that is separate from the cytosol. Dividing the cell into functional compartments, each of which may require different conditions, is an important aspect of the endomembrane system.

? **Which structure includes all others in the list: rough ER, smooth ER, endomembrane system, nuclear envelope?**

● Endomembrane system

4.8 The endoplasmic reticulum is a biosynthetic workshop

One of the major manufacturing sites in a cell is the endoplasmic reticulum. The diagram in **Figure 4.8A** shows a cutaway view of the interconnecting membranes of the smooth and rough ER, which can be distinguished in the superimposed electron micrograph. **Smooth endoplasmic reticulum** is called *smooth* because its outer surface lacks attached ribosomes. **Rough endoplasmic reticulum** has bound ribosomes that stud the outer surface of the membrane; thus, it appears *rough* in the electron micrograph.

Smooth ER   The smooth ER of various cell types functions in a variety of metabolic processes. Enzymes of the smooth ER are important in the synthesis of lipids, including oils, phospholipids, and steroids. In vertebrates, for example, cells of the ovaries and testes synthesize the steroid sex hormones. These cells are rich in smooth ER, a structural feature that fits their function by providing ample machinery for steroid synthesis.

Our liver cells also have large amounts of smooth ER, with enzymes that help process drugs, alcohol, and other potentially harmful substances. The sedative phenobarbital and other barbiturates are examples of drugs detoxified by these enzymes. As liver cells are exposed to such chemicals, the amount of smooth ER and its detoxifying enzymes increases, thereby increasing the rate of detoxification and thus the body's tolerance to the drugs. The result is a need for higher doses of a drug to achieve a particular effect, such as sedation. Also, because detoxifying enzymes often cannot distinguish among related chemicals, the growth of smooth ER in response to one drug can increase the need for higher doses of other drugs. Barbiturate abuse, for example, can decrease the effectiveness of certain antibiotics and other useful drugs.

Smooth ER has yet another function, the storage of calcium ions. In muscle cells, for example, a specialized smooth ER membrane pumps calcium ions into the interior of the ER. When a nerve signal stimulates a muscle cell, calcium ions rush from the smooth ER into the cytosol and trigger contraction of the cell.

Rough ER   Many types of cells secrete proteins produced by ribosomes attached to rough ER. An example of a secretory protein is insulin, a hormone produced and secreted by certain cells of the pancreas and transported in the bloodstream. Type 1 diabetes results when these cells are destroyed and a lack of insulin disrupts glucose metabolism in the body.

Figure 4.8B follows the synthesis, modification, and packaging of a secretory protein. ❶ As the polypeptide is synthesized by a bound ribosome following the instructions of an mRNA, it is threaded into the cavity of the rough ER. As it enters, the new protein folds into its three-dimensional shape. ❷ Short chains of sugars are often linked to the polypeptide, making the molecule a **glycoprotein** (*glyco* means "sugar"). ❸ When the molecule is ready for export from the ER, it is packaged in a **transport vesicle**, a vesicle that moves from one part of the cell to another. ❹ This vesicle buds off from the ER membrane.

▲ **Figure 4.8A**   A diagram and TEM of smooth and rough endoplasmic reticulum

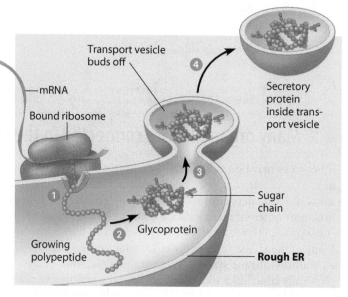

▲ **Figure 4.8B**   Synthesis and packaging of a secretory protein by the rough ER

Try This   Explain where the protein-making instructions carried by the mRNA came from.

The vesicle now carries the protein to the Golgi apparatus for further processing. From there, a transport vesicle containing the finished molecule makes its way to the plasma membrane and releases its contents from the cell.

In addition to making secretory proteins, rough ER is a membrane-making machine for the cell. It grows in place by adding membrane proteins and phospholipids to its own membrane. As polypeptides destined to be membrane proteins grow from bound ribosomes, they are inserted into the ER membrane. Phospholipids are made by enzymes of the rough ER and also inserted into the membrane. Thus, the ER membrane grows, and portions of it are transferred to other components of the endomembrane system in the form of transport vesicles.

Now let's follow a transport vesicle carrying products of the rough ER to the Golgi apparatus.

? **Explain why we say that the endoplasmic reticulum is a biosynthetic workshop.**

● The ER produces a huge variety of molecules, including phospholipids for cell membranes, steroid hormones, and proteins (synthesized by bound ribosomes) for membranes, other organelles, and secretion by the cell.

4.9 The Golgi apparatus modifies, sorts, and ships cell products

After leaving the ER, many transport vesicles travel to the **Golgi apparatus**. Using a light microscope and a staining technique he developed, Italian scientist Camillo Golgi discovered this membranous organelle in 1898. The electron microscope confirmed his discovery more than 50 years later, revealing a stack of flattened sacs, looking much like a pile of pita bread. A cell may contain many, even hundreds, of these stacks. The number of Golgi stacks correlates with how active the cell is in secreting proteins—a multistep process that, as you have just seen, is initiated in the rough ER.

The Golgi apparatus serves as a molecular warehouse and processing station for products manufactured by the ER. You can follow these activities in **Figure 4.9**. Note that the flattened Golgi sacs are not connected, as are ER sacs. **1** One side of a Golgi stack serves as a receiving dock for transport vesicles produced by the ER. **2** A vesicle fuses with a Golgi sac, adding its membrane and contents to the "receiving" side. **3** Products of the ER are modified as a Golgi sac progresses through the stack. **4** The "shipping" side of the Golgi

functions as a depot, dispatching its products in vesicles that bud off and travel to other sites.

How might ER products be processed during their transit through the Golgi? Various Golgi enzymes modify the carbohydrate portions of the glycoproteins made in the ER, removing some sugars and substituting others. Molecular identification tags, such as phosphate groups, may be added that help the Golgi sort molecules into different batches for different destinations.

Finished secretory products, packaged in transport vesicles, move to the plasma membrane for export from the cell. Alternatively, finished products may become part of the plasma membrane itself or part of another organelle, such as a lysosome, which we discuss next.

? **What is the relationship of the Golgi apparatus to the ER in a protein-secreting cell?**

● The Golgi receives transport vesicles budded from the ER that contain proteins synthesized by bound ribosomes. The Golgi finishes processing the proteins and dispatches transport vesicles to the plasma membrane, where the proteins are secreted.

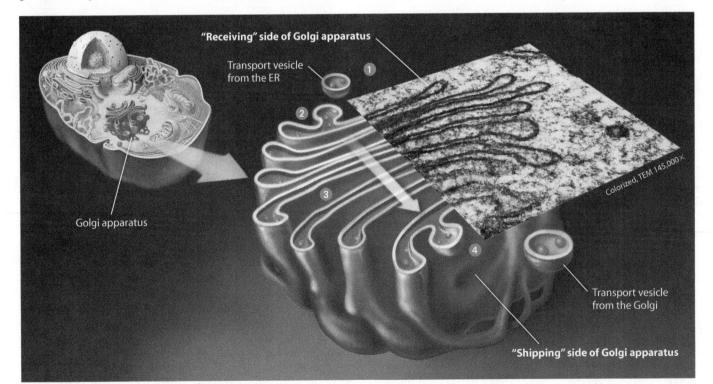

"Receiving" side of Golgi apparatus

Transport vesicle from the ER

1

2

3

4

Golgi apparatus

Colorized, TEM 145,000✕

Transport vesicle from the Golgi

"Shipping" side of Golgi apparatus

▲ **Figure 4.9** The Golgi apparatus receiving, processing, and shipping products

4.10 Lysosomes are digestive compartments within a cell

A **lysosome** is a membrane-enclosed sac of digestive enzymes. The name *lysosome* is derived from two Greek words meaning "breakdown body." The enzymes and membranes of lysosomes are made by rough ER and processed in the Golgi apparatus. Illustrating a main theme of eukaryotic cell structure—compartmentalization—a lysosome provides an acidic environment for its enzymes, while safely isolating them from the rest of the cell.

Lysosomes have several types of digestive functions. Many protists engulf food particles into membranous sacs called food vacuoles. As **Figure 4.10A** shows, lysosomes fuse with food vacuoles and digest the food. The nutrients are then released into the cytosol. Our white blood cells engulf bacteria and then destroy them using lysosomes. Lysosomes also serve as recycling centers. Cells enclose damaged organelles or small amounts of cytosol in membrane sacs. A lysosome fuses with such a vesicle (**Figure 4.10B**) and dismantles its contents, making organic molecules available for reuse. With the help of lysosomes, a cell continually renews itself.

The cells of people with inherited lysosomal storage diseases lack one or more lysosomal enzymes. The lysosomes become engorged with undigested material, eventually interfering with cellular function. In Tay-Sachs disease, for example, a lipid-digesting enzyme is missing, and brain cells become impaired by an accumulation of lipids. Fortunately, lysosomal storage diseases are rare, as they are often fatal in early childhood.

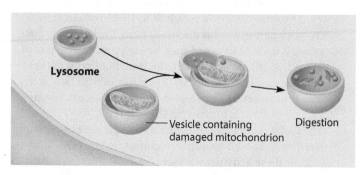

▲ **Figure 4.10A** Lysosome fusing with a food vacuole and digesting food, after which nutrients are released to the cytosol

▲ **Figure 4.10B** Lysosome fusing with a vesicle containing a damaged organelle and then digesting and recycling its contents

? **How is a lysosome like a recycling center?**

● It breaks down damaged organelles and recycles their molecules.

4.11 Vacuoles function in the general maintenance of the cell

Vacuoles are large vesicles that have a variety of functions. In Figure 4.10A, you saw how a food vacuole forms as a cell ingests food. **Figure 4.11A** shows two contractile vacuoles in the protist *Paramecium*, looking somewhat like wheel hubs with radiating spokes. The "spokes" collect water from the cell, and the hub expels it to the outside. Freshwater protists constantly take in water from their environment. Without a way to get rid of the excess water, the cell would swell and burst.

In plants, some vacuoles have a digestive function similar to that of lysosomes in animal cells. Vacuoles in flower petals contain pigments that attract pollinating insects. Vacuoles may also contain poisons or unpalatable compounds that protect the plant against herbivores;

▲ **Figure 4.11A** Contractile vacuoles in *Paramecium*, a unicellular eukaryote

examples include nicotine, caffeine, and various chemicals we use as pharmaceutical drugs.

Figure 4.11B shows a plant cell's large **central vacuole**, which helps the cell grow in size by absorbing water and enlarging. It also stockpiles vital chemicals and may act as a trash can, safely storing toxic waste products.

▶ **Figure 4.11B** Central vacuole in a plant cell

? **Is a food vacuole part of the endomembrane system? Explain.**

● Yes; it forms by pinching in from the plasma membrane, which is part of the endomembrane system.

4.12 A review of the structures involved in manufacturing and breakdown

Figure 4.12 summarizes the relationships within the endomembrane system. You can see the direct *structural* connections between the nuclear envelope, rough ER, and smooth ER. The red arrows show the *functional* connections, as membranes and proteins produced by the ER travel in transport vesicles to the Golgi and on to other destinations. Some vesicles develop into lysosomes or vacuoles. Others travel to and fuse with the plasma membrane, secreting their contents and adding their membrane to the plasma membrane.

Peroxisomes (see Figures 4.4A and B) are metabolic compartments that do not originate from the endomembrane system. In fact, how they are related to other organelles is still unknown. Some peroxisomes break down fatty acids to be used as cellular fuel. In your liver, peroxisomes detoxify harmful compounds. In these processes, enzymes transfer hydrogen from the compounds to oxygen, producing hydrogen peroxide (H_2O_2). Other enzymes in the peroxisome convert this toxic by-product to water—another example of the importance of a cell's compartmental structure.

A cell requires a continuous supply of energy to perform the work of life. Next we consider two organelles that act as cellular power stations—mitochondria and chloroplasts.

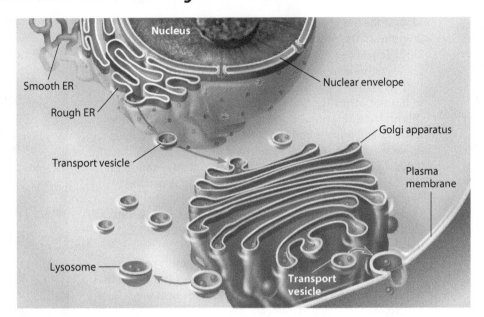

▲ **Figure 4.12** Review of the endomembrane system

Try This Explain the role of transport vesicles in the endomembrane system.

? **How do transport vesicles help tie together the endomembrane system?**

● Transport vesicles move membranes and the substances they enclose between components of the endomembrane system.

▷ Energy-Converting Organelles

4.13 Mitochondria harvest chemical energy from food

Mitochondria (singular, *mitochondrion*) are organelles that carry out cellular respiration in nearly all eukaryotic cells, converting the chemical energy of foods such as sugars to the chemical energy of the molecule called ATP (adenosine triphosphate). ATP is the main energy source for cellular work.

A mitochondrion is enclosed by two membranes, each a phospholipid bilayer with a unique collection of embedded proteins (Figure 4.13). The mitochondrion has two internal compartments. The first is the intermembrane space, the narrow region between the inner and outer membranes. The inner membrane encloses the second compartment, the **mitochondrial matrix**, which contains mitochondrial DNA and ribosomes, as well as enzymes that catalyze some of the reactions of cellular respiration. The inner membrane is highly folded and contains many embedded protein molecules that function in ATP synthesis. The folds, called **cristae**, increase the membrane's surface area, enhancing the mitochondrion's ability to produce ATP.

? **What is cellular respiration?**

● A process that converts the chemical energy of sugars and other food molecules to the chemical energy of ATP

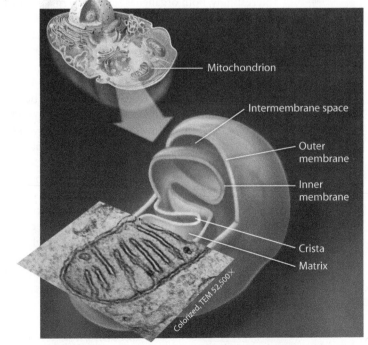

▲ **Figure 4.13** The mitochondrion, site of cellular respiration

4.14 Chloroplasts convert solar energy to chemical energy

Most of the living world runs on the energy provided by photosynthesis, the conversion of light energy from the sun to the chemical energy of sugar molecules. **Chloroplasts** are the photosynthesizing organelles of plants and algae.

This organelle carries out complex, multistep processes, so it is not surprising that internal membranes partition the chloroplast into compartments (**Figure 4.14**). It is enclosed by an inner and outer membrane separated by a thin intermembrane space. The compartment inside the inner membrane holds a thick fluid called **stroma**, which contains chloroplast DNA and ribosomes as well as many enzymes. A network of interconnected sacs called **thylakoids** is suspended in the stroma. The sacs are often stacked like poker chips; each stack is called a **granum** (plural, *grana*). The compartment inside the thylakoids is called the thylakoid space.

The thylakoids are the chloroplast's solar power packs—the sites where the green chlorophyll molecules embedded in thylakoid membranes trap solar energy. In the next module, we explore the origin of mitochondria and chloroplasts.

> **?** Which membrane in a chloroplast appears to be the most extensive? Why might this be so?

⊙ The thylakoid membranes contain chlorophyll for photosynthesis.

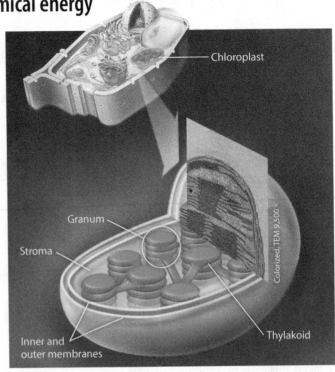

Colorized TEM 9,500×

▲ **Figure 4.14** The chloroplast, site of photosynthesis

4.15 Mitochondria and chloroplasts evolved by endosymbiosis

EVOLUTION CONNECTION

Mitochondria and chloroplasts contain a single circular DNA molecule, similar in structure to a prokaryotic chromosome, and ribosomes more similar to prokaryotic ribosomes than to eukaryotic ones. Interestingly, both organelles reproduce in a cell by a process resembling that of certain prokaryotes.

The **endosymbiont theory** states that mitochondria and chloroplasts were formerly small prokaryotes that began living within larger cells. These prokaryotes may have gained entry to the larger cell as undigested prey or parasites (**Figure 4.15**).

We can hypothesize how the symbiosis could have been beneficial. In a world that was becoming increasingly aerobic from the oxygen-generating photosynthesis of prokaryotes, a host would have benefited from an endosymbiont that was able to use oxygen to release large amounts of energy from organic molecules. Over the course of evolution, the host cell and its endosymbiont merged into a single organism—a eukaryotic cell with a mitochondrion. If one of these cells acquired a photosynthetic prokaryote, the prokaryote could provide the host cell with nourishment. An increasingly interdependent host and endosymbiont, over many generations, could become a eukaryotic cell containing chloroplasts.

> **?** All eukaryotes have mitochondria, but not all have chloroplasts. What is the evolutionary explanation?

⊙ The first endosymbiosis would have given rise to eukaryotic cells containing mitochondria. A second endosymbiotic event gave rise to cells containing chloroplasts as well as mitochondria.

▲ **Figure 4.15** Endosymbiotic origin of mitochondria and chloroplasts

▷ The Cytoskeleton and Cell Surfaces

4.16 The cell's internal skeleton helps organize its structure and activities

As you saw in the chapter introduction, networks of protein fibers extend throughout a cell. Collectively called the **cytoskeleton**, these fibers play a major role in organizing the structures and activities of the cell. And like a skeleton, they provide for structural support as well as movement, including both the internal movement of cell parts and the swimming or crawling motility of some cells.

Three main kinds of fibers make up the cytoskeleton: microtubules, the thickest fiber; microfilaments, the thinnest; and intermediate filaments, in between in thickness. **Figure 4.16** shows three micrographs of cells of the same type, each stained with a different fluorescent dye that selectively highlights one of these types of fibers.

Microtubules are straight, hollow tubes composed of globular proteins called tubulins. As indicated in the bottom left of Figure 4.16, microtubules elongate by the addition of tubulin proteins. They are readily disassembled, and their subunits can be reused elsewhere in the cell. In animal cells, microtubules grow out from a region near the nucleus called the **centrosome**, which contains a pair of centrioles, each composed of a ring of microtubules (see Figure 4.4A). Plant cells lack centrosomes with centrioles and organize microtubules by other means.

Microtubules shape and support the cell and also act as tracks along which organelles equipped with motor proteins move. For example, a lysosome might use its motor protein "feet" to "walk" along a microtubule to reach a food vacuole. Microtubules also guide the movement of chromosomes when cells divide, and they are the main components of cilia and flagella. We will return to the structure of these locomotive appendages in Module 4.18.

Intermediate filaments are found in the cells of most animals. They are made of various fibrous proteins that supercoil into cables. Intermediate filaments reinforce cell shape and anchor some organelles. For example, the nucleus typically sits in a cage made of intermediate filaments. While microtubules may be disassembled and reassembled elsewhere, intermediate filaments are often more permanent fixtures in the cell. The outer layer of your skin consists of dead skin cells packed full of intermediate filaments.

Microfilaments, also called actin filaments, are solid rods composed mainly of globular proteins called actin, arranged in a twisted double chain (bottom right of Figure 4.16). Microfilaments form a three-dimensional network just inside the plasma membrane that helps support the cell's shape. This is especially important for animal cells, which lack cell walls.

Microfilaments are also involved in cell movements. Actin filaments and thicker filaments made of a type of motor protein called myosin interact to cause contraction of muscle cells (see Figure 30.9B). Localized contractions brought about by actin and myosin are involved in the amoeboid (crawling) movement of the protist *Amoeba* and some of your white blood cells.

In the next module, we survey some of the techniques that led to the discovery of the cytoskeleton.

? Which component of the cytoskeleton is most important in (a) holding the nucleus in place within the cell; (b) guiding transport vesicles from the Golgi to the plasma membrane; (c) contracting muscle cells?

(a) Intermediate filaments; (b) microtubules; (c) microfilaments

▲ **Figure 4.16** Three types of fibers of the cytoskeleton: microtubules labeled with green fluorescent molecules (left), intermediate filaments labeled yellow-green (center), and microfilaments labeled red (right)

4.17 Scientists discovered the cytoskeleton using the tools of biochemistry and microscopy

SCIENTIFIC THINKING

As you learned in Module 4.1, improvements in microscopes and staining techniques led to the discovery of organelles. But biologists originally thought that these structures floated freely in the cell. Let's trace the progressive sequence of new techniques that led to the discovery of microfilaments, the component of the cytoskeleton built from actin.

In the 1940s, biochemists first isolated and identified the proteins actin and myosin from muscle cells. In 1954, scientists, using newly developed techniques of microscopy, established how filaments of actin and myosin interact in muscle contraction. In the next decade, researchers developed a technique to stain and identify actin filaments with the electron microscope. Imagine their surprise when they found actin not just in the muscle cells they were studying but also in other cells present in their samples. Further study identified actin filaments in all types of cells.

Today we take for granted our ability to "see" the cytoskeleton (as you saw in the chapter introduction). But intact networks of microfilaments were not visualized in cells until 1974. Using a technique called immunofluorescence microscopy, scientists developed antibody proteins that would bind to actin and attached fluorescent molecules to

How has our knowledge of cells grown?

them. When fluorescent molecules absorb light, they "glow" because they emit light of a specific wavelength or color. When injected into cells, the fluorescent antibodies revealed a remarkable and beautiful web of microfilaments. Figure 4.17 shows how different fluorescent tags can attach to various components of the cytoskeleton.

Researchers then tagged actin proteins themselves with fluorescent molecules and injected them into living cells. Instead of just marking where proteins are found, this technique, known as molecular cytochemistry, enabled scientists to visualize the dynamic behavior of cytoskeletal proteins in living cells.

In the early 1980s, biologists first paired a video camera with a microscope. Suddenly they could "watch" what was happening in cells over time and follow the changing architecture of the cytoskeleton.

As scientists develop new techniques, our understanding of the structure and function of the cytoskeleton will continue to grow.

▲ **Figure 4.17** A fluorescence micrograph of the cytoskeleton (microtubules are green, microfilaments are red)

? **What is the difference between immunofluorescence microscopy and molecular cytochemistry?**

● In the former, fluorescently labeled antibodies show the locations of specific molecules. In the latter, the molecules themselves are labeled, and their behavior within a living cell can be tracked.

4.18 Cilia and flagella move when microtubules bend

The role of the cytoskeleton in movement is clearly seen in the motile appendages that protrude from certain cells. The short, numerous appendages that propel protists such as *Paramecium* (see Figure 4.1B) are called **cilia** (singular, *cilium*).

Other protists may move using flagella, which are longer than cilia and usually limited to one or a few per cell.

Some cells of multicellular organisms also have cilia or flagella. For example, Figure 4.18A shows cilia on cells lining the trachea (windpipe). These cilia sweep mucus containing trapped debris out of your lungs. (This cleaning function is impaired by cigarette smoke, which paralyzes the cilia.) Most animals and

some plants have flagellated sperm. A flagellum, shown in Figure 4.18B, propels the cell by an undulating whiplike motion. In contrast, cilia work more like the coordinated oars of a rowing team.

Though different in length and beating pattern, cilia and flagella have a common structure and mechanism of movement (Figure 4.18C). Both are composed of microtubules wrapped in an extension of the plasma membrane. In nearly all eukaryotic cilia and flagella, a ring of nine microtubule doublets surrounds a central pair of microtubules. This arrangement is called the "9 + 2" pattern. The microtubule assembly is anchored in the cell by a

Colorized SEM 940×

Flagellum

Colorized SEM 2,400×

Cilia

▲ **Figure 4.18A** Cilia on cells lining the respiratory tract

▲ **Figure 4.18B** Undulating flagellum on a human sperm cell

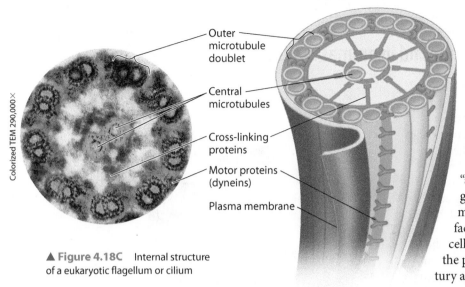

- Outer microtubule doublet
- Central microtubules
- Cross-linking proteins
- Motor proteins (dyneins)
- Plasma membrane

Colorized TEM 290,000×

▲ **Figure 4.18C** Internal structure of a eukaryotic flagellum or cilium

basal body (not shown in the figure), which is structurally very similar to a centriole. In fact, in humans and many other animals, the basal body of the fertilizing sperm's flagellum enters the egg and becomes a centriole.

How does the microtubule assembly shown in Figure 4.18C produce the movement of cilia and flagella? Large motor proteins called dyneins (red in the figure) are attached along each outer microtubule doublet. A dynein protein has two "feet" that "walk" along an adjacent doublet. The walking

movement is coordinated so that it happens on one side at a time. The microtubules are held together by flexible cross-linking proteins (purple in the diagram). If the doublets were not held in place, they would slide past each other. Instead, the "walking" of the dynein feet causes the microtubules—and consequently the cilium or flagellum—to bend.

A cilium may also serve as a signal-receiving "antenna" for the cell. Cilia with this function are generally nonmotile (they lack the central pair of microtubules), and there is only one per cell. In fact, in vertebrate animals, it appears that almost all cells have what is called a *primary cilium*. Although the primary cilium was discovered more than a century ago, its importance to embryonic development, sensory reception, and cell function is only now being recognized. Defective primary cilia have been linked to polycystic kidney disease and other human disorders.

? **Primary ciliary dyskinesia (PCD), also known as immotile cilia syndrome, is a fairly rare disease in which cilia and flagella are lacking motor proteins. PCD is characterized by recurrent respiratory tract infections and immotile sperm. How would you explain these seemingly unrelated symptoms?**

● Without motor proteins, microtubules cannot bend. Thus cilia cannot cleanse the respiratory tract, and sperm cannot swim.

4.19 The extracellular matrix of animal cells functions in support and regulation

The plasma membrane is usually regarded as the boundary of the cell, but most cells synthesize and secrete materials that are external to the plasma membrane. These extracellular structures are essential to many cell functions.

Animal cells produce an **extracellular matrix (ECM)** (Figure 4.19). This elaborate layer helps hold cells together in tissues and protects and supports the plasma membrane. The main components of the ECM are glycoproteins, proteins bonded with carbohydrates. The most abundant glycoprotein is collagen, which forms strong fibers outside the cell. In fact, collagen accounts for about 40% of the protein in your body. The collagen fibers are embedded in a network woven from other types of glycoproteins. Large complexes form when hundreds of small glycoproteins connect to a central long polysaccharide molecule (shown as green in the figure). The ECM may attach to the cell through other glycoproteins that then bind to membrane proteins called **integrins**. Integrins span the membrane, attaching on the other side to proteins connected to microfilaments of the cytoskeleton.

As their name implies, integrins have the function of integration: They transmit signals between the ECM and the cytoskeleton. Thus, the cytoskeleton can influence the organization of the ECM and vice versa. For example, research shows that the ECM can regulate a cell's behavior, directing the path along which embryonic cells move and even influencing the activity of genes through the signals it relays. Genetic changes in cancer cells may result in a change in the composition of

- Glycoprotein complex with long polysaccharide
- Collagen fiber
- Connecting glycoprotein
- Integrin
- Plasma membrane
- Microfilaments of cytoskeleton
- EXTRACELLULAR FLUID
- CYTOPLASM

▲ **Figure 4.19** The extracellular matrix (ECM) of an animal cell

the ECM they produce, causing such cells to lose their connections and spread to other tissues.

? **Referring to Figure 4.19, describe the structures that provide support to the plasma membrane.**

● The membrane is attached through membrane proteins (integrins) to microfilaments in the cytoskeleton and collagen fibers of the ECM.

4.20 Three types of cell junctions are found in animal tissues

Neighboring cells in animal tissues often adhere, interact, and communicate through specialized junctions between them. Figure 4.20 uses cells lining the digestive tract to illustrate three types of cell junctions. (The projections at the top of the cells increase the surface area for absorption of nutrients.)

At tight junctions, the plasma membranes of neighboring cells are knit tightly together by proteins. Tight junctions prevent leakage of fluid across a layer of cells. The dotted green arrows show how tight junctions prevent the contents of the digestive tract from leaking into surrounding tissues.

Anchoring junctions function like rivets, fastening cells together into strong sheets. Intermediate filaments made of sturdy proteins anchor these junctions in the cytoplasm. Anchoring junctions are common in tissues subject to stretching or mechanical stress, such as skin and muscle.

Gap junctions, also called communicating junctions, are channels that allow small molecules to flow through protein-lined pores between cells. The flow of ions through gap junctions in the cells of heart muscle coordinates their contraction. Gap junctions are common in embryos, where communication between cells is essential for development.

> **?** A muscle tear injury would probably involve the rupture of which type of cell junction?
>
> ● Anchoring junction

Tight junctions prevent fluid from moving across a layer of cells

Tight junction

Anchoring junction

Gap junction

Plasma membranes of adjacent cells

Ions or small molecules

Extracellular matrix

▲ **Figure 4.20**   Three types of cell junctions in animal tissues

4.21 Cell walls enclose and support plant cells

The **cell wall** is one of the features that distinguishes plant cells from animal cells. This rigid extracellular structure not only protects the cells but also provides the skeletal support that keeps plants upright on land. Plant cell walls consist of fibers of cellulose (see Figure 3.7) embedded in a matrix of other polysaccharides and proteins. This fibers-in-a-matrix construction resembles that of steel-reinforced concrete, which is also noted for its strength.

Figure 4.21 shows the layered structure of plant cell walls. Cells initially lay down a relatively thin and flexible primary wall, which allows the growing cell to continue to enlarge. Between adjacent cells is a layer of sticky polysaccharides called pectins (shown here in dark brown), which glue the cells together. (Pectin is used to thicken jams and jellies.) When a cell stops growing, it strengthens its wall. Some cells add a secondary wall deposited in laminated layers next to the plasma membrane. Wood consists mainly of secondary walls, which are strengthened with rigid molecules called lignin.

Despite their thickness, plant cell walls do not totally isolate the cells from each other. Figure 4.21 shows the numerous channels that connect adjacent plant cells, called **plasmodesmata** (singular, *plasmodesma*). Cytosol passing through the plasmodesmata allows water and other small molecules to freely move from cell to cell. Through

Plant cell walls

Vacuole

Plasmodesmata

Primary cell wall

Secondary cell wall

Plasma membrane

Cytosol

▲ **Figure 4.21**   Plant cell walls and plasmodesmata

plasmodesmata, the cells of a plant tissue share water, nourishment, and chemical messages.

> **?** Which animal cell junction is analogous to a plasmodesma?
>
> ● A gap junction

4.22 Review: Eukaryotic cell structures can be grouped on the basis of four main functions

Congratulations: You have completed the grand tour of the cell. In the process, you have been introduced to many important cell structures. To provide a framework for this information and reinforce the theme that structure is correlated with function, we have grouped the eukaryotic cell structures into four categories by general function, as reviewed in **Table 4.22**.

The first category is genetic control. Here we include the nucleus that houses a cell's genetic instructions and the ribosomes that produce the proteins coded for in those instructions. The second category includes organelles of the endomembrane system that are involved in the manufacture, distribution, and breakdown of materials. The third category includes the two energy-processing organelles, mitochondria and chloroplasts. And the fourth category—structural support, movement, and intercellular communication—includes the cytoskeleton, extracellular structures, and connections between cells.

Within most of these categories, a structural similarity underlies the general function of each component. Manufacturing depends heavily on a network of structurally and functionally connected membranes. All the organelles involved in the breakdown or recycling of materials are membranous sacs, inside of which enzymatic digestion can safely occur. In the energy-processing category, expanses of metabolically active membranes and intermembrane compartments within the organelles enable chloroplasts and mitochondria to perform the complex energy conversions that power the cell. Even in the diverse fourth category, there is a common structural theme in the various protein fibers of most of these cellular systems.

We can summarize further by noting that the overall structure of a cell is closely related to its specific function. Thus, cells that produce proteins for export contain a large quantity of ribosomes and rough ER, while muscle cells are packed with microfilaments, myosin motor proteins, and mitochondria. And, finally, let us emphasize that these cellular structures form an integrated team—with the property of life emerging at the level of the cell from the coordinated functions of the team members.

? How do mitochondria, smooth ER, and the cytoskeleton all contribute to the contraction of a muscle cell?

● Mitochondria supply energy in the form of ATP. The smooth ER helps regulate contraction by the uptake and release of calcium ions. Microfilaments function in the actual contractile apparatus.

TABLE 4.22 | EUKARYOTIC CELL STRUCTURES AND FUNCTIONS

1. Genetic Control	
Nucleus	DNA replication, RNA synthesis; assembly of ribosomal subunits (in nucleolus)
Ribosomes	Polypeptide (protein) synthesis
2. Manufacturing, Distribution, and Breakdown	
Rough ER	Synthesis of membrane lipids and proteins, secretory proteins, and hydrolytic enzymes; formation of transport vesicles
Smooth ER	Lipid synthesis; detoxification in liver cells; calcium ion storage
Golgi apparatus	Modification and sorting of macromolecules; formation of lysosomes and transport vesicles
Lysosomes (in animal cells and some protists)	Digestion of ingested food or bacteria and recycling of a cell's damaged organelles and macromolecules
Vacuoles	Digestion (food vacuole); storage of chemicals and cell enlargement (central vacuole); water balance (contractile vacuole)
Peroxisomes (not part of endomembrane system)	Diverse metabolic processes, with breakdown of toxic hydrogen peroxide by-product
3. Energy Processing	
Mitochondria	Conversion of chemical energy in food to chemical energy of ATP
Chloroplasts (in plants and algae)	Conversion of light energy to chemical energy of sugars
4. Structural Support, Movement, and Communication Between Cells	
Cytoskeleton (microfilaments, intermediate filaments, and microtubules)	Maintenance of cell shape; anchorage for organelles; movement of organelles within cells; cell movement (crawling, muscle contraction, bending of cilia and flagella)
Plasma membrane	Regulate traffic in and out of cell
Extracellular matrix (in animals)	Support; regulation of cellular activities
Cell junctions	Communication between cells; binding of cells in tissues
Cell walls (in plants)	Support and protection; binding of cells in tissues

CHAPTER 4 REVIEW

For practice quizzes, BioFlix animations, MP3 tutorials, video tutors, and more study tools designed for this textbook, go to
MasteringBiology®

Reviewing the Concepts

Introduction to the Cell (4.1–4.4)

4.1 Microscopes reveal the world of the cell. The light microscope can display living cells. The greater magnification and resolution of the scanning and transmission electron microscopes reveal the ultrastructure of cells.

4.2 The small size of cells relates to the need to exchange materials across the plasma membrane. The microscopic size of most cells provides a large surface-to-volume ratio. The plasma membrane is a phospholipid bilayer with embedded proteins.

4.3 Prokaryotic cells are structurally simpler than eukaryotic cells. All cells have a plasma membrane, DNA, ribosomes, and cytosol. Prokaryotic cells lack organelles.

4.4 Eukaryotic cells are partitioned into functional compartments. Membrane-enclosed organelles compartmentalize a cell's activities.

The Nucleus and Ribosomes (4.5–4.6)

4.5 The nucleus contains the cell's genetic instructions. The nucleus houses the cell's DNA, which directs protein synthesis via messenger RNA. Subunits of ribosomes are assembled in the nucleolus.

4.6 Ribosomes make proteins for use in the cell and for export. Composed of ribosomal RNA and proteins, ribosomes synthesize proteins according to directions from DNA.

The Endomembrane System (4.7–4.12)

4.7 Many organelles are connected in the endomembrane system.

4.8 The endoplasmic reticulum is a biosynthetic workshop. The ER is a membranous network of tubes and sacs. Smooth ER synthesizes lipids and processes toxins. Rough ER produces membranes, and ribosomes on its surface make membrane and secretory proteins.

4.9 The Golgi apparatus modifies, sorts, and ships cell products. The Golgi apparatus consists of stacks of sacs in which products of the ER are processed and then sent to other organelles or to the cell surface.

4.10 Lysosomes are digestive compartments within a cell. Lysosomes house enzymes that break down ingested substances and damaged organelles for recycling.

4.11 Vacuoles function in the general maintenance of the cell. Some protists have contractile vacuoles. Plant cells contain a large central vacuole that stores molecules and wastes and facilitates growth.

4.12 A review of the structures involved in manufacturing and breakdown. The organelles of the endomembrane system are interconnected structurally and functionally.

Energy-Converting Organelles (4.13–4.15)

4.13 Mitochondria harvest chemical energy from food.

4.14 Chloroplasts convert solar energy to chemical energy.

4.15 Mitochondria and chloroplasts evolved by endosymbiosis. These organelles originated from prokaryotic cells that became residents in a host cell.

The Cytoskeleton and Cell Surfaces (4.16–4.22)

4.16 The cell's internal skeleton helps organize its structure and activities. The cytoskeleton includes microfilaments, intermediate filaments, and microtubules. Their functions include muscle contraction, anchorage and movement of organelles, and maintenance of cell shape.

4.17 Scientists discovered the cytoskeleton using the tools of biochemistry and microscopy.

4.18 Cilia and flagella move when microtubules bend. Eukaryotic cilia and flagella are locomotor appendages made of microtubules in a "9 + 2" arrangement.

4.19 The extracellular matrix of animal cells functions in support and regulation. The ECM consists mainly of glycoproteins, which bind tissue cells together, support the membrane, and communicate with the cytoskeleton.

4.20 Three types of cell junctions are found in animal tissues. Tight junctions bind cells to form leakproof sheets. Anchoring junctions rivet cells into strong tissues. Gap junctions allow substances to flow from cell to cell.

4.21 Cell walls enclose and support plant cells. Plant cell walls are made largely of cellulose. Plasmodesmata are connecting channels between cells.

4.22 Review: Eukaryotic cell structures can be grouped on the basis of four main functions. These functions are (1) genetic control; (2) manufacturing, distribution, and breakdown; (3) energy processing; and (4) structural support, movement, and communication between cells.

Connecting the Concepts

1. Label the structures in this diagram of an animal cell. Review the functions of each of these organelles.

a. _____
b. _____
c. _____
d. _____
e. _____
f. _____
g. _____
h. _____
i. _____
j. _____
k. _____
l. _____

Testing Your Knowledge

Level 1: Knowledge/Comprehension

2. The ultrastructure of a chloroplast is best studied using a
   a. light microscope.
   b. scanning electron microscope.
   c. transmission electron microscope.
   d. light microscope and fluorescent dyes.
3. The cells of an ant and an elephant are, on average, the same small size; an elephant just has more of them. What is the main advantage of small cell size? (*Explain your reasoning.*)
   a. A small cell has a larger plasma membrane surface area than does a large cell.
   b. Small cells can better take up sufficient nutrients and oxygen to service their cell volume.
   c. It takes less energy to make an organism out of small cells.
   d. Small cells require less oxygen than do large cells.
4. Which of the following clues would tell you whether a cell is prokaryotic or eukaryotic?
   a. the presence or absence of a rigid cell wall
   b. whether or not the cell is partitioned by internal membranes
   c. the presence or absence of ribosomes
   d. Both a and b are important clues.
5. Which of the following is one of the major components of the plasma membrane of a plant cell?
   a. phospholipids
   b. cellulose fibers
   c. collagen fibers
   d. pectins
6. What four cellular components are shared by prokaryotic and eukaryotic cells?
7. Describe two different ways in which cilia can function in organisms.

Level 2: Application/Analysis

Choose from the following cells for questions 8–11:
   a. pancreatic cell that secretes digestive enzymes
   b. ovarian cell that produces estrogen (a steroid hormone)
   c. muscle cell in the thigh of a long-distance runner
   d. white blood cell that engulfs bacteria

8. In which cell would you find the most lysosomes?
9. In which cell would you find the most smooth ER?
10. In which cell would you find the most rough ER?
11. In which cell would you find the most mitochondria?
12. In what ways do the internal membranes of a eukaryotic cell contribute to the functioning of the cell?
13. Is this statement true or false? "Animal cells have mitochondria; plant cells have chloroplasts." Explain your answer, and describe the functions of these organelles.
14. Describe the structure of the plasma membrane of an animal cell. What would be found directly inside and outside the membrane?
15. Imagine a spherical cell with a radius of 10 μm. What is the cell's surface area in μm^2? Its volume, in μm^3? (*Note:* For a sphere of radius *r*, surface area $= 4\pi r^2$ and volume $= \pi r^3$. Remember that the value of π is 3.14.) What is the ratio of surface area to volume for this cell? Now do the same calculations for a second cell, this one with a radius of 20 μm. Compare the surface-to-volume ratios of the two cells. How is this comparison significant to the functioning of cells?

16. Describe the pathway of the protein hormone insulin from its gene to its export from a cell of your pancreas.

Level 3: Synthesis/Evaluation

17. How might the phrase "ingested but not digested" be used in a description of the endosymbiotic theory?
18. Cilia are found on cells in almost every organ of the human body, and the malfunction of cilia is involved in several human disorders. During embryological development, for example, cilia generate a leftward flow of fluid that initiates the left-right organization of the body organs. Some individuals with primary ciliary dyskinesia (see Module 4.18 checkpoint question) exhibit *situs inversus*, in which internal organs such as the heart are on the wrong side of the body. Explain why this reversed arrangement may be a symptom of PCD.
19. **SCIENTIFIC THINKING** Microtubules often produce movement through their interaction with motor proteins. But in some cases, microtubules move cell components when the length of the microtubule changes. Through a series of experiments, researchers determined that microtubules grow and shorten as tubulin proteins are added or removed from their ends. Other experiments showed that microtubules make up the spindle apparatus that "pulls" chromosomes toward opposite ends (poles) of a dividing cell. The figures below describe a clever experiment done in 1987 to determine whether a spindle microtubule shortens (depolymerizes) at the end holding a chromosome or at the pole end of a dividing cell.

    Experimenters labeled the microtubules of a dividing cell from a pig kidney with a yellow fluorescent dye. As shown on the left half of the diagram below, they then marked a region halfway along the microtubules by using a laser to eliminate the fluorescence from that region. They did not mark the other side of the spindle (right side of the figure).

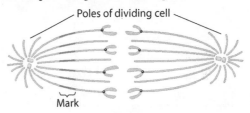

The figure below illustrates the results they observed as the chromosomes moved toward the opposite poles of the cell.

Describe these results. What would you conclude about where the microtubules depolymerize from comparing the length of the microtubules on either side of the mark? How could the experimenters determine whether this is the mechanism of chromosome movement in all cells?

Source: G. J. Gorbsky et al. Chromosomes move poleward in anaphase along stationary microtubules that coordinately disassemble from their kinetochore ends, *Journal of Cell Biology* 104:9–18 (1987).

Answers to all questions can be found in Appendix 4.

5

The Working Cell

How can water flow through a membrane?

The illustration below is beautiful and intriguing—but what does it represent? This computer model shows a small section of a membrane in a human cell; notice the water molecules (depicted with red and gray balls) streaming single file across the membrane. Notice also the phospholipids that make up the lipid bilayer of this membrane: The yellow balls represent the phosphate heads and the green squiggles are the fatty acid tails of the phospholipids. The blue ribbons embedded in the membrane represent regions of a membrane protein called aquaporin that function as water channels. Just one molecule of this protein enables billions of water molecules to flow through the membrane every second—many more than could wander through the lipid bilayer on their own.

Aquaporins are common in cells involved in water balance. For example, your kidneys must filter and reabsorb many liters of water a day, and aquaporins are vital to their proper functioning. There are rare cases of people with defective aquaporins whose kidneys can't reabsorb water and must drink 20 liters of water every day to prevent dehydration. On the other hand, if kidney cells have too many aquaporins, excess water is reabsorbed and body tissues may swell. A common complication of pregnancy is fluid retention, and it is likely caused by increased synthesis of aquaporin proteins. Later in the chapter you will learn about the serendipitous discovery of these water channels.

But aquaporins are only one example of how the plasma membrane and its proteins enable cells to survive and function. We begin this chapter by examining membranes. A cell expends energy to build membranes, and many of a membrane's functions require energy. A cell's energy conversions involve enzymes, which control all of its chemical reactions. Indeed, everything that is depicted in this computer model of water molecules zipping through a membrane relates to how working cells use membranes, energy, and enzymes—which are the topics of this chapter.

BIG IDEAS

Membrane Structure and Function
(5.1–5.9)

A cell membrane's structure enables its many functions, such as regulating traffic across the membrane.

Energy and the Cell
(5.10–5.12)

A cell's metabolic reactions transform energy, using ATP to drive cellular work.

How Enzymes Function
(5.13–5.16)

Enzymes speed up a cell's chemical reactions and provide precise control of metabolism.

5.1 Membranes are fluid mosaics of lipids and proteins with many functions

Biologists use the **fluid mosaic model** to describe a membrane's structure—diverse protein molecules suspended in a fluid phospholipid bilayer. This module illustrates the structure and function of a plasma membrane, the boundary that encloses a living cell. Like all cellular membranes,

the plasma membrane exhibits **selective permeability**; that is, it allows some substances to cross more easily than others. But the plasma membrane does more than just regulate the exchange of materials. This figure will help you visualize all the activity taking place in and across the membranes of two adjacent cells.

DIVERSE FUNCTIONS OF THE PLASMA MEMBRANE

CYTOPLASMIC SIDE OF MEMBRANE
EXTRACELLULAR SIDE OF MEMBRANE

O_2 CO_2

Initial reactant

Small nonpolar molecules may diffuse across the lipid bilayer.

Fibers of extracellular matrices (ECM)

Enzyme

Enzyme

Some membrane proteins are enzymes, which may be grouped to carry out sequential reactions.

Product of reaction

Phospholipid

What keeps a membrane "fluid"? Kinks in the unsaturated fatty acid tails of some phospholipids and the presence of cholesterol (in animal cells) keep phospholipids from packing too tightly.

Cholesterol

Solute molecules

Membrane proteins may form intercellular junctions that attach adjacent cells.

Signaling molecule

Receptor protein

Attachment protein

Channel protein

Junction protein

Active transport protein

Junction protein

Attached sugars

ATP

Glycoprotein

Protein that recognizes neighboring cell

Proteins that attach to the extracellular matrix and cytoskeleton help support the membrane and can coordinate external and internal changes.

Signaling molecules bind to receptor proteins, which relay the message by activating other molecules inside the cell.

Transport proteins allow specific ions or molecules to enter or exit the cell.

Glycoproteins may serve as ID tags that are recognized by membrane proteins of other cells.

Microfilaments of cytoskeleton

What makes this membrane a "mosaic"? Note the diverse proteins, each with a specific function.

? Can you identify six different types of functions of proteins in a plasma membrane?

Attachment to the cytoskeleton and ECM, signal reception and relay, enzymatic activity, cell-cell recognition, intercellular joining, and transport

5.2 The spontaneous formation of membranes was a critical step in the origin of life

EVOLUTION CONNECTION

Phospholipids, the key ingredients of biological membranes, were probably among the first organic molecules that formed from chemical reactions on early Earth (see Module 15.2). These lipids could spontaneously self-assemble into simple membranes, as can be demonstrated in a test tube. When a mixture of phospholipids and water is shaken, the phospholipids organize into bilayers surrounding water-filled bubbles (Figure 5.2). This assembly requires neither genes nor other information beyond the properties of the phospholipids themselves.

The formation of membrane-enclosed collections of molecules would have been a critical step in the evolution of the first cells. A membrane can enclose a solution that is different in composition from its surroundings. A plasma membrane that allows cells to regulate their chemical exchanges with the environment is a basic requirement for life. Indeed, all cells are enclosed by a plasma membrane that is similar in structure and function—illustrating the evolutionary unity of life.

Water-filled bubble made of phospholipids

▲ **Figure 5.2** Artificial membrane-bounded sacs

? In the origin of a cell, why would the formation of a simple lipid bilayer membrane not be sufficient? What else would have to be part of such a membrane?

● The membrane would need embedded proteins that could regulate the movement of substances into and out of the cell.

5.3 Passive transport is diffusion across a membrane with no energy investment

Molecules have a type of energy called thermal energy, due to their constant motion. One result of this motion is **diffusion**, the tendency for particles of any substance to spread out into the available space. How might diffusion affect the movement of substances into or out of a cell?

The figures to the right will help you visualize diffusion across a membrane. **Figure 5.3A** shows a solution of green dye separated from pure water by an artificial membrane. Assume that this membrane has microscopic pores through which dye molecules can move. Thus, we say the membrane is permeable to the dye. Although each molecule moves randomly, there will be a *net* movement from the side of the membrane where dye molecules are more concentrated to the side where they are less concentrated. Put another way, the dye diffuses down its **concentration gradient**. Eventually, the solutions on both sides will have equal concentrations of dye. At this dynamic equilibrium, molecules still move back and forth, but there is no *net* change in concentration on either side of the membrane.

Figure 5.3B illustrates the important point that two or more substances diffuse independently of each other; that is, each diffuses down its own concentration gradient.

Because a cell does not have to do work when molecules diffuse across its membrane, such movement across a membrane is called **passive transport**. Much of the traffic across cell membranes occurs by diffusion. For example, diffusion down concentration gradients is the sole means by which oxygen (O_2), essential for metabolism, enters your cells and carbon dioxide (CO_2), a metabolic waste, passes out of them.

Both O_2 and CO_2 are small, nonpolar molecules that diffuse easily across the phospholipid bilayer of a membrane. But can ions and polar molecules also diffuse across the

Molecules of dye   Membrane

Pores

Net diffusion   Net diffusion   Equilibrium

▲ **Figure 5.3A** Diffusion of one type of molecule across a membrane

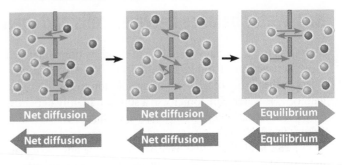

Net diffusion   Net diffusion   Equilibrium
Net diffusion   Net diffusion   Equilibrium

▲ **Figure 5.3B** Diffusion of two types of molecules across a membrane

Try This Explain why these two types of molecules are moving in opposite directions.

hydrophobic interior of a membrane? They can if they are moving down their concentration gradients and if they have transport proteins to help them cross.

? Why is diffusion across a membrane called passive transport?

● The cell does not expend energy to transport substances that are diffusing down their concentration gradients.

5.4 Osmosis is the diffusion of water across a membrane

One of the most important substances that crosses membranes by passive transport is water. In the next module, we consider the critical balance of water between a cell and its environment. But first let's explore a physical model of the diffusion of water across a selectively permeable membrane, a process called **osmosis**. Remember that a selectively permeable membrane allows some substances to cross more easily than others.

The top of **Figure 5.4** shows what happens if a membrane permeable to water but not to a solute (such as glucose) separates two solutions that have different concentrations of solute. (A solute is a substance that dissolves in a liquid solvent. The resulting mixture is a solution.) The solution on the right side initially has a higher concentration of solute than that on the left. As you can see, water crosses the membrane until the solute concentrations are more nearly equal on both sides.

In the close-up view at the bottom of Figure 5.4, you can see what happens at the molecular level. Polar water molecules cluster around hydrophilic (water-loving) solute molecules. The effect is that on the right side, there are fewer water molecules that are *free* to cross the membrane. The less concentrated solution on the left has fewer solute molecules but more *free* water molecules available to move. There is a net movement of water down its own concentration gradient, from the solution with more free water molecules (and lower solute concentration) to that with fewer free water molecules (and higher solute concentration). The result of this water movement is the difference in water levels you see at the top right of Figure 5.4.

Let's now apply to living cells what we have learned about osmosis in artificial systems.

▲ **Figure 5.4**   Osmosis, the diffusion of water across a membrane

Try This   Identify the solution that has more free water molecules. Predict which way water will move.

? Indicate the direction of net water movement between two solutions—a 0.5% sucrose solution and a 2% sucrose solution—separated by a membrane not permeable to sucrose.

● From the 0.5% sucrose solution (lower solute concentration) to the 2% sucrose solution (higher solute concentration)

5.5 Water balance between cells and their surroundings is crucial to organisms

Biologists use a special vocabulary to describe how water will move between a cell and its surroundings. The term **tonicity** refers to the ability of a surrounding solution to cause a cell to gain or lose water. The tonicity of a solution mainly depends on its concentration of solutes relative to the concentration of solutes inside the cell.

Figure 5.5, on the facing page, illustrates the effects of placing animal and plant cells in solutions of various tonicities.

When an animal cell, such as the red blood cell shown in the top center of the figure, is immersed in a solution that is **isotonic** to the cell (*iso*, same, and *tonos*, tension), the cell's volume remains constant. The solute concentration of a cell and its isotonic environment are essentially equal, and the cell gains water at the same rate that it loses it. In your body, red blood cells are transported in the isotonic plasma of the blood. Intravenous (IV) fluids administered in hospitals must also be isotonic to blood cells. The body cells of most animals are bathed in an extracellular fluid that is isotonic to the cells.

And seawater is isotonic to the cells of many marine animals, such as sea stars and crabs.

What happens when an animal cell is placed in a **hypotonic** solution (*hypo*, below), a solution with a solute concentration lower than that of the cell? As shown in the upper left of the figure, the cell gains water, swells, and may burst (lyse) like an overfilled balloon. The upper right shows the opposite case—an animal cell placed in a **hypertonic** solution (*hyper*, above), a solution with a higher solute concentration. In which direction will water move? The cell shrivels and can die from water loss.

For an animal to survive in a hypotonic or hypertonic environment, it must have a way to prevent excessive uptake or loss of water and regulate the solute concentration of its body fluids. The control of water balance is called **osmoregulation**. For example, a freshwater fish, which lives in a hypotonic environment, takes up water by osmosis across the cells of its gills. Its kidneys work constantly to remove excess water from the body. (We will discuss osmoregulation further in Module 25.4.)

Water balance issues are somewhat different for the cells of plants, prokaryotes, and fungi because of their cell walls. As shown in the bottom of Figure 5.5, in a hypotonic environment a plant cell is turgid (very firm), which is the healthy state for most plant cells. Although the plant cell swells as water enters by osmosis, the cell wall exerts a back pressure, called turgor pressure, which prevents the cell from taking in too much water and bursting. Plants that are not woody, such as most houseplants, depend on their turgid cells for mechanical support. In contrast, when a plant cell is surrounded by an isotonic solution, there is no net movement of water into the cell, and the cell is flaccid (limp).

In a hypertonic environment (bottom right), a plant cell is no better off than an animal cell. As a plant cell loses water, it shrivels, and its plasma membrane pulls away from the cell wall. This process, called plasmolysis, causes the plant to wilt and can be lethal to the cell and the plant. The walled cells of bacteria and fungi also plasmolyze in hypertonic environments. Thus, meats and other foods can be preserved with

Hypotonic solution (lower solute levels)

Isotonic solution (equal solute levels)

Hypertonic solution (higher solute levels)

Animal cell

H_2O
Lysed

H_2O H_2O
Normal

H_2O
Shriveled

Plant cell

H_2O
Turgid (normal)

H_2O
Flaccid

Plasma membrane H_2O
Shriveled (plasmolyzed)

▲ **Figure 5.5** How animal and plant cells react to changes in tonicity

concentrated salt solutions because the cells of food-spoiling bacteria or fungi become plasmolyzed and eventually die.

In the next module, we explore how water and other polar solutes move across cell membranes.

? Explain the function of the contractile vacuoles in a freshwater *Paramecium* (shown in Figure 4.11A) in terms of what you have just learned about water balance in cells.

● The pond water in which *Paramecium* lives is hypotonic to the cell. The contractile vacuoles expel the water that constantly enters the cell by osmosis.

5.6 Transport proteins can facilitate diffusion across membranes

Recall that nonpolar molecules, such as O_2 and CO_2, can dissolve in the lipid bilayer of a membrane and diffuse through it with ease. But how do polar or charged substances make it past the hydrophobic center of a membrane? Hydrophilic molecules and ions require the help of specific transport proteins to move across a membrane. This assisted transport, called **facilitated diffusion**, is a type of passive transport because it does not require energy. As in all passive transport, the driving force is the concentration gradient.

Figure 5.6 shows a common type of transport protein, which provides a channel that specific molecules or ions use as a passageway through a membrane. Another type of transport protein binds its passenger, changes shape, and releases the transported molecule on the other side. In both cases, the transport protein helps a specific substance diffuse across the membrane down its concentration gradient and, thus, requires no input of energy.

Substances that use facilitated diffusion for crossing cell membranes include a number of sugars, amino acids, ions— and even water. The water molecule is very small, but because it is polar (see Module 2.6), its diffusion through a membrane's hydrophobic interior is relatively slow. For many cells, this slow diffusion of water is adequate. Cells such as plant

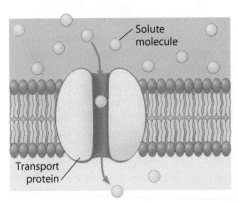

Solute molecule

Transport protein

◀ **Figure 5.6** Transport protein providing a channel for the diffusion of a specific solute across a membrane

cells, red blood cells, and the cells lining your kidney tubules, however, have greater water-permeability needs. As you saw in the chapter introduction, the very rapid diffusion of water into and out of such cells is made possible by a protein channel called an **aquaporin**. In the next module, we explore the discovery of these transport proteins.

? How do transport proteins contribute to a membrane's selective permeability?

● Because they are specific for the solutes they transport, the numbers and kinds of transport proteins affect a membrane's permeability to various solutes.

5.7 Research on another membrane protein led to the discovery of aquaporins

SCIENTIFIC THINKING

Sometimes major advances in science occur when a scientist is studying something else but makes the wise decision to explore an unexpected finding. Peter Agre received the 2003 Nobel Prize in Chemistry for this sort of discovery of aquaporins. In an interview, Dr. Agre described his research that led to this discovery:

How can water flow through a membrane?

> When I joined the faculty at the Johns Hopkins School of Medicine, I began to study the Rh blood antigens. Rh is of medical importance . . . when Rh-negative mothers have Rh-positive babies. Membrane-spanning proteins are really messy to work with. But we worked out a method to isolate the Rh protein. Our sample seemed to consist of two proteins, but we were sure that the smaller one was just a breakdown product of the larger one. We were completely wrong.

Dr. Agre's research team made antibodies that would specifically bind to and label this smaller protein. They found two interesting results: The antibody did not bind to any part of the Rh protein, indicating that the smaller protein wasn't part of the Rh protein. And the antibody did bind in huge quantities to red blood cells, showing that this new protein is one of the most abundant proteins in red cell membranes. Agre and his team also determined that the protein was identical to and even more abundant in certain kidney cells. But they didn't know what this protein did.

A colleague suggested that the protein might be the elusive water channel that physiologists had predicted would explain the rapid transport of water in some cells. To test this hypothesis, the researchers injected messenger RNA for the protein into frog eggs, whose plasma membranes are known to be quite water impermeable. Biochemical tests showed that within 72 hours, the frog egg cells had translated the mRNA into the new protein. They transferred a group of RNA-injected frog eggs and a control group of eggs injected with only a buffer solution to a hypotonic solution and monitored the eggs with videomicroscopy. The osmotic swelling of RNA-injected and control cells is plotted in **Figure 5.7**. The experimental egg cells exploded in three minutes; the control eggs showed minimal swelling, even for time periods exceeding an hour. The researchers concluded that the newly discovered protein enabled the rapid movement of water into the cells.

Since the results of that experiment were reported in 1992, much research has been done on aquaporins, determining their structure and dynamic functioning. The chapter introduction presented a model of aquaporin structure. Molecular biophysicists have produced computer simulations that show water molecules flipping their way single file through an aquaporin. Such simulations have revealed how aquaporins allow only water molecules to pass through them. Aquaporins have been found in bacteria, plants, and animals, and evolutionary biologists are tracing the relationships of these various aquaporins. Medical researchers study the function and occasional malfunction of aquaporins in the human kidney, lungs, brain, and lens of the eye. The serendipitous discovery of aquaporins has led to a broad range of scientific research.

? **Why are aquaporins important in kidney cells?**

● Kidney cells must reabsorb a large amount of water when producing urine.

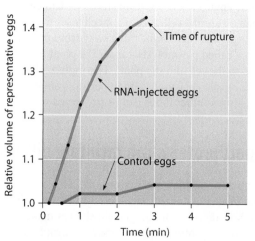

Source: Adaptation of Figure 2A from "Appearance of Water Channels in Xenopus Oocytes Expressing Red Cell CHIP28 Protein" by Gregory Preston et al., from *Science*, April 1992, Volume 256(5055). Copyright © 1992 by AAAS. Reprinted with permission.

▲ **Figure 5.7** Osmotic swelling of representative aquaporin RNA-injected and control-injected oocytes following transfer to a hypotonic medium

5.8 Cells expend energy in the active transport of a solute

In **active transport**, a cell must expend energy to move a solute *against* its concentration gradient—that is, across a membrane toward the side where the solute is more concentrated. The energy molecule ATP (described in more detail in Module 5.12) supplies the energy for most active transport.

Active transport allows a cell to maintain internal concentrations of small molecules and ions that are different from concentrations in its surroundings. For example, the inside of an animal cell has a higher concentration of potassium ions (K^+) and a lower concentration of sodium ions (Na^+) than the solution outside the cell. The generation of nerve signals depends on these concentration differences, which a transport protein called the sodium-potassium pump maintains by actively moving Na^+ out of the cell and K^+ into the cell.

① Solute binds to transport protein.

② ATP provides energy for change in protein shape.

③ Protein returns to original shape and more solute can bind.

▲ **Figure 5.8** Active transport of a solute across a membrane

Figure 5.8 shows a simple model of an active transport system that pumps a solute out of the cell against its concentration gradient. ① The process begins when solute molecules on the cytoplasmic side of the plasma membrane attach to specific binding sites on the transport protein. ② With energy provided by ATP, the transport protein changes shape in such a way that the solute is released on the other side of the membrane. ③ The transport protein returns to its original shape, ready for its next passengers.

? Cells actively transport Ca^{2+} out of the cell. Is calcium more concentrated inside or outside of the cell? Explain.

⊘ Outside: Active transport moves calcium against its concentration gradient.

5.9 Exocytosis and endocytosis transport large molecules across membranes

So far, we've focused on how water and small solutes enter and leave cells. The story is different for large molecules.

A cell uses the process of **exocytosis** (from the Greek *exo*, outside, and *kytos*, cell) to export bulky materials such as proteins or polysaccharides. A transport vesicle filled with macromolecules buds from the Golgi apparatus and moves to the plasma membrane (see Figure 4.12). Once there, the vesicle fuses with the plasma membrane, and the vesicle's contents spill out of the cell when the vesicle membrane becomes part of the plasma membrane. For example, the cells in your pancreas that manufacture the hormone insulin secrete it into the extracellular fluid by exocytosis, where it is picked up by the bloodstream.

Endocytosis (*endo*, inside) is a transport process through which a cell takes in large molecules. **Figure 5.9** shows two kinds of endocytosis. The top diagram illustrates **phagocytosis**, or "cellular eating." A cell engulfs a particle by wrapping extensions called pseudopodia around it and packaging it within a membrane-enclosed sac called a vacuole. The vacuole then fuses with a lysosome, whose hydrolytic enzymes digest the contents of the vacuole (see Figure 4.10A). Protists such as amoeba take in food particles this way, and some of your white blood cells engulf invading bacteria via phagocytosis.

The bottom diagram illustrates **receptor-mediated endocytosis**, which enables a cell to acquire specific solutes. Receptor proteins for specific molecules are embedded in regions of the membrane that are lined by a layer of coat proteins. The plasma membrane indents to form a coated pit, whose receptor proteins pick up particular molecules from the extracellular fluid. The coated pit pinches closed to form a vesicle, which then releases the molecules into the cytoplasm.

Your cells use receptor-mediated endocytosis to take in cholesterol from the blood for synthesis of membranes and as a precursor for other steroids. Cholesterol circulates in the blood in particles called low-density lipoproteins (LDLs). LDLs bind to receptor proteins and then enter cells by

Phagocytosis

Receptor-mediated endocytosis

▲ **Figure 5.9** Two kinds of endocytosis

endocytosis. In humans with the inherited disease familial hypercholesterolemia, LDL receptor proteins are defective or missing. Cholesterol accumulates to high levels in the blood, leading to atherosclerosis, the buildup of fatty deposits in the walls of blood vessels (see Module 9.11).

? As a cell grows, its plasma membrane expands. Does this involve endocytosis or exocytosis? Explain.

⊘ Exocytosis: When a transport vesicle fuses with the plasma membrane, its contents are released and the vesicle membrane adds to the plasma membrane.

▷ Energy and the Cell

5.10 Cells transform energy as they perform work

The title of this chapter is "The Working Cell." But just what type of work does a cell do? You just learned that a cell can actively transport substances across membranes. The cell also builds those membranes and the proteins embedded in them. A cell is a miniature chemical factory in which thousands of reactions occur within a microscopic space. Some of these reactions release energy; others require energy. But before you can understand how the cell works, you must have a basic knowledge of energy.

Forms of Energy   **Energy** is the capacity to cause change or to perform work. There are two basic forms of energy: kinetic energy and potential energy. **Kinetic energy** is the energy of motion. Moving objects can perform work by transferring motion to other matter. For example, the movement of your legs can push bicycle pedals, turning the wheels and moving you and your bike up a hill. **Thermal energy** is a type of kinetic energy associated with the random movement of atoms or molecules. Thermal energy in transfer from one object to another is called **heat**. Light, which is also a type of kinetic energy, can be harnessed to power photosynthesis.

Potential energy, the second main form of energy, is energy that matter possesses as a result of its location or structure. Water behind a dam and you on your bicycle at the top of a hill possess potential energy. Molecules possess potential energy because of the arrangement of electrons in the bonds between their atoms. **Chemical energy** is the potential energy available for release in a chemical reaction. Chemical energy is the most important type of energy for living organisms; it is the energy that can be transformed to power the work of the cell.

Energy Transformations   The study of energy transformations that occur in a collection of matter is called **thermodynamics**. Scientists use the word *system* for the matter under study and refer to the rest of the universe—everything outside the system—as the *surroundings*. A system can be an electric power plant, a single cell, or the entire planet. An organism is an open system; that is, it exchanges both energy and matter with its surroundings.

The **first law of thermodynamics**, also known as the law of energy conservation, states that the energy in the universe is constant. Energy can be transferred and transformed, but it cannot be created or

destroyed. A power plant does not create energy; it merely converts it from one form (such as the energy stored in coal) to the more convenient form of electricity. A plant cell converts light energy to chemical energy; the plant cell, too, is an energy transformer, not an energy producer.

If energy cannot be destroyed, then why can't organisms simply recycle their energy? It turns out that during every transfer or transformation, some energy becomes unavailable to do work—it is converted to thermal energy (random molecular motion) and released as heat. Scientists use a quantity called **entropy** as a measure of disorder, or randomness. The more randomly arranged a collection of matter is, the greater its entropy. According to the **second law of thermodynamics**, energy conversions increase the entropy (disorder) of the universe.

Figure 5.10 compares a car and a cell to show how energy can be transformed and how entropy increases as a result. Automobile engines and cells use the same basic process to make the chemical energy of their fuel available for work. The engine mixes oxygen with gasoline in an explosive chemical reaction that pushes the pistons, which eventually move the wheels. The waste products emitted from the exhaust pipe are carbon dioxide and water, energy-poor, simple molecules. Only about

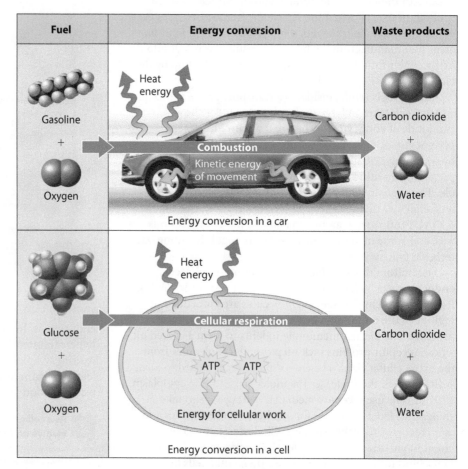

▲ **Figure 5.10**   Energy transformations in a car and a cell

25% of the energy stored in gasoline is converted to the kinetic energy of the car's movement; the rest is lost as heat.

Cells also use oxygen in reactions that release energy from fuel molecules. In the process called **cellular respiration**, the chemical energy stored in organic molecules is used to produce ATP, which the cell can use to perform work. Just like for the car, the waste products are carbon dioxide and water. Cells are more efficient than cars, however, converting about 34% of the chemical energy in their fuel to energy for cellular work. The other 66% generates heat, which explains why vigorous exercise makes you so warm.

According to the second law of thermodynamics, energy transformations result in the universe becoming more disordered. How, then, can we account for biological order?

Although the intricate structures of a cell correspond to a decrease in entropy, their production is accomplished at the expense of ordered forms of matter and energy taken in from the surroundings. As shown in Figure 5.10, cells extract the chemical energy of glucose and return disordered heat and lower-energy carbon dioxide and water to the surroundings. In a thermodynamic sense, a cell is an island of low entropy in an increasingly random universe.

> **?** How does the second law of thermodynamics explain the diffusion of a solute across a membrane?

● Diffusion across a membrane results in equal concentrations of solute, which is a more disordered arrangement (higher entropy) than a high concentration on one side and a low concentration on the other.

5.11 Chemical reactions either release or store energy

Chemical reactions are of two types: exergonic or endergonic. An **exergonic reaction** releases energy (*exergonic* means "energy outward"). As **Figure 5.11A** shows, an exergonic reaction begins with reactants whose covalent bonds contain more potential energy than those in the products. The reaction releases to the surroundings an amount of energy equal to the difference in potential energy between the reactants and the products.

Consider what happens when wood burns. One of the major components of wood is cellulose, a large energy-rich carbohydrate composed of many glucose monomers. Burning wood releases the energy of glucose as heat and light. Carbon dioxide and water are the products of the reaction.

As you learned in Module 5.10, cells release energy from fuel molecules in the process called cellular respiration. Burning and cellular respiration are alike in being exergonic. They differ in that burning is essentially a one-step process that releases all of a substance's energy at once. Cellular respiration, on the other hand, involves many steps, each a separate chemical reaction; you can think of it as a "slow burn." Some of the energy released by cellular respiration escapes as heat, but a substantial amount is stored in ATP, the immediate source of energy for a cell.

Endergonic reactions require a net input of energy and yield products that are rich in potential energy (*endergonic* means "energy inward"). As shown in **Figure 5.11B**, an endergonic reaction starts with reactants that contain relatively little potential energy. Energy is absorbed from the surroundings as the reaction occurs, so the products of an endergonic reaction contain more chemical energy than the reactants did.

Photosynthesis, the process by which plant cells make sugar, is an example of an endergonic process. Photosynthesis starts with energy-poor reactants (carbon dioxide and water molecules) and, using energy absorbed from sunlight, produces energy-rich sugar molecules.

Living cells carry out thousands of exergonic and endergonic reactions. The total of an organism's chemical reactions is called **metabolism**. We can picture a cell's metabolism as a road map of thousands of chemical reactions arranged as intersecting highways or metabolic pathways. A **metabolic pathway** is a series of chemical reactions that either builds a

▲ **Figure 5.11A**   Exergonic reaction, energy released

▲ **Figure 5.11B**   Endergonic reaction, energy required

complex molecule or breaks down a complex molecule into simpler compounds. The "slow burn" of cellular respiration is an example of a metabolic pathway in which a sequence of reactions slowly releases the potential energy stored in sugar.

All of an organism's activities require energy, which is obtained from sugar and other molecules by the exergonic reactions of cellular respiration. Cells then use that energy in endergonic reactions to make molecules and do the work of the cell. **Energy coupling**—the use of energy released from exergonic reactions to drive endergonic reactions—is crucial in all cells. ATP molecules are the key to energy coupling. In the next module, we explore the structure and function of ATP.

> **?** Cellular respiration is an exergonic process. Remembering that energy must be conserved, what do you think becomes of the energy extracted from food during this process?

● Some of it is stored in ATP molecules; the rest is released as heat.

5.12 ATP drives cellular work by coupling exergonic and endergonic reactions

ATP powers nearly all forms of cellular work. The abbreviation ATP stands for adenosine triphosphate, and as Figure 5.12A shows, ATP consists of an organic molecule called adenosine and a triphosphate tail of three phosphate groups (each symbolized by (P)). All three phosphate groups are negatively charged (see Table 3.2). These like charges are crowded together, and their mutual repulsion makes the triphosphate tail of ATP the chemical equivalent of a compressed spring.

As a result, the bonds connecting the phosphate groups are unstable and can readily be broken by hydrolysis, the addition of water. Notice in Figure 5.12A that when the bond to the third group breaks, a phosphate group leaves ATP—which becomes ADP (adenosine diphosphate)—and energy is released.

Thus, the hydrolysis of ATP is exergonic—it releases energy. How does a cell couple this reaction to an endergonic

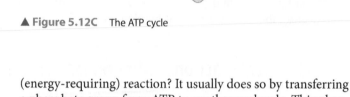

▲ **Figure 5.12C** The ATP cycle

(energy-requiring) reaction? It usually does so by transferring a phosphate group from ATP to another molecule. This phosphate transfer is called **phosphorylation**, and most cellular work depends on ATP energizing molecules by phosphorylating them.

What types of work does a cell do? As Figure 5.12B shows, the chemical, transport, and mechanical work of a cell are all driven by ATP. In chemical work, the phosphorylation of reactants provides energy to drive the endergonic synthesis of products. In transport work, ATP drives the active transport of solutes across a membrane against their concentration gradients by phosphorylating transport proteins. And in an example of mechanical work, the transfer of phosphate groups to special motor proteins in muscle cells causes the proteins to change shape and pull on other protein filaments, in turn causing the cells to contract.

ATP is a renewable resource. A cell uses and regenerates ATP continuously. Figure 5.12C shows the ATP cycle. Each side of this cycle illustrates energy coupling. Energy released in exergonic reactions, such as the breakdown of glucose during cellular respiration, is used to generate ATP from ADP. In this endergonic process, a phosphate group is bonded to ADP, forming ATP. The hydrolysis of ATP releases energy that drives endergonic reactions. The ATP cycle runs at an astonishing pace. In fact, a working muscle cell may consume and regenerate 10 million ATP molecules each second.

▲ **Figure 5.12A** The hydrolysis of ATP yielding ADP, a phosphate group, and energy.

Chemical work

Reactants   Product formed

Transport work

Transport protein   Solute transported

Mechanical work

Motor protein   Protein filament moved

▲ **Figure 5.12B** How ATP powers cellular work

Try This Examine this figure and identify the way in which all three types of cellular work are similar.

> **?** Explain how ATP transfers energy from exergonic to endergonic processes in the cell.

● Exergonic processes phosphorylate ADP to form ATP. ATP transfers energy to endergonic processes by phosphorylating other molecules.

5.13 Enzymes speed up the cell's chemical reactions by lowering energy barriers

Your room gets messier; water flows downhill; sugar crystals dissolve in your coffee. Ordered structures tend toward disorder, and high-energy systems tend to change toward a more stable state of low energy. Proteins, DNA, carbohydrates, lipids—most of the complex molecules of your cells are rich in potential energy. Why don't these high-energy, ordered molecules spontaneously break down into less ordered, lower-energy molecules? They remain intact for the same reason that wood doesn't normally burst into flames or the gas in an automobile's gas tank doesn't spontaneously explode.

There is an energy barrier that must be overcome before a chemical reaction can begin. Energy must be absorbed to contort or weaken bonds in reactant molecules so that they can break and new bonds can form. We call this the **activation energy** (because it activates the reactants). We can think of activation energy as the amount of energy needed for reactant molecules to move "uphill" to a higher-energy, unstable state so that the "downhill" part of a reaction can begin.

The activation energy barrier protects the highly ordered molecules of your cells from spontaneously breaking down. But now we have a dilemma. Life depends on countless chemical reactions that constantly change a cell's molecular makeup. Most of the essential reactions of metabolism must occur quickly and precisely for a cell to survive. How can the specific reactions that a cell requires get over that energy barrier?

One way to speed reactions is to add heat. Heat speeds up molecules and agitates atoms so that bonds break more easily and reactions can proceed. Certainly, adding a match to kindling will start a fire, and the firing of a spark plug ignites gasoline in an engine. But heating a cell would speed up all chemical reactions, not just the necessary ones, and too much heat would kill the cell.

The answer to this dilemma lies in **enzymes**—molecules that function as biological catalysts, increasing the rate of a reaction without being consumed by the reaction. Almost all enzymes are proteins. (Some RNA molecules can also function as enzymes.) An enzyme speeds up a reaction by lowering the activation energy needed for a reaction to begin. **Figure 5.13** compares a reaction without an enzyme (left) and with an enzyme (right). Notice how much easier it is for the reactant to get over the activation energy barrier when an enzyme is involved. In the next module, we explore how the structure of an enzyme enables it to lower the activation energy, allowing a reaction to proceed.

? The graph below illustrates the course of a reaction with and without an enzyme. Which curve represents the enzyme-catalyzed reaction? What energy changes are represented by the lines labeled a, b, and c?

● The lower (red) curve. Line a is the activation energy without enzyme; b is the activation energy with enzyme; c is the change in energy between reactants and products, which is the same for both the catalyzed and uncatalyzed reactions.

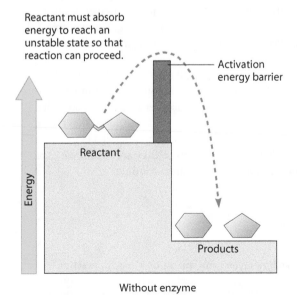

Reactant must absorb energy to reach an unstable state so that reaction can proceed.

Activation energy barrier

Reactant

Products

Energy

Without enzyme

Enzyme helps reactant overcome the activation energy barrier.

Enzyme

Activation energy barrier reduced by enzyme

Reactant

Products

Energy

With enzyme

▲ **Figure 5.13** The effect of an enzyme in lowering the activation energy

5.14 A specific enzyme catalyzes each cellular reaction

You just learned that an enzyme catalyzes a reaction by lowering the activation energy barrier. How does it do that? With the aid of an enzyme, the bonds in a reactant are contorted into the higher-energy, unstable state from which the reaction can proceed. Without an enzyme, the activation energy barrier might never be breached. For example, a solution of sucrose (table sugar) can sit for years at room temperature with no appreciable hydrolysis into its components glucose and fructose. But if we add a small amount of the enzyme sucrase, all the sucrose will be hydrolyzed within seconds.

An enzyme is very selective in the reaction it catalyzes. As a protein, an enzyme has a unique three-dimensional shape, and that shape determines the enzyme's specificity. The specific reactant that an enzyme acts on is called the enzyme's **substrate**. A substrate fits into a region of the enzyme called the **active site**—typically a pocket or groove on the surface of the enzyme. Enzymes are specific because only specific substrate molecules fit into their active sites.

The Catalytic Cycle   Figure 5.14 illustrates the catalytic cycle of an enzyme. Our example is the enzyme sucrase, which catalyzes the hydrolysis of sucrose. (Most enzymes have names that end in *-ase*, and many are named for their substrate.) ❶ The enzyme starts with an empty active site. ❷ Sucrose enters the active site, attaching by weak bonds. The active site changes shape slightly, embracing the substrate more snugly, like a firm handshake. This **induced fit** may contort substrate bonds or place chemical groups of the amino acids making up the active site in position to catalyze the reaction. (In reactions involving two or more reactants, the active site holds the substrates in the proper orientation for a reaction to occur.)

❸ The strained bond of sucrose reacts with water, and the substrate is converted (hydrolyzed) to the products glucose and fructose. ❹ The enzyme releases the products and emerges unchanged from the reaction. Its active site is now available for another substrate molecule, and another round of the cycle can begin. A single enzyme molecule may act on thousands or even millions of substrate molecules per second.

Optimal Conditions for Enzymes   As with all proteins, an enzyme's shape is central to its function, and this three-dimensional shape is affected by the environment. For every enzyme, there are optimal conditions under which it is most effective. Temperature, for instance, affects molecular motion, and an enzyme's optimal temperature produces the highest rate of contact between reactant molecules and the enzyme's active site. Higher temperatures denature the enzyme, altering its specific shape and destroying its function. Most human enzymes work best at 35–40°C (95–104°F), close to our normal body temperature of 37°C. Prokaryotes that live in hot springs, however, contain enzymes with optimal temperatures of 70°C (158°F) or higher. Scientists make use of the enzymes of these bacteria in a technique that rapidly replicates DNA sequences from small samples (see Module 12.12).

The optimal pH for most enzymes is near neutrality, in the range of 6–8. There are exceptions, of course. Pepsin, a digestive enzyme in your stomach, works best at pH 2. Such an environment would denature most enzymes, but the structure of pepsin is most stable and active in this acidic environment.

Cofactors   Many enzymes require nonprotein helpers called **cofactors**, which bind to the active site and function in catalysis. The cofactors of some enzymes are inorganic, such as the ions of zinc, iron, and copper. If the cofactor is an organic molecule, it is called a **coenzyme**. Most vitamins are important in nutrition because they function as coenzymes or raw materials from which coenzymes are made. For example, folic acid is a coenzyme for a number of enzymes involved in the synthesis of nucleic acids.

Chemical chaos would result if all of a cell's metabolic pathways were operating simultaneously. A cell must tightly control when and where its various enzymes are active. It does this either by switching on or off the genes that encode specific enzymes (as you will learn in Chapter 11) or by regulating the activity of enzymes once they are made. We explore this second mechanism in the next module.

❶ The enzyme available with an empty active site

Active site

Substrate (sucrose)

❷ The substrate enters the active site, which enfolds the substrate with an induced fit

Enzyme (sucrase)

Glucose

Fructose

H_2O

❹ The products are released

❸ The substrate is converted to products

▲ Figure 5.14   The catalytic cycle of an enzyme

? Explain how an enzyme speeds up a specific reaction.

An enzyme lowers the activation energy needed for a reaction when its specific substrate enters its active site. With an induced fit, the enzyme strains bonds that need to break or positions substrates in an orientation that aids the conversion of reactants to products.

5.15 Enzyme inhibition can regulate enzyme activity in a cell

A chemical that interferes with an enzyme's activity is called an inhibitor. Scientists have learned a great deal about enzyme function by studying the effects of such chemicals. Some inhibitors resemble the enzyme's normal substrate and compete for entry into the active site. As shown in the lower left of **Figure 5.15A**, such a **competitive inhibitor** reduces an enzyme's productivity by blocking substrate molecules from entering the active site. Competitive inhibition can be overcome by increasing the concentration of the substrate, making it more likely that a substrate molecule rather than an inhibitor will be nearby when an active site becomes vacant.

Normal binding of substrate

Enzyme inhibition

▲ **Figure 5.15A** How inhibitors interfere with substrate binding

In contrast, a **noncompetitive inhibitor** does not enter the active site. Instead, it binds to a site elsewhere on the enzyme, and its binding changes the enzyme's shape so that the active site no longer fits the substrate (lower right of Figure 5.15A).

Although enzyme inhibition sounds harmful, cells use inhibitors as important regulators of cellular metabolism. Many of a cell's chemical reactions are organized into metabolic pathways in which a molecule is altered in a series of steps, each catalyzed by a specific enzyme, to form a final product. If a cell is producing more of that product than it needs, the product may act as an inhibitor of one of the enzymes early in the pathway. **Figure 5.15B** illustrates this sort of inhibition, called **feedback inhibition**. Because only weak interactions bind inhibitor and enzyme, this inhibition is reversible. When the product is used up by the cell, the enzyme is no longer inhibited and the pathway functions again.

In the next module, we explore some uses that people make of enzyme inhibitors.

? Explain an advantage of feedback inhibition to a cell.

● It prevents the cell from wasting valuable resources by synthesizing more of a particular product than is needed.

▲ **Figure 5.15B** Feedback inhibition of a metabolic pathway in which product D acts as an inhibitor of enzyme 1

5.16 Many drugs, pesticides, and poisons are enzyme inhibitors

CONNECTION

Many beneficial drugs act as enzyme inhibitors. Ibuprofen (**Figure 5.16**) is a common drug that inhibits an enzyme involved in the production of prostaglandins—messenger molecules that increase the sensation of pain and inflammation. Other drugs that function as enzyme inhibitors include some blood pressure medicines and antidepressants. Many antibiotics work by inhibiting enzymes of disease-causing bacteria. Penicillin, for example, blocks the active site of an enzyme that many bacteria use in making cell walls. Protease inhibitors are HIV drugs that target a key viral enzyme. And many cancer drugs are inhibitors of enzymes that promote cell division.

Humans have developed enzyme inhibitors as pesticides, and occasionally as deadly poisons for use in warfare. Poisons

▲ **Figure 5.16** Ibuprofen, an enzyme inhibitor

often attach to an enzyme by covalent bonds, making the inhibition irreversible. Poisons called nerve gases bind in the active site of an enzyme vital to the transmission of nerve impulses. The inhibition of this enzyme leads to rapid paralysis of vital functions and death. Pesticides such as malathion and parathion are toxic to insects (and dangerous to the people who apply them) because they also irreversibly inhibit this enzyme. Interestingly, some drugs reversibly inhibit this same enzyme and are used in anesthesia and treatment of certain diseases.

? What determines whether enzyme inhibition is reversible or irreversible?

● If the inhibitor binds to the enzyme with covalent bonds, the inhibition is usually irreversible. When weak chemical interactions bind inhibitor and enzyme, the inhibition is reversible.

CHAPTER **5** REVIEW

For practice quizzes, BioFlix animations, MP3 tutorials, video tutors, and more study tools designed for this textbook, go to

MasteringBiology®

Reviewing the Concepts

Membrane Structure and Function (5.1–5.9)

5.1 Membranes are fluid mosaics of lipids and proteins with many functions. The proteins embedded in a membrane's phospholipid bilayer perform various functions.

5.2 The spontaneous formation of membranes was a critical step in the origin of life.

5.3 Passive transport is diffusion across a membrane with no energy investment. Solutes diffuse across membranes down their concentration gradients.

5.4 Osmosis is the diffusion of water across a membrane.

5.5 Water balance between cells and their surroundings is crucial to organisms. Cells shrink in a hypertonic solution and swell in a hypotonic solution. In isotonic solutions, animal cells are normal, but plant cells are flaccid.

5.6 Transport proteins can facilitate diffusion across membranes.

5.7 Research on another membrane protein led to the discovery of aquaporins.

5.8 Cells expend energy in the active transport of a solute.

5.9 Exocytosis and endocytosis transport large molecules across membranes. A vesicle may fuse with the membrane and expel its contents (exocytosis), or the membrane may fold inward, enclosing material from the outside (endocytosis).

Energy and the Cell (5.10–5.12)

5.10 Cells transform energy as they perform work. Kinetic energy is the energy of motion. Potential energy is energy stored in the location or structure of matter and includes chemical energy. According to the laws of thermodynamics, energy can change form but cannot be created or destroyed, and energy transfers or transformations increase disorder, or entropy, with some energy being lost as heat.

5.11 Chemical reactions either release or store energy. Exergonic reactions release energy. Endergonic reactions require energy and yield products rich in potential energy. Metabolism encompasses all of a cell's chemical reactions.

5.12 ATP drives cellular work by coupling exergonic and endergonic reactions. The transfer of a phosphate group from ATP is involved in chemical, transport, and mechanical work.

How Enzymes Function (5.13–5.16)

5.13 Enzymes speed up the cell's chemical reactions by lowering energy barriers. Enzymes are protein catalysts that decrease the activation energy needed to begin a reaction.

5.14 A specific enzyme catalyzes each cellular reaction. An enzyme's substrate fits specifically in its active site.

5.15 Enzyme inhibition can regulate enzyme activity in a cell. A competitive inhibitor competes with the substrate for the active site. A noncompetitive inhibitor alters an enzyme's function by changing its shape. Feedback inhibition helps regulate metabolism.

5.16 Many drugs, pesticides, and poisons are enzyme inhibitors.

Connecting the Concepts

1. Fill in the following concept map to review the processes by which molecules move across membranes.

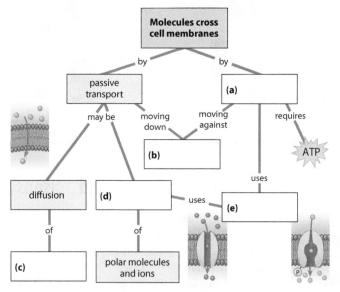

2. Label the parts of the following diagram illustrating the catalytic cycle of an enzyme.

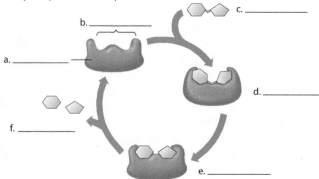

Testing Your Knowledge

Level 1: Knowledge/Comprehension

3. Which best describes the structure of a cell membrane?
   a. proteins between two bilayers of phospholipids
   b. proteins embedded in a bilayer of phospholipids
   c. a bilayer of protein coating a layer of phospholipids
   d. cholesterol embedded in a bilayer of phospholipids

4. A plant cell placed in distilled water will _____; an animal cell placed in distilled water will _____.
   a. burst . . . burst
   b. become flaccid . . . shrivel
   c. become turgid . . . be normal in shape
   d. become turgid . . . burst

5. The sodium concentration in a cell is 10 times less than the concentration in the surrounding fluid. How can the cell move sodium out of the cell? (*Explain your answer.*)
   a. passive transport
   b. receptor-mediated endocytosis
   c. active transport
   d. facilitated diffusion

6. The synthesis of ATP from ADP and (P)
   a. stores energy in a form that can drive cellular work.
   b. involves the hydrolysis of a phosphate bond.
   c. transfers a phosphate, priming a protein to do work.
   d. is an exergonic process.

7. Facilitated diffusion across a membrane requires _____ and moves a solute _____ its concentration gradient.
   a. transport proteins . . . up (against)
   b. transport proteins . . . down
   c. energy and transport proteins . . . up
   d. energy and transport proteins . . . down

8. What are the main types of cellular work? How does ATP provide the energy for this work?

Level 2: Application/Analysis

9. Why is the barrier of the activation energy beneficial for cells? Explain how enzymes lower activation energy.
10. Relate the laws of thermodynamics to living organisms.
11. How do the components and structure of cell membranes relate to the functions of membranes?
12. Sometimes inhibitors can be harmful to a cell; often they are beneficial. Explain.

Level 3: Synthesis/Evaluation

13. Cells lining kidney tubules function in the reabsorption of water from urine. In response to chemical signals, they reversibly insert additional aquaporins into their plasma membranes. In which of these situations would your tubule cells have the most aquaporins: after a long run on a hot day, right after a large meal, or after drinking a large bottle of water? Explain.

14. **SCIENTIFIC THINKING** Mercury is known to inhibit the permeability of water channels. To help establish that the protein isolated by Agre's group was a water channel (see Module 5.7), the researchers incubated groups of RNA-injected oocytes (which then made aquaporin proteins) in four different solutions: plain buffer, low concentration and high concentration of a mercury chloride ($HgCl_2$) solution, and a low concentration of a mercury solution followed by an agent (ME)

known to reverse the effects of mercury. The water permeability of the cells was determined by the rate of their osmotic swelling. Interpret the results of this experiment, which are presented in the graph below.

Data from G. M. Preston et al., Appearance of water channels in *Xenopus* oocytes expressing red cell CHIP28 protein, *Science* 256: 3385–7 (1992).

Control oocytes not injected with aquaporin RNA were also incubated with buffer and the two concentrations of mercury. Predict what the results of these treatments would be.

15. A biologist performed two series of experiments on lactase, the enzyme that hydrolyzes lactose to glucose and galactose. First, she made up 10% lactose solutions containing different concentrations of enzyme and measured the rate at which galactose was produced (grams of galactose per minute). Results of these experiments are shown in Table A below. In the second series of experiments (Table B), she prepared 2% enzyme solutions containing different concentrations of lactose and again measured the rate of galactose production.

Table A Rate and Enzyme Concentration					
Lactose concentration	10%	10%	10%	10%	10%
Enzyme concentration	0%	1%	2%	4%	8%
Reaction rate	0	25	50	100	200

Table B Rate and Substrate Concentration					
Lactose concentration	0%	5%	10%	20%	30%
Enzyme concentration	2%	2%	2%	2%	2%
Reaction rate	0	25	50	65	65

   a. Graph and explain the relationship between the reaction rate and the enzyme concentration.
   b. Graph and explain the relationship between the reaction rate and the substrate concentration. How and why did the results of the two experiments differ?

16. Organophosphates (organic compounds containing phosphate groups) are commonly used as insecticides to improve crop yield. Organophosphates typically interfere with nerve signal transmission by inhibiting the enzymes that degrade transmitter molecules. They affect humans and other vertebrates as well as insects. Thus, the use of organophosphate pesticides poses some health risks. On the other hand, these molecules break down rapidly upon exposure to air and sunlight. As a consumer, what level of risk are you willing to accept in exchange for an abundant and affordable food supply?

Answers to all questions can be found in Appendix 4.

6

How Cells Harvest Chemical Energy

A baby's first cry! This welcome sound shows that the baby is breathing and taking in oxygen. But why is oxygen necessary for life? Oxygen is a reactant in cellular respiration—the process that breaks down sugar and other food molecules and generates ATP, the energy currency of cells.

Cellular respiration occurred in this baby's cells before she was born, but the oxygen and sugar her cells required were delivered from her mother's blood. Now this baby takes in her own oxygen—although she still can't obtain her own food. The process of cellular respiration produces heat as well as ATP, which helps maintain a warm body temperature. But if this baby is exposed to the cold, she can't keep herself warm. If you get cold, you put on more clothes, move to a warmer place, or shiver—generating heat as your contracting muscles increase their production of ATP and heat. This baby can't do any of those things yet. Instead, along her back she has a layer of a special kind of "baby fat," called brown fat, that helps keep her warm. The cells of brown fat have a "short circuit" in their cellular respiration—they consume oxygen and burn fuel, but generate only heat, not ATP.

? *Can brown fat keep a newborn warm* and *help keep an adult thin?*

Scientists have long known that brown fat is important for heat production in small mammals, hibernating bears, and newborn infants. Studies have also shown brown fat to be involved in weight regulation in mice. As you will learn later in the chapter, brown fat deposits have only recently been discovered in adult humans. Scientists are now exploring whether this heat-generating, calorie-burning tissue may be tapped in the fight against obesity.

We begin this chapter with an overview of cellular respiration and then focus on its stages: glycolysis, the citric acid cycle, and oxidative phosphorylation. We also consider fermentation, an extension of glycolysis that has deep evolutionary roots. We complete the chapter with a comparison of the metabolic pathways that break down and build up the organic molecules of your body.

BIG IDEAS

Cellular Respiration: Aerobic Harvesting of Energy
(6.1–6.5)

Cellular respiration oxidizes fuel molecules and generates ATP for cellular work.

Stages of Cellular Respiration
(6.6–6.12)

The main stages of cellular respiration are glycolysis, the citric acid cycle, and oxidative phosphorylation.

Fermentation: Anaerobic Harvesting of Energy
(6.13–6.14)

Fermentation regenerates NAD^+, allowing glycolysis and ATP production to continue without oxygen.

Connections Between Metabolic Pathways
(6.15–6.16)

The breakdown pathways of cellular respiration intersect with biosynthetic pathways.

▷ Cellular Respiration: Aerobic Harvesting of Energy

6.1 Photosynthesis and cellular respiration provide energy for life

Life requires energy. In almost all ecosystems, that energy ultimately comes from the sun. (Photosynthesis, the process by which the sun's energy is captured, will be explored later, in Chapter 7.) **Figure 6.1** illustrates how photosynthesis and cellular respiration together provide energy for living organisms. In photosynthesis, which takes place in a plant cell's chloroplasts, the energy of sunlight is used to rearrange the atoms of carbon dioxide (CO_2) and water (H_2O) to produce sugar and oxygen (O_2). In **cellular respiration**, O_2 is consumed as sugar is broken down to CO_2 and H_2O; the cell captures the energy released in ATP. Cellular respiration takes place in the mitochondria of almost all eukaryotic cells—in the cells of plants, animals, fungi, and protists. (Although prokaryotes don't have mitochondria, some do break down sugar in a similar type of oxygen-using respiration.)

This figure also shows that in these energy conversions, some energy is lost as heat. Life on Earth is solar powered, and energy makes a one-way trip through an ecosystem. Chemicals, however, are recycled. The CO_2 and H_2O released by cellular respiration are converted through photosynthesis to sugar and O_2, which are then used in respiration.

> **?** What is misleading about the following statement? "Plant cells perform photosynthesis, and animal cells perform cellular respiration."

● The statement implies that cellular respiration does not occur in plant cells. In fact, almost all eukaryotic cells use cellular respiration to obtain energy for their cellular work.

▲ **Figure 6.1** The connection between photosynthesis and cellular respiration

6.2 Breathing supplies O_2 for use in cellular respiration and removes CO_2

We often use the word *respiration* as a synonym for "breathing," the meaning of its Latin root. In that case, respiration refers to an exchange of gases: An organism obtains O_2 from its environment and releases CO_2 as a waste product. Biologists also define respiration as the aerobic (oxygen-requiring) harvesting of energy from food molecules by cells. This process is called cellular respiration to distinguish it from breathing.

Breathing and cellular respiration are closely related. As the runner in **Figure 6.2** breathes in air, her lungs take up O_2 and pass it to her bloodstream. The bloodstream carries the O_2 to her muscle cells. Mitochondria in the muscle cells use the O_2 in cellular respiration to harvest energy from glucose and other organic molecules and generate ATP. Muscle cells use ATP to fuel contractions. The runner's bloodstream and lungs also perform the vital function of disposing of the CO_2 waste, which is produced in cellular respiration. You can see the roles of O_2 and CO_2 in the equation for cellular respiration at the bottom of the figure.

> **?** How is your breathing related to your cellular respiration?

● In breathing, CO_2 and O_2 are exchanged between your lungs and the air. In cellular respiration, cells use the O_2 obtained through breathing to break down fuel, releasing CO_2 as a waste product.

▲ **Figure 6.2** The connection between breathing and cellular respiration

6.3 Cellular respiration banks energy in ATP molecules

You breathe air and eat food to supply your cells with the reactants for cellular respiration—the process that generates ATP for cellular work.

$$C_6H_{12}O_6 + 6\ O_2 \longrightarrow 6\ CO_2 + 6\ H_2O + ATP + Heat$$

Glucose   Oxygen   Carbon   Water
                                  dioxide

▲ **Figure 6.3**   Summary equation for cellular respiration

The chemical equation in **Figure 6.3** summarizes cellular respiration. The simple sugar glucose ($C_6H_{12}O_6$) is the fuel that cells use most often, although other organic molecules can also be "burned" in cellular respiration. The equation tells us that the atoms of the reactant molecules $C_6H_{12}O_6$ and O_2 are rearranged to form the products CO_2 and H_2O. In this exergonic (energy-releasing) process, the chemical energy of the bonds in glucose is released and stored (or "banked") in the chemical bonds of ATP (see Module 5.12). The series of arrows in Figure 6.3 indicates that cellular respiration consists of many steps, not just a single reaction.

Cellular respiration can produce up to 32 ATP molecules for each glucose molecule, a capture of about 34% of the energy originally stored in glucose. The rest of the energy is released as heat (see Module 5.10). This may seem inefficient, but it compares very well with the efficiency of most energy-conversion systems. For instance, the average automobile engine is able to convert only about 25% of the energy in gasoline to the kinetic energy of movement. And, as you learned in the chapter introduction, heat released in cellular respiration helps maintain your warm body temperature.

How great are the energy needs of a cell? If ATP could not be regenerated through cellular respiration, you would use up nearly your body weight in ATP each day. Let's consider the energy requirements for various human activities next.

? **Why are sweating and other body-cooling mechanisms necessary during vigorous exercise?**

● The demand for ATP is supported by an increased rate of cellular respiration, but about 66% of the energy released from food produces heat instead of ATP.

6.4 The human body uses energy from ATP for all its activities

CONNECTION

Your body requires a continuous supply of energy just to stay alive—to keep your heart pumping and to keep you breathing. Your brain especially requires a huge amount of energy; its cells burn about 120 grams (g)—a quarter of a pound!—of glucose a day, accounting for about 15% of total oxygen consumption. Maintaining brain cells and other life-sustaining activities uses as much as 75% of the energy a person takes in as food during a typical day.

Above and beyond the energy you need for body maintenance, cellular respiration provides energy for voluntary activities. **Figure 6.4** shows the amount of energy it takes to perform some of these activities. The energy units are **kilocalories (kcal)**, a measure of the quantity of heat required to raise the temperature of 1 kilogram (kg) of water by 1°C. (The "Calories" listed on food packages are actually kilocalories, usually signified by a capital C.) The values shown do not include the energy the body consumes for its basic life-sustaining activities. Even sleeping or lying quietly requires energy for metabolism.

The U.S. National Academy of Sciences estimates that the average adult needs to take in food that provides about 2,200 kcal of energy per day, although the number varies based on age, sex, and activity level. A balance of energy intake and expenditure is required to maintain a healthy weight. (We will explore nutritional needs further in Chapter 21.) Now we begin the study of how cells liberate the energy stored in fuel molecules to produce the ATP used to power the work of your cells and thus the activities of your body.

Activity	kcal consumed per hour by a 67.5-kg (150-lb) person*
Running (8–9 mph)	979
Dancing (fast)	510
Bicycling (10 mph)	490
Swimming (2 mph)	408
Walking (4 mph)	341
Walking (3 mph)	245
Dancing (slow)	204
Driving a car	61
Sitting (writing)	28

*Not including kcal needed for body maintenance

▲ **Figure 6.4**   Energy consumed by various activities

? **Walking at 3 mph, how far would you have to travel to "burn off" the equivalent of an extra slice of pizza, which has about 475 kcal? How long would that take?**

● You would have to walk about 6 miles, which would take you about 2 hours. (Now you understand why the most effective exercise for losing weight is pushing away from the table!)

6.5 Cells capture energy from electrons "falling" from organic fuels to oxygen

How do your cells extract energy from glucose? The answer involves the transfer of electrons during chemical reactions.

Redox Reactions   During cellular respiration, electrons are transferred from glucose to oxygen, releasing energy. Oxygen attracts electrons very strongly, and an electron loses potential energy when it is transferred to oxygen. If you burn a cube of sugar, this electron "fall" happens very rapidly, releasing energy in the form of heat and light. Cellular respiration is a more controlled descent of electrons—more like rolling down an energy hill, with energy released in small amounts that can be stored in the chemical bonds of ATP.

The movement of electrons from one molecule to another is an oxidation-reduction reaction, or **redox reaction** for short. In a redox reaction, the loss of electrons from one substance is called **oxidation**, and the addition of electrons to another substance is called **reduction**. A molecule is said to become oxidized when it loses one or more electrons and reduced when it gains one or more electrons. Because an electron transfer requires both a donor and an acceptor, oxidation and reduction always go together.

In the cellular respiration equation in **Figure 6.5A** below, you cannot see any electron transfers. What you do see are changes in the location of hydrogen atoms. These hydrogen movements represent electron transfers because each hydrogen atom consists of an electron (e^-) and a proton (hydrogen ion, or H^+). Glucose ($C_6H_{12}O_6$) loses hydrogen atoms (electrons) as it becomes oxidized to CO_2; simultaneously, O_2 gains hydrogen atoms (electrons) as it becomes reduced to H_2O. As they pass from glucose to oxygen, the electrons lose energy, some of which cells capture.

NADH and Electron Transport Chains   An important player in the process of oxidizing glucose is a coenzyme called **NAD$^+$**, which accepts electrons and becomes reduced to NADH. NAD$^+$ (nicotinamide adenine dinucleotide) is an organic molecule that cells make from the vitamin niacin and use to shuttle electrons in redox reactions. The top equation in **Figure 6.5B** depicts the oxidation of an organic molecule. We show only its three carbons (●) and a few of its other atoms. An enzyme called dehydrogenase strips two hydrogen atoms from this molecule. Simultaneously, as shown in the lower equation, NAD$^+$ picks up the two electrons (●) and becomes reduced to NADH. One hydrogen ion (H$^+$) also becomes part of the NADH, and the other is released. (NADH

▲ **Figure 6.5B**   A pair of redox reactions occurring simultaneously

Try This   Circle the two atoms that will be removed from the molecule on the left as it becomes oxidized to the molecule on the right. Explain why we say that a hydrogen atom consists of a hydrogen ion (H$^+$) and an electron.

is represented throughout this chapter as a light brown box carrying two blue electrons.)

Using the energy hill analogy for electrons rolling from glucose to oxygen, the transfer of electrons from an organic molecule to NAD$^+$ is just the beginning. **Figure 6.5C** shows NADH delivering these electrons to a string of electron carrier molecules, shown here as purple ovals, that lead down the hill. At the bottom of the hill is oxygen ($\frac{1}{2} O_2$), which accepts two electrons, picks up two H$^+$, and becomes reduced to water.

These carrier molecules form an **electron transport chain**. In a cell, they are built into the inner membrane of a mitochondrion. Through a series of redox reactions, electrons are passed from carrier to carrier, releasing energy in amounts small enough to be used by the cell to make ATP.

With an understanding of this basic mechanism of electron transfer and energy release, we can now explore cellular respiration in more detail.

> **?**   **What chemical characteristic of the element oxygen accounts for its function in cellular respiration?**
>
> ● Oxygen is extremely electronegative (see Module 2.6), making it very powerful in pulling electrons down the electron transport chain.

▲ **Figure 6.5A**   Rearrangement of hydrogen atoms (with their electrons) in the redox reactions of cellular respiration

▲ **Figure 6.5C**   Electrons releasing energy for ATP synthesis as they roll down an energy hill from NADH through an electron transport chain to O_2

⊳ Stages of Cellular Respiration

6.6 Overview: Cellular respiration occurs in three main stages

Cellular respiration consists of a sequence of many chemical reactions that we can divide into three main stages. **Figure 6.6** gives an overview of these stages and shows where they occur in a eukaryotic cell. (In prokaryotic cells that use aerobic respiration, these steps occur in the cytosol, and the electron transport chain is built into the plasma membrane.)

Stage 1: Glycolysis (shown with a teal background throughout this chapter) occurs in the cytosol of the cell. Glycolysis begins cellular respiration by breaking glucose into two molecules of a three-carbon compound called pyruvate.

Stage 2: Pyruvate oxidation and the **citric acid cycle** (shown in shades of orange) take place within the mitochondria. Pyruvate is oxidized to a two-carbon compound. The citric acid cycle then completes the breakdown of glucose to carbon dioxide. Thus, the CO_2 that you exhale is formed in the mitochondria of your cells during this second stage of respiration.

As suggested by the smaller ATP symbols in the diagram, the cell makes a small amount of ATP during glycolysis and the citric acid cycle. The main function of these first two stages, however, is to supply the third stage of respiration with electrons (shown with gold arrows).

Stage 3: Oxidative phosphorylation (purple background) involves electron transport and a process known as chemiosmosis. NADH and a related electron carrier, $FADH_2$ (flavin adenine dinucleotide), shuttle electrons to an electron transport chain embedded in the inner mitochondrial membrane. Most of the

ATP produced by cellular respiration is generated by oxidative phosphorylation, which uses the energy released by the downhill fall of electrons from NADH and $FADH_2$ to oxygen to phosphorylate ADP. (Recall from Module 5.12 that cells generate ATP by adding a phosphate group to ADP.)

What couples the electron transport chain to ATP synthesis? As the electron transport chain passes electrons down the energy hill, it also pumps hydrogen ions (H^+) across the inner mitochondrial membrane into the narrow intermembrane space. The result is a concentration gradient of H^+ across the membrane. In **chemiosmosis**, the potential energy of this concentration gradient is used to make ATP. The details of this process are explored in Module 6.10.

The small amount of ATP produced in glycolysis and the citric acid cycle is made by substrate-level phosphorylation, a process we discuss in the next module. In the next several modules, we look more closely at the stages of cellular respiration and the mechanisms of ATP synthesis.

? **Of the three main stages of cellular respiration, which is the only one that uses oxygen?**

● Oxidative phosphorylation, in which the electron transport chain ultimately transfers electrons to oxygen

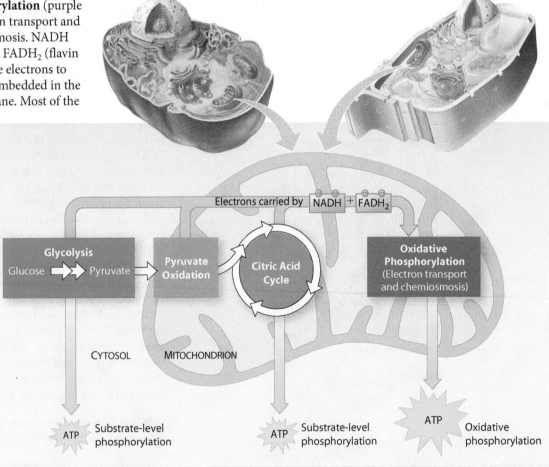

▶ **Figure 6.6** An overview of cellular respiration

6.7 Glycolysis harvests chemical energy by oxidizing glucose to pyruvate

Now that you have been introduced to the major players and processes, it's time to focus on the individual stages of cellular respiration. The term for the first stage, *glycolysis*, means "splitting of sugar" (*glyco*, sweet, and *lysis*, split), and that's exactly what happens during this phase.

Figure 6.7A below gives an overview of glycolysis, which begins with a single molecule of glucose and concludes with two molecules of pyruvate. (Pyruvate is the ionized form of pyruvic acid.) Each ● represents a carbon atom in the molecules; glucose has six carbons, and these same six carbons end up in the two molecules of pyruvate (three carbons in each). The straight arrow shown running from glucose to pyruvate actually represents nine chemical steps, each catalyzed by its own enzyme. As these reactions occur, two molecules of NAD⁺ are reduced to two molecules of NADH, and a net gain of two molecules of ATP is produced.

Figure 6.7B illustrates how ATP is formed in glycolysis by the process called **substrate-level phosphorylation**. In this process, an enzyme transfers a phosphate group (Ⓟ) from a substrate molecule directly to ADP, forming ATP. You will come across substrate-level phosphorylation again in our discussion of the citric acid cycle, in which a small amount of ATP is generated by this process.

The oxidation of glucose to pyruvate during glycolysis releases energy, which is stored in ATP and in NADH. The cell can use the energy in ATP immediately, but for it to use the energy in NADH, electrons from NADH must pass down an electron transport chain located in the inner mitochondrial membrane. And the pyruvate molecules still hold most of the energy of glucose; these molecules will be oxidized in the citric acid cycle.

Let's take a closer look at glycolysis. **Figure 6.7C**, on the next page, names and shows simplified structures for all the

▲ **Figure 6.7B**   Substrate-level phosphorylation: transfer of a phosphate group from a substrate to ADP, producing ATP

organic compounds that form in the nine chemical reactions of glycolysis. Commentary on the left highlights the main features of these reactions.

Compounds that form between the initial reactant, glucose, and the final product, pyruvate, are known as **intermediates**. Glycolysis is an example of a metabolic pathway in which each chemical step feeds into the next one. For instance, the intermediate glucose 6-phosphate is the product of step 1 and the reactant for step 2. Similarly, fructose 6-phosphate is the product of step 2 and the reactant for step 3. Also essential are the specific enzymes that catalyze each chemical step; however, the figure does not include the enzymes.

As indicated in Figure 6.7C, the steps of glycolysis can be grouped into two main phases. Steps ❶–❹, the energy investment phase, actually *consume* energy. In this phase, two molecules of ATP are used to energize a glucose molecule, which is then split into two small sugars. The figure follows each of these three-carbon sugars through the second phase.

Steps ❺–❾, the energy payoff phase, *yield* energy for the cell. In this phase, two NADH molecules are produced for each initial glucose molecule, and four ATP molecules are generated. Remember that the first phase used two molecules of ATP, so the net gain to the cell is two ATP molecules for each glucose molecule that enters glycolysis.

These two ATP molecules from glycolysis account for only about 6% of the energy that a cell can harvest from a glucose molecule. The two NADH molecules generated during step 5 represent about another 16%, but their stored energy is not available for use without oxygen. Some organisms—yeasts and certain bacteria, for instance—can satisfy their energy needs with the ATP produced by glycolysis alone. And some cells, such as your muscle cells, may use this anaerobic production of ATP for short periods when they do not have sufficient O_2. Most cells and organisms, however, have far greater energy demands. The stages of cellular respiration that follow glycolysis release much more energy. In the next modules, we see what happens in most organisms after glucose is oxidized to pyruvate in glycolysis.

?   **For each glucose molecule processed, what are the net molecular products of glycolysis?**

● Two molecules of pyruvate, two molecules of ATP, and two molecules of NADH

▶ **Figure 6.7A**
An overview
of glycolysis

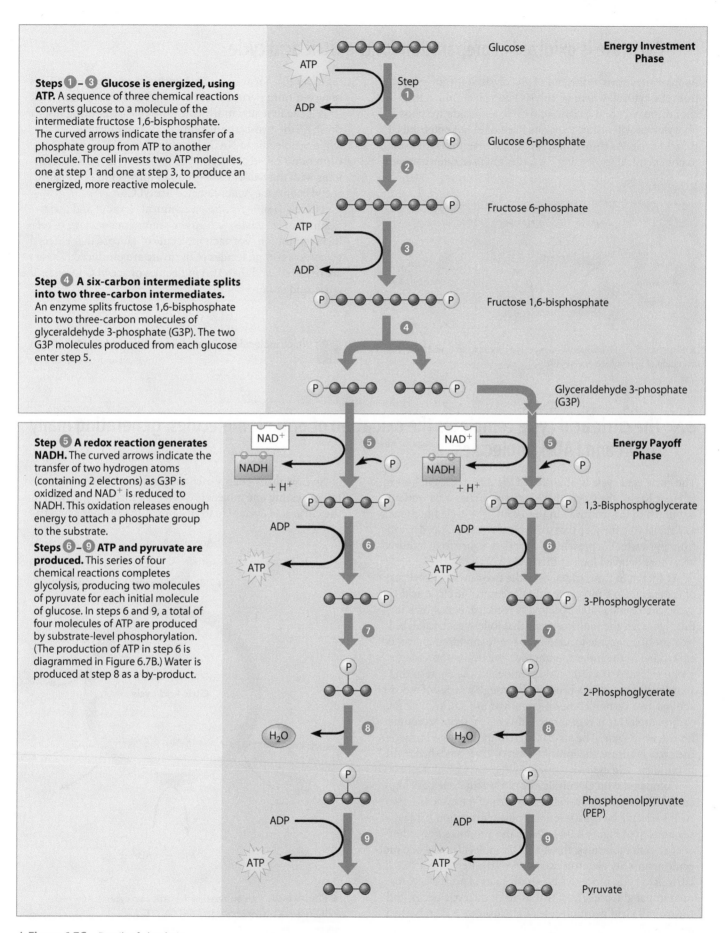

Steps ① – ③ Glucose is energized, using ATP. A sequence of three chemical reactions converts glucose to a molecule of the intermediate fructose 1,6-bisphosphate. The curved arrows indicate the transfer of a phosphate group from ATP to another molecule. The cell invests two ATP molecules, one at step 1 and one at step 3, to produce an energized, more reactive molecule.

Step ④ A six-carbon intermediate splits into two three-carbon intermediates. An enzyme splits fructose 1,6-bisphosphate into two three-carbon molecules of glyceraldehyde 3-phosphate (G3P). The two G3P molecules produced from each glucose enter step 5.

Step ⑤ A redox reaction generates NADH. The curved arrows indicate the transfer of two hydrogen atoms (containing 2 electrons) as G3P is oxidized and NAD⁺ is reduced to NADH. This oxidation releases enough energy to attach a phosphate group to the substrate.

Steps ⑥ – ⑨ ATP and pyruvate are produced. This series of four chemical reactions completes glycolysis, producing two molecules of pyruvate for each initial molecule of glucose. In steps 6 and 9, a total of four molecules of ATP are produced by substrate-level phosphorylation. (The production of ATP in step 6 is diagrammed in Figure 6.7B.) Water is produced at step 8 as a by-product.

Energy Investment Phase

Glucose

Step ①

ATP → ADP

Glucose 6-phosphate

②

Fructose 6-phosphate

ATP → ADP ③

Fructose 1,6-bisphosphate

④

Glyceraldehyde 3-phosphate (G3P)

Energy Payoff Phase

NAD⁺ → NADH + H⁺ ⑤

1,3-Bisphosphoglycerate

ADP → ATP ⑥

3-Phosphoglycerate

⑦

2-Phosphoglycerate

H₂O ⑧

Phosphoenolpyruvate (PEP)

ADP → ATP ⑨

Pyruvate

▲ **Figure 6.7C**   Details of glycolysis

6.8 Pyruvate is oxidized in preparation for the citric acid cycle

As pyruvate forms at the end of glycolysis, it is transported from the cytosol, where glycolysis takes place, into a mitochondrion, where the citric acid cycle and oxidative phosphorylation will occur. Pyruvate itself does not enter the citric acid cycle. As shown in **Figure 6.8**, it first undergoes some major chemical "grooming." A large, multi-enzyme complex

catalyzes three reactions: ❶ A carboxyl group (—COO⁻) is removed from pyruvate and given off as a molecule of CO_2 (this is the first step in which CO_2 is released during respiration); ❷ the two-carbon compound remaining is oxidized while a molecule of NAD^+ is reduced to NADH; and ❸ a compound called coenzyme A, derived from a B vitamin, joins with the two-carbon group to form a molecule called acetyl coenzyme A, abbreviated **acetyl CoA**.

These grooming steps—a chemical "haircut and conditioning" of pyruvate—set up the second major stage of cellular respiration. For each molecule of glucose that enters glycolysis, two molecules of pyruvate are produced. These are oxidized, and then two molecules of acetyl CoA enter the citric acid cycle.

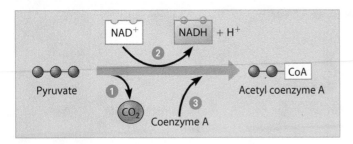

▲ **Figure 6.8** The link between glycolysis and the citric acid cycle: the oxidation of pyruvate to acetyl CoA

? **Which molecule in Figure 6.8 has been reduced?**

● NAD⁺ has been reduced to NADH.

6.9 The citric acid cycle completes the oxidation of organic molecules, generating many NADH and FADH₂ molecules

The citric acid cycle is often called the Krebs cycle in honor of Hans Krebs, the German-British researcher who worked out much of this pathway in the 1930s. The cycle functions as a metabolic furnace that oxidizes the acetyl CoA derived from pyruvate. We present an overview figure first, followed by a more detailed look at this cycle.

As shown in **Figure 6.9A**, only the two-carbon acetyl part of the acetyl CoA molecule actually enters the citric acid cycle; coenzyme A splits off and is recycled. Not shown in this figure are the multiple steps that follow, each catalyzed by a specific enzyme located in the mitochondrial matrix or embedded in the inner membrane. The two-carbon acetyl group is joined to a four-carbon molecule. As the resulting six-carbon molecule is processed through a series of redox reactions, two carbon atoms are removed as CO_2, and the four-carbon molecule is regenerated; this regeneration accounts for the word *cycle*. The six-carbon compound first formed in the cycle is citrate, the ionized form of citric acid; hence the name *citric acid cycle*.

Compared with glycolysis, the citric acid cycle pays big energy dividends to the cell. Each turn of the cycle makes one ATP molecule by substrate-level phosphorylation (shown at the bottom of Figure 6.9A). But it also produces four other energy-rich molecules: three NADH molecules and one molecule of another electron carrier, FADH₂. Remember that the citric acid cycle processes two molecules of acetyl CoA for each initial glucose. Thus, two turns of the cycle occur, and the overall yield per molecule of glucose is 2 ATP, 6 NADH, and 2 FADH₂.

So how many energy-rich molecules have been produced by processing one molecule of glucose through glycolysis and the citric acid cycle? Up to this point, the cell has gained a

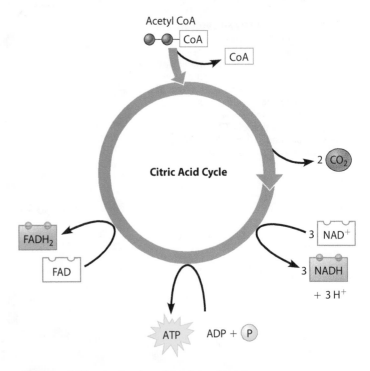

▲ **Figure 6.9A** An overview of the citric acid cycle

Try This Remember that 2 acetyl CoA are produced from each glucose. Use this figure to determine the per-glucose return from the citric acid cycle.

total of 4 ATP (all from substrate-level phosphorylation), 10 NADH, and 2 FADH$_2$. For the cell to be able to harvest the energy banked in NADH and FADH$_2$, these molecules must shuttle their high-energy electrons to an electron transport chain. There the energy from the *oxidation* of organic molecules is used to *phosphorylate* ADP to ATP—hence the name *oxidative phosphorylation*. Before we look at how oxidative phosphorylation works, you may want to examine the inner workings of the citric acid cycle in **Figure 6.9B**, below.

? What is the total number of NADH and FADH$_2$ molecules generated during the complete breakdown of one glucose molecule to six molecules of CO$_2$? (Hint: Combine the outputs discussed in Modules 6.7–6.9.)

● 10 NADH: 2 from glycolysis; 2 from the oxidation of pyruvate; 6 from the citric acid cycle; and 2 FADH$_2$ from the citric acid cycle. (Did you remember to double the output after to the sugar-splitting step of glycolysis?)

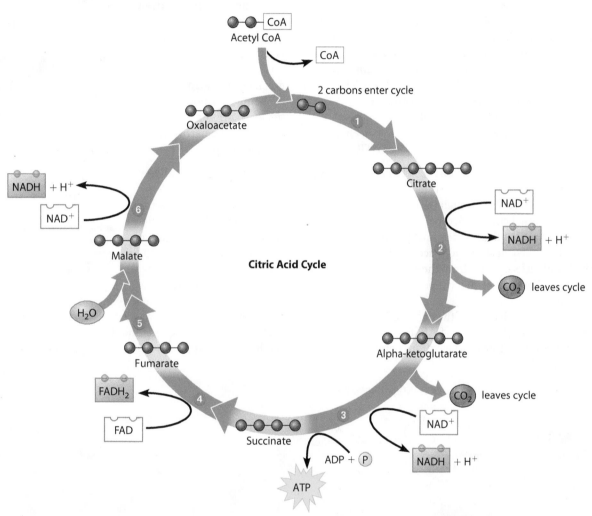

Step ①
Acetyl CoA stokes the furnace.

A turn of the citric acid cycle begins (top center) as enzymes strip the CoA portion from acetyl CoA and combine the remaining two-carbon group with the four-carbon molecule oxaloacetate (top left) already present in the mitochondrion. The product of this reaction is the six-carbon molecule citrate. All the acid compounds in this cycle exist in the cell in their ionized form, hence the suffix *-ate*.

Steps ② – ③
NADH, ATP, and CO$_2$ are generated during redox reactions.

Successive redox reactions harvest energy by stripping hydrogen atoms from citrate and then alpha-ketoglutarate and producing energy-laden NADH molecules. In two places, an intermediate compound loses a CO$_2$ molecule. Energy is harvested by substrate-level phosphorylation of ADP to produce ATP. A four-carbon compound called succinate emerges at the end of step 3.

Steps ④ – ⑥
Further redox reactions generate FADH$_2$ and more NADH.

Succinate is oxidized as the electron carrier FAD is reduced to FADH$_2$. Fumarate is converted to malate, which is then oxidized as one last NAD$^+$ is reduced to NADH. One turn of the citric acid cycle is completed with the regeneration of oxaloacetate, which is then ready to start the next cycle by accepting an acetyl group from acetyl CoA.

▲ **Figure 6.9B** A closer look at the citric acid cycle. (Remember that the cycle runs two times for each glucose molecule oxidized.)

6.10 Most ATP production occurs by oxidative phosphorylation

Your main objective in this chapter is to learn how cells harvest the energy of glucose to make ATP. But so far, you've seen the production of only 4 ATP per glucose molecule. Now it's time for the big energy payoff. The final stage of cellular respiration is oxidative phosphorylation, which uses the electron transport chain and chemiosmosis—a process introduced in Module 6.6. Oxidative phosphorylation clearly illustrates the concept of structure fitting function: The arrangement of electron carriers built into a membrane makes it possible to create an H^+ concentration gradient across the membrane and then use the energy of that gradient to drive ATP synthesis.

Figure 6.10A shows how an electron transport chain is arranged in the inner membrane of the mitochondrion. The folds (cristae) of this membrane enlarge its surface area, providing space for thousands of copies of the chain. Also embedded in the membrane are multiple copies of an enzyme complex called **ATP synthase**, which synthesizes ATP.

Electron Transport Chain   Starting on the left in Figure 6.10A, the gold arrow traces the transport of electrons from the shuttle molecules NADH and $FADH_2$ through the electron transport chain to oxygen, the final electron acceptor. It is in this end stage of cellular respiration that oxygen finally steps in to play its critical role. Each oxygen atom ($\frac{1}{2}O_2$) accepts 2 electrons from the chain and picks up 2 H^+ from the surrounding solution, forming H_2O. You can see that happening in the center right of the figure.

Most of the carrier molecules of the chain reside in four main protein complexes (labeled I to IV in the diagram), while two mobile carriers transport electrons between the complexes. All of the carriers bind and release electrons in redox reactions, passing electrons down the "energy hill." Three of the protein complexes use the energy released from these electron transfers to actively transport H^+ across the membrane, from where H^+ is less concentrated to where it is more concentrated. The green vertical arrows show H^+ being transported from the matrix of the mitochondrion into the narrow intermembrane space.

Chemiosmosis   Recall that chemiosmosis is a process that uses the energy stored in a hydrogen ion gradient across a membrane to drive ATP synthesis. **Figure 6.10B** shows the role of ATP synthase in chemiosmosis. The H^+ concentration gradient across the membrane stores potential energy, much the way a dam stores energy by holding back the elevated water behind it. The energy stored by a dam can be harnessed to do work (such as generating electricity)

▲ **Figure 6.10B**   ATP synthase—a molecular rotary motor

Try This   Identify the power source that runs this motor. Explain where this "power" comes from.

▲ **Figure 6.10A**   Oxidative phosphorylation: electron transport and chemiosmosis in a mitochondrion when the water is allowed to rush downhill, turning giant wheels called turbines. The ATP synthases built into the inner mitochondrial membrane act like miniature turbines, with the rush of H^+ ions down their concentration gradient turning the wheels. Indeed, ATP synthase is considered the smallest molecular rotary motor known in nature.

As Figure 6.10B shows, hydrogen ions move one by one into binding sites within this protein complex (the rotor), causing it to spin. After once around, they are spit out into the mitochondrial matrix. The spinning rotor turns an internal rod, which activates sites in the catalytic knob that phosphorylate ADP to ATP.

We will make a final tally of ATP production in Module 6.12. But first, let's consider how cellular respiration can sometimes be used primarily to generate heat.

> **?** What effect would an absence of oxygen (O_2) have on the process illustrated in Figure 6.10A?
>
> ● Without oxygen to "pull" electrons down the electron transport chain, the energy stored in NADH and $FADH_2$ could not be harnessed for ATP synthesis.

6.11 Scientists have discovered heat-producing, calorie-burning brown fat in adults

SCIENTIFIC THINKING

Ordinary body fat, called white fat, has little metabolic activity. Each cell is filled with a single large droplet of fat. Brown fat, on the other hand, actively burns energy. You learned in the chapter introduction that brown fat helps keep infants warm. Brown fat is named for its color, which comes from the brownish mitochondria that pack its cells. These mitochondria are unique in that they can burn fuel and produce heat without making ATP. How can they do that? Look back at Figure 6.10A and imagine ion channels spanning the inner mitochondrial membrane that allow H^+ to flow freely across the membrane. Such channels would dissipate the H^+ gradient that the electron transport chain had produced. Without that gradient, ATP synthase could not make ATP, and all the energy from the burning of fuel molecules would be released as heat. The mitochondria of brown fat cells have just such channels.

Can brown fat keep a newborn warm and help keep an adult thin?

Until recently, brown fat in humans was thought to disappear after infancy. The presence of unidentified tissue in the PET scans of cancer patients, however, caused researchers to question that conclusion. Could the tissues in the scans be brown fat? To test that hypothesis, researchers analyzed 3,640 PET-CT scans that had been performed on 1,972 patients for various diagnostic reasons. PET is a technique that identifies areas with high uptake of radioactively labeled glucose, and CT scans can detect adipose (fat) tissue. The combined PET-CT scans revealed small areas in the neck and chest of some patients that fit the criteria for brown fat—adipose tissue that was metabolically active (burning glucose). The researchers correlated the presence or absence of brown fat with patients' sex, age, weight, and other parameters, including the outdoor temperature. The results showed that 7.5% of the women and 3% of the men examined had deposits of brown fat. The tissues were found to be more prevalent both in patients who were thinner and when the scans had been taken in cold weather.

As is typical in science, the results from one study led to new questions and new research. Is brown fat activated by cold temperatures and, thus, could a much higher percentage of adults have brown fat than shown in scans of patients who were presumably *not* cold? Is the prevalence of this fat-burning tissue in thinner individuals related to why some people are thin and others are obese?

A second study involving 24 men looked at the presence and activity of brown fat during cold exposure. Ten participants were classified as lean (based on a BMI [body mass index] of less than 25) and 14 were identified as overweight or obese. Combined PET-CT scans were taken of all research participants following a two-hour exposure at 16°C (60.8°F). The scans of all but one participant (the one with the highest BMI) revealed activated brown fat tissues. As shown in Figure 6.11, the measured brown fat activity of the lean group was significantly higher than that of the overweight/obese group.

These results indicate that brown fat may be present in most people, and, when activated by cold, the brown fat of lean individuals is more active (burns more calories). What questions does this study raise? Does the more active brown fat of thin individuals help keep them thin? Are there other ways to turn on brown fat besides exposure to cold? Could brown fat be a target for obesity-fighting drugs?

▲ **Figure 6.11** Activity level of brown fat of lean and overweight/obese participants after cold exposure

Data from W. D. van Marken Lichtenbelt et al., Cold-activated brown adipose tissue in healthy men, *New England Journal of Medicine* 360: 1500–8 (2009).

Research continues on brown fat and on the signals (temperature, hormonal, and nervous) that activate it. But as the popular press reports this potential link between calorie-burning brown fat and weight loss, be prepared to see new diets, supplements, exercise routines, and perhaps even cold spa treatments that promise to rev up your brown fat furnace. As always when evaluating such information, look for the science behind those claims.

Data from A. M. Cypess et al., Identification and importance of brown adipose tissue in adult humans, *New England Journal of Medicine* 360: 1509–17 (2009).

> **?** The initial study discussed identified brown fat in less than 10% of the patients whose scans were analyzed. The second study identified brown fat in 96% of participants. What accounts for this difference?
>
> ● Brown fat is activated in response to cold temperature, and the second study involved cold treatment.

6.12 Review: Each molecule of glucose yields many molecules of ATP

Let's review what you have learned about cellular respiration by following the oxidation of one molecule of glucose. Starting on the left in **Figure 6.12**, glycolysis, which occurs in the cytosol, oxidizes glucose to two molecules of pyruvate, produces 2 NADH, and produces a net of 2 ATP by substrate-level phosphorylation. Within the mitochondrion, the oxidation of 2 pyruvate yields 2 NADH and 2 acetyl CoA. The 2 acetyl CoA feed into the citric acid cycle, which yields 6 NADH and 2 FADH$_2$, as well as 2 ATP by substrate-level phosphorylation. NADH and FADH$_2$ deliver electrons to the electron transport chain, where they are finally passed to O$_2$, forming H$_2$O. The electron transport chain pumps H$^+$ into the intermembrane space. The resulting H$^+$ gradient is tapped by ATP synthase to produce about 28 molecules of ATP by oxidative phosphorylation (according to current experimental data). Thus, the total yield of ATP molecules per glucose is about 32.

The number of ATP molecules cannot be stated exactly for several reasons. The NADH produced in glycolysis passes its

electrons across the mitochondrial membrane to either NAD$^+$ or FAD. Because FADH$_2$ adds its electrons farther along the electron transport chain (see Figure 6.10A), it contributes less to the H$^+$ gradient and thus generates less ATP. In addition, some of the energy of the H$^+$ gradient may be used for work other than ATP production, such as the active transport of pyruvate into the mitochondrion.

Because most of the ATP generated by cellular respiration results from oxidative phosphorylation, the ATP yield depends on an adequate supply of oxygen to the cell. Without oxygen to function as the final electron acceptor, electron transport and ATP production stop. But as we see next, some cells can oxidize organic fuel and generate ATP *without* oxygen.

? Explain where O$_2$ is used and CO$_2$ is produced in cellular respiration.

O$_2$ accepts electrons at the end of the electron transport chain. CO$_2$ is released during the oxidation of intermediate compounds in pyruvate oxidation and the citric acid cycle.

▶ **Figure 6.12**
An estimated tally of the ATP produced per molecule of glucose by substrate-level and oxidative phosphorylation in cellular respiration

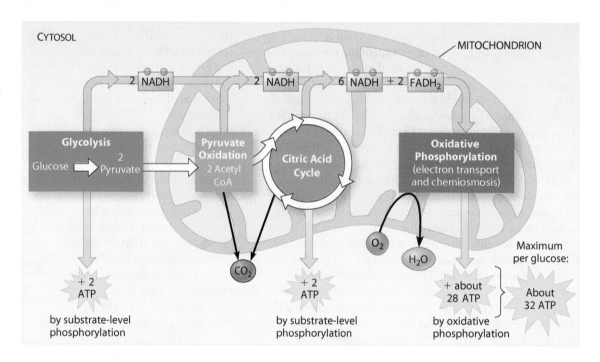

▷ Fermentation: Anaerobic Harvesting of Energy

6.13 Fermentation enables cells to produce ATP without oxygen

Fermentation is a way of harvesting chemical energy that does not require oxygen. The metabolic pathway that generates ATP during fermentation is glycolysis, the same pathway that functions in the first stage of cellular respiration. Remember that glycolysis uses no oxygen; it simply generates a net gain of 2 ATP while oxidizing glucose to two molecules of pyruvate and reducing NAD$^+$ to NADH. The yield of 2 ATP

is certainly a lot less than the possible 32 ATP per glucose generated during aerobic respiration, but it is enough to keep your muscles contracting for a short period of time when oxygen is scarce. And many microorganisms supply all their energy needs with the 2 ATP per glucose yield of glycolysis.

There is more to fermentation, however, than just glycolysis. To oxidize glucose in glycolysis, NAD$^+$ must be present as an electron acceptor. This is no problem under aerobic conditions, because the cell regenerates its pool of NAD$^+$ when NADH passes its electrons into the mitochondrion, to be transported to the electron transport chain. Fermentation provides an anaerobic path for recycling NADH back to NAD$^+$.

Lactic Acid Fermentation One common type of fermentation is called **lactic acid fermentation**. Your muscle cells and certain bacteria can regenerate NAD$^+$ by this process, as illustrated in **Figure 6.13A**. You can see that NADH is oxidized back to NAD$^+$ as pyruvate is reduced to lactate (the ionized form of lactic acid). Muscle cells can switch to lactic acid fermentation when the need for ATP outpaces the delivery of O$_2$ via the bloodstream. The lactate that builds up in muscle cells during strenuous exercise was previously thought to cause muscle fatigue and pain, but research now indicates that increased levels of other ions may be to blame. In any case, the lactate is gradually carried away by the blood to the liver, where it is converted back to pyruvate and oxidized in the mitochondria of liver cells.

The dairy industry uses lactic acid fermentation by bacteria to make cheese and yogurt. Other types of microbial fermentation turn soybeans into soy sauce and cabbage into sauerkraut.

Alcohol Fermentation For thousands of years, people have used **alcohol fermentation** in brewing, winemaking, and baking. Yeasts are single-celled fungi that normally use aerobic respiration to process their food. But they are also able to survive in anaerobic environments. Yeasts and certain bacteria recycle their NADH back to NAD$^+$ while converting pyruvate to CO$_2$ and ethanol **(Figure 6.13B)**. The CO$_2$ provides the bubbles in beer and champagne. Bubbles of CO$_2$ generated by baker's yeast cause bread dough to rise. Ethanol (ethyl alcohol), the two-carbon end product, is toxic to the organisms that produce it. Yeasts release their alcohol wastes to their surroundings, where it usually diffuses away. When yeasts are confined in a wine vat, they die when the alcohol concentration reaches 14%.

Types of Anaerobes Unlike muscle cells and yeasts, many prokaryotes that live in stagnant ponds and deep in the soil are *obligate anaerobes*, meaning they require anaerobic conditions and are poisoned by oxygen. Yeasts and many other bacteria are facultative anaerobes. A *facultative anaerobe* can make ATP either by fermentation or by oxidative phosphorylation, depending on whether O$_2$ is available. On the cellular level, our muscle cells behave as facultative anaerobes.

For a facultative anaerobe, pyruvate is a fork in the metabolic road. If oxygen is available, the organism will always use the more productive aerobic respiration. Thus, to make wine and beer, yeasts must be grown anaerobically so that they will ferment sugars and produce ethanol. For this reason, the wine barrels and beer fermentation vats in **Figure 6.13C** are designed to keep air out.

> **?** A glucose-fed yeast cell is moved from an aerobic environment to an anaerobic one. For the cell to continue generating ATP at the same rate, how would its rate of glucose consumption need to change?

⊙ The cell would have to consume glucose at a rate about 16 times the consumption rate in the aerobic environment (2 ATP per glucose molecule is made by fermentation versus 32 ATP by cellular respiration).

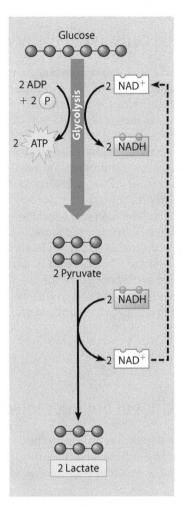

▲ **Figure 6.13A** Lactic acid fermentation: NAD$^+$ is regenerated as pyruvate is reduced to lactate

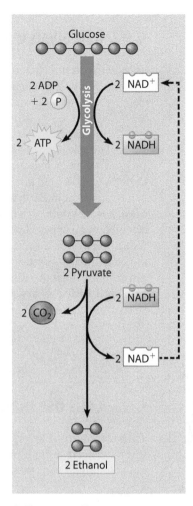

▲ **Figure 6.13B** Alcohol fermentation: NAD$^+$ is regenerated as pyruvate is broken down to CO$_2$ and ethanol

▲ **Figure 6.13C** Wine barrels and beer fermentation vats

6.14 Glycolysis evolved early in the history of life on Earth

EVOLUTION CONNECTION

Glycolysis is the universal energy-harvesting process of life. If you looked inside a bacterial cell, inside one of your body cells, or inside virtually any other living cell, you would find the metabolic machinery of glycolysis.

The role of glycolysis in both fermentation and respiration has an evolutionary basis. Ancient prokaryotes are thought to have used glycolysis to make ATP long before oxygen was present in Earth's atmosphere. The oldest known fossils of bacteria date back more than 3.5 billion years, and they resemble some types of photosynthetic bacteria still found today. The evidence indicates, however, that significant levels of O_2, formed as a by-product of bacterial photosynthesis, did not accumulate in the atmosphere until about 2.7 billion years ago. Thus, early prokaryotes most likely generated ATP exclusively from glycolysis, a process that does not require oxygen.

The fact that glycolysis is the most widespread metabolic pathway found in Earth's organisms today suggests that it evolved very early in the history of life. The location of glycolysis within the cell also implies great antiquity; the pathway does not require any of the membrane-enclosed organelles of the eukaryotic cell, which evolved about a billion years after the prokaryotic cell. Glycolysis is a metabolic heirloom from early cells that continues to function in fermentation and as the first stage in the breakdown of organic molecules by cellular respiration.

? List some of the characteristics of glycolysis that indicate that it is an ancient metabolic pathway.

● Glycolysis occurs universally (functioning in both fermentation and respiration), does not require oxygen, and does not occur in a membrane-enclosed organelle.

▷ Connections Between Metabolic Pathways

6.15 Cells use many kinds of organic molecules as fuel for cellular respiration

Throughout this chapter, we have spoken of glucose as the fuel for cellular respiration. But free glucose molecules are not common in your diet. You obtain most of your calories as carbohydrates (such as sucrose and other disaccharide sugars and starch, a polysaccharide), fats, and proteins. You consume all three of these classes of organic molecules when you eat a handful of peanuts, for instance.

Figure 6.15 uses color-coded arrows to illustrate how a cell can use these three types of molecules to make ATP. A wide range of carbohydrates can be funneled into glycolysis, as indicated by the blue arrows on the far left of the diagram. For example, enzymes in your digestive tract hydrolyze starch to glucose, which is then broken down by glycolysis and the citric acid cycle. Similarly, glycogen, the polysaccharide stored in your liver and muscle cells, can be hydrolyzed to glucose to serve as fuel between meals.

Fats make excellent cellular fuel because they contain many hydrogen atoms and thus many energy-rich electrons. As the diagram shows (tan arrows), a cell first hydrolyzes fats to glycerol and fatty acids. It then converts the glycerol to glyceraldehyde 3-phosphate (G3P), one of the intermediates in glycolysis. The fatty acids are broken into two-carbon fragments that enter the citric acid cycle as acetyl CoA. A gram of fat yields more than twice as much ATP as a gram of carbohydrate. Because so many calories are stockpiled in each gram of fat, you must expend a large amount of energy to burn fat stored in your body. This helps explain why it is so difficult for a dieter to lose excess fat.

Proteins (purple arrows in Figure 6.15) can also be used for

▲ Figure 6.15 Pathways that break down various food molecules

fuel, although your body preferentially burns sugars and fats first. To be oxidized as fuel, proteins must first be digested to their constituent amino acids. Typically, a cell will use most of these amino acids to make its own proteins. Enzymes can convert excess amino acids to intermediates of glycolysis or the citric acid cycle, and their energy is then harvested by cellular respiration. During the conversion, the amino groups are stripped off and later disposed of in urine.

? Animals store most of their energy reserves as fats, not as polysaccharides. What is the advantage of this mode of storage for an animal?

● Most animals are mobile and benefit from a compact and concentrated form of energy storage. Also, because fats are hydrophobic, they can be stored without extra water associated with them (see Module 3.8).

6.16 Organic molecules from food provide raw materials for biosynthesis

Not all food molecules are destined to be oxidized as fuel for making ATP. Food also provides the raw materials your cells use for biosynthesis—the production of organic molecules using energy-requiring metabolic pathways. A cell must be able to make its own molecules to build its structures and perform its functions. Some raw materials, such as amino acids, can be incorporated directly into your macromolecules. However, your cells also need to make molecules that are not present in your food. Indeed, glycolysis and the citric acid cycle function as metabolic interchanges that enable your cells to convert some kinds of molecules to others as you need them.

Figure 6.16 outlines the pathways by which your cells can make three classes of organic molecules using some of the intermediate molecules of glycolysis and the citric acid cycle. By comparing Figures 6.15 and 6.16, you can see clear connections between the energy-harvesting pathways of cellular respiration and the biosynthetic pathways used to construct the organic molecules of the cell.

Basic principles of supply and demand regulate these pathways. If there is an excess of a certain amino acid, for example, the pathway that synthesizes it is switched off. The most common mechanism for this control is feedback inhibition: The end product inhibits an enzyme that catalyzes an early step in the pathway (see Module 5.15). Feedback inhibition also controls cellular respiration. If ATP accumulates in a cell, it inhibits an early enzyme in glycolysis, slowing down respiration and conserving resources. On the other hand, the same enzyme is activated by a buildup of ADP in the cell, signaling the need for more energy.

The cells of all living organisms—including those of the panda shown in Figure 6.16 and the plants they eat—have the ability to harvest energy from the breakdown of organic molecules. When the process is cellular respiration, the atoms of the starting materials end up in carbon dioxide and water. In contrast, the ability to make organic molecules from carbon dioxide and water is not universal. Animal cells lack this ability, but plant cells can actually produce organic molecules from inorganic ones using the energy of sunlight in the process of photosynthesis. (We explore photosynthesis in Chapter 7.)

▲ **Figure 6.16** Biosynthesis of large organic molecules from intermediates of cellular respiration

? Explain how someone can gain weight and store fat even when on a low-fat diet. (Hint: Look for G3P and acetyl CoA in Figures 6.15 and 6.16.)

● If caloric intake is excessive, body cells use metabolic pathways to convert the excess to fat. The glycerol and fatty acids of fats are made from G3P and acetyl CoA, respectively, both produced from the oxidation of carbohydrates.

CHAPTER **6** REVIEW

For practice quizzes, BioFlix animations, MP3 tutorials, video tutors, and more study tools designed for this textbook, go to

MasteringBiology®

Reviewing the Concepts

Cellular Respiration: Aerobic Harvesting of Energy (6.1–6.5)

6.1 Photosynthesis and cellular respiration provide energy for life. Photosynthesis uses solar energy to produce glucose and O_2 from CO_2 and H_2O. In cellular respiration, O_2 is consumed during the breakdown of glucose to CO_2 and H_2O, and energy is released.

6.2 Breathing supplies O_2 for use in cellular respiration and removes CO_2.

6.3 Cellular respiration banks energy in ATP molecules.

$C_6H_{12}O_6$ + 6 O_2 → → → 6 CO_2 + 6 H_2O + ATP + Heat

Glucose   Oxygen   Carbon dioxide   Water

6.4 The human body uses energy from ATP for all its activities.

6.5 Cells capture energy from electrons "falling" from organic fuels to oxygen. Electrons removed from fuel molecules (oxidation) are transferred to NAD^+ (reduction). NADH passes electrons to an electron transport chain. As electrons "fall" from carrier to carrier and finally to O_2, energy is released.

Stages of Cellular Respiration (6.6–6.12)

6.6 Overview: Cellular respiration occurs in three main stages.

6.7 Glycolysis harvests chemical energy by oxidizing glucose to pyruvate. ATP is used to prime a glucose molecule, which is split in two. These three-carbon intermediates are oxidized to two molecules of pyruvate, yielding a net of 2 ATP and 2 NADH. ATP is formed by substrate-level phosphorylation, in which a phosphate group is transferred from an organic molecule to ADP.

6.8 Pyruvate is oxidized in preparation for the citric acid cycle. The oxidation of pyruvate yields acetyl CoA, CO_2, and NADH.

6.9 The citric acid cycle completes the oxidation of organic molecules, generating many NADH and $FADH_2$ molecules. For each turn of the cycle, two carbons from acetyl CoA are added and 2 CO_2 are released.

6.10 Most ATP production occurs by oxidative phosphorylation. In mitochondria, electrons from NADH and $FADH_2$ are passed down the electron transport chain to O_2, which picks up H^+ to

form water. Energy released by these redox reactions is used to pump H^+ into the intermembrane space. In chemiosmosis, the H^+ gradient drives H^+ back through ATP synthase complexes in the inner membrane, synthesizing ATP.

6.11 Scientists have discovered heat-producing, calorie-burning brown fat in adults.

6.12 Review: Each molecule of glucose yields many molecules of ATP. Substrate-level phosphorylation and oxidative phosphorylation produce up to 32 ATP molecules for every glucose molecule oxidized in cellular respiration.

Fermentation: Anaerobic Harvesting of Energy (6.13–6.14)

6.13 Fermentation enables cells to produce ATP without oxygen. Under anaerobic conditions, muscle cells, yeasts, and certain bacteria produce ATP by glycolysis. NAD^+ is recycled from NADH as pyruvate is reduced to lactate (lactic acid fermentation) or alcohol and CO_2 (alcohol fermentation).

6.14 Glycolysis evolved early in the history of life on Earth. Glycolysis occurs in the cytosol of the cells of nearly all organisms and is thought to have evolved in ancient prokaryotes.

Connections Between Metabolic Pathways (6.15–6.16)

6.15 Cells use many kinds of organic molecules as fuel for cellular respiration.

6.16 Organic molecules from food provide raw materials for biosynthesis. Cells use intermediates from cellular respiration and ATP for biosynthesis of other organic molecules. Metabolic pathways are often regulated by feedback inhibition.

Connecting the Concepts

1. Fill in the blanks in this summary map to help you review the key concepts of cellular respiration.

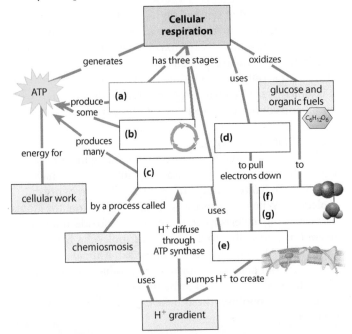

Testing Your Knowledge

Level 1: Knowledge/Comprehension

2. A biochemist wanted to study how various substances were used in cellular respiration. In one experiment, she allowed a mouse to breathe air containing O_2 "labeled" by a particular isotope. In the mouse, the labeled oxygen first showed up in
   a. ATP.
   b. NADH.
   c. CO_2.
   d. H_2O.

3. In glycolysis, _____ is oxidized and _____ is reduced.
   a. NAD^+ . . . glucose
   b. glucose . . . oxygen
   c. ATP . . . ADP
   d. glucose . . . NAD^+

4. Which of the following is the most immediate source of energy for making most of the ATP in your cells?
   a. the transfer of Ⓟ from intermediate substrates to ADP
   b. the movement of H^+ across a membrane down its concentration gradient
   c. the splitting of glucose into two molecules of pyruvate
   d. electrons moving through the electron transport chain

5. Which of the following is a true distinction between cellular respiration and fermentation?
   a. NADH is oxidized by passing electrons to the electron transport chain in respiration only.
   b. Only respiration oxidizes glucose.
   c. Substrate-level phosphorylation is unique to fermentation; cellular respiration uses oxidative phosphorylation.
   d. Fermentation is the metabolic pathway found in prokaryotes; cellular respiration is unique to eukaryotes.

Level 2: Application/Analysis

6. The poison cyanide binds to an electron carrier within the electron transport chain and blocks the movement of electrons. When this happens, glycolysis and the citric acid cycle soon grind to a halt as well. Why do you think these other two stages of cellular respiration stop? (*Explain your answer.*)
   a. They run out of ATP.
   b. Unused O_2 interferes with cellular respiration.
   c. They run out of NAD^+ and FAD.
   d. Electrons are no longer available.

7. In which of the following is the first molecule becoming reduced to the second molecule?
   a. pyruvate → acetyl CoA
   b. pyruvate → lactate
   c. glucose → pyruvate
   d. $NADH + H^+ → NAD^+ + 2\,H$

8. Which of the three stages of cellular respiration is considered the most ancient? Explain your answer.

9. Compare and contrast fermentation as it occurs in your muscle cells and in yeast cells.

10. Explain how your body can convert excess carbohydrates in the diet to fats. Can excess carbohydrates be converted to protein? What else must be supplied?

11. An average adult human requires 2,200 kcal of energy per day. Suppose your diet provides an average of 2,300 kcal per day. How many hours per week would you have to walk to burn off the extra calories? Swim? Run? (See Figure 6.4.)

12. Your body makes NAD^+ and FAD from two B vitamins, niacin and riboflavin. The Recommended Dietary Allowance for niacin is 20 mg and for riboflavin, 1.7 mg. These amounts are thousands of times less than the amount of glucose your body needs each day to fuel its energy needs. Why is the daily requirement for these vitamins so small?

Level 3: Synthesis/Evaluation

13. In the citric acid cycle, an enzyme oxidizes malate to oxaloacetate, with the production of NADH and the release of H^+. You are studying this reaction using a suspension of bean cell mitochondria and a blue dye that loses its color as it takes up H^+. You know that the higher the concentration of malate, the more rapid the decolorization of the dye. You set up reaction mixtures with mitochondria, dye, and three different concentrations of malate (0.1 mg/L, 0.2 mg/L, and 0.3 mg/L). Which of the following graphs represents the results you would expect, and why?

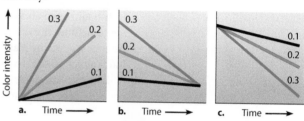

14. ATP synthase enzymes are found in the prokaryotic plasma membrane and in the inner membrane of a mitochondrion. What does this suggest about the evolutionary relationship of this eukaryotic organelle to prokaryotes?

15. **SCIENTIFIC THINKING** Several studies have found a correlation between the activity levels of brown fat tissue in research participants following exposure to cold and their percentage of body fat (see Module 6.11). Devise a graph that would present the results from such a study, labeling the axes and drawing a line to show whether the results show a positive or negative correlation between the variables. Propose two hypotheses that could explain these results.

16. For a short time in the 1930s, some physicians prescribed low doses of a compound called dinitrophenol (DNP) to help patients lose weight. This unsafe method was abandoned after some patients died. DNP uncouples the chemiosmotic machinery by making the inner mitochondrial membrane leaky to H^+. Explain how this drug could cause profuse sweating, weight loss, and possibly death.

17. Explain how the mechanism of brown fat metabolism is similar to the effect that the drug DNP described above has on mitochondria. Pharmaceutical companies may start targeting brown fat for weight loss drugs. How might such drugs help patients lose weight? What dangers might such drugs pose?

Answers to all questions can be found in Appendix 4.

7

Photosynthesis: *Using Light to Make Food*

? *Will global climate change make you itch?*

If you are among the 80% of people allergic to poison ivy, the thick patch of three-leaved plants pictured below may make you want to scrub with soap and water and rush to find calamine lotion. A close encounter with this noxious weed often leads to itchy and oozing blisters that can last for weeks. The allergic component of poison ivy sap, urushiol, binds to skin, clothing, and pet fur on contact, where it remains active until washed off. Even dead leaves or vines retain active urushiol for several years.

Poison ivy is found throughout much of North America, often growing along the ground in both woods and open areas. It can also grow as a vine, climbing high up trees with its lateral branches that are sometimes mistaken for tree limbs. The rhymes "hairy vine, no friend of mine" and "raggy rope, don't be a dope" help alert hikers to the danger around them when the characteristic shiny leaves are hidden high in the tree foliage.

Like all plants, poison ivy produces energy for its growth by photosynthesis, the process that converts light energy to the chemical energy of sugar. Photosynthesis removes CO_2 from the atmosphere and stores it in plant matter. The burning of sugar in the cellular respiration of almost all organisms releases CO_2 back to the environment. Burning fossil fuels and deforestation also release CO_2, and these activities are contributing to the current rise in atmospheric CO_2 and the accompanying global climate change. How might higher CO_2 levels affect plant growth? Unfortunately, many studies indicate that weeds grow faster under such conditions than do our crop plants or trees. Later in the chapter we will discuss one such study concerning the growth of poison ivy.

But first, let's learn how photosynthesis works. We begin with some basic concepts and then look more closely at the two stages of photosynthesis: the light reactions and the Calvin cycle. Finally, we explore ways in which photosynthesis affects our global environment.

▷ An Introduction to Photosynthesis

7.1 Photosynthesis fuels the biosphere

Life on Earth is solar powered. The chloroplasts in plant cells capture light energy that has traveled 150 million kilometers from the sun. Through the process of **photosynthesis**, plants use solar energy to convert CO_2 and H_2O to sugars and other organic molecules, and they release O_2 as a by-product. Plants are **autotrophs** (meaning "self-feeders" in Greek) in that they make their own food. Autotrophs not only feed themselves, but they are the ultimate source of organic molecules for almost all other organisms. Because they use the energy of light, plants and other photosynthesizers are specifically called **photoautotrophs**.

Photoautotrophs are often referred to as the producers of the biosphere because they produce its food supply. (In Chapter 16, you will learn about chemoautotrophs—prokaryotes that use inorganic chemicals as their energy source and are the producers in deep-sea vent communities.) Producers feed the consumers of the biosphere—the **heterotrophs** that cannot make their own food but must consume plants or animals or decompose organic material (*hetero* means "other"). You and almost all other heterotrophs are completely dependent on photoautotrophs for the raw materials and organic fuel necessary to maintain life and for the oxygen required to burn that fuel in cellular respiration.

Photoautotrophs not only feed us; they also clothe us (think cotton), house us (think wood), and provide energy for warmth, light, transport, and manufacturing. The fossil fuels we use as energy sources represent stores of the sun's energy captured by photoautotrophs in the far distant past.

The photographs shown on this page illustrate some of the diversity among today's photoautotrophs. On land, plants, such as those in the tropical forest in **Figure 7.1A**, are the producers. In aquatic environments, photoautotrophs include unicellular and multicellular algae, as well as photosynthetic prokaryotes. **Figure 7.1B** shows kelp, a large alga that forms extensive underwater "forests" off the coast of California. **Figure 7.1C** is a micrograph of cyanobacteria, which are important producers in freshwater and marine ecosystems.

In this chapter, we focus on photosynthesis in plants, which takes place in chloroplasts. The remarkable ability of these organelles to harness light energy and use it to drive the synthesis of organic compounds emerges from their structural organization: Photosynthetic pigments and enzymes are grouped together in membranes or compartments, facilitating the complex series of chemical reactions in photosynthesis. Photosynthetic bacteria have infolded regions of the plasma membrane containing such clusters of pigments and enzymes. In fact, according to the widely accepted theory of endosymbiosis, chloroplasts originated from a photosynthetic prokaryote that took up residence inside a eukaryotic cell (see Module 4.15).

Let's begin our study of photosynthesis with an overview of the location and structure of plant chloroplasts.

> **?** **What do "self-feeding" photoautotrophs require from the environment to make their own food?**

● Light, carbon dioxide, and water. (Minerals are also required; you'll learn about the needs of plants in Chapter 32.)

▲ **Figure 7.1A**   Tropical forest plants

▲ **Figure 7.1B**   Kelp, a large, multicellular alga

▲ **Figure 7.1C**   Cyanobacteria (photosynthetic bacteria) LM 980X

7.2 Photosynthesis occurs in chloroplasts in plant cells

All green parts of a plant have chloroplasts in their cells, but leaves are the major sites of photosynthesis in most plants. Indeed, a section of leaf with a top surface area of 1 mm^2 has about a half million chloroplasts. A leaf's green color comes from **chlorophyll**, a light-absorbing pigment in the chloroplasts that plays a central role in converting solar energy to chemical energy.

Figure 7.2 zooms in on a leaf to show the actual sites of photosynthesis. As you can see in the leaf cross section, chloroplasts are concentrated in the cells of the **mesophyll**, the green tissue in the interior of the leaf. Carbon dioxide enters the leaf, and oxygen exits, by way of tiny pores called **stomata** (singular, *stoma*, meaning "mouth"). Water absorbed by the roots is delivered to the leaves in veins. Leaves also use veins to export sugar to roots and other parts of the plant.

As you will notice in the light micrograph of a single mesophyll cell, each cell has numerous chloroplasts. A typical mesophyll cell has about 30 to 40 chloroplasts. The bottom drawing and the electron micrograph show the structures in a single chloroplast. Membranes in the chloroplast form the framework within which many of the reactions of photosynthesis occur, just as mitochondrial membranes are the site for much of the energy-harvesting machinery in cellular respiration (see Module 6.10). In the chloroplast, an envelope of two membranes encloses an inner compartment, which is filled with a thick fluid called **stroma**. Suspended in the stroma is a system of interconnected membranous sacs, called **thylakoids**, which enclose another internal compartment, called the thylakoid space. (As you will see later, this thylakoid space plays a role analogous to the intermembrane space of a mitochondrion in the generation of ATP.) In many places, thylakoids are concentrated in stacks called grana (singular, *granum*). Built into the thylakoid membranes are the chlorophyll molecules that capture light energy. The thylakoid membranes also house much of the machinery that converts light energy to chemical energy, which is used in the stroma to make sugar.

Later in the chapter, we examine the function of these structures in more detail. But first, let's look more closely at the general process of photosynthesis.

▲ **Figure 7.2** Zooming in on the location and structure of chloroplasts

---

? How do the reactant molecules of photosynthesis reach the chloroplasts in leaves?

⊛ CO$_2$ enters leaves through stomata, and H$_2$O enters the roots and is carried to leaves through veins.

7.3 Scientists traced the process of photosynthesis using isotopes

The leaves of plants that live in lakes and ponds are often covered with bubbles like the ones shown in **Figure 7.3**. The bubbles are oxygen gas (O_2) produced during photosynthesis. But where does this O_2 come from?

The overall process of photosynthesis has been known since the 1800s: In the presence of light, green plants produce sugar and oxygen from carbon dioxide and water. Consider the basic equation for photosynthesis:

$$6\,CO_2 + 6\,H_2O \rightarrow C_6H_{12}O_6 + 6\,O_2$$

Looking at this equation, you can understand why scientists hypothesized that photosynthesis first splits carbon dioxide ($CO_2 \rightarrow C + O_2$), releasing oxygen gas, and then adds water (H_2O) to the carbon to produce sugar. In the 1930s, this idea was challenged by C. B. van Niel, who was working with photosynthesizing bacteria that produce sugar from CO_2 but do not release O_2 in the process. These bacteria obviously did not split CO_2 in their photosynthesis. He hypothesized that in plants, it is H_2O that is split, with the hydrogen becoming incorporated into sugar and the O_2 released as gas.

In the 1950s, scientists confirmed van Niel's hypothesis by using a heavy isotope of oxygen, O-18, to follow the fate of oxygen atoms during photosynthesis. Isotopes are atoms with differing numbers of neutrons: O-18 has two more neutrons in the nucleus of its atom than the more common isotope O-16. The summary of the results of these experiments follows. (Note that these equations are slightly more detailed than the equation written above because, as it turns out, water is both a reactant and a product in photosynthesis.)

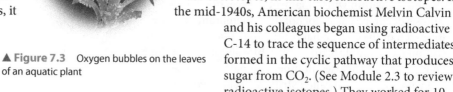

▲ **Figure 7.3** Oxygen bubbles on the leaves of an aquatic plant

Experiment 1: $6\,CO_2 + 12\,H_2O \rightarrow C_6H_{12}O_6 + 6\,H_2O + 6\,O_2$

Experiment 2: $6\,CO_2 + 12\,H_2O \rightarrow C_6H_{12}O_6 + 6\,H_2O + 6\,O_2$

The red type in the equations above denotes the source and ending location of O-18, the tracer used in these experiments. In experiment 1, a plant given CO_2 containing O-18 gave off no labeled (containing O-18) oxygen gas. But in experiment 2, a plant given H_2O containing O-18 did produce labeled O_2. What did these experiments show? As you can see, the O_2 released during photosynthesis comes from water and not from CO_2. Additional experiments have revealed that the oxygen atoms from CO_2 and the hydrogen atoms from the reactant H_2O molecules end up in both the sugar molecule and the H_2O molecules that are formed as a product.

The synthesis of sugar in photosynthesis involves numerous chemical reactions. Working out the details of these reactions also involved the use of isotopes, in this case, radioactive isotopes. In the mid-1940s, American biochemist Melvin Calvin and his colleagues began using radioactive C-14 to trace the sequence of intermediates formed in the cyclic pathway that produces sugar from CO_2. (See Module 2.3 to review radioactive isotopes.) They worked for 10 years to elucidate this cycle, which is now called the Calvin cycle. Calvin received the Nobel Prize in 1961 for this work.

 Photosynthesis produces billions of tons of carbohydrate a year. Where does most of the mass of this huge amount of organic matter come from?

⊙ Mostly from CO_2 in the air, which provides both the carbon and oxygen in carbohydrate. Water supplies only the hydrogen.

7.4 Photosynthesis is a redox process, as is cellular respiration

What actually happens when CO_2 and water are converted to sugar and O_2? Photosynthesis is a redox (oxidation-reduction) process, just as cellular respiration is (see Module 6.5). As indicated in the summary equation for photosynthesis (**Figure 7.4A**), CO_2 becomes reduced to sugar as electrons, along with hydrogen ions (H^+) from water, are added to it. Meanwhile, water molecules are oxidized; that is, they lose

electrons, along with hydrogen ions. Recall that oxidation and reduction always go hand in hand.

Now compare the food-producing equation for photosynthesis with the energy-releasing equation for cellular respiration (**Figure 7.4B**). Cellular respiration harvests energy stored in a glucose molecule by oxidizing the sugar and reducing O_2 to H_2O. This process involves a number of energy-releasing

┌── Becomes reduced ──┐
$6\,CO_2 + 6\,H_2O \longrightarrow C_6H_{12}O_6 + 6\,O_2$
└── Becomes oxidized ──┘

▲ **Figure 7.4A** Photosynthesis (uses light energy)

┌── Becomes oxidized ──┐
$C_6H_{12}O_6 + 6\,O_2 \longrightarrow 6\,CO_2 + 6\,H_2O$
└── Becomes reduced ──┘

▲ **Figure 7.4B** Cellular respiration (releases chemical energy)

redox reactions, with electrons losing potential energy as they are passed down an electron transport chain to O_2. Along the way, the mitochondrion uses some of the energy to synthesize ATP.

In contrast, the food-producing redox reactions of photosynthesis require energy. The potential energy of electrons increases as they move from H_2O to CO_2 during photosynthesis. The light energy captured by chlorophyll molecules in the chloroplast provides this energy boost. Photosynthesis converts light energy to chemical energy and stores it in the chemical bonds of sugar molecules, which can provide energy for later use or raw materials for biosynthesis.

? **Which redox process, photosynthesis or cellular respiration, is endergonic? (*Hint*: See Module 5.11.)**

● Photosynthesis

7.5 The two stages of photosynthesis are linked by ATP and NADPH

The equation for photosynthesis is a simple summary of a rather complex process. Photosynthesis occurs in two stages, each with multiple steps. Let's begin our study of photosynthesis with an overview of the two stages. **Figure 7.5** shows the inputs and outputs of the light reactions and the Calvin cycle and how these two stages are related.

The **light reactions**, which occur in the thylakoids, include the steps that convert light energy to chemical energy and release O_2. Water is split, providing a source of electrons and giving off O_2 as a by-product. Light energy absorbed by chlorophyll molecules built into the thylakoid membranes is used to drive the transfer of electrons and H^+ from water to the electron acceptor **NADP⁺**, reducing it to NADPH. NADPH is first cousin to NADH, which transports electrons in cellular respiration; the two differ only in the extra phosphate group in NADPH. NADPH temporarily stores electrons and hydrogen ions and provides "reducing power" to the Calvin cycle. The light reactions also generate ATP from ADP and a phosphate group.

In summary, the light reactions absorb solar energy and convert it to chemical energy stored in both ATP and NADPH. Notice that these reactions produce no sugar; sugar is not made until the Calvin cycle, which is the second stage of photosynthesis.

The **Calvin cycle** occurs in the stroma of the chloroplast. It is a cyclic series of reactions that assembles sugar molecules using CO_2 and the energy-rich products of the light reactions. The incorporation of carbon from CO_2 into organic compounds, shown in the figure as CO_2 entering the Calvin cycle, is called **carbon fixation**. After carbon fixation, the carbon compounds are reduced to sugars.

As the figure suggests, it is NADPH produced by the light reactions that provides the electrons for reducing carbon compounds in the Calvin cycle. And ATP from the light reactions provides chemical energy that powers several of the steps of the Calvin cycle. The Calvin cycle is sometimes referred to as the dark reactions, or light-independent

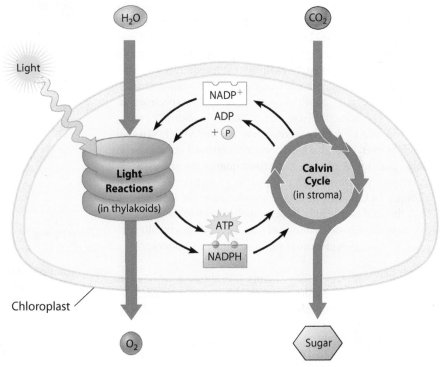

▲ **Figure 7.5** An overview of the two stages of photosynthesis in a chloroplast
Try This Relate the summary equation for photosynthesis to this overview diagram.

reactions, because none of the steps requires light directly. However, in most plants, the Calvin cycle occurs during daylight, when the light reactions power the cycle's sugar assembly line by supplying it with NADPH and ATP.

The word *photosynthesis* encapsulates the two stages. *Photo*, from the Greek word for "light," refers to the light reactions; *synthesis*, meaning "putting together," refers to sugar construction by the Calvin cycle. In the next several modules, we look at these two stages in more detail. But first, let's consider some of the properties of light, the energy source that powers photosynthesis.

? **For chloroplasts to produce sugar from carbon dioxide in the dark, they would need to be supplied with _____ and _____.**

● ATP . . . NADPH

7.6 Visible radiation absorbed by pigments drives the light reactions

What do we mean when we say that photosynthesis is powered by light energy from the sun?

The Nature of Sunlight Sunlight is a type of energy called electromagnetic energy or radiation. Electromagnetic energy travels in space as rhythmic waves analogous to those made by a pebble dropped in a puddle of water. The distance between the crests of electromagnetic waves is called a **wavelength**. Figure 7.6A shows the **electromagnetic spectrum**, the full range of electromagnetic wavelengths from the very short gamma rays to the very long-wavelength radio waves. As you can see in the center of the figure, visible light—the radiation your eyes see as different colors—is only a small fraction of the spectrum. It consists of wavelengths from about 380 nm to about 750 nm.

The model of light as waves explains many of light's properties. However, light also behaves as discrete packets of energy called photons. A **photon** has a fixed quantity of energy, and the shorter the wavelength of light, the greater the energy of its photons. In fact, the photons of wavelengths that are shorter than those of visible light have enough energy to damage molecules such as proteins and nucleic acids. This is why ultraviolet (UV) radiation can cause sunburns and skin cancer.

Photosynthetic Pigments Figure 7.6B shows what happens to visible light in the chloroplast. Light-absorbing molecules called pigments, built into the thylakoid membranes, absorb some wavelengths of light and reflect or transmit other wavelengths. We do not see the absorbed wavelengths; their energy has been absorbed by pigment molecules. What we see when we look at a leaf are the green wavelengths that are not absorbed but are transmitted and reflected by the pigments.

Different pigments absorb light of different wavelengths, and chloroplasts contain more than one type of pigment. Chlorophyll *a*, which participates directly in the light

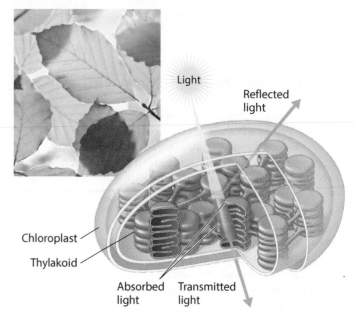

Chloroplast
Thylakoid
Light
Reflected light
Absorbed light
Transmitted light

▲ **Figure 7.6B** The interaction of light with chlorophyll in a chloroplast
Try This Use this diagram to explain why leaves are green.

reactions, absorbs mainly blue-violet and red light. It looks blue-green because it reflects mainly green light. A very similar molecule, chlorophyll *b*, absorbs mainly blue and orange light and reflects (appears) olive green. Chlorophyll *b* broadens the range of light that a plant can use by conveying absorbed energy to chlorophyll *a*, which then puts the energy to work in the light reactions.

Chloroplasts also contain pigments called carotenoids, which are various shades of yellow and orange. The spectacular colors of fall foliage in certain parts of the world are due partly to the yellow-orange hues of longer-lasting carotenoids that show through once the green chlorophyll breaks down. Carotenoids may broaden the spectrum of colors that can drive photosynthesis. However, a more important function seems to be photoprotection: Some carotenoids absorb and dissipate excessive light energy that would otherwise damage chlorophyll or interact with oxygen to form reactive oxidative molecules that can damage cell molecules. Similar carotenoids, which we obtain from carrots and other vegetables and fruits, have a photoprotective role in our eyes.

Each type of pigment absorbs certain wavelengths of light because it is able to absorb the specific amounts of energy in those photons. Next we see what happens when a pigment molecule such as chlorophyll absorbs a photon of light.

? What color of light is least effective at driving photosynthesis? Explain.

Shorter wavelength ⟶ Longer wavelength
Higher energy ⟵ Lower energy

10^{-5} nm 10^{-3} nm   1 nm 10^3 nm 10^6 nm   1 m 10^3 m

| Gamma rays | X-rays | UV | Infrared | Micro-waves | Radio waves |

Visible light

380 400   500   600   700 750
Wavelength (nm)

▲ **Figure 7.6A** The electromagnetic spectrum and the wavelengths of visible light

● Green, because it is mostly transmitted and reflected—not absorbed—by photosynthetic pigments.

7.7 Photosystems capture solar energy

Energy cannot be created or destroyed, but it can be transferred or transformed (see Module 5.10). Let's examine how light energy can be transformed to other types of energy. When a pigment molecule absorbs a photon of light, one of the pigment's electrons jumps to an energy level farther from the nucleus. In this location, the electron has more potential energy, and we say that the electron has been raised from a ground state to an excited state. The excited state, like all high-energy states, is unstable. Generally, when isolated pigment molecules absorb light, their excited electrons drop back down to the ground state in a billionth of a second, releasing their excess energy as heat. This conversion of light energy to heat is what makes a black car so hot on a sunny day (black pigments absorb all wavelengths of light).

Some isolated pigments, including chlorophyll, emit light as well as heat after absorbing photons. We can demonstrate this phenomenon in the laboratory with a chlorophyll solution, as shown on the left in **Figure 7.7A**. When brightly illuminated, the chlorophyll emits photons of light that produce a reddish afterglow called fluorescence. The right side of Figure 7.7A illustrates what happens in fluorescence: An absorbed photon boosts an electron of chlorophyll to an excited state, from which it falls back to the ground state, emitting its energy as heat and light.

But chlorophyll behaves very differently in isolation than it does in an intact chloroplast. In their native habitat of the thylakoid membrane, chlorophyll and other pigments that absorb photons transfer the energy to other pigment molecules and eventually to a special pair of chlorophyll molecules. This pair passes off an excited electron to a neighboring molecule before it has a chance to drop back to the ground state.

In the thylakoid membrane, chlorophyll molecules are organized along with other pigments and proteins into clusters called photosystems (**Figure 7.7B**). A **photosystem** consists of a number of light-harvesting complexes surrounding a reaction-center

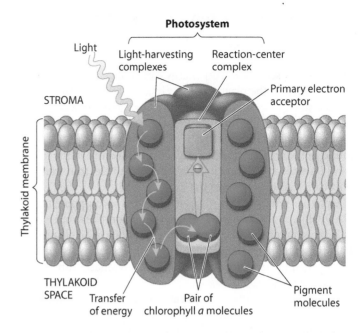

▲ **Figure 7.7B**   A light-excited pair of chlorophyll molecules in the reaction center of a photosystem passing an excited electron to a primary electron acceptor

complex. A light-harvesting complex contains various pigment molecules bound to proteins. Collectively, the light-harvesting complexes function as a light-gathering antenna. The pigments absorb photons and pass the energy from molecule to molecule, somewhat like a human "wave" at a sporting event, until it reaches the reaction center. The reaction-center complex contains a pair of special chlorophyll *a* molecules and a molecule called the primary electron acceptor, which is capable of accepting electrons and becoming reduced. The solar-powered transfer of an electron from the reaction-center chlorophyll *a* pair to the primary electron acceptor is the first step in the transformation of light energy to chemical energy in the light reactions.

Two types of photosystems have been identified, and they cooperate in the light reactions. They are referred to as photosystem I and photosystem II, in order of their discovery, although photosystem II actually functions first in the sequence of steps that make up the light reactions. Each photosystem has a characteristic reaction-center complex, with a special pair of chlorophyll *a* molecules associated with a particular primary electron acceptor. Now let's see how the two photosystems work together in the light reactions to generate ATP and NADPH.

> **?** Compared with a solution of isolated chlorophyll, why do intact chloroplasts release less heat and fluorescence when illuminated?

▲ **Figure 7.7A**   A solution of chlorophyll glowing red when illuminated (left); a diagram of an isolated, light-excited chlorophyll molecule that releases heat and a photon of red light when it falls back to ground state (right)

● In the chloroplasts, a light-excited electron from the reaction-center chlorophyll molecules is trapped by a primary electron acceptor rather than giving up its energy as heat and light.

7.8 Two photosystems connected by an electron transport chain generate ATP and NADPH

You have just seen how light energy can boost an electron of chlorophyll *a* in the reaction center of a photosystem to an excited state, from which it is captured by a primary electron acceptor. But how do these captured electrons lead to the production of ATP and NADPH? Part of the explanation is found in the arrangement of photosystems II and I in the thylakoid membrane and their connection via an electron transport chain. Another part of the explanation involves the flow of electrons removed from H_2O through these components to NADPH. And the final part of the explanation, the synthesis of ATP, is linked (as it is in cellular respiration) to an electron transport chain pumping H^+ into a membrane compartment, from which the ions flow through an ATP synthase embedded in the membrane.

To unpack this rather complicated system, let's start with the simple mechanical analogy illustrated in **Figure 7.8**. Starting on the left, you see that the large yellow photon mallet provides the energy to boost an electron from photosystem II to a higher energy level, where it is caught by the primary electron acceptor standing on the platform. The electron is loaded onto an electron transport chain "ramp" leading to photosystem I. (Recall that photosystem II precedes photosystem I in the light reactions.) As electrons roll down the ramp, they release energy that is used for the production of ATP. When an electron reaches photosystem I, another photon mallet pumps it up to a higher energy level, where it is caught by a primary electron acceptor on the photosystem I platform. From there, the photoexcited electrons are thrown into a bucket to produce NADPH. This construction analogy shows how the coupling of two photosystems and an electron transport chain can transform the energy of light to the chemical energy of ATP and NADPH.

The simple analogy in Figure 7.8 does leave a few important unanswered questions: What is the source of the electrons that are moving through the photosystems to NADPH? Don't the light reactions produce O_2—where does that happen? And how does the flow of electrons down that ramp produce ATP?

The electrons that end up reducing $NADP^+$ to NADPH originally come from water. An enzyme in the thylakoid space splits H_2O into 2 electrons, 2 hydrogen ions (H^+), and 1 oxygen atom ($\frac{1}{2} O_2$). The H^+ stay in the thylakoid space. The oxygen atom immediately joins with another oxygen to form O_2. As you learned in Module 7.3, water is the source of the O_2 produced in photosynthesis, and these oxygen molecules diffuse out of the thylakoids, the chloroplast, and the plant cell, finally exiting the leaf through its stomata. The all-important electrons from water are passed, one by one, to the reaction center chlorophyll *a* molecules in photosystem II, replacing the photoexcited electron that was just captured by the primary electron acceptor. From photosystem II, the electrons pass through an electron transport chain to the reaction center chlorophyll *a* molecules in photosystem I, again replacing photoexcited electrons that had been captured by its primary electron acceptor. Although the illustration shows these electrons being dropped in a bucket, they actually are passed through a short electron transport chain to $NADP^+$, reducing it to NADPH.

Now that we have accounted for NADPH and O_2, all that is left is ATP. Making ATP in the light reactions involves an electron transport chain and chemiosmosis—the same players and process you met in the synthesis of ATP in cellular respiration. Recall that in chemiosmosis, the potential energy of a concentration gradient of H^+ across a membrane powers ATP synthesis. This gradient is created when an electron transport chain uses the energy released as it passes electrons down the chain to pump H^+ across a membrane. The energy of the concentration gradient drives H^+ back across the membrane through ATP synthase, spinning this rotary motor and phosphorylating ADP to produce ATP (see Figure 6.10B).

The next module presents a slightly more realistic model of the light reactions than this mechanical analogy, which should help you visualize how photosystem II, the electron transport chain, photosystem I, and ATP synthase function together within the thylakoid membranes of a chloroplast to produce NADPH and ATP.

▲ Figure 7.8 A mechanical analogy of the light reactions

? **Looking at the model of the light reactions in Figure 7.8, explain why two photons of light are required in the movement of electrons from water to NADPH.**

● One photon excites an electron from photosystem II, which is then passed down an electron transfer chain to photosystem I. A second photon excites an electron from photosystem I, which is then used in the reduction of $NADP^+$ to NADPH.

7.9 The light reactions take place within the thylakoid membranes

The diagram below shows the relationship between chloroplast structure and function in the light reactions. Depicted here is a small portion of a thylakoid sac showing how the two photosystems and electron transport chain are embedded in a thylakoid membrane. All of the components shown here are present in numerous copies in each thylakoid. Moving from left to right, you can see how light energy absorbed by the two photosystems drives the flow of electrons from water to NADPH. The electron transport chain helps to produce the concentration gradient of H^+ across the thylakoid membrane, which drives H^+ through ATP synthase, producing ATP. Because the initial energy input is light (*photo-*), this chemiosmotic production of ATP is called **photophosphorylation**.

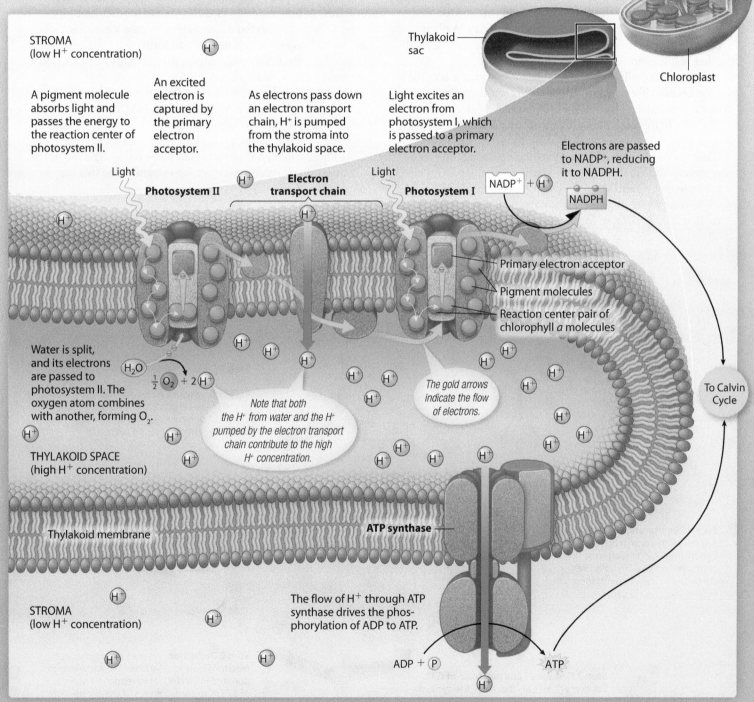

STROMA (low H^+ concentration)

Thylakoid sac

Chloroplast

A pigment molecule absorbs light and passes the energy to the reaction center of photosystem II.

An excited electron is captured by the primary electron acceptor.

As electrons pass down an electron transport chain, H^+ is pumped from the stroma into the thylakoid space.

Light excites an electron from photosystem I, which is passed to a primary electron acceptor.

Electrons are passed to $NADP^+$, reducing it to NADPH.

Light

Photosystem II

Electron transport chain

Light

Photosystem I

$NADP^+ + H^+$

NADPH

Primary electron acceptor

Pigment molecules

Reaction center pair of chlorophyll *a* molecules

Water is split, and its electrons are passed to photosystem II. The oxygen atom combines with another, forming O_2.

H_2O $\frac{1}{2} O_2 + 2 H^+$

Note that both the H^+ from water and the H^+ pumped by the electron transport chain contribute to the high H^+ concentration.

The gold arrows indicate the flow of electrons.

To Calvin Cycle

THYLAKOID SPACE (high H^+ concentration)

Thylakoid membrane

ATP synthase

STROMA (low H^+ concentration)

The flow of H^+ through ATP synthase drives the phosphorylation of ADP to ATP.

$ADP + P$ ATP

? What is the advantage of the light reactions producing NADPH and ATP on the stroma side of the thylakoid membrane?

● The Calvin cycle, which uses the NADPH and ATP, occurs in the stroma.

7.10 ATP and NADPH power sugar synthesis in the Calvin cycle

The Calvin cycle functions like a sugar factory within a chloroplast. The inputs to this all-important food-making process are CO$_2$ (from the air) and ATP and NADPH (both generated by the light reactions). ATP is used as an energy source and NADPH provides high-energy electrons for reducing CO$_2$ to sugar. The output of the Calvin cycle is an energy-rich, three-carbon sugar, glyceraldehyde 3-phosphate (G3P). A plant cell uses G3P to make glucose, the disaccharide sucrose, and other organic molecules as needed.

Figure 7.10 outlines the steps of the Calvin cycle. It is called a cycle because, like the citric acid cycle in cellular respiration, the starting material is regenerated after molecules enter and leave the cycle. In this case, the starting material is a five-carbon sugar named ribulose bisphosphate (RuBP). To make a molecule of G3P, the cycle must turn three times, incorporating three molecules of CO$_2$. We show the cycle starting with three CO$_2$ molecules so that we end up with a complete G3P molecule.

As you can see in step 1, carbon fixation, the enzyme rubisco attaches CO$_2$ to RuBP. (Recall that carbon fixation refers to the initial incorporation of CO$_2$ into organic compounds.) This unstable six-carbon molecule splits into two three-carbon molecules. In step 2, reduction, ATP and NADPH are used to reduce the three-carbon molecule to G3P.

For this to be a cycle, RuBP must be regenerated. In step 3, release of one molecule of G3P, you can see that for every three CO$_2$ molecules fixed, one G3P molecule leaves the cycle as product. In step 4, regeneration of RuBP, the remaining five G3P molecules are rearranged, using energy from ATP, to regenerate three molecules of RuBP.

Note that for the net synthesis of one G3P molecule, the Calvin cycle consumes nine ATP and six NADPH molecules, which were provided by the light reactions. Neither the light reactions nor the Calvin cycle alone can make sugar from CO$_2$. Photosynthesis is an emergent property of the structural organization of a chloroplast, which integrates the two stages of photosynthesis.

?
To synthesize one glucose molecule, the Calvin cycle uses _____ CO$_2$, _____ ATP, and _____ NADPH. Explain why this high number of ATP and NADPH molecules is consistent with the value of glucose as an energy source.

● 6 . . . 18 . . . 12. Glucose is a highly reduced molecule, storing lots of potential energy in its electrons. The more energy a molecule stores, the more energy and reducing power required to produce that molecule.

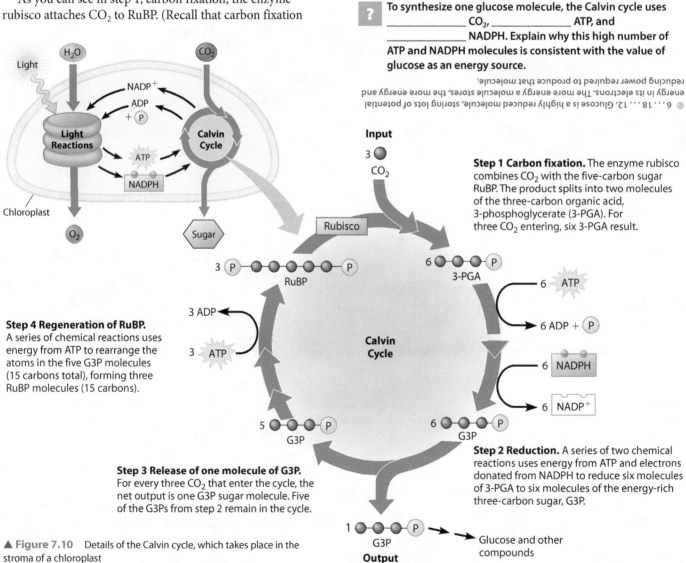

▲ **Figure 7.10** Details of the Calvin cycle, which takes place in the stroma of a chloroplast

Step 1 Carbon fixation. The enzyme rubisco combines CO$_2$ with the five-carbon sugar RuBP. The product splits into two molecules of the three-carbon organic acid, 3-phosphoglycerate (3-PGA). For three CO$_2$ entering, six 3-PGA result.

Step 2 Reduction. A series of two chemical reactions uses energy from ATP and electrons donated from NADPH to reduce six molecules of 3-PGA to six molecules of the energy-rich three-carbon sugar, G3P.

Step 3 Release of one molecule of G3P. For every three CO$_2$ that enter the cycle, the net output is one G3P sugar molecule. Five of the G3Ps from step 2 remain in the cycle.

Step 4 Regeneration of RuBP. A series of chemical reactions uses energy from ATP to rearrange the atoms in the five G3P molecules (15 carbons total), forming three RuBP molecules (15 carbons).

7.11 Other methods of carbon fixation have evolved in hot, dry climates

EVOLUTION CONNECTION

As you learned in the previous module, the first step of the Calvin cycle is carbon fixation. Most plants use CO_2 directly from the air, and carbon fixation occurs when the enzyme rubisco adds CO_2 to RuBP (see step 1 of Figure 7.10). Such plants are called **C_3 plants** because the first product of carbon fixation is the three-carbon compound 3-PGA. C_3 plants are widely distributed; they include such important agricultural crops as soybeans, oats, wheat, and rice. One problem that farmers face in growing C_3 plants is that hot, dry weather can decrease crop yield. In response to such conditions, plants close their stomata, the pores in their leaves. This adaptation reduces water loss and helps prevent dehydration, but it also prevents CO_2 from entering the leaf and O_2 from exiting. As a result, CO_2 levels get very low in the leaf and photosynthesis slows. And the O_2 released from the light reactions begins to accumulate, creating another problem.

As O_2 builds up in a leaf, rubisco adds O_2 instead of CO_2 to RuBP. A two-carbon product of this reaction is then broken down in the cell. This process is called **photorespiration** because it occurs in the light and, like respiration, it consumes O_2 and releases CO_2. But unlike cellular respiration, it uses ATP instead of producing it; and unlike photosynthesis, it yields no sugar. Photorespiration can, however, drain away as much as 50% of the carbon fixed by the Calvin cycle.

According to one hypothesis, photorespiration is an evolutionary relic from when the atmosphere had less O_2 than it does today. In the ancient atmosphere that prevailed when rubisco first evolved, the inability of the enzyme's active site to exclude O_2 would have made little difference. It is only after O_2 became so concentrated in the atmosphere that the "sloppiness" of rubisco presented a problem. New evidence also indicates that photorespiration may play a protective role when the products of the light reactions build up in a cell (as occurs when the Calvin cycle slows due to a lack of CO_2).

C_4 Plants   In some plant species found in hot, dry climates, alternate modes of carbon fixation have evolved that minimize photorespiration and optimize the Calvin cycle. **C_4 plants** are so named because they first fix CO_2 into a four-carbon compound. When the weather is hot and dry, a C_4 plant keeps its stomata mostly closed, thus conserving water. It continues making sugars by photosynthesis using the pathway and the two types of cells shown on the left side of Figure 7.11. An enzyme in the mesophyll cells has a high affinity for CO_2 and can fix carbon even when the CO_2 concentration in the leaf is low. The resulting four-carbon compound then acts as a carbon shuttle; it moves into bundle-sheath cells, which are packed around the veins of the leaf, and releases CO_2. Thus, the CO_2 concentration in these cells remains high enough for the Calvin cycle to make sugars and avoid photorespiration. Corn and sugarcane are examples of agriculturally important C_4 plants.

CAM Plants   A second photosynthetic adaptation has evolved in pineapples, many cacti, and other succulent (water-storing)

▲ **Figure 7.11**   Adaptations for photosynthesis in hot, dry climates

Try This Use these diagrams to explain the differences between C_4 and CAM photosynthesis.

plants, such as aloe and jade plants. Called **CAM plants**, these species are adapted to very dry climates. A CAM plant (right side of Figure 7.11) conserves water by opening its stomata and admitting CO_2 only at night. CO_2 is fixed into a four-carbon compound, which banks CO_2 at night and releases it during the day. Thus, the Calvin cycle can operate, even with the leaf's stomata closed during the day.

In C_4 plants, carbon fixation and the Calvin cycle occur in different types of cells. In CAM plants, these processes occur in the same cells, but at different times of the day. Keep in mind that CAM, C_4, and C_3 plants all eventually use the Calvin cycle to make sugar from CO_2. The C_4 and CAM pathways are two evolutionary adaptations that minimize photorespiration and maximize photosynthesis in hot, dry climates.

? **Why would you expect photorespiration on a hot, dry day to occur less in C_4 and CAM plants than in C_3 plants?**

Because of their initial fixing of carbon, both C_4 and CAM plants can supply rubisco with CO_2. When a C_3 plant closes its stomata, CO_2 levels drop and O_2 rises, making it more likely that rubisco will add O_2 to RuBP.

7.12 Photosynthesis makes sugar from CO_2 and H_2O, providing food and O_2 for almost all living organisms

Now that we have made our way from photons to food, let's step back and review the process of photosynthesis and then discuss its importance. Starting on the left of the overview diagram shown in **Figure 7.12**, you see a summary of the light reactions, which occur in the thylakoid membranes. Two photosystems in the membranes capture solar energy, energizing electrons in chlorophyll molecules. Simultaneously, water is split, O_2 is released, and electrons are funneled to the photosystems. The photoexcited electrons are transferred through an electron transport chain, where energy is harvested to make ATP by the process of chemiosmosis, and finally to $NADP^+$, reducing it to the high-energy compound NADPH.

The chloroplast's sugar factory is the Calvin cycle, the second stage of photosynthesis. In the stroma, the enzyme rubisco combines CO_2 with RuBP. ATP and NADPH are used to reduce 3-PGA to G3P. Sugar molecules made from G3P serve as a plant's own food supply.

About 50% of the carbohydrate made by photosynthesis is consumed as fuel for cellular respiration in the mitochondria of plant cells. Sugars also serve as starting material for making other organic molecules, such as a plant's proteins and lipids. Many glucose molecules are linked together to make cellulose, the main component of cell walls. Cellulose is the most abundant organic molecule in a plant—and probably on the surface of the planet. Most plants make much more food each day than they need. They store the excess in roots, tubers, seeds, and fruits.

Plants (and other photosynthesizers) not only feed themselves but also are the ultimate source of food for virtually all other organisms. Humans and other animals make none of their own food and are totally dependent on the organic matter made by photosynthesizers. Even the energy we acquire when we eat meat was originally captured by photosynthesis. The energy in a steak, for instance, came from sunlight that was originally converted to a chemical form in the grasses eaten by cattle.

The collective productivity of the tiny chloroplasts is truly amazing: Photosynthesis makes an estimated 150 billion metric tons of carbohydrate per year (about 165 billion tons). That's equivalent in mass to a stack of about 100 trillion copies of this textbook—10 stacks of books reaching from Earth to the sun!

The products of photosynthesis provide us with more than just food. For most of human history, burning plant material has been a major source of heat, light, and cooking fuel. The use of fossil fuels is a relatively recent development, and these sources of energy come from the remains of ancient organisms that removed CO_2 from the atmosphere by photosynthesis over the course of hundreds of millions of years. The burning of these ancient carbon stores is increasing the atmospheric level of CO_2, which has risen more than 40% since 1850, the start of the Industrial Revolution, changing the global climate and affecting current-day photosynthesizers. In the next module, we explore how scientists study the effects of rising CO_2 levels on plants.

> ? **Explain this statement: No process is more important to the welfare of life on Earth than photosynthesis.**

● Photosynthesis is the ultimate source of the food for almost all organisms and the oxygen they need for cellular respiration.

▶ **Figure 7.12** A summary of photosynthesis

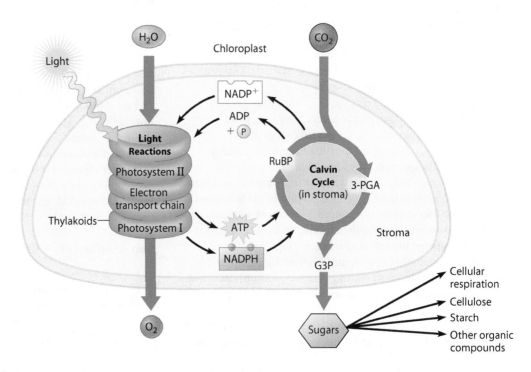

7.13 Rising atmospheric levels of carbon dioxide and global climate change will affect plants in various ways

SCIENTIFIC THINKING

How is the increase in atmospheric carbon dioxide affecting Earth's climate? First, let's consider the role of CO_2 as a so-called greenhouse gas. As you probably know, greenhouses are used to grow plants when the weather outside is too cold. Solar radiation can pass through their transparent walls, and much of the heat that accumulates inside is trapped.

An analogous process, called the **greenhouse effect**, operates on a global scale. Solar radiation passes through the atmosphere and warms Earth's surface. Heat radiating from the warmed planet is absorbed by greenhouse gases, such as CO_2, water vapor, and methane, which then reflect some of the heat back to Earth. Without this natural heating effect, the average air temperature would be a frigid $-18°C$ ($-0.4°F$), and most life as we know it could not exist. But this insulating blanket of greenhouse gases is starting to warm Earth *too* much.

Increasing concentrations of greenhouse gases have been linked to **global climate change**, of which one major aspect is global warming. The predicted consequences of global climate change include melting of polar ice, rising sea levels, extreme weather patterns, droughts, increased extinction rates, and the spread of tropical diseases. Indeed, many of these effects are already being documented.

How may global climate change affect plants? You might predict that, as a raw material for photosynthesis, increasing CO_2 levels would increase plant productivity. Indeed, research has documented such an increase, although results often indicate that the growth rates of weeds, such as the poison ivy described in the chapter introduction, increase more than those of crop plants and trees.

How do scientists study the effects of increasing CO_2 on plants? As is so often the case, scientists use different types of experiments to test their hypotheses. Many experiments are done in small growth chambers in which variables can be carefully controlled. But the availability of facilities and resources often limits such studies in scope and length. Some creative researchers have made use of study areas that naturally vary in CO_2 levels, such as comparing plant diversity and growth in experimental plots set in urban, suburban, and country locations.

Other scientists are turning to long-term field studies that include large-scale manipulations of CO_2 levels. In the Free-Air CO_2 Enrichment (FACE) experiment set up in Duke University's experimental forest, scientists monitored the effects of elevated CO_2 levels on an intact forest ecosystem over a period of 15 years. Six study sites were established, each 30 m in diameter and ringed by 16 towers (**Figure 7.13A**). In three of the plots, the towers released air containing CO_2 concentrations about $1\frac{1}{2}$ times

Source: Adaptation of Figure 1A from "Biomass and Toxicity Responses of Poison Ivy (*Toxicodendron Radicans*) to Elevated Atmospheric CO_2" by Jacqueline E. Mohan, et al., from *PNAS*, June 2006, Volume 103(24). Copyright © 2006 by National Academy of Sciences. Reprinted with permission.

▲ **Figure 7.13B** The mean poison ivy biomass in control plots and elevated CO_2 plots (with error bars showing the variation around the mean)

present-day levels. Monitoring instruments on a tall tower in the center of each plot adjusted the distribution of CO_2 to maintain a stable concentration. All other factors, such as temperature, precipitation, and wind patterns, varied normally for both experimental plots and adjacent control plots.

Figure 7.13B shows some results from a study that compared the growth of poison ivy in experimental and control plots. The poison ivy in the elevated CO_2 plots showed an average annual growth increase of 149% compared to control plots. This increase is much greater than the increase for woody plants that similar studies have documented. Indeed, over a 12-year monitoring period, the trees in the FACE experimental plots produced only about 15% more wood per year than those in the control plots.

Will global climate change make you itch?

There was one other significant finding of the poison ivy study. A chemical analysis showed that the high-CO_2 plants produced a more potent form of poison ivy's allergenic compound. Thus, poison ivy is predicted to become both more abundant and more toxic ("itchy") as CO_2 levels rise.

▲ **Figure 7.13A** Large-scale experiment in the Duke University Experimental Forest on the effects of elevated CO_2 concentration. (Rings of towers emit CO_2-enriched air in three of the plots.)

? **Describe three research methods that scientists use to test the hypothesis that increasing CO_2 levels will affect the growth of plants.**

● Laboratory growth chambers, field studies in areas where CO_2 levels vary naturally, and large-scale field studies in which CO_2 levels are manipulated

7.14 Scientific research and international treaties have helped slow the depletion of Earth's ozone layer

The importance of science is illustrated by the story of how synthetic chemicals were destroying Earth's protective ozone layer and how the work of many scientists led to changes in worldwide environmental policies. As you now know, photosynthesis produces the O_2 on which almost all organisms depend for cellular respiration. This O_2 has another benefit: High in the atmosphere, high-energy solar radiation converts it to ozone (O_3). Acting as sunscreen for the planet, the ozone layer shields Earth from ultraviolet radiation. The balance between ozone formation and its natural destruction in the atmosphere, however, has been upset by human actions.

Chlorofluorocarbons (CFCs) are chemicals developed in the 1930s that became widely used in aerosol sprays, refrigerators, and Styrofoam production. In 1970, a scientist wondered whether CFCs were accumulating in the environment and sent a homemade detector on a boat trip to Antarctica. He found CFCs in the air all along the journey. When he reported his findings at a scientific meeting in 1972, two chemists, Sherwood Rowland and Mario Molina, further wondered what happened to CFCs once they entered the atmosphere. A search of the literature found that these chemicals were not broken down in the lower atmosphere.

But the intense solar radiation in the upper atmosphere could break down CFCs, releasing chlorine atoms. Molina learned that chlorine reacts with ozone, reducing it to O_2. Other reactions liberate the chlorine, allowing it to destroy more ozone. In 1974, Molina and Rowland published their work predicting that the release of CFCs would damage the ozone layer.

As other researchers tested the CFC-ozone depletion hypothesis, the evidence accumulated, and more people became concerned about ozone depletion. Others worried about the economic impact of banning CFCs, and many chemical manufacturers mounted a campaign to cast doubt on the Molina-Rowland hypothesis in any way they could.

Then, in 1985, scientists from the British Antarctic Survey published their observations that the ozone level above Antarctica had decreased drastically. A reanalysis of data collected by the National Aeronautics and Space Administration (NASA) over that period confirmed a gigantic hole in the ozone layer. This hole has appeared every spring over Antarctica since the late 1970s and continues today. **Figure 7.14A** shows an image produced from atmospheric data from 2012. Dark blue colors show where there is the least ozone. The ozone depletion turned out to be much greater than had been predicted by Molina and Rowland. How could that be explained?

Susan Solomon (**Figure 7.14B**), with the National Oceanic and Atmospheric Administration (NOAA), developed a hypothesis that the unique ice clouds that develop during the cold winter in Antarctica could be involved in speeding up the reactions that destroy ozone. The then 30-year-old scientist led two research expeditions to the Antarctic. The data that she and her team collected indicated that chemical reactions occurring on the icy particles when the spring sun hits them made CFCs destroy ozone at an astonishing rate. Once the clouds warm and disperse, these reactions slow.

Further laboratory tests and field measurements taken from the ground, balloons, and airplanes supported Solomon's hypothesis. In response to these scientific findings, the first treaty to address Earth's environment was signed in 1987. In the original Montreal Protocol, more than two dozen nations agreed to phase out CFCs. As research continued to establish the extent and danger of ozone depletion, these agreements were strengthened in 1990, and now nearly 200 nations participate in the protocol. In 1995, Molina and Rowland shared a Nobel Prize for their work in determining how CFCs were damaging the atmosphere.

Global emissions of CFCs are near zero now, but because these compounds are so stable, recovery of the ozone layer is not expected until around 2060. Meanwhile, unblocked UV radiation is predicted to increase skin cancer and cataracts, as well as damage crops and phytoplankton in the oceans.

In addition to being ozone destroyers, CFCs are also potent greenhouse gases. The phaseout of CFCs has avoided what would have been the equivalent of adding 10 gigatons of CO_2 to the atmosphere. (For comparison, the Kyoto Protocol of 1997 set a 2012 target of a reduction of 2 gigatons of CO_2 emissions.)

Whether an environmental problem involves CFCs or CO_2, the scientific research is often complicated and the solutions complex. The connections between science, technology, and society, so clearly exemplified by the work of the scientists studying the ozone layer, are a major theme of this book.

▲ **Figure 7.14B** Susan Solomon at her cold research site

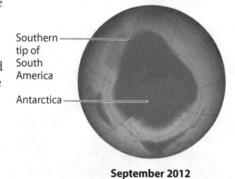

Southern tip of South America

Antarctica

September 2012

▲ **Figure 7.14A** The ozone hole in the Southern Hemisphere, fall 2012

> ? Where does the ozone layer come from, and why is it so important to life on Earth?

● High in the atmosphere, radiation from the sun converts O_2 to ozone. The ozone layer absorbs potentially damaging UV radiation before it can reach Earth's surface.

For practice quizzes, BioFlix animations, MP3 tutorials, video tutors, and more study tools designed for this textbook, go to

MasteringBiology®

Reviewing the Concepts

An Introduction to Photosynthesis (7.1–7.5)

7.1 Photosynthesis fuels the biosphere. Plants, algae, and some bacteria are photoautotrophs, the producers of food consumed by virtually all heterotrophic organisms.

7.2 Photosynthesis occurs in chloroplasts in plant cells. Chloroplasts are surrounded by a double membrane and contain stacks of thylakoids and a thick fluid called stroma.

7.3 Scientists traced the process of photosynthesis using isotopes. Experiments using both heavy and radioactive isotopes helped determine the details of the process of photosynthesis.

$$6\ CO_2 + 6\ H_2O \xrightarrow[\textbf{Photosynthesis}]{\text{Light energy}} C_6H_{12}O_6 + 6\ O_2$$

Carbon dioxide Water   Glucose   Oxygen gas

7.4 Photosynthesis is a redox process, as is cellular respiration. In photosynthesis, H_2O is oxidized and CO_2 is reduced.

7.5 The two stages of photosynthesis are linked by ATP and NADPH. The light reactions occur in the thylakoids, producing ATP and NADPH for the Calvin cycle, which takes place in the stroma.

The Light Reactions: Converting Solar Energy to Chemical Energy (7.6–7.9)

7.6 Visible radiation absorbed by pigments drives the light reactions. Certain wavelengths of visible light are absorbed by chlorophyll and other pigments. Carotenoids also function in photoprotection from excessive light.

7.7 Photosystems capture solar energy. Thylakoid membranes contain photosystems, each consisting of light-harvesting complexes and a reaction-center complex. A primary electron acceptor receives photoexcited electrons from chlorophyll.

7.8 Two photosystems connected by an electron transport chain generate ATP and NADPH. Electrons shuttle from photosystem II to photosystem I, providing energy to make ATP, and then reduce $NADP^+$ to NADPH. Photosystem II regains electrons as water is split and O_2 released.

7.9 The light reactions take place within the thylakoid membranes. In photophosphorylation, the electron transport chain pumps H^+ into the thylakoid space. The concentration gradient drives H^+ back through ATP synthase, powering the synthesis of ATP.

The Calvin Cycle: Reducing CO_2 to Sugar (7.10–7.11)

7.10 ATP and NADPH power sugar synthesis in the Calvin cycle. The steps of the Calvin cycle include carbon fixation, reduction, release of G3P, and regeneration of RuBP. Using carbon from CO_2, electrons from NADPH, and energy from ATP, the cycle constructs G3P, which is used to build glucose and other organic molecules.

7.11 Other methods of carbon fixation have evolved in hot, dry climates. In C_3 plants, a drop in CO_2 and rise in O_2 when stomata close divert the Calvin cycle to photorespiration. C_4 plants and CAM plants first fix CO_2 into four-carbon compounds that provide CO_2 to the Calvin cycle even when stomata close on hot, dry days.

The Global Significance of Photosynthesis (7.12–7.14)

7.12 Photosynthesis makes sugar from CO_2 and H_2O, providing food and O_2 for almost all living organisms.

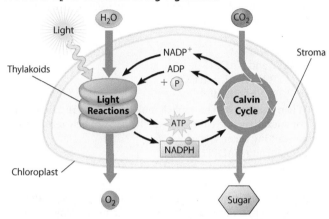

7.13 Rising atmospheric levels of carbon dioxide and global climate change will affect plants in various ways. Scientists study the effects of rising CO_2 levels using laboratory growth chambers and field studies. Long-term field projects enable scientists to assess the effects of CO_2 levels on natural ecosystems.

7.14 Scientific research and international treaties have helped slow the depletion of Earth's ozone layer. Solar radiation converts O_2 high in the atmosphere to ozone (O_3), which shields organisms from damaging UV radiation. Industrial chemicals called CFCs caused dangerous thinning of the ozone layer, but international restrictions on CFC use are allowing its recovery.

Connecting the Concepts

1. Complete this summary map of photosynthesis.

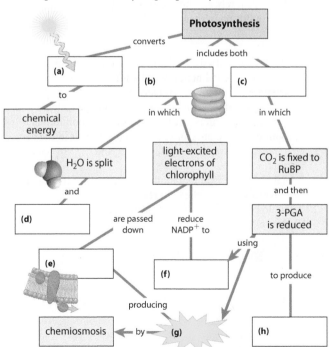

Testing Your Knowledge

Level 1: Knowledge/Comprehension

2. In photosynthesis, _____ is oxidized and _____ is reduced.
   a. water . . . oxygen
   b. carbon dioxide . . . water
   c. water . . . carbon dioxide
   d. glucose . . . carbon dioxide

3. Which of the following are produced by reactions that take place in the thylakoids and consumed by reactions in the stroma?
   a. CO_2 and H_2O
   b. ATP and NADPH
   c. ATP, NADPH, and CO_2
   d. ATP, NADPH, and O_2

4. When light strikes chlorophyll molecules in the reaction-center complex, they lose electrons, which are ultimately replaced by
   a. splitting water.
   b. oxidizing NADPH.
   c. the primary electron acceptor.
   d. the electron transport chain.

5. The reactions of the Calvin cycle are not directly dependent on light, but they usually do not occur at night. Why? (*Explain your answer.*)
   a. It is often too cold at night for these reactions to take place.
   b. Carbon dioxide concentrations decrease at night.
   c. The Calvin cycle depends on products of the light reactions.
   d. Plants usually close their stomata at night.

6. Which of the following does *not* occur during the Calvin cycle?
   a. carbon fixation
   b. oxidation of NADPH
   c. consumption of ATP
   d. release of oxygen

7. Why is it difficult for C_3 plants to carry out photosynthesis in very hot, dry environments such as deserts?
   a. The light is too intense and destroys the pigment molecules.
   b. The closing of stomata keeps CO_2 from entering and O_2 from leaving the plant.
   c. They must rely on photorespiration to make ATP.
   d. CO_2 builds up in the leaves, blocking carbon fixation.

Level 2: Application/Analysis

8. How is photosynthesis similar in C_4 plants and CAM plants?
   a. In both cases, the light reactions and the Calvin cycle are separated in both time and location.
   b. Both types of plants make sugar without the Calvin cycle.
   c. In both cases, rubisco is not used to fix carbon initially.
   d. Both types of plants make most of their sugar in the dark.

9. Compare and describe the roles of CO_2 and H_2O in cellular respiration and photosynthesis.

10. Explain why a poison that inhibits an enzyme of the Calvin cycle will also inhibit the light reactions.

11. What do plants do with the sugar they produce in photosynthesis?

Level 3: Synthesis/Evaluation

12. The following diagram compares the chemiosmotic synthesis of ATP in mitochondria and chloroplasts. Identify the components that are shared by both organelles and indicate which side of the membrane has the higher H^+ concentration. Then label on the right the locations within the chloroplast.

13. Continue your comparison of electron transport and chemiosmosis in mitochondria and chloroplasts. In each case,
    a. where do the electrons come from?
    b. how do the electrons get their high potential energy?
    c. what picks up the electrons at the end of the chain?
    d. how is the energy given up by the electrons used?

14. **SCIENTIFIC THINKING** Will global climate change make you sneeze as well as itch? Scientists studying the effects of rising CO_2 levels have looked at ragweed, whose pollen is the primary allergen for fall hay fever. They grew ragweed in three levels of CO_2: a pre-industrial concentration of 280 ppm, a year 2000 level of 370 ppm, and a projected level of 600 ppm. They found that pollen production increased by 131% and 320% in the plants exposed to the recent and projected CO_2 levels, respectively. What was the hypothesis of this experiment? Do the results support the hypothesis? Given what you know about global climate change, what other variables would you like to test, and what other measurements would you like to take?

15. Most experts agree that global climate change is already occurring and that global warming will increase rapidly in this century. Recent international negotiations, however, including a 2012 meeting in Doha, Qatar, have yet to reach a global consensus on how to reduce greenhouse gas emissions. Some countries have resisted taking action because a very few scientists and policymakers think that the warming trend may be just a random fluctuation and/or not related to human activities or that cutting CO_2 emissions would sacrifice economic growth. Do you think we need more evidence before taking action? Or is it better to act now to reduce CO_2 emissions? What are the possible costs and benefits of each of these two strategies?

Answers to all questions can be found in Appendix 4.

Cellular Reproduction and Genetics

The Cellular Basis of Reproduction and Inheritance

The photo below shows a cancer cell dividing. Cancer cells start as normal body cells, but genetic mutations cause them to lose the ability to regulate the tempo of their own division. Like a car careening downhill without brakes, unconstrained body cells will likely wreak havoc. If left untreated, cancer cells will continue to divide and spread, invading other tissues, disrupting organ function, and eventually killing the host.

How can cancer be stopped? Most cancer treatments seek to disrupt one or more steps in cell division. Some anticancer drugs target dividing DNA; others disrupt the cellular structures that assist in cell division. Recent advances in cancer therapy have sought to match particular patients with specific therapies. For example, about two-thirds of human breast tumors contain cells that bear receptors for the sex hormone estrogen, which enhances breast cell division, thereby accelerating the growth of the tumor. Patients with such tumors may be treated with tamoxifen, a drug that specifically blocks estrogen receptors. Women who lack estrogen receptors on their tumor cells (about one-third of breast cancer patients)

Can cancer therapy be personalized?

will not respond to this therapy. As more is learned about the underlying biology of cancer cells, cancer therapy will become even more personalized, with the most reliable drugs chosen for each patient.

Although uncontrolled cell division in cancer cells is harmful, normal cell division is necessary in all forms of life. Some organisms, such as single-celled prokaryotes, reproduce themselves via cell division, creating two genetically identical offspring. In the bodies of all multicellular organisms, cell division allows for growth, replacement of damaged cells, and development of an embryo into an adult. In sexually reproducing organisms, eggs and sperm are produced by a particular type of cell division. In this chapter, we discuss the two main types of cell division—mitosis and meiosis—and explore how they function within organisms.

BIG IDEAS

Cell Division and Reproduction
(8.1–8.2)

Cell division underlies many of life's important processes.

The Eukaryotic Cell Cycle and Mitosis
(8.3–8.10)

Cells produce genetic duplicates through an ordered, tightly controlled series of steps.

Meiosis and Crossing Over
(8.11–8.17)

The process of meiosis produces genetically varied haploid gametes from diploid cells.

Alterations of Chromosome Number and Structure
(8.18–8.23)

Errors in cell division can produce organisms with abnormal numbers of chromosomes.

Cell Division and Reproduction

8.1 Cell division plays many important roles in the lives of organisms

The ability of organisms to reproduce their own kind is the characteristic that best distinguishes living things from non-living matter (see Module 1.1 to review the characteristics of life). Only amoebas produce more amoebas, only people make more people, and only maple trees produce more maple trees. However, reproduction actually occurs much more often at the cellular level. When a cell undergoes reproduction, or **cell division**, the two "daughter" cells that result are genetically identical to each other and to the original "parent" cell. (Biologists traditionally use the word *daughter* in this context; it does not imply gender.) Before the parent cell splits into two, it duplicates its **chromosomes**, the structures that contain most of the cell's DNA. Then, during the division process, one set of chromosomes is distributed to each daughter cell. As a rule, the daughter cells receive identical sets of chromosomes from the lone, original parent cell. Each offspring cell will thus be genetically identical to the other and to the original parent cell.

Sometimes, cell division results in the reproduction of a whole organism. Many single-celled organisms, such as prokaryotes or the eukaryotic yeast cell in **Figure 8.1A**, reproduce by dividing in half, and the offspring are genetic replicas. This is an example of **asexual reproduction**, the creation of genetically identical offspring by a single parent, without the participation of sperm and egg. Many multicellular organisms can reproduce asexually as well. For example, some sea star species have the ability to grow new individuals from fragmented pieces (**Figure 8.1B**). And if you've ever grown a houseplant from a clipping, you've observed asexual reproduction

in plants (**Figure 8.1C**). In asexual reproduction, there is one simple principle of inheritance: The lone parent and each of its offspring have identical genes.

Sexual reproduction is different; it requires fertilization of an egg by a sperm. The production of gametes—egg and sperm— involves a particular type of cell division that occurs only in reproductive organs (testes and ovaries in humans). A gamete has only half as many chromosomes as the parent cell that gave rise to it (see Module 8.13), and these chromosomes contain unique combinations of genes. Therefore, offspring produced by sexual reproduction generally resemble their parents more closely than they resemble unrelated individuals of the same species, but they are not identical to their parents or (with the exception of identical twins) to each other (**Figure 8.1D**). Each offspring inherits a unique combination of genes from its two parents, and this one-and-only set of genes programs a unique combination of traits. As a result, sexual reproduction can produce great variation among offspring.

Colorized TEM 5,000×

▲ **Figure 8.1A**
A yeast cell producing a genetically identical daughter cell by asexual reproduction

▲ **Figure 8.1B**　A sea star reproducing asexually via fragmentation and regeneration of the body from the fragmented arm

▲ **Figure 8.1C**　An African violet reproducing asexually from a cutting (the large leaf on the left)

▼ **Figure 8.1D**　Sexual reproduction produces offspring with unique combinations of genes

In multicellular organisms, cell division plays other important roles, in addition to the production of gametes. Cell division enables sexually reproducing organisms to develop from a single cell—the fertilized egg, or zygote (**Figure 8.1E**)—into an adult organism. All of the trillions of cells in your body arose via repeated cell divisions that began in your mother's body with a single fertilized egg cell. After an organism is fully grown, cell division continues to function in renewal and repair, replacing cells that die from normal wear and tear or from accidents. Within your body, millions of cells must divide every second to replace damaged or lost cells (**Figure 8.1F**). For example, dividing cells within your epidermis continuously replace dead cells that slough off the surface of your skin.

750×

▲ **Figure 8.1E**   Dividing cells in an early human embryo

The type of cell division responsible for the growth and maintenance of multicellular organisms and for asexual reproduction involves a process called mitosis. The production of egg and sperm cells involves a different type of cell division called meiosis. In the remainder of this chapter, you will learn the details of both mitosis and meiosis. To start, we'll look briefly at prokaryotic cell division.

LM 850×

▲ **Figure 8.1F**   A human kidney cell dividing

> **?** What function does cell division play in an amoeba (a single-celled protist)? What functions does it play in your body?
>
> ● Reproduction; development, growth, and repair

8.2 Prokaryotes reproduce by binary fission

Prokaryotes (single-celled bacteria and archaea) reproduce by a type of cell division called **binary fission**, a term that means "dividing in half." In typical prokaryotes, the majority of genes are carried on a single circular DNA molecule that, with associated proteins, constitutes the organism's

▲ **Figure 8.2A**   Binary fission of a prokaryotic cell

chromosome. Although prokaryotic chromosomes are much smaller than those of eukaryotes, duplicating them in an orderly fashion and distributing the copies equally to two daughter cells are still formidable tasks. Consider, for example, that when stretched out, the chromosome of the bacterium *Escherichia coli* (*E. coli*) is about 500 times longer than the cell itself. It is no small achievement to accurately replicate this molecule when it is coiled and packed inside the cell.

Figure 8.2A illustrates binary fission in a prokaryote. **1** As the chromosome is duplicating, the copies move toward the opposite ends of the cell. **2** Meanwhile, the cell elongates. **3** When chromosome duplication is complete and the cell has reached about twice its initial size, the plasma membrane grows inward and more cell wall is made, which eventually divides the parent cell into two daughter cells (**Figure 8.2B**).

> **?** Why is binary fission classified as asexual reproduction?
>
> ● Because the genetically identical offspring inherit their DNA from a single parent

Prokaryotic chromosomes

Colorized TEM 32,500×

▲ **Figure 8.2B**   An electron micrograph of a bacterium in a late stage of dividing

▷ **The Eukaryotic Cell Cycle and Mitosis**

8.3 The large, complex chromosomes of eukaryotes duplicate with each cell division

Eukaryotic cells, in general, are more complex and much larger than prokaryotic cells. In addition, eukaryotic cells usually have many more genes, the units of information that specify an organism's inherited traits. Human cells, for example, carry just under 21,000 genes, versus about 3,000 for a typical bacterium. Almost all the genes in the cells of humans, and in all other eukaryotes, are found in the cell nucleus, grouped into multiple chromosomes. (The exceptions include genes on the small DNA molecules within mitochondria and, in plants, within chloroplasts.) Each eukaryotic species has a characteristic number of chromosomes in each cell nucleus. For example, human body cells have 46 chromosomes, while the body cells of a dog have 78 and those of a hedgehog have 90.

Each eukaryotic chromosome consists of one long DNA molecule—bearing hundreds or thousands of genes—and a number of protein molecules, which are attached to the DNA. The proteins help maintain the chromosome's structure and control the activity of its genes. Together, the entire complex—consisting of roughly equal amounts of DNA and protein—is called **chromatin**.

Most of the time, chromatin exists as a diffuse mass of long, thin fibers that, if stretched out, would be far too long to fit in a cell's nucleus. In fact, the total length of DNA in just one of your cells exceeds your height! Chromatin in this state is too thin to be seen using a light microscope.

As a cell prepares to divide, its chromatin coils up, forming tight, distinct chromosomes that are visible under a light microscope. Why is it necessary for a cell's chromosomes to be compacted in this way? Imagine an analogy from your own life: Your belongings are spread throughout your home, but as you prepare to move, you gather them up and pack them into small containers to make them more easily sorted and transported. Similarly, before a cell can undergo division, it must compact all its DNA into manageable packages. **Figure 8.3A** is a micrograph of a plant cell that is about to divide; each thick

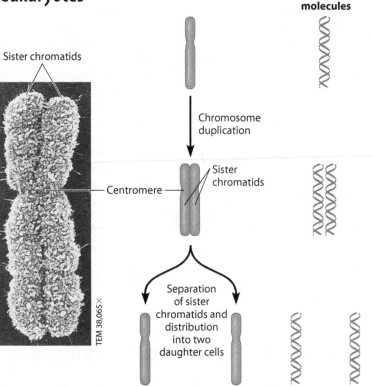

Chromosomes **Chromosomal DNA molecules**

Sister chromatids

Chromosome duplication

Centromere — Sister chromatids

Separation of sister chromatids and distribution into two daughter cells

TEM 38,065×

▲ **Figure 8.3B** Chromosome duplication and distribution

purple thread is actually an individual chromosome consisting of a single DNA molecule tightly wrapped around proteins.

The chromosomes of a eukaryotic cell are duplicated before they condense and the cell divides. The DNA molecule of each chromosome is replicated (as you'll learn in Chapter 10), and new protein molecules attach as needed to maintain the chromosome's structure and regulate its genes. Each chromosome now consists of two copies called **sister chromatids**, joined copies of the original chromosome (**Figure 8.3B**). The two sister chromatids are attached together along their lengths by proteins and are cinched especially tightly at a region called the **centromere** (visible as a narrow "waist" near the center of each chromosome shown in the figure).

When the cell divides, the sister chromatids of a duplicated chromosome separate from each other. Once separated from its sister, each chromatid is considered an individual chromosome, and it is identical to the cell's original chromosome. During cell division, one of the newly separated chromosomes goes to one daughter cell, and the other goes to the other daughter cell. In this way, each daughter cell receives a complete and identical set of chromosomes. In humans, for example, a typical dividing cell has 46 duplicated chromosomes (and thus 92 chromatids), and each of the two daughter cells that results from it has 46 single chromosomes.

▶ **Figure 8.3A**
A plant cell (from an African blood lily (*Scadoxus multiflorus*) just before cell division

LM 565×

? **When does a chromosome consist of two identical chromatids?**

● When the cell is preparing to divide and has duplicated its chromosomes but before the duplicates actually separate

8.4 The cell cycle includes growing and division phases

How do chromosome duplication and cell division fit into the life of a cell—and the life of an organism? As discussed in Module 8.1, all life depends on cell division: Cell division is the basis of reproduction for every organism; it enables a multicellular organism to grow to adult size; and it replaces worn-out or damaged cells, keeping the total number of cells in an adult animal relatively constant. In your body, for example, millions of cells must divide every second to maintain the total number of about 10 trillion cells. Some cells divide once a day, others less often; and highly specialized cells, such as mature muscle cells, do not divide at all. The fact that some mature cells never divide explains why some kinds of damage—such as the death of cardiac muscle during a heart attack or the death of brain cells during a stroke—can never be reversed.

The process of cell division is a key component of the **cell cycle**, an ordered sequence of events that extends from the instant a cell is first formed from a dividing parent cell until its own division into two cells. The cell cycle consists of two main stages: a growing stage (called interphase), during which the cell approximately doubles everything in its cytoplasm and precisely replicates its chromosomal DNA, and the actual cell division (called the mitotic phase).

As **Figure 8.4** indicates, most of the cell cycle is spent in **interphase**. This is an interval when a cell's metabolic activity is very high and the cell performs its normal functions. For example, a cell in your small intestine might release digestive enzymes and absorb nutrients. Your intestinal cell also grows in size during interphase, making more cytoplasm, increasing its supply of digestive proteins, and creating more cytoplasmic organelles (such as mitochondria and ribosomes). In addition, the cell duplicates its chromosomes during this period. Typically, interphase lasts for at least 90% of the total time required for the cell cycle.

Interphase (illustrated in the beige portion of the figure) can be divided into three subphases: the G_1 phase ("first gap"), the S phase ("synthesis" of DNA—also known as DNA replication), and the G_2 phase ("second gap"). During all three subphases, the cell grows. The chromosomes are duplicated during the S phase: At the beginning of the S phase, each chromosome is single. At the end of this subphase, after DNA replication, the chromosomes are doubled, each consisting of two sister chromatids joined along their lengths. During the G_2 phase, the cell grows more as it completes preparations for cell division.

The **mitotic phase** (**M phase**; illustrated in the blue portion of the figure), the interval of the cell cycle when the cell physically divides, accounts for only about 10% of the total time required for the cell cycle. The mitotic phase is divided into two overlapping stages, called mitosis and cytokinesis. In **mitosis**, the nucleus and its contents—most important, the duplicated chromosomes—divide and are evenly distributed, forming two daughter nuclei. During **cytokinesis**, which usually begins before mitosis ends, the cytoplasm is divided in

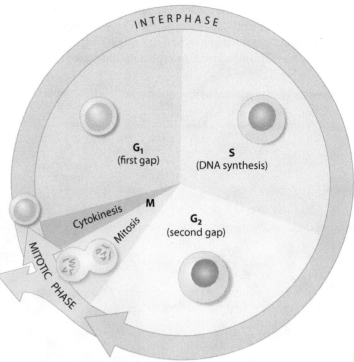

▲ **Figure 8.4**   The eukaryotic cell cycle

two. The combination of mitosis and cytokinesis produces two genetically identical daughter cells, each with a single nucleus, surrounding cytoplasm stocked with organelles, and a plasma membrane. Each newly produced daughter cell may then proceed through G_1 and repeat the cycle.

Mitosis is unique to eukaryotes and is the evolutionary solution to the problem of allocating an identical copy of the whole set of chromosomes to two daughter cells. Mitosis is a remarkably accurate mechanism. Experiments with yeast, for example, indicate that an error in chromosome distribution occurs only once in about 100,000 cell divisions.

The extreme accuracy of mitosis is essential to the development of your own body. You began as a single cell. Mitotic cell division ensures that all your body cells receive copies of the 46 chromosomes that were found in this original cell. Thus, every one of the trillions of cells in your body today can trace its ancestry back through mitotic divisions to that first cell produced when your father's sperm and mother's egg fused about nine months before your birth.

During the mitotic phase, a living cell viewed through a light microscope undergoes dramatic changes in the appearance of the chromosomes and other structures. In the next module, we'll use these visible changes as a guide to the stages of mitosis.

> **?**   A researcher treats cells with a chemical that prevents DNA synthesis from starting. This treatment would trap the cells in which part of the cell cycle?

G₁

8.5 Cell division is a continuum of dynamic changes

Figure 8.5 illustrates the cell cycle for an animal cell using micrographs from a newt (with chromosomes shown in blue and the mitotic spindle stained green) and drawings (simplified to include just four chromosomes). Interphase is illustrated here, but the emphasis is on the dramatic changes that occur during cell division, the mitotic phase. Mitosis is a continuum, but biologists can distinguish five main stages: **prophase**, **prometaphase**, **metaphase**, **anaphase**, and **telophase**.

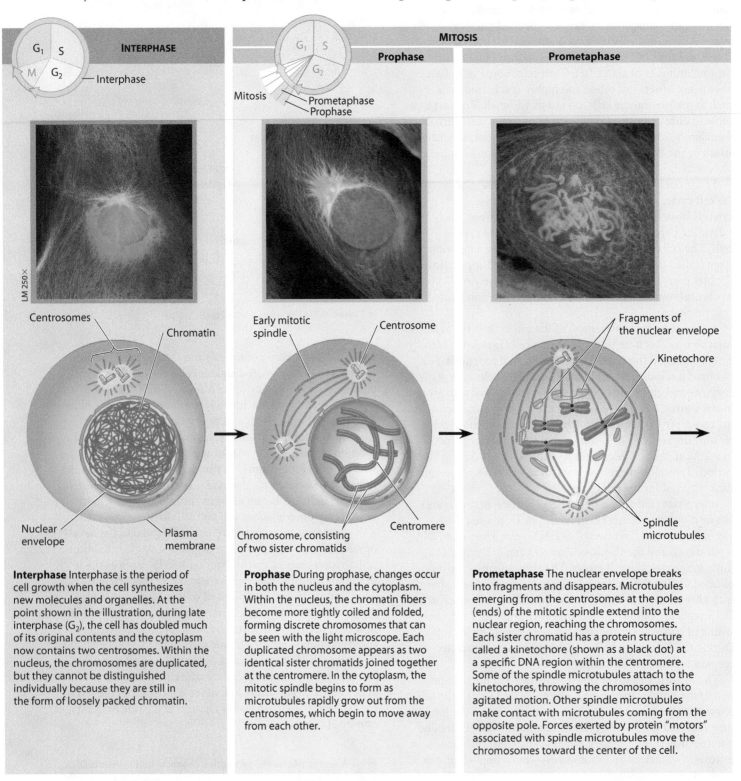

Interphase Interphase is the period of cell growth when the cell synthesizes new molecules and organelles. At the point shown in the illustration, during late interphase (G_2), the cell has doubled much of its original contents and the cytoplasm now contains two centrosomes. Within the nucleus, the chromosomes are duplicated, but they cannot be distinguished individually because they are still in the form of loosely packed chromatin.

Prophase During prophase, changes occur in both the nucleus and the cytoplasm. Within the nucleus, the chromatin fibers become more tightly coiled and folded, forming discrete chromosomes that can be seen with the light microscope. Each duplicated chromosome appears as two identical sister chromatids joined together at the centromere. In the cytoplasm, the mitotic spindle begins to form as microtubules rapidly grow out from the centrosomes, which begin to move away from each other.

Prometaphase The nuclear envelope breaks into fragments and disappears. Microtubules emerging from the centrosomes at the poles (ends) of the mitotic spindle extend into the nuclear region, reaching the chromosomes. Each sister chromatid has a protein structure called a kinetochore (shown as a black dot) at a specific DNA region within the centromere. Some of the spindle microtubules attach to the kinetochores, throwing the chromosomes into agitated motion. Other spindle microtubules make contact with microtubules coming from the opposite pole. Forces exerted by protein "motors" associated with spindle microtubules move the chromosomes toward the center of the cell.

▲ **Figure 8.5**   The stages of cell division by mitosis

Try This   Using simple drawings, illustrate the stages of mitosis for a cell that has six chromosomes.

The chromosomes are the stars of the mitotic drama. Their movements depend on the **mitotic spindle**, a football-shaped structure of microtubules and associated proteins that guides the separation of the two sets of daughter chromosomes. The spindle microtubules emerge from two **centrosomes**, microtubule-organizing regions in the cytoplasm of eukaryotic cells.

? You view an animal cell through a microscope and observe dense, duplicated chromosomes scattered throughout the cell. Which state of mitosis are you witnessing?

⊙ Prophase (because the chromosomes are condensed but not yet aligned)

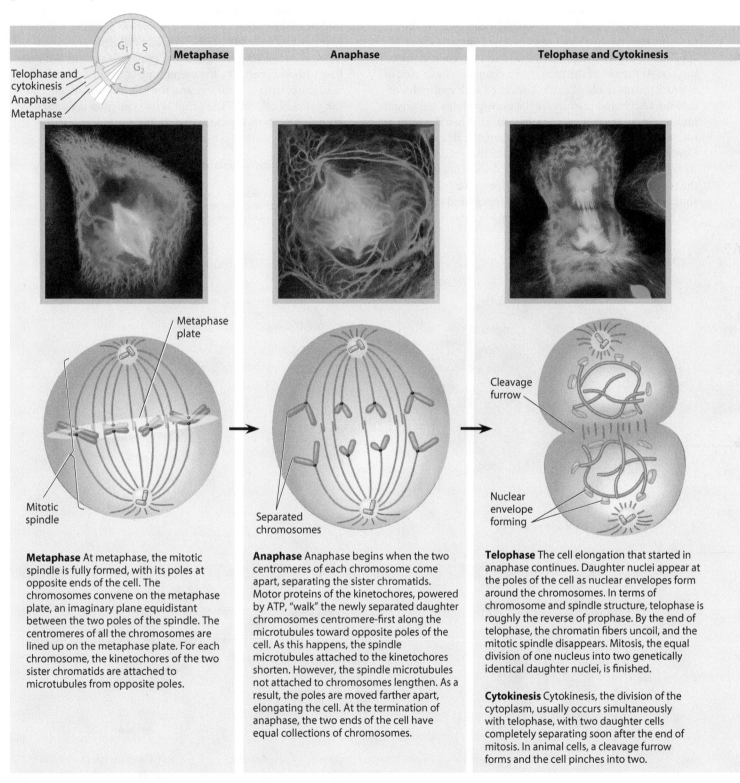

Metaphase

Anaphase

Telophase and Cytokinesis

Telophase and cytokinesis
Anaphase
Metaphase

Metaphase plate

Mitotic spindle

Separated chromosomes

Cleavage furrow

Nuclear envelope forming

Metaphase At metaphase, the mitotic spindle is fully formed, with its poles at opposite ends of the cell. The chromosomes convene on the metaphase plate, an imaginary plane equidistant between the two poles of the spindle. The centromeres of all the chromosomes are lined up on the metaphase plate. For each chromosome, the kinetochores of the two sister chromatids are attached to microtubules from opposite poles.

Anaphase Anaphase begins when the two centromeres of each chromosome come apart, separating the sister chromatids. Motor proteins of the kinetochores, powered by ATP, "walk" the newly separated daughter chromosomes centromere-first along the microtubules toward opposite poles of the cell. As this happens, the spindle microtubules attached to the kinetochores shorten. However, the spindle microtubules not attached to chromosomes lengthen. As a result, the poles are moved farther apart, elongating the cell. At the termination of anaphase, the two ends of the cell have equal collections of chromosomes.

Telophase The cell elongation that started in anaphase continues. Daughter nuclei appear at the poles of the cell as nuclear envelopes form around the chromosomes. In terms of chromosome and spindle structure, telophase is roughly the reverse of prophase. By the end of telophase, the chromatin fibers uncoil, and the mitotic spindle disappears. Mitosis, the equal division of one nucleus into two genetically identical daughter nuclei, is finished.

Cytokinesis Cytokinesis, the division of the cytoplasm, usually occurs simultaneously with telophase, with two daughter cells completely separating soon after the end of mitosis. In animal cells, a cleavage furrow forms and the cell pinches into two.

8.6 Cytokinesis differs for plant and animal cells

As discussed in the previous module, cytokinesis typically overlaps with telophase. Given the differences between animal and plant cells—particularly the stiff cell wall in plant cells—it isn't surprising that cytokinesis proceeds differently for these two types of eukaryotic cells.

In animal cells, cytokinesis occurs by cleavage. As shown in Figure 8.6A, the first sign of cleavage in animal cells is the appearance of a **cleavage furrow**, a shallow groove in the cell surface. At the site of the furrow, the cytoplasm has a ring of microfilaments made of actin, associated with molecules of myosin. (Actin and myosin are the same proteins responsible for muscle contraction; see Module 30.8.) When the actin microfilaments interact with the myosin, the ring contracts. Contraction of the myosin ring is much like pulling a drawstring on a hooded sweatshirt: As the drawstring is pulled, the ring of the hood contracts inward, eventually pinching shut. Similarly, the cleavage furrow deepens and eventually pinches the parent cell in two, resulting in two completely separate daughter cells, each with its own nucleus and share of cytoplasm.

Cytokinesis is markedly different in plant cells, which possess stiff cell walls (Figure 8.6B). During telophase, membranous vesicles containing cell wall material collect at the middle of the parent cell. The vesicles fuse, forming a membranous disk called the **cell plate**. The cell plate grows outward, accumulating more cell wall materials as more vesicles fuse with it. Eventually, the membrane of the cell plate fuses with the plasma membrane, and the cell plate's contents join the parental cell wall. The result is two daughter cells, each bounded by its own plasma membrane and cell wall.

? | **Contrast cytokinesis in animals with cytokinesis in plants.**

● In animals, cytokinesis involves a cleavage furrow in which contracting microfilaments pinch the cell in two. In plants, it involves formation of a cell plate, a fusion of vesicles that forms new plasma membranes and new cell walls between the cells.

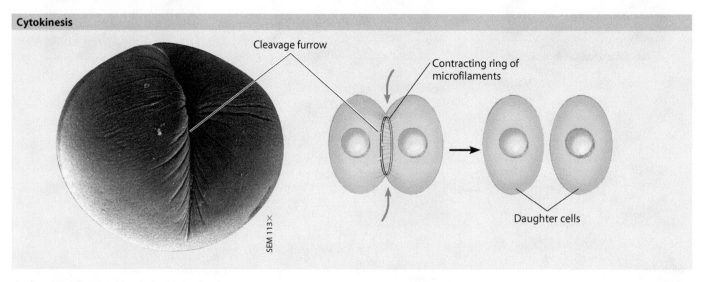

Cytokinesis

Cleavage furrow

Contracting ring of microfilaments

SEM 113×

Daughter cells

▲ Figure 8.6A   Cleavage of an animal cell

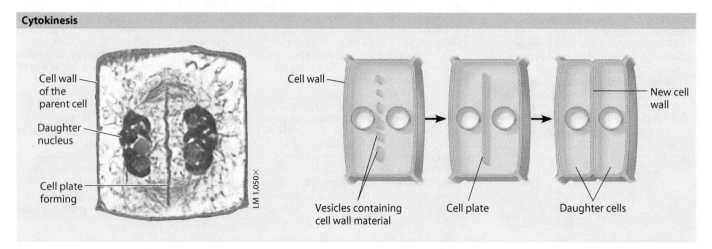

Cytokinesis

Cell wall of the parent cell

Daughter nucleus

Cell plate forming

LM 1,050×

Cell wall

Vesicles containing cell wall material

Cell plate

New cell wall

Daughter cells

▲ Figure 8.6B   Cell plate formation in a plant cell

8.7 Anchorage, cell density, and chemical growth factors affect cell division

For a plant or an animal to grow, develop normally, and maintain its tissues once fully grown, it must be able to control the timing of cell division in different parts of its body. For example, in your body, skin cells and the cells lining your digestive tract divide frequently, replacing cells that are constantly being abraded and sloughed off. In contrast, cells in your liver usually do not divide unless the liver is damaged.

By growing animal cells in culture, researchers have been able to identify many factors, both chemical and physical, that influence cell division. For example, most animal cells exhibit **anchorage dependence**; they must be in contact with a solid surface—such as the inside of a culture dish or the extracellular matrix of a tissue—to divide. One of the characteristics that distinguishes cancerous cells from normal body cells is their failure to exhibit anchorage dependence; they grow whether or not they are in contact with a suitable surface.

Another physical factor that can regulate growth rate is **density-dependent inhibition**, a phenomenon in which crowded cells stop dividing (Figure 8.7A). Animal cells growing on the surface of a dish multiply to form a single layer and usually stop dividing when they touch one another. If some cells are removed, those bordering the open space begin dividing again and continue until the vacancy is filled. What actually causes the inhibition of growth? Studies of cultured cells suggest that physical contact of cell-surface proteins between adjacent cells is responsible for inhibiting cell division. As with anchorage dependence, density-dependent inhibition fails in tumors; cancer cells continue to divide even at high densities, piling up on one another (bottom of Figure 8.7A).

Chemical factors can also influence the rate of cell growth. For example, when grown in the laboratory, cells fail to divide if an essential nutrient is left out of the culture medium. And most types of mammalian cells divide in culture only if certain specific growth factors are included. A **growth factor** is a protein secreted by certain body cells that stimulates other cells to divide (Figure 8.7B). Researchers have discovered at least 50 different growth factors that can trigger cell division. Different cell types respond specifically to certain growth factors or a combination of growth factors. For example, injury to the skin causes blood platelets to release a protein called platelet-derived growth factor. This protein promotes the rapid growth of connective tissue cells that help seal the wound. Another well-studied example is a protein called vascular endothelial growth factor (VEGF), which stimulates the growth of new blood vessels during fetal development and after injury. Interestingly, VEGF overproduction is a hallmark of many dangerous cancers; several anticancer drug therapies work by inhibiting the action of VEGF.

How do growth factors work? We will explore this question in the next module.

Cells anchor to the dish surface and divide (anchorage dependence).

When the cells have formed a complete single layer, they stop dividing (density-dependent inhibition).

If some cells are scraped away, the remaining cells divide to fill the dish with a single layer and then stop once they contact each other (density-dependent inhibition).

Cancer cells keep dividing even when they have filled a layer, forming a clump of overlapping cells.

▲ Figure 8.7A   An experiment demonstrating density-dependent inhibition, using animal cells grown in culture

Cultured cells suspended in liquid

The addition of growth factor

Cells fail to divide

Cells divide in presence of growth factor

▲ Figure 8.7B   An experiment demonstrating the effect of growth factors on the division of cultured animal cells

? Compared to a control culture, the cells in an experimental culture are fewer but much larger in size when they cover the dish surface and stop growing. What is a reasonable hypothesis for this difference?

The experimental culture is deficient in one or more growth factors.

8.8 Growth factors signal the cell cycle control system

In a living animal, most cells are anchored in a fixed position and bathed in a solution of nutrients supplied by the blood, yet they usually do not divide unless they are signaled by other cells to do so. Growth factors are the main signals, and their role in promoting cell division leads us back to our earlier discussion of the cell cycle.

The sequential events of the cell cycle, represented by the circle in **Figure 8.8A**, are directed by a distinct cell cycle control system, represented by the gray circle in the center of the art. The thin gray bar extending from the circle represents the current position in the cell cycle. The **cell cycle control system** is a cyclically operating set of molecules in the cell that both triggers and coordinates key events in the cell cycle. The cell cycle is *not* like a row of falling dominoes, with each event causing the next one in line. Within the M phase, for example, metaphase does not automatically lead to anaphase. Instead, proteins of the cell cycle control system must trigger the separation of sister chromatids that marks the start of anaphase.

A checkpoint in the cell cycle is a critical control point where stop and go-ahead signals (represented by stop/go lights in the figure) can regulate the cycle. The default action in most animal cells is to halt the cell cycle at these checkpoints unless overridden by specific go-ahead signals.

The red and white gates in Figure 8.8A represent major checkpoints in the cell cycle: during the G_1 and G_2 subphases of interphase and in the M phase. Intracellular signals detected by the control system tell the system whether key cellular processes up to each point have been completed and whether the cell cycle should proceed past that point. The control system also receives messages from outside the cell, indicating general environmental conditions and the presence of specific signal molecules from other cells. For many cells, the G_1 checkpoint seems to be the most important in cell division. If a cell receives a go-ahead signal—for example, from a growth factor—at the G_1 checkpoint, it will usually enter the S phase, eventually going on to complete its cycle and divide. If such a signal never arrives, the cell will switch to a permanently nondividing state called the G_0 phase. Many cells in the human body, such as mature nerve cells and muscle cells, are in the G_0 phase.

Figure 8.8B shows a simplified model for how a growth factor might affect the cell cycle control system at the G_1 checkpoint. A cell that responds to a growth factor (▽) has molecules of a specific receptor protein in its plasma membrane. Binding of the growth factor to the receptor (◗) triggers a signal transduction pathway in the cell. A signal transduction pathway is a series of protein molecules that conveys a message (see Modules 5.1 and 11.10). In this case, that message leads to cell division. The "signals" are

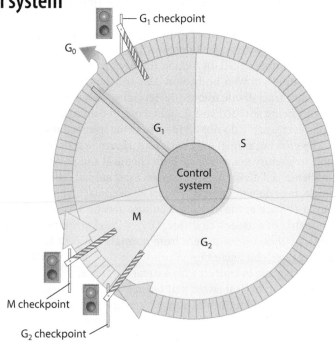

▲ **Figure 8.8A** A schematic model for the cell cycle control system

changes that each protein molecule induces in the next molecule in the pathway. Via a series of relay proteins, a signal finally reaches the cell cycle control system and overrides the brakes that otherwise prevent progress of the cell cycle.

Research on the control of the cell cycle is one of the hottest areas in biology today. This research is leading to a better understanding of cancer, which we discuss next.

> **?** At which of the three checkpoints described in this module do the chromosomes exist as duplicated sister chromatids?
>
> ● G_2 and M checkpoints

▲ **Figure 8.8B** How a growth factor signals the cell cycle control system

8.9 Growing out of control, cancer cells produce malignant tumors

CONNECTION

Cancer, which claims the lives of one out of every five people in the United States, is a disease of the cell cycle. Cancer cells do not heed the normal signals that regulate the cell cycle; they divide excessively and invade other tissues of the body. If unchecked, cancer cells may continue to grow and spread until they kill the organism.

The abnormal behavior of cancer cells begins when a single cell undergoes transformation, a process that converts a normal cell to a cancer cell. Transformation occurs following a mutation in one or more genes that encode for proteins in the cell cycle control system. Because a transformed cell grows abnormally, the immune system usually recognizes it as such and destroys it. However, if the cell evades destruction, it may multiply to form a **tumor**, a mass of abnormally growing cells within otherwise normal tissue. If the abnormal cells remain at their original site, the lump is called a **benign tumor**. Benign tumors can cause problems if they grow in and disrupt certain organs, such as the brain, but often they can be completely removed by surgery or even (in cases in which they pose no imminent threat) left alone.

In contrast, a **malignant tumor** can spread into neighboring tissues and invade other parts of the body, displacing normal tissue and interrupting organ function as it grows (Figure 8.9). An individual with a malignant tumor is said to have **cancer**. Cancer cells may separate from the original tumor or secrete signal molecules that cause blood vessels to grow toward the tumor. A few tumor cells may then enter the blood and lymph vessels and move to other parts of the body, where they may proliferate and form new tumors. The spread of cancer cells beyond their original site is called **metastasis**.

Cancers are named according to the organ or tissue in which they originate. Liver cancer, for example, starts in liver tissue and may or may not spread from there. Carcinomas are cancers that originate in the external or internal coverings of the body, such as the skin or the lining of the intestine. Leukemia is a broad term covering a number of diseases that originate in immature white blood cells within the blood or bone marrow.

From studying cancer cells in culture, researchers have learned that cancer cells do not heed the normal signals that regulate the cell cycle. For example, many cancer cells have defective cell cycle control systems that proceed past checkpoints even in the absence of growth factors. Other cancer cells synthesize growth factors themselves, causing the cells to divide continuously. If cancer cells do stop dividing, they seem to do so at random points in the cell cycle, rather than at the normal cell cycle checkpoints. Moreover, in the

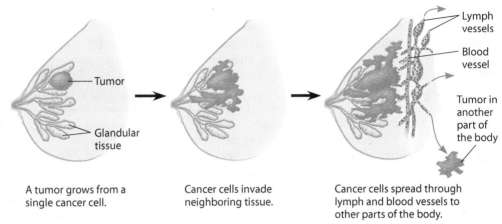

A tumor grows from a single cancer cell.

Cancer cells invade neighboring tissue.

Cancer cells spread through lymph and blood vessels to other parts of the body.

▲ **Figure 8.9** Growth and metastasis of a malignant tumor of the breast

laboratory, cancer cells are "immortal"; they can go on dividing indefinitely, as long as they have a supply of nutrients (whereas normal mammalian cells divide only about 20 to 50 times before they stop). A striking example of the immortality of cancer cells is a line that has been continuously multiplying in culture since 1951. Cells of this line are called HeLa cells, named for the original donor, Henrietta Lacks, who died of cervical cancer more than 60 years ago.

Luckily, many tumors can be successfully treated. A tumor that appears to be localized may be removed surgically. Alternatively, it can be treated with concentrated beams of high-energy radiation, which usually damages DNA in cancer cells more than it does in normal cells, perhaps because cancer cells have lost the ability to repair such damage. However, radiation also damages normal body cells, producing harmful side effects. For example, radiation damage to cells of the ovaries or testes can lead to sterility.

Chemotherapy is used to treat widespread or metastatic tumors. During periodic chemotherapy treatments, drugs are administered that disrupt specific steps in the cell cycle. For instance, the drug paclitaxel (trade name Taxol) freezes the mitotic spindle after it forms, which stops actively dividing cells from proceeding past metaphase. Vinblastin, a chemotherapeutic drug first obtained from the periwinkle plant, prevents the mitotic spindle from forming.

The side effects of chemotherapy are due to the drugs' effects on normal cells that rapidly divide. Nausea results from chemotherapy's effects on intestinal cells; hair loss comes from effects on hair follicle cells; and susceptibility to infection results from effects on immune cell production. (We will return to the topic of cancer—specifically, how mutations in genes that control cell division can lead to cancer—in Chapter 11.)

In the next module, you'll learn how understanding such mutations may aid in cancer treatment.

? **What is metastasis?**

● Metastasis is the spread of cancer cells from their original site of formation to other sites in the body.

8.10 Tailoring treatment to each patient may improve cancer therapy

SCIENTIFIC THINKING

Although several forms of cancer treatment are available, oncologists (doctors who treat cancer) have observed that different patients respond in drastically different ways to the same treatment. Medicines that are ineffective for most patients may have profound effects in a few, and vice versa.

Recently, researchers have amassed a flood of data about specific DNA mutations that disable the cell cycle control system and thereby promote the development of cancer. In addition, the time and cost required to sequence genes from a given individual have decreased dramatically. Thus, with increased understanding of DNA mutations and better access to gene sequencing, it is increasingly possible for physicians to personalize cancer treatment. The goal in moving toward personalized treatment is to identify and administer drugs that have the best chance of success in combating a given tumor's specific genetic profile.

Can cancer therapy be personalized?

A study that examined personalized cancer treatment was conducted at Memorial Sloan-Kettering Cancer Center in New York in 2012. Researchers sequenced the complete genome of tumor cells taken from a patient with metastasized bladder cancer. This patient, unlike most individuals with this type of cancer, responded well to a drug called everolimus. The researchers hoped that a genetic profile could provide insight into this unexpected result. Their next step was to identify 140 distinct mutations within the protein-coding genes of this patient's tumor cells. One of these mutations—in a gene called *TSC1*—affects a pathway that is targeted by the drug. The researchers hypothesized that mutations in this gene might be predictive of the drug's effect in cancer patients; those with the mutation would fare well when taking everolimus, whereas those who lack the mutation would not.

Because their hypothesis was based on a single case—and researchers are careful never to draw broad conclusions from

TABLE 8.10	NUMBERS OF CANCER PATIENTS RESPONDING TO THE DRUG EVEROLIMUS ($N = 13$)	
	Patients Responding to Everolimus	**Patients *Not* Responding to Everolimus**
Patients who had *TSC1* mutation	3	1
Patients who *did not* have *TSC1* mutation	1	8

Source: Data from G. Iyer et al., Genome sequencing identifies a basis for everolimus sensitivity, *Science* 338: 221 (2012).

just one case—the Sloan-Kettering researchers expanded their study by analyzing the *TSC1* gene in tumors from 13 additional bladder cancer patients. Their results (Table 8.10) suggest that the drug may indeed be most effective in patients who harbor mutations in the *TSC1* gene: three out of four patients with the mutation responded to the drug, whereas only one out of nine patients without the mutation responded.

Critics caution that the *TSC1* mutation is sufficiently rare that enough data to draw reliable conclusions may never be obtained. The nature of the evidence—scant and difficult to generalize—is typical of personalized cancer therapy trials. But small advances are continuously being made that may lead to improved treatment for a variety of cancer patients.

? Think critically about the data presented in Table 8.10: Which data in Table 8.10 do not support the hypothesis that everolimus works *only* in patients who harbor a *TSC1* mutation?

One patient without the mutation responded to the drug, and one patient with the mutation did not respond to the drug.

▷ Meiosis and Crossing Over

8.11 Chromosomes are matched in homologous pairs

In humans, a typical body cell, called a **somatic cell**, has 46 chromosomes. When chromosomes from a cell in metaphase (when the chromosomes are most condensed) are viewed with a microscope, they can be arranged into matching pairs; Figure 8.11 illustrates one pair of metaphase chromosomes consisting of two joined sister chromatids. A human cell at metaphase contains 23 sets of duplicated chromosomes. Other species have different numbers of chromosomes, but these, too, usually occur in matched pairs. Moreover, when treated with special dyes, the chromosomes of a pair display matching staining patterns (represented by colored stripes in Figure 8.11).

Almost every chromosome has a twin that resembles it in length, centromere position, and staining (coloration)

pattern. The two chromosomes of such a matching pair are **homologous chromosomes** (or homologs) because each chromosome carries genes controlling the same inherited characteristics. For example, if a gene for freckles is located at a particular place, or **locus** (plural, *loci*), on one chromosome—within the

▲ **Figure 8.11** A pair of homologous chromosomes

Try This Cover the figure, then draw a pair of homologous chromosomes and label sister chromatids, the centromere, and one chromosome.

narrow orange band in our drawing—then the homologous chromosome has that same gene at that same locus. However, the two chromosomes of a homologous pair may have different versions of the same gene.

The two distinct chromosomes referred to as X and Y are an important exception to the general pattern of homologous chromosomes in human somatic cells. Human females have a homologous pair of X chromosomes (XX), but males have one X and one Y chromosome (XY). Only small parts of the

X and Y are homologous. Most of the genes carried on the X chromosome do not appear on the tiny Y, and the Y chromosome has genes not present on the X. Because they determine an individual's sex, the X and Y chromosomes are called **sex chromosomes**. Chromosomes other than sex chromosomes are called **autosomes**.

? **Are all of *your* chromosomes fully homologous?**

● If you are female, yes. If you are male, no.

8.12 Gametes have a single set of chromosomes

The development of a fertilized egg into a new adult organism is one phase of a multicellular organism's **life cycle**, the sequence of stages leading from the adults of one generation to the adults of the next (**Figure 8.12A**). Having two sets of chromosomes, one inherited from each parent, is a key factor in the life cycle of all species that reproduce sexually.

Most animals and plants are said to be **diploid** organisms because all somatic cells contain pairs of homologous chromosomes. The total number of chromosomes is called the diploid number (abbreviated $2n$). For humans, the diploid number is 46; that is, $2n = 46$. The exceptions are the egg and sperm cells, collectively known as **gametes**. Each gamete has a single set of chromosomes: 22 autosomes plus a sex chromosome, either X or Y. A cell with a

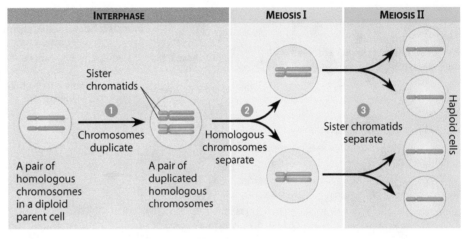

▲ **Figure 8.12B**   How meiosis halves chromosome number through two sequential divisions

single chromosome set is called a **haploid** cell; it has only one member of each homologous pair. For humans, the haploid number (abbreviated n) is 23; that is, $n = 23$.

The human life cycle begins when a haploid sperm cell from the father fuses with a haploid egg cell from the mother in the process of **fertilization**. The resulting fertilized egg, called a **zygote**, has one set of homologous chromosomes from each parent, and so is diploid. As a human develops into an adult, mitosis of the zygote and its descendants generates all the somatic cells.

The only cells of the human body not produced by mitosis are the gametes. Gametes are made by a different form of cell division called meiosis, which occurs only in reproductive organs. Whereas mitosis produces daughter cells with the same number of chromosomes as the parent cell, meiosis reduces the chromosome number by half. **Figure 8.12B** tracks one pair of homologous chromosomes through the two divisions of meiosis. ❶ Each of the chromosomes is duplicated during interphase (before meiosis). ❷ The first division, meiosis I, segregates the two chromosomes of the homologous pair, packaging them in separate (haploid) daughter cells. But each chromosome is still doubled. ❸ Meiosis II separates the sister chromatids. Each of the four daughter cells is haploid and contains only a single chromosome from the homologous pair.

Next, we'll take a closer look at the process of meiosis.

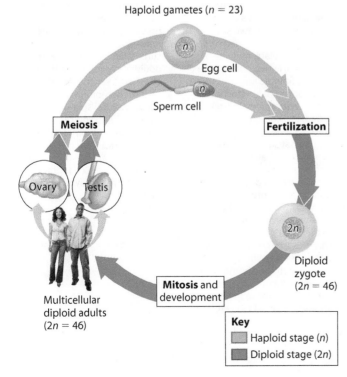

▲ **Figure 8.12A**   The human life cycle

? **How many autosomes are found in a human sperm cell? How many and which sex chromosomes?**

● 22 autosomes plus either an X or Y sex chromosome

8.13 Meiosis reduces the chromosome number from diploid to haploid

Meiosis is a type of cell division that produces haploid gametes in diploid organisms. Two haploid gametes may then combine via fertilization to restore the diploid state in the zygote. Fertilization and meiosis alternate in sexual life cycles, which serves to maintain a constant number of chromosomes in each species from one generation to the next.

Many of the stages of meiosis closely resemble corresponding stages in mitosis. Meiosis, like mitosis, is preceded by the duplication of chromosomes. However, this single duplication is followed by not one but two consecutive cell divisions,

called meiosis I and meiosis II. Because one duplication of the chromosomes is followed by two divisions, the result is four daughter cells, each with half as many chromosomes as the parent cell. The illustrations in **Figure 8.13** show the two meiotic divisions for an animal cell with a diploid number of 6. The members of a pair of homologous chromosomes in Figure 8.13 (and later figures) are colored red and blue to help distinguish them. (Imagine that the red chromosomes were inherited from the mother and the blue chromosomes from the father.) One of the most important events in meiosis

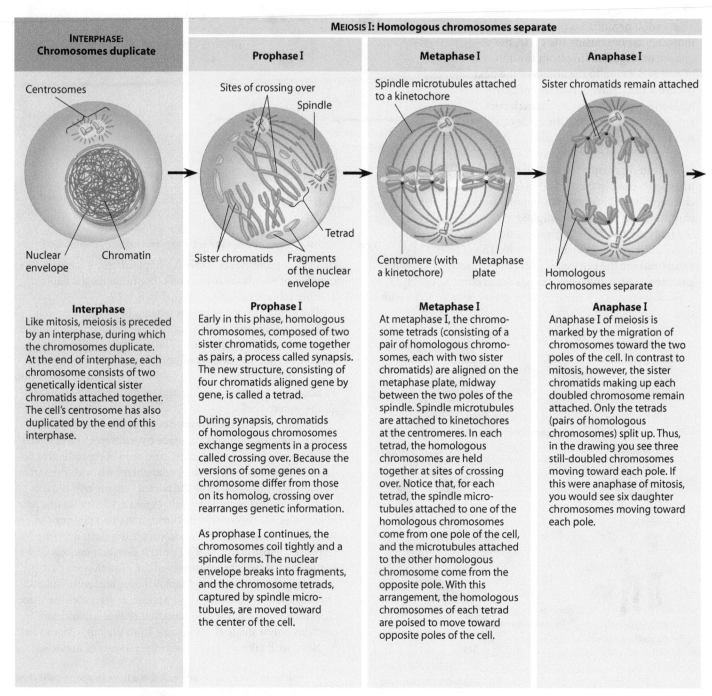

INTERPHASE: Chromosomes duplicate

Centrosomes

Nuclear envelope   Chromatin

MEIOSIS I: Homologous chromosomes separate

Prophase I

Sites of crossing over
Spindle
Tetrad
Sister chromatids   Fragments of the nuclear envelope

Metaphase I

Spindle microtubules attached to a kinetochore
Centromere (with a kinetochore)   Metaphase plate

Anaphase I

Sister chromatids remain attached
Homologous chromosomes separate

Interphase
Like mitosis, meiosis is preceded by an interphase, during which the chromosomes duplicate. At the end of interphase, each chromosome consists of two genetically identical sister chromatids attached together. The cell's centrosome has also duplicated by the end of this interphase.

Prophase I
Early in this phase, homologous chromosomes, composed of two sister chromatids, come together as pairs, a process called synapsis. The new structure, consisting of four chromatids aligned gene by gene, is called a tetrad.

During synapsis, chromatids of homologous chromosomes exchange segments in a process called crossing over. Because the versions of some genes on a chromosome differ from those on its homolog, crossing over rearranges genetic information.

As prophase I continues, the chromosomes coil tightly and a spindle forms. The nuclear envelope breaks into fragments, and the chromosome tetrads, captured by spindle microtubules, are moved toward the center of the cell.

Metaphase I
At metaphase I, the chromosome tetrads (consisting of a pair of homologous chromosomes, each with two sister chromatids) are aligned on the metaphase plate, midway between the two poles of the spindle. Spindle microtubules are attached to kinetochores at the centromeres. In each tetrad, the homologous chromosomes are held together at sites of crossing over. Notice that, for each tetrad, the spindle microtubules attached to one of the homologous chromosomes come from one pole of the cell, and the microtubules attached to the other homologous chromosome come from the opposite pole. With this arrangement, the homologous chromosomes of each tetrad are poised to move toward opposite poles of the cell.

Anaphase I
Anaphase I of meiosis is marked by the migration of chromosomes toward the two poles of the cell. In contrast to mitosis, however, the sister chromatids making up each doubled chromosome remain attached. Only the tetrads (pairs of homologous chromosomes) split up. Thus, in the drawing you see three still-doubled chromosomes moving toward each pole. If this were anaphase of mitosis, you would see six daughter chromosomes moving toward each pole.

▲ Figure 8.13   The stages of meiosis

occurs during prophase I. At this stage, four chromatids (two sets of sister chromatids) are aligned and physically touching each other. When in this configuration, nonsister chromatids may trade segments. As you will learn in Module 8.17, this exchange of chromosome segments—called crossing over—shuffles genes, making an important contribution to the genetic variability that results from sexual reproduction.

? A cell has the haploid number of chromosomes, but each chromosome has two chromatids. The chromosomes are arranged singly at the center of the spindle. What is the meiotic stage?

● Metaphase II (because the chromosomes line up two by two in metaphase I)

Two lily cells undergo meiosis II

LM 670×

Telophase I and Cytokinesis	MEIOSIS II: Sister chromatids separate			
	Prophase II	**Metaphase II**	**Anaphase II**	**Telophase II and Cytokinesis**

Cleavage furrow

Sister chromatids separate

Haploid daughter cells forming

Telophase I and Cytokinesis

In telophase I, the chromosomes arrive at the poles of the cell. When the chromosomes finish their journey, each pole of the cell has a haploid chromosome set, although each chromosome is still in duplicate form (with two sister chromatids) at this point. Usually, cytokinesis (division of the cytoplasm) occurs along with telophase I, and two haploid daughter cells are formed.

Following telophase I in some organisms, there is an interphase between telophase I and meiosis II. In other species, meiosis I immediately leads to meiosis II. In either case, no chromosome duplication occurs between telophase I and the onset of meiosis II.

Meiosis II

Meiosis II is essentially the same as mitosis. The important difference is that meiosis II starts with a haploid cell.

During prophase II, a spindle forms and moves the chromosomes toward the middle of the cell. During metaphase II, the chromosomes are aligned on the metaphase plate as they are in mitosis, with the kinetochores of the sister chromatids of each chromosome pointing toward opposite poles. In anaphase II, the centromeres of sister chromatids separate, and the sister chromatids of each pair, now individual chromosomes, move toward opposite poles of the cell. In telophase II, nuclei form at the cell poles, and cytokinesis occurs at the same time. There are now four daughter cells, each with the haploid number of (single) chromosomes.

8.14 Mitosis and meiosis have important similarities and differences

Carefully review this module, which compares mitosis and meiosis starting from a diploid parent cell with four chromosomes. Homologous chromosomes match in size. Color distinguishes the two chromosomes of each homologous pair.

MITOSIS   **MEIOSIS I**

Parent cell
(before chromosome duplication)
$2n = 4$
Chromosome duplication
(Occurs once, during S phase of preceding interphase)

Prophase   Prophase I

Duplicated chromosome (two sister chromatids)

In prophase of mitosis, each duplicated chromosome remains separate, while in prophase I of meiosis, chromosomes are associated with their homologs.

Homologous chromosomes come together in pairs

Site of crossing over between homologous (nonsister) chromatids

Metaphase   Metaphase I

Individual chromosomes line up at the metaphase plate

In metaphase of mitosis, duplicated chromosomes line up singly, while in metaphase I of meiosis, duplicated homologous chromosomes line up in pairs.

Tetrads (pairs of homologous chromosomes) line up at the metaphase plate

Anaphase Telophase   Anaphase I Telophase I

In anaphase of mitosis, sister chromatids separate, while in anaphase I of meiosis, pairs of homologous chromosomes separate.

Sister chromatids separate during anaphase

$2n$ $2n$

Homologous chromosomes separate during anaphase I; sister chromatids remain attached

$n = 2$

Mitosis involves one division of the nucleus and cytoplasm, while meiosis involves two divisions.

MEIOSIS II

Sister chromatids separate

Sister chromatids separate during anaphase II

n n n n

Result: Two genetically identical diploid cells
Used for: Growth, tissue repair, asexual reproduction

Result: Four genetically unique haploid cells
Used for: Sexual reproduction

? **Which stage of meiosis shown here most closely resembles mitosis?**

● The movement of chromosomes during meiosis II very closely matches mitosis (except with half as many chromosomes).

8.15 Independent orientation of chromosomes in meiosis and random fertilization lead to varied offspring

Offspring that result from sexual reproduction are highly varied (see Module 8.1); they are genetically different from their parents and from one another. How does this genetic variation result from meiosis?

Figure 8.15 illustrates one way: The arrangement of homologous chromosome pairs at metaphase I affects the resulting gametes. Once again, our example is from a diploid organism with four chromosomes (two homologous pairs, with one set larger than the other to help make them distinct), and red represents chromosomes inherited from the mother, whereas blue represents chromosomes inherited from the father.

Recall that joined homologous chromosomes form tetrads, a set of four chromatids. At metaphase, the orientation of these tetrads—whether the maternal or paternal chromosome is closer to a given pole—is as random as the flip of a coin. Thus, there is a 50% chance that a particular daughter cell will get the maternal chromosome of a certain homologous pair and a 50% chance that it will receive the paternal chromosome. In this example, there are two possible ways that the two tetrads can align during metaphase I. In possibility A, the tetrads are oriented with both red chromosomes on the same side of the metaphase plate. Therefore, the gametes produced in possibility A can each have either two red *or* two blue chromosomes (bottom row, combinations 1 and 2).

In possibility B, the tetrads are oriented differently (blue/red and red/blue). This arrangement produces gametes that each have one red and one blue chromosome. Furthermore, half the gametes have a big blue chromosome and a small red one (combination 3), and half have a big red chromosome and a small blue one (combination 4).

So we see that for this example, four chromosome combinations are possible in the gametes. In fact, the organism will produce gametes of all four types in equal quantities. For a species with more than two pairs of chromosomes, such as humans, *all* the chromosome pairs orient independently at metaphase I. (Chromosomes X and Y behave as a homologous pair in meiosis.)

For any species, the total number of combinations of chromosomes that meiosis can produce in gametes is 2^n, where n is the haploid number. For the organism in this figure, $n = 2$, so the number of chromosome combinations is 2^2, or 4. For a human ($n = 23$), there are 2^{23}, or about 8 million possible chromosome combinations! This means that each gamete you produce contains one of roughly 8 million possible combinations of chromosomes.

How many possibilities are there when a gamete from one individual unites with a gamete from another individual in fertilization? In humans, the random fusion of a single sperm with a single egg during fertilization will produce a zygote with any of about 64 trillion (8 million $\times$ 8 million) combinations of chromosomes! Although the random nature of fertilization adds a huge amount of potential variability to the offspring of sexual reproduction, there is in fact even more variety created during meiosis, as we see in the next two modules.

> **?** A particular species of worm has a diploid number of 10. How many chromosomal combinations are possible for gametes formed by meiosis?

● 32; 2n = 10, so n = 5 and 2^n = 32

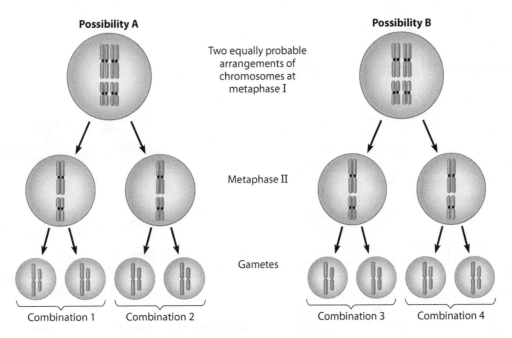

▲ Figure 8.15   Results of the independent orientation of chromosomes at metaphase I

8.16 Homologous chromosomes may carry different versions of genes

So far, we have focused on genetic variability in gametes and zygotes at the whole-chromosome level. We have yet to discuss the actual genetic information—the genes—contained in the chromosomes. The question we need to answer now is: What is the significance of the independent orientation of metaphase chromosomes at the level of genes?

Let's take a simple example, the single tetrad in Figure 8.16. The letters on the homologous chromosomes represent genes. Recall that homologous chromosomes have genes for the same characteristic at corresponding loci. Our example involves hypothetical genes controlling the appearance of mice. *C* and *c* indicate different versions of a gene for one characteristic, coat color; *E* and *e* are different versions of a gene for another characteristic, eye color. (As you'll learn in later chapters, different versions of a gene contain slightly different nucleotide sequences in the chromosomal DNA.)

Let's say that *C* represents the gene for a brown coat and that *c* represents the gene for a white coat. In the chromosome diagram, notice that *C* is at the same locus on the red chromosome as *c* is on the blue one. Likewise, gene *E* (for black eyes) is at the same locus as *e* (pink eyes).

The fact that homologous chromosomes can bear two different kinds of genetic information for the same characteristic (for instance, coat color) is what really makes gametes—and therefore offspring—different from one another. In our example, a gamete carrying a red chromosome would have genes specifying brown coat color and

black eye color, whereas a gamete with the homologous blue chromosome would have genes for white coat and pink eyes. Thus, we see that a tetrad can yield two genetically different kinds of gametes. In the next module, we go a step further and see how this same tetrad can actually yield *four* different kinds of gametes.

> **?** In the tetrad of Figure 8.16, use labels to distinguish the pair of homologous chromosomes from sister chromatids.

Sister chromatids
Sister chromatids
Pair of homologous chromosomes

▲ Figure 8.16 Differing genetic information (coat color and eye color) on homologous chromosomes

8.17 Crossing over further increases genetic variability

Crossing over is an exchange of corresponding segments between nonsister chromatids of homologous chromosomes. The micrograph and drawing in Figure 8.17A show the results of crossing over between two homologous chromosomes during prophase I of meiosis. The chromosomes are a tetrad. The sites of crossing over appear as X-shaped regions; each of these sites is called a **chiasma**. A chiasma (plural, *chiasmata*) is a place where two homologous (nonsister) chromatids are attached to each other. Figure 8.17B on the next page illustrates how crossing over can produce new combinations of genes, using as examples the hypothetical mouse genes mentioned in the previous module.

Crossing over begins very early in prophase I of meiosis. At that time, homologous chromosomes are paired all along their lengths, with a precise gene-by-gene alignment. Notice

▲ Figure 8.17A Chiasmata, the sites of crossing over

at the top of the figure a tetrad with coat-color (*C, c*) and eye-color (*E, e*) genes labeled. **1** The DNA molecules of two nonsister chromatids—one maternal (red) and one paternal (blue)—break at the same place. **2** Immediately, the two broken chromatids join together in a new way (red to blue and blue to red). In effect, the two homologous segments trade places, or cross over, producing hybrid chromosomes (red/blue and blue/red) with new combinations of maternal and paternal genes. **3** When the homologous chromosomes separate in anaphase I, each contains a new segment originating from its homolog. **4** Finally, during anaphase II, the sister chromatids separate, each going to a different gamete.

In this example, if there were no crossing over, meiosis could produce only two genetic types of gametes. These would be the ones ending up with the "parental" types of chromosomes (either all blue or all red), carrying either genes *C* and *E* or genes *c* and *e*. These are the same two kinds of gametes we saw in Figure 8.16. With crossing over, two other types of gametes can result, ones that are part blue and part red. One of these carries genes *C* and *e* and the other carries genes *c* and *E*. Chromosomes with these combinations of genes would not exist if not for crossing over. They are called "recombinant" because they result from **genetic recombination**, the production of gene combinations different from those carried by the original parental chromosomes.

In meiosis in humans, an average of one to three crossover events occur per chromosome pair. Thus, if you were to examine a chromosome from one of your gametes, you would most likely find that it is not exactly like any one of your own chromosomes. Rather, it is probably a patchwork of segments derived from a pair of homologous chromosomes, in essence cut and pasted together to form a hybrid chromosome with a unique combination of genes.

We have now examined three sources of genetic variability in sexually reproducing organisms: independent orientation of chromosomes at metaphase I, random fertilization, and crossing over during prophase I of meiosis. The different versions of genes that homologous chromosomes may have at each locus originally arise from mutations (changes in the sequence of DNA), so mutations are ultimately responsible for genetic diversity in living organisms. Once these differences arise, reshuffling of the different versions during sexual reproduction increases genetic variation. (When we discuss natural selection and evolution in Unit III, we will see that this genetic variety in offspring is the raw material for natural selection.)

Our discussion of meiosis to this point has focused on the process as it normally occurs. In the next section, we consider some of the consequences of errors in the process.

1 Breakage of nonsister chromatids

2 Joining of nonsister chromatids

Chiasma

3 Separation of homologous chromosomes at anaphase I

4 Separation of chromatids at anaphase II and completion of meiosis

Parental type of chromosome

Recombinant chromosome

Recombinant chromosome

Parental type of chromosome

Gametes of four genetic types

▲ **Figure 8.17B** How crossing over leads to genetic recombination

? Describe how crossing over and the random alignment of homologous chromosomes on the metaphase I plate account for the genetic variation among gametes formed by meiosis.

● Crossing over creates recombinant chromosomes having a combination of genes that were originally on different, though homologous, chromosomes. Homologous chromosome pairs are oriented randomly at metaphase of meiosis I.

8.18 Accidents during meiosis can alter chromosome number

Within the human body, meiosis occurs repeatedly as the testes or ovaries produce gametes. In the vast majority of cases, the process distributes chromosomes to daughter cells without error. But there is an occasional mishap, called a **nondisjunction**, in which the members of a chromosome pair fail to separate. After a nondisjunction, one gamete receives two of the same type of chromosome and another gamete receives no copy of that chromosome. The other chromosomes (those not involved in the nondisjunction) are distributed normally.

Imagine a hypothetical organism whose diploid chromosome number is 4. In such an organism, the somatic cells are diploid ($2n = 4$), with two pairs of homologous chromosomes. Sometimes, a pair of homologous chromosomes does not separate during meiosis I (see left side of **Figure 8.18**). In this case, even though the rest of meiosis occurs normally, all the resulting gametes end up with abnormal numbers of chromosomes. Two of the gametes have three chromosomes; the other two gametes have only one chromosome each.

Alternatively, sometimes meiosis I procedes normally, but one pair of sister chromatids fails to separate during meiosis II (see right side of Figure 8.18). In this case, two of the resulting gametes are abnormal—one with an extra chromosome and one that is missing a chromosome; the other two gametes are normal.

If an abnormal gamete produced by nondisjunction unites with a normal gamete during fertilization, the result is a zygote with an abnormal number of chromosomes. Mitosis will then transmit the mistake to all embryonic cells. If the organism survived, it would most likely display a syndrome of disorders caused by the abnormal number of genes. Biologists can detect such syndromes by taking an inventory of the chromosomes in a person's cells, as we'll see next.

> **?** **Explain how nondisjunction could result in a diploid gamete.**
>
> ● A diploid gamete would result if the nondisjunction affected all the chromosomes during one of the meiotic divisions.

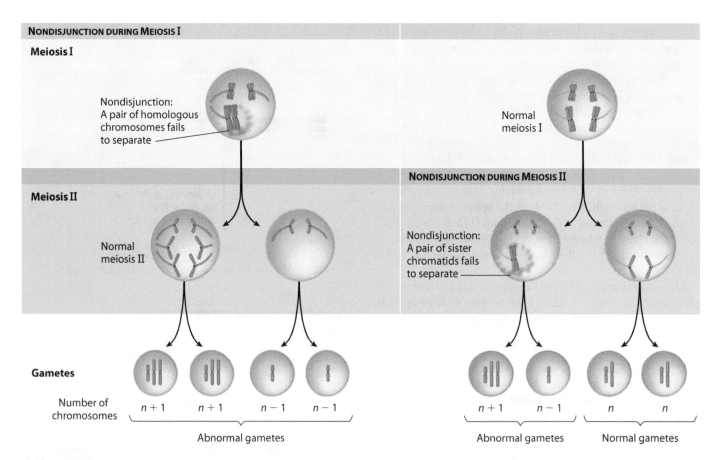

NONDISJUNCTION DURING MEIOSIS I

Meiosis I

Nondisjunction: A pair of homologous chromosomes fails to separate

Normal meiosis I

Meiosis II

Normal meiosis II

NONDISJUNCTION DURING MEIOSIS II

Nondisjunction: A pair of sister chromatids fails to separate

Gametes

Number of chromosomes $n + 1$ $n + 1$ $n - 1$ $n - 1$ $n + 1$ $n - 1$ n n

Abnormal gametes   Abnormal gametes   Normal gametes

▲ **Figure 8.18** Nondisjunction in meiosis I and meiosis II

8.19 A karyotype is a photographic inventory of an individual's chromosomes

Chromosomal abnormalities can be readily detected in a **karyotype**, an ordered display of magnified images of an individual's chromosomes arranged in pairs. A karyotype shows the chromosomes condensed and doubled, as they appear in metaphase of mitosis.

To prepare a karyotype, scientists often use lymphocytes, a type of white blood cell. A blood sample is treated with a chemical that stimulates mitosis. After growing in culture for several days, the cells are treated with another chemical to arrest mitosis at metaphase, when the chromosomes, each consisting of two joined sister chromatids, are most highly condensed. Figure 8.19 outlines the steps of one method for the preparation of a karyotype from a blood sample.

The photograph on the right shows the karyotype of a normal human male. Images of the 46 chromosomes from a single diploid cell are arranged in 23 homologous pairs: autosomes numbered from 1 to 22 (starting with the largest) and one pair of sex chromosomes (X and Y in this case). The chromosomes have been stained to reveal band patterns, which are helpful in differentiating the chromosomes and in detecting structural abnormalities. Among the alterations that can be detected by karyotyping is trisomy 21, the basis of Down syndrome, which we discuss next.

? How would the karyotype of a human female differ from the male karyotype in Figure 8.19?

● Instead of an XY combination for the sex chromosomes, there would be a homologous pair of X chromosomes (XX).

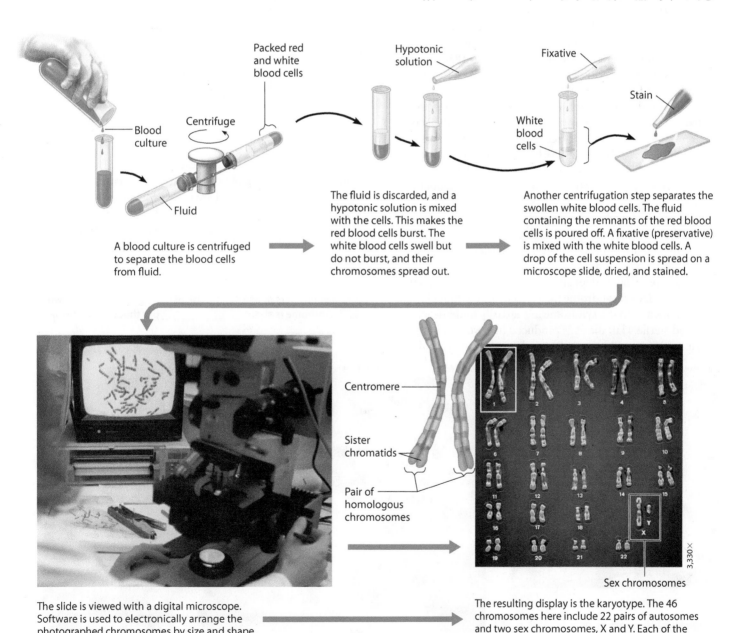

A blood culture is centrifuged to separate the blood cells from fluid.

The fluid is discarded, and a hypotonic solution is mixed with the cells. This makes the red blood cells burst. The white blood cells swell but do not burst, and their chromosomes spread out.

Another centrifugation step separates the swollen white blood cells. The fluid containing the remnants of the red blood cells is poured off. A fixative (preservative) is mixed with the white blood cells. A drop of the cell suspension is spread on a microscope slide, dried, and stained.

The slide is viewed with a digital microscope. Software is used to electronically arrange the photographed chromosomes by size and shape.

The resulting display is the karyotype. The 46 chromosomes here include 22 pairs of autosomes and two sex chromosomes, X and Y. Each of the chromosomes consists of two sister chromatids joined along their lengths (as shown in the diagram).

▲ Figure 8.19 Preparation of a karyotype from a blood sample

8.20 An extra copy of chromosome 21 causes Down syndrome

CONNECTION

The karyotype in Figure 8.19 shows the normal human complement of 23 pairs of chromosomes. Compare this figure with the karyotype shown in **Figure 8.20A**; besides having two X chromosomes (because it's from a female), notice that there are three number 21 chromosomes, making 47 chromosomes in total. This condition is called **trisomy 21**.

In most cases, an abnormal number of chromosomes is so harmful to development that an affected embryo is spontaneously aborted (miscarried) long before birth. But some aberrations in chromosome number, including trisomy 21, appear to upset the genetic balance less drastically, and individuals carrying such chromosomal abnormalities can survive into adulthood. Individuals with chromosomal abnormalities have a characteristic set of symptoms, collectively called a syndrome. A person with trisomy 21, for instance, has a condition called **Down syndrome**, named after John Langdon Down, a doctor who described the syndrome in 1866.

Trisomy 21 is the most common chromosome number abnormality. Affecting about one out of every 700 children, it is also the most common serious birth defect in the United States. Down syndrome includes characteristic facial features—frequently a round face, a skin fold at the inner corner of the eye, a flattened nose bridge, and small, irregular teeth—as well as short stature, heart defects, and susceptibility to respiratory infections, leukemia, and Alzheimer's disease.

People with Down syndrome usually have a life span shorter than normal. They also exhibit varying degrees of developmental disabilities. However, with proper care, many individuals with the syndrome live to middle age or beyond, and many are socially adept and are able to hold jobs. A few women with Down syndrome have had children, though nearly all men with the syndrome are sexually underdeveloped and sterile. Half the eggs produced by a woman with Down syndrome will have the extra chromosome 21, so there

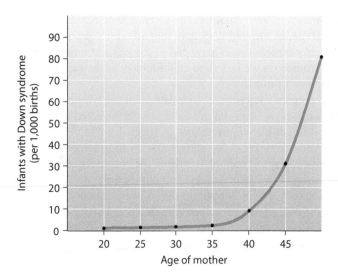

▲ **Figure 8.20B**   Maternal age and incidence of Down syndrome

Source: Adapted from C. A. Huether et al., Maternal age specific risk rate estimates for Down syndrome among live births in whites and other races from Ohio and Metropolitan Atlanta, 1970–1989, *Journal of Medical Genetics* 35: 482–90 (1998).

is a 50% chance that she will transmit the syndrome to her child.

As indicated in **Figure 8.20B**, the incidence of Down syndrome in the offspring of normal parents increases markedly with the age of the mother. Down syndrome affects less than 0.05% of children (fewer than one in 2,000) born to women under age 30. The risk climbs to 1% (10 in 1,000) for mothers at age 40 and is even higher for older mothers. Prenatal screening for chromosomal defects in the embryo is now offered to all pregnant women.

?   For mothers of age 47, the risk of having a baby with Down syndrome is about _____ per thousand births, or _____ %.

4...40 ●

Trisomy 21

▲ **Figure 8.20A**   A karyotype showing trisomy 21 and an individual with Down syndrome

8.21 Abnormal numbers of sex chromosomes do not usually affect survival

CONNECTION

Nondisjunction can result in abnormal numbers of sex chromosomes, X and Y. Unusual numbers of sex chromosomes seem to upset the genetic balance less than unusual numbers of autosomes. This may be because the Y chromosome is very small and carries relatively few genes. Furthermore, mammalian cells usually operate with only one functioning X chromosome because other copies of the chromosome become inactivated in each cell (as you'll learn in Module 11.2).

Table 8.21 lists the most common human sex chromosome abnormalities. An extra X chromosome in a male, making him XXY, occurs approximately once in every 1,000 live male births. Men with this disorder, called Klinefelter syndrome, have male sex organs, but the testes are abnormally small, the individual is sterile, and he often has female body characteristics. Affected individuals may have subnormal intelligence. Klinefelter syndrome is also found in individuals with more than three sex chromosomes, such as XXYY, XXXY, or XXXXY. These abnormal numbers of sex chromosomes result from multiple nondisjunctions; such men are more likely to have developmental disabilities than XY or XXY individuals.

Human males with an extra Y chromosome do not have any well-defined syndrome, although they tend to be taller than average. Females with an extra X chromosome cannot be distinguished from XX females except by karyotype.

Females who lack an X chromosome are designated XO; the O indicates the absence of a second sex chromosome. These women have Turner syndrome. They have a characteristic appearance, including short stature and often a web of skin extending between the neck and the shoulders. Women with Turner syndrome are sterile because their sex organs do not fully mature at adolescence. If left untreated, girls with Turner syndrome have poor development of breasts and other secondary sexual characteristics. Artificial administration of estrogen can alleviate these symptoms. Women with Turner syndrome have normal intelligence. The XO condition is the sole known case where having only 45 chromosomes is not fatal in humans.

? What is the total number of autosomes you would expect to find in the karyotype of a female with Turner syndrome?

44 (plus one sex chromosome)

TABLE 8.21 | ABNORMALITIES OF SEX CHROMOSOME NUMBER IN HUMANS

Sex Chromosomes	Syndrome	Origin of Nondisjunction	Frequency in Population
XXY	Klinefelter syndrome (male)	Meiosis in egg or sperm formation	1/1,000 live male births
XYY	None (normal male)	Meiosis in sperm formation	1/1,000 live male births
XXX	None (normal female)	Meiosis in egg or sperm formation	1/1,000 live female births
XO	Turner syndrome (female)	Meiosis in egg or sperm formation	1/2,500 live female births

8.22 New species can arise from errors in cell division

EVOLUTION CONNECTION

Errors in meiosis or mitosis do not always lead to problems. In fact, biologists hypothesize that such errors have been instrumental in the evolution of many species. Such new species are polyploid, meaning that they have more than two sets of homologous chromosomes in each somatic cell. At least half of all species of flowering plants are polyploid, including such crops as wheat, potatoes, and cotton.

Let's consider one scenario by which a diploid ($2n$) plant species might generate a tetraploid ($4n$) plant. Imagine that, like many plants, our diploid plant produces both sperm and egg cells and can self-fertilize. If meiosis fails to occur in the plant's reproductive organs and gametes are instead produced by mitosis, the gametes will be diploid. The union of a diploid ($2n$) sperm with a diploid ($2n$) egg during self-fertilization will produce a tetraploid ($4n$) zygote, which may develop into a mature tetraploid plant that can itself reproduce by self-fertilization. The tetraploid plants will constitute a new species, one that has evolved in just one generation. Although polyploid animal species are less common than polyploid plants, they are known to occur among the fishes and amphibians (Figure 8.22). Moreover, researchers in Chile have identified the first candidate for polyploidy among the mammals—the Viscacha rat (*Tympanoctomys barrerae*), a rodent whose cells seem to be tetraploid. Tetraploid organisms are sometimes strikingly different from their recent diploid ancestors. Scientists don't yet understand exactly how polyploidy brings about such differences.

▲ **Figure 8.22** The gray tree frog (*Hyla versicolor*), a tetraploid organism

? What is a polyploid organism?

An organism with more than two sets of homologous chromosomes in its body cells

8.23 Alterations of chromosome structure can cause birth defects and cancer

Errors in meiosis or damaging agents such as radiation can cause a chromosome to break, which can lead to four types of changes in chromosome structure (**Figure 8.23A**). A **deletion** occurs when a chromosomal fragment (along with its genes) becomes detached. The "deleted" fragment may disappear from the cell, or it may become attached as an extra segment to its sister chromatid or a homologous chromosome, producing a **duplication**. A chromosomal fragment may also reattach to the original chromosome but in the reverse orientation, producing an **inversion**. A fourth possible result of chromosomal breakage is for the fragment to join a nonhomologous chromosome, a rearrangement called a **translocation**. As shown in the figure, a translocation may be reciprocal; that is, two nonhomologous chromosomes may exchange segments.

Inversions are less likely than deletions or duplications to produce harmful effects, because in inversions all genes are still present in their normal number. Many deletions in human chromosomes, however, cause serious physical and mental problems. One example is a specific deletion in chromosome 5 that causes *cri du chat* ("cat-cry") syndrome. A child born with this syndrome has severe developmental disabilities, a small head with unusual facial features, and a cry that sounds like the mewing of a distressed cat. Such individuals usually die in infancy or early childhood.

Like inversions, translocations may or may not be harmful. Some people with Down syndrome have only part of a third chromosome 21; as the result of a translocation, this partial chromosome is attached to another (nonhomologous) chromosome. Other chromosomal translocations have been implicated in certain cancers, including chronic myelogenous leukemia (CML). CML develops after a reciprocal translocation during mitosis of cells that will become white blood cells. In these cells, the exchange of a large portion of chromosome 22 with a small fragment from a tip of chromosome 9 produces a much shortened, easily recognized chromosome 22 (**Figure 8.23B**). Such an exchange causes cancer by activating a gene that leads to uncontrolled cell cycle progression.

Because the chromosomal changes in cancer are usually confined to somatic cells, cancer is not usually inherited. (We'll return to cancer in Chapter 11.) We continue our study of genetic principles (in Chapter 9), looking first at the historical development of the science of genetics and then at the rules governing the way traits are passed from parents to offspring.

? How is reciprocal translocation different from crossing over?

Reciprocal translocation swaps chromosome segments between nonhomologous chromosomes. Crossing over exchanges corresponding segments between homologous chromosomes.

Chromosome 9

Chromosome 22

Reciprocal translocation

Activated cancer-causing gene

▲ **Figure 8.23B** The translocation associated with chronic myelogenous leukemia

Deletion	Inversion
A segment of a chromosome is removed	A segment of a chromosome is removed and then reinserted opposite to its original orientation
Duplication	**Reciprocal translocation**
A segment of a chromosome is copied and inserted into the homologous chromosome	Segments of two nonhomologous chromosomes swap locations with each other
Homologous chromosomes	Nonhomologous chromosomes

▲ **Figure 8.23A** Alterations of chromosome structure

CHAPTER 8 REVIEW

For practice quizzes, BioFlix animations, MP3 tutorials, video tutors, and more study tools designed for this textbook, go to

MasteringBiology®

Reviewing the Concepts

Cell Division and Reproduction (8.1–8.2)

8.1 Cell division plays many important roles in the lives of organisms. Cell division is at the heart of the reproduction of cells and organisms because cells originate only from preexisting cells. Some organisms reproduce through asexual reproduction, and in such instances their offspring are all genetic copies of the parent and identical to each other. Other organisms reproduce through sexual reproduction, creating a variety of offspring.

8.2 Prokaryotes reproduce by binary fission. Prokaryotic cells reproduce asexually by cell division. As the cell replicates its single chromosome, the copies move apart; the growing membrane then divides the cell.

The Eukaryotic Cell Cycle and Mitosis (8.3–8.10)

8.3 The large, complex chromosomes of eukaryotes duplicate with each cell division. A eukaryotic cell has many more genes than a prokaryotic cell, and they are grouped into multiple chromosomes in the nucleus. Each chromosome contains one long DNA molecule. Individual chromosomes are visible under a light microscope only when the cell is in the process of dividing; otherwise, chromosomes are thin, loosely packed chromatin fibers too small to be seen. Before a cell starts dividing, the chromosomes duplicate, producing sister chromatids (containing identical DNA) that are joined together along their lengths. Cell division involves the separation of sister chromatids and results in two daughter cells, each containing a complete and identical set of chromosomes.

8.4 The cell cycle includes growing and division phases.

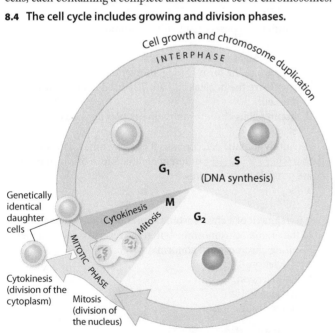

8.5 Cell division is a continuum of dynamic changes. Mitosis distributes duplicated chromosomes into two daughter nuclei. After the chromosomes are coiled up, a mitotic spindle made of microtubules moves the chromosomes to the middle of the cell. The sister chromatids then separate and move to opposite poles of the cell, at which point two new nuclei form.

8.6 Cytokinesis differs for plant and animal cells. Cytokinesis, in which the cell divides in two, overlaps the end of mitosis. In animals, cytokinesis occurs when a cell constricts, forming a cleavage furrow. In plants, a membranous cell plate forms and then splits the cell in two.

8.7 Anchorage, cell density, and chemical growth factors affect cell division. In laboratory cultures, most normal cells divide only when attached to a surface. The cultured cells continue dividing until they touch one another. Most animal cells divide only when stimulated by growth factors, and some do not divide at all. Growth factors stimulate other cells to divide.

8.8 Growth factors signal the cell cycle control system. A set of proteins within the cell controls the cell cycle. Signals affecting critical checkpoints in the cell cycle determine whether a cell will go through the complete cycle and divide. The binding of growth factors to specific receptors on the plasma membrane is usually necessary for cell division.

8.9 Growing out of control, cancer cells produce malignant tumors. Cancer cells divide excessively to form masses called tumors. Malignant tumors can invade other tissues. Radiation and chemotherapy are effective as cancer treatments because they interfere with cell division.

8.10 Tailoring treatment to each patient may improve cancer therapy. Determination of specific mutations within the cells of an individual tumor may aid in treatment. Although reliable data are scant today, such personalized medicine may prove to be an important treatment regimen in the future.

Meiosis and Crossing Over (8.11–8.17)

8.11 Chromosomes are matched in homologous pairs. The somatic (body) cells of each species contain a specific number of chromosomes; for example, human cells have 46, consisting of 23 pairs of homologous chromosomes. The chromosomes of a homologous pair of autosomes carry genes for the same characteristics at the same place, or locus.

8.12 Gametes have a single set of chromosomes. Cells with two sets of homologous chromosomes are diploid. Gametes—eggs and sperm—are haploid cells with a single set of chromosomes. Sexual life cycles involve the alternation of haploid and diploid stages.

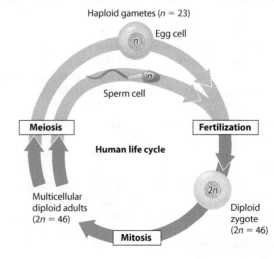

8.13 Meiosis reduces the chromosome number from diploid to haploid. Meiosis, like mitosis, is preceded by chromosome duplication, but in meiosis, the cell divides twice to form four daughter cells. The first division, meiosis I, starts with the pairing of homologous chromosomes. In crossing over, homologous chromosomes exchange corresponding segments. Meiosis I separates the members of each homologous pair and produces two daughter cells, each with one set of chromosomes. Meiosis II is essentially the same as mitosis: In each of the cells, the sister chromatids of each chromosome separate. The result is a total of four haploid cells.

8.14 Mitosis and meiosis have important similarities and differences. Both mitosis and meiosis begin with diploid parent cells that have chromosomes duplicated during the previous interphase. Mitosis produces two genetically identical diploid somatic daughter cells, whereas meiosis produces four genetically unique haploid gametes.

8.15 Independent orientation of chromosomes in meiosis and random fertilization lead to varied offspring. Each chromosome of a homologous pair differs at many points from the other member of the pair. Random arrangements of chromosome pairs at metaphase I of meiosis lead to many different combinations of chromosomes in eggs and sperm. Random fertilization of eggs by sperm greatly increases this variation.

8.16 Homologous chromosomes may carry different versions of genes. The differences between homologous chromosomes come from the fact that they can bear different versions of genes at corresponding loci.

8.17 Crossing over further increases genetic variability. Genetic recombination, which results from crossing over during prophase I of meiosis, increases variation still further.

Alterations of Chromosome Number and Structure (8.18–8.23)

8.18 Accidents during meiosis can alter chromosome number. An abnormal chromosome count is the result of nondisjunction, which can result from the failure of a pair of homologous chromosomes to separate during meiosis I or from the failure of sister chromatids to separate during meiosis II.

8.19 A karyotype is a photographic inventory of an individual's chromosomes. To prepare a karyotype, white blood cells are isolated, stimulated to grow, arrested at metaphase, and photographed under a microscope. The chromosomes are arranged into ordered pairs so that any chromosomal abnormalities can be detected.

8.20 An extra copy of chromosome 21 causes Down syndrome. Trisomy 21, the most common chromosome number abnormality, results in a condition called Down syndrome.

8.21 Abnormal numbers of sex chromosomes do not usually affect survival. Nondisjunction of the sex chromosomes during meiosis can result in individuals with a missing or extra X or Y chromosome. In some cases (such as XXY), this leads to syndromes; in other cases (such as XXX), the body is normal.

8.22 New species can arise from errors in cell division. Nondisjunction can produce polyploid organisms, organisms with extra sets of chromosomes. Such errors in cell division can be important in the evolution of new species.

8.23 Alterations of chromosome structure can cause birth defects and cancer. Chromosome breakage can lead to rearrangements—deletions, duplications, inversions, and translocations—that can produce genetic disorders or, if the changes occur in somatic cells, cancer.

Connecting the Concepts

1. Complete the following table to compare mitosis and meiosis.

	Mitosis	Meiosis
Number of chromosomal duplications		
Number of cell divisions		
Number of daughter cells produced		
Number of chromosomes in the daughter cells		
How the chromosomes line up during metaphase		
Genetic relationship of the daughter cells to the parent cell		
Functions performed in the human body		

Testing Your Knowledge

Level 1: Knowledge/Comprehension

2. If an intestinal cell in a grasshopper contains 24 chromosomes, then a grasshopper sperm cell contains _____ chromosomes.
   a. 6
   b. 12
   c. 24
   d. 48

3. Which of the following is *not* a function of mitosis in humans?
   a. repair of wounds
   b. growth
   c. production of gametes from diploid cells
   d. replacement of lost or damaged cells

4. It is difficult to observe individual chromosomes during interphase because
   a. the DNA has not been replicated yet.
   b. they are in the form of long, thin strands.
   c. they leave the nucleus and are dispersed to other parts of the cell.
   d. homologous chromosomes do not pair up until division starts.

5. A fruit fly somatic cell contains 8 chromosomes. This means that _____ different combinations of chromosomes are possible in its gametes.
   a. 8
   b. 16
   c. 32
   d. 64

6. If a fragment of a chromosome breaks off and then reattaches to the original chromosome but in the reverse direction, the resulting chromosomal abnormality is called
   a. a deletion.
   b. an inversion.
   c. a translocation.
   d. a nondisjunction.

Level 2: Application/Analysis

7. Which of the following phases of mitosis is essentially the opposite of prophase in terms of changes within the nucleus?
   a. telophase
   b. metaphase
   c. interphase
   d. anaphase

8. A biochemist measured the amount of DNA in cells growing in the laboratory and found that the quantity of DNA in a cell doubled
   a. between prophase and anaphase of mitosis.
   b. between the G_1 and G_2 phases of the cell cycle.
   c. during the M phase of the cell cycle.
   d. between prophase I and prophase II of meiosis.
9. A micrograph of a dividing cell from a mouse showed 19 chromosomes, each consisting of two sister chromatids. During which of the following stages of cell division could such a picture have been taken? (*Explain your answer.*)
   a. prophase of mitosis
   b. telophase II of meiosis
   c. prophase I of meiosis
   d. prophase II of meiosis
10. Cytochalasin B is a chemical that disrupts microfilament formation. This chemical would interfere with
    a. DNA replication.
    b. formation of the mitotic spindle.
    c. cleavage.
    d. formation of the cell plate.
11. Why are individuals with an extra chromosome 21, which causes Down syndrome, more numerous than individuals with an extra chromosome 3 or chromosome 16?
    a. There are probably more genes on chromosome 21 than on the others.
    b. Chromosome 21 is a sex chromosome and chromosomes 3 and 16 are not.
    c. Down syndrome is not more common, just more serious.
    d. Extra copies of the other chromosomes are probably fatal.
12. In the light micrograph below of dividing cells near the tip of an onion root, identify a cell in interphase, prophase, metaphase, anaphase, and telophase. Describe the major events occurring at each stage.

Level 3: Synthesis/Evaluation

13. An organism called a plasmodial slime mold is one large cytoplasmic mass with many nuclei. Explain how such a "megacell" could form.
14. Briefly describe how three different processes that occur during a sexual life cycle increase the genetic diversity of offspring.
15. Discuss the factors that control the division of eukaryotic cells grown in the laboratory. Cancer cells are easier to grow in the lab than other cells. Why do you suppose this is?
16. Compare cytokinesis in plant and animal cells. In what ways are the two processes similar? In what ways are they different?
17. Sketch a cell with three pairs of chromosomes undergoing meiosis, and show how nondisjunction can result in the production of gametes with extra or missing chromosomes.

18. Suppose you read in the newspaper that a genetic engineering laboratory has developed a procedure for fusing two gametes from the same person (two eggs or two sperm) to form a zygote. The article mentions that an early step in the procedure prevents crossing over from occurring during the formation of the gametes in the donor's body. The researchers are in the process of determining the genetic makeup of one of their new zygotes. Which of the following predictions do you think they would make? Justify your choice, and explain why you rejected each of the other choices.
    a. The zygote would have 46 chromosomes, all of which came from the gamete donor (its one parent), so the zygote would be genetically identical to the gamete donor.
    b. The zygote *could* be genetically identical to the gamete donor, but it is much more likely that it would have an unpredictable mixture of chromosomes from the gamete donor's parents.
    c. The zygote would not be genetically identical to the gamete donor, but it would be genetically identical to one of the donor's parents.
    d. The zygote would not be genetically identical to the gamete donor, but it would be genetically identical to one of the donor's grandparents.
19. Bacteria are able to divide on a faster schedule than eukaryotic cells. Some bacteria can divide every 20 minutes, while the minimum time required by eukaryotic cells in a rapidly developing embryo is about once per hour, and most cells divide much less often than that. State several testable hypotheses explaining why bacteria can divide at a faster rate than eukaryotic cells.
20. Red blood cells, which carry oxygen to body tissues, live for only about 120 days. Replacement cells are produced by cell division in bone marrow. How many cell divisions must occur each second in your bone marrow just to replace red blood cells? Here is some information to use in calculating your answer: There are about 5 million red blood cells per cubic millimeter (mm^3) of blood. An average adult has about 5 L (5,000 cm^3) of blood. (*Hint*: What is the total number of red blood cells in the body? What fraction of them must be replaced each day if all are replaced in 120 days?)
21. A mule is the offspring of a horse and a donkey. A donkey sperm contains 31 chromosomes and a horse egg cell contains 32 chromosomes, so the zygote contains a total of 63 chromosomes. The zygote develops normally. The combined set of chromosomes is not a problem in mitosis, and the mule combines some of the best characteristics of horses and donkeys. However, a mule is sterile; meiosis cannot occur normally in its testes (or ovaries). Explain why mitosis is normal in cells containing both horse and donkey chromosomes but the mixed set of chromosomes interferes with meiosis.
22. **SCIENTIFIC THINKING** The personalized cancer therapy study described in Module 8.10 began with a single bladder cancer patient. This patient, unlike many others, responded well to treatment with the drug everolimus. Many scientific studies begin with a detailed examination of an unusual case like this; the goal is to understand the underlying cause and use this information to understand (and help) more individuals. How could this approach be extended from the data presented in Table 8.10? Do you see any unusual results that could prompt another round of study? How might such a study be designed?

Answers to all questions can be found in Appendix 4.

9

Patterns of Inheritance

The people of Tibet occupy a high-altitude region of the Himalayan mountains and are renowned for their mountaineering skills. For centuries, westerners have marveled at their uncanny ability to live and work at altitudes above 13,000 feet, where the amount of oxygen that reaches the blood is 40% less than at sea level. Without extensive conditioning, most people from other regions can hardly walk under such conditions, let alone carry heavy loads.

What makes the Tibetan people so able to tolerate their harsh surroundings? The answer lies, at least in part, in their genes: Over the last several thousand years, the Tibetan population has accumulated several dozen genetic mutations that affect their circulatory and respiratory systems. Tibetans commonly have versions of these genes that are rare among their low-dwelling Chinese neighbors. A newborn with such mutations is three times more likely to survive a high-altitude infancy, an advantage that clearly increases fitness in this environment and so is favored by natural selection.

Are humans evolving?

In this chapter, we'll examine the rules that govern how inherited traits are passed from parents to offspring. We'll look at several different patterns of inheritance and investigate how we can predict the ratios of offspring with particular traits. Most important, we'll uncover a basic biological concept: how the behavior of chromosomes during gamete formation and fertilization (discussed in Chapter 8) accounts for the patterns of inheritance we observe. Along the way, we'll consider many examples of how genetic principles can help us understand the biology of humans, plants, and many other familiar creatures.

BIG IDEAS

Mendel's Laws
(9.1–9.10)

A few simple and long-established rules explain many aspects of heredity.

Variations on Mendel's Laws
(9.11–9.15)

Some inheritance patterns are more complex than the ones described by Mendel.

The Chromosomal Basis of Inheritance
(9.16–9.19)

Hereditary rules can be understood by following the behavior of chromosomes.

Sex Chromosomes and Sex-Linked Genes
(9.20–9.23)

Genes found on sex chromosomes display unique patterns of inheritance.

▷ Mendel's Laws

9.1 The study of genetics has ancient roots

Attempts to explain inheritance date back at least to the ancient Greek physician Hippocrates (**Figure 9.1**). He suggested that particles called "pangenes" travel from each part of an organism's body to the eggs or sperm and then are passed to the next generation; moreover, Hippocrates argued, changes that occur in the body during an organism's life are passed on in this way.

Hippocrates's idea is incorrect in several respects. The reproductive cells are not composed of particles from somatic (body) cells, and changes in somatic cells do not influence eggs and sperm. For instance, no matter how many years you endure orthodontic braces, cells in your mouth do not transmit genetic information to your gametes, and there is no higher likelihood that your offspring will have straight teeth just because you wore braces. This may seem like common sense today, but the idea that traits acquired during an individual's lifetime are passed on to offspring prevailed well into the 19th century.

By observing inheritance patterns in ornamental plants, biologists of the early 19th century established that offspring inherit traits from both parents. The favored explanation of

▲ **Figure 9.1**   Hippocrates (approximately 460–370 BCE)

inheritance then became the "blending" hypothesis, the idea that the hereditary materials contributed by the male and female parents mix in forming the offspring similar to the way that blue and yellow paints blend to make green. For example, according to this hypothesis, after the genetic information for the colors of black and chocolate brown Labrador retrievers is blended, the colors should be as inseparable as paint pigments. But this is not what happens: Instead, the offspring of a purebred black Lab and a purebred brown Lab will all be black, but some of the dogs in the next generation will be brown (you'll learn why in Module 9.5). The blending hypothesis was finally rejected because it does not explain how traits that disappear in one generation can reappear in later ones.

> **?**   Imagine you have two different houseplants of the same species, one of which blooms with white flowers and the other with red flowers. Design a simple experiment to test the blending hypothesis.
>
> ● Cross the two plants and observe the resulting flower color in the offspring. The blending hypothesis predicts the appearance of pink flowers.

9.2 The science of genetics began in an abbey garden

Heredity is the transmission of traits from one generation to the next. The field of **genetics**, the scientific study of heredity, began in the 1860s, when an Augustinian monk named Gregor Mendel (**Figure 9.2A**) deduced the fundamental principles of genetics by breeding garden peas. Mendel lived and worked in an abbey in Brunn, Austria (now Brno, in the Czech Republic). His research was strongly influenced by his study of physics, mathematics, and chemistry at the University of Vienna; the research was both experimentally and mathematically rigorous, and these qualities were largely responsible for his success.

▲ **Figure 9.2A**   Gregor Mendel

In a classic paper published in 1866, Mendel correctly argued that parents pass discrete "heritable factors" on to their offspring. (It is interesting to note that Mendel's landmark publication appeared just seven years after Darwin's 1859 publication of *The Origin of Species*, making the 1860s a banner decade in the development of modern biology.) Mendel stressed that the heritable factors, today called genes,

retain their individuality generation after generation. That is, genes are like playing cards: A deck may be shuffled, but the cards always retain their original identities, and no card is ever blended with another. Similarly, genes may be sorted, but each gene permanently retains its identity.

Mendel probably chose to study garden peas because they had short generation times, produced large numbers of offspring from each mating, and came in many readily distinguishable varieties. For example, one variety has purple flowers, and another variety has white flowers. A heritable feature that varies among individuals, such as flower color, is called a **character**. Each variant for a character, such as purple or white flowers, is called a **trait**. Perhaps the most important advantage of pea plants as an experimental model was that Mendel could strictly control matings. As **Figure 9.2B** shows, the petals of the pea flower almost completely enclose the reproductive organs: the stamens and carpel.

Petal

Carpel (contains eggs)

Stamens (release sperm-containing pollen)

◀ **Figure 9.2B**   The anatomy of a garden pea flower (with one petal removed to improve visibility)

① Mendel removed the stamens from a purple flower.

② He transferred pollen from the stamens of a white flower to the carpel of the purple flower.

Parents (P)

Carpel

Stamens

③ The pollinated carpel matured into a pod.

④ Mendel planted seeds from the pod.

Offspring (F₁)

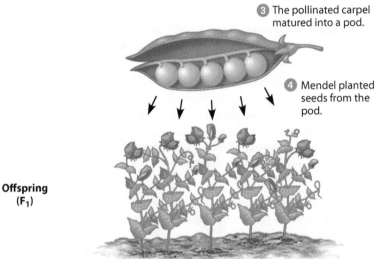

▲ Figure 9.2C Mendel's technique for cross-fertilization of pea plants

Consequently, pea plants usually are able to self-fertilize in nature. That is, sperm-carrying pollen grains released from the stamens land on the egg-containing carpel of the same flower. Mendel could ensure self-fertilization by covering a flower with a small bag so that no pollen from another plant could reach the carpel. When he wanted cross-fertilization (fertilization of one plant by pollen from a different plant), he used the method shown in **Figure 9.2C**. ① He prevented self-fertilization by cutting off the immature stamens of a plant before they produced pollen. ② To cross-fertilize the stameless flower, he dusted its carpel with pollen from another plant. After pollination, ③ the carpel developed into a pod, containing seeds (peas) that ④ he later planted. The seeds grew into offspring plants. Through these methods, Mendel could always be sure of the parentage of new plants.

Mendel's success was due to his experimental approach and choice of organism and to his selection of characters to study. He chose to observe seven characters, each of which occurred as two distinct traits (**Figure 9.2D**). Mendel worked with his plants until he was sure he had **true-breeding** varieties—that is, varieties for which self-fertilization produced offspring all identical to the parent. For instance, he identified a purple-flowered variety that, when self-fertilized, produced offspring plants that all had purple flowers.

Mendel was then ready to ask what would happen when he crossed his different true-breeding varieties with each other. For example, what offspring would result if plants with purple flowers and plants with white flowers were cross-fertilized? The offspring of two different varieties are called **hybrids**, and the cross-fertilization itself is referred to as a hybridization, or simply a genetic **cross**. The true-breeding parents are called the **P generation** (P for parental), and their hybrid offspring are called the **F₁ generation** (F for *filial*, from the Latin word for "son"). When F₁ plants self-fertilize or fertilize each other, their offspring are the **F₂ generation**.

Mendel's quantitative analysis of the F₂ plants from thousands of genetic crosses allowed him to deduce the fundamental principles of heredity. We turn to Mendel's results next.

? Describe three generations of your own family using the terminology of a genetic cross (P, F₁, F₂).

● The P generation is your grandparents, the F₁ your parents, and the F₂ is you (and any siblings).

Character	Traits	
	Dominant	**Recessive**
Flower color	Purple	White
Flower position	Axial	Terminal
Seed color	Yellow	Green
Seed shape	Round	Wrinkled
Pod shape	Inflated	Constricted
Pod color	Green	Yellow
Stem length	Tall	Dwarf

▲ Figure 9.2D   The seven pea characters studied by Mendel

9.3 Mendel's law of segregation describes the inheritance of a single character

Mendel performed many experiments in which he tracked the inheritance of characters that occur in two forms, such as flower color. The results led him to formulate several hypotheses about inheritance. Let's look at some of his experiments and follow the reasoning that led to his hypotheses.

Figure 9.3A starts with a cross between a true-breeding pea plant with purple flowers and a true-breeding pea plant with white flowers. This is an example of a **monohybrid cross** because it follows just one character—flower color. Mendel observed that F_1 plants all had purple flowers. Was the white-flowered plant's genetic contribution to the hybrids lost? By mating the F_1 plants with each other, Mendel found the answer to be no. Out of 929 F_2 plants, 705 (about $\frac{3}{4}$) had purple flowers and 224 (about $\frac{1}{4}$) had white flowers. That is, there are about three plants with purple flowers for every one with white flowers, or a 3:1 ratio of purple to white. Mendel reasoned that the heritable factor for white flowers did not disappear in the F_1 plants but was masked when the purple-flower factor was present. He also deduced that the F_1 plants must have carried two factors for the flower-color character, one for purple and one for white. From these results and others, Mendel developed four hypotheses, described here using modern terminology, such as "gene" instead of "heritable factor."

1. *There are alternative versions of genes that account for variations in inherited characters.* For example, the gene for flower color in pea plants exists in two versions: one for purple and the other for white. Alternative versions of a gene are called **alleles**.

2. *For each character, an organism inherits two alleles, one from each parent.* These alleles may be identical or they may differ. An organism that has two identical alleles for a gene is said to be **homozygous** for that gene (and is a "homozygote" for that trait). An organism that has two different alleles for a gene is said to be **heterozygous** for that gene (and is a "heterozygote").

3. *If the two alleles of an inherited pair differ, then one determines the organism's appearance and is called the* **dominant allele**; *the other has no noticeable effect on the organism's appearance and is called the* **recessive allele**. Geneticists use uppercase italic letters to represent dominant alleles and lowercase italic letters to represent recessive alleles.

4. *A sperm or egg carries only one allele for each inherited character because allele pairs separate (segregate) from each other during the production of gametes.* This statement is called the **law of segregation**. When sperm and egg unite at fertilization, each contributes its allele, restoring the paired condition in the offspring.

Do Mendel's hypotheses account for the 3:1 ratio he observed in the F_2 generation? Figure 9.3B illustrates Mendel's law

▲ Figure 9.3A   A monohybrid cross that tracks one character (flower color)

▲ Figure 9.3B   An explanation of the crosses in Figure 9.3A of segregation, which explains the inheritance pattern shown in Figure 9.3A. Mendel's hypotheses predict that when alleles segregate during gamete formation in the F_1 plants, half the gametes will receive a purple-flower allele (P) and the other half a white-flower allele (p). During pollination among the F_1 plants, the gametes unite randomly. An egg with a purple-flower allele has an equal chance of being fertilized by a sperm with a purple-flower allele or one with a white-flower allele (that is, a P egg may fuse with a P sperm or a p sperm). Because the same is true for an egg with a white-flower allele (a p egg with a P sperm or p sperm), there are a total of four equally likely combinations of sperm and egg in the F_2 generation.

The diagram at the bottom of Figure 9.3B, called a **Punnett square**, repeats the cross shown in Figure 9.3A in a way that highlights the four possible combinations of gametes and the resulting four possible offspring in the F_2 generation. Each square represents an equally probable product of fertilization. For example, the box in the upper right corner of the Punnett square shows the genetic combination resulting from a p sperm fertilizing a P egg.

According to the Punnett square, what will be the physical appearance of these F_2 offspring? One-fourth of the plants have two alleles specifying purple flowers (PP); clearly, these plants will have purple flowers. One-half (two-fourths) of the F_2 offspring have inherited one allele for purple flowers and one allele for white flowers (Pp); like the F_1 plants, these plants will also have purple flowers, the dominant trait. (Note that Pp and pP are equivalent and usually written as Pp.) Finally, one-fourth of the F_2 plants have inherited two alleles specifying white flowers (pp) and will express this recessive

trait. Thus, Mendel's model accounts for the 3:1 ratio that he observed in the F_2 generation.

Because an organism's appearance does not always reveal its genetic composition, geneticists distinguish between an organism's physical traits, called its **phenotype** (such as purple or white flowers), and its genetic makeup, its **genotype** (in this example, PP, Pp, or pp). So now we see that Figure 9.3A shows just phenotypes, whereas Figure 9.3B shows both phenotypes and genotypes in our sample crosses. For the F_2 plants, the ratio of plants with purple flowers to those with white flowers (3:1) is called the phenotypic ratio. The genotypic ratio, as shown by the Punnett square, is $1PP : 2Pp : 1pp$.

Mendel found that each of the seven characters he studied exhibited the same inheritance pattern: One parental trait disappeared in the F_1 generation, only to reappear in $\frac{1}{4}$ of the F_2 offspring. The mechanism underlying this inheritance pattern is stated by Mendel's law of segregation: *Pairs of alleles segregate (separate) during gamete formation; the fusion of gametes at fertilization creates allele pairs once again.* Research since Mendel's time has established that the law of segregation applies to all sexually reproducing organisms, including humans.

Later in this chapter, we'll return to Mendel and his experiments with pea plants (in Module 9.5). But first, we'll investigate how cell division (the topic of Chapter 8) fits with what we've learned about genetics so far.

> **?** How can two plants with different genotypes for a particular inherited character be identical in phenotype?
>
> ● One could be homozygous for the dominant allele and the other heterozygous.

9.4 Homologous chromosomes bear the alleles for each character

Figure 9.4 shows a pair of homologous chromosomes. The chromosomes in a homologous pair—chromosomes that carry alleles of the same genes—are also called homologs. Recall that every diploid cell, whether from a pea plant or a person, has pairs of homologous chromosomes. One member of each pair comes from the organism's female parent and the other member of each pair comes from the male parent.

Each labeled band on the chromosomes in Figure 9.4 represents a gene **locus** (plural, *loci*), a specific location of a gene along the chromosome. You can see the connection between Mendel's law of segregation and homologous chromosomes: Alleles (alternative versions) of a gene reside at the same locus on homologous chromosomes. However, the two chromosomes may bear either identical alleles at a locus (as in the P/P and a/a loci) or different alleles (as in the B/b locus)—the organisms may be homozygous or heterozygous for the gene at any particular locus. We will return to the chromosomal basis of Mendel's law later in the chapter.

> **?** An individual is heterozygous, *Bb*, for a gene. According to the law of segregation, each gamete formed by this individual will have *either* the *B* allele *or* the *b* allele. Which step in the process of meiosis is the physical basis for this segregation of alleles? (*Hint*: See Figure 8.12.)
>
> ● The *B* and *b* alleles are located at the same gene locus on homologous chromosomes, which separate during meiosis I and are packaged in separate gametes during meiosis II.

Genotype:

PP	aa	Bb
Homozygous for the dominant allele	**Homozygous** for the recessive allele	**Heterozygous**, with one dominant and one recessive allele

▲ **Figure 9.4** Three gene loci on homologous chromosomes

9.5 The law of independent assortment is revealed by tracking two characters at once

Recall from Module 9.3 that Mendel deduced his law of segregation by following through the F_1 and F_2 generations one character from the P generation. From such monohybrid crosses, Mendel knew that the allele for round seed shape (designated R) was dominant to the allele for wrinkled seed shape (r) and that the allele for yellow seed color (Y) was dominant to the allele for green seed color (y). Mendel wondered: What would happen if he crossed plants that differ in both seed shape and seed color?

To find out, Mendel set up a **dihybrid cross**, a mating of parental varieties differing in two characters. Mendel crossed homozygous plants having round yellow seeds (genotype *RRYY*) with plants having wrinkled green seeds (*rryy*). Mendel knew that an *RRYY* plant would produce only gametes with *RY* alleles; an *rryy* plant would produce only gametes with *ry* alleles. Therefore, Mendel knew there was only one possible outcome for the F_1 generation: The union of *RY* and *ry* gametes would yield hybrids heterozygous for both characters (*RrYy*)—that is, dihybrids. All of these *RrYy* offspring would have round yellow seeds, the double dominant phenotype.

The F_2 generation is trickier to predict. To find out if genes for seed color and shape would be transmitted as a package, Mendel crossed the *RrYy* F_1 plants with each other. He hypothesized two outcomes from this experiment: Either the dihybrid cross would exhibit *dependent* assortment, with the alleles for seed color and seed shape inherited together as they came from the P generation, or it would exhibit *independent* assortment, with the genes inherited independently.

As shown on the left side of **Figure 9.5A**, the hypothesis of dependent assortment leads to the prediction that each F_2 plant would inherit one of two possible sperm (*RY* or *ry*) and one of two possible eggs (*RY* or *ry*), for a total of four combinations. The Punnett square shows that there could be only

two F_2 phenotypes—round yellow or wrinkled green—in a 3:1 ratio. However, when Mendel actually performed this cross, he did not obtain these results, thus refuting the hypothesis of dependent assortment.

The alternative hypothesis—that the genes would exhibit independent assortment—is shown on the right side of Figure 9.5A. This leads to the prediction that the F_1 plants would produce four different gametes: *RY, rY, Ry,* and *ry*. Each F_2 plant would inherit one of four possible sperm and one of four possible eggs, for a total of 16 possible combinations. Fertilization among these gametes would lead to four different seed phenotypes—round yellow, round green, wrinkled yellow, or wrinkled green—in a 9:3:3:1 ratio. In fact, Mendel observed such a ratio in the F_2 plants, indicating that each pair of alleles segregates independently of the other.

From the 9:3:3:1 ratio, we can see that there are 12 plants with round seeds to 4 with wrinkled seeds, and 12 yellow-seeded plants to 4 green-seeded ones. These 12:4 ratios each reduce to 3:1, which is the F_2 ratio for a monohybrid cross. In other words, an independent monohybrid cross is occurring for each of the two characters. Mendel tried his seven pea characters in various dihybrid combinations and always obtained data close to the predicted 9:3:3:1 ratio. These results supported the hypothesis that each pair of alleles segregates independently of other pairs of alleles during gamete formation. Put another way, the inheritance of one character has no effect on the inheritance of another. This is referred to as Mendel's **law of independent assortment**.

Figure 9.5B shows how this law applies to the inheritance of two characters controlled by separate genes in Labrador retrievers: black versus chocolate coat color and normal vision versus progressive retinal atrophy (PRA), an eye disorder that leads to blindness. Black Labs have at least one copy of an allele, B, that gives their hairs densely packed granules of a dark pigment. The B allele is dominant to the b allele, which leads to a less tightly packed distribution of pigment. As a result, the coats of dogs with genotype *bb* are chocolate in color. The

▼ **Figure 9.5A**
Two hypotheses for segregation in a dihybrid cross

The hypothesis of dependent assortment
Not actually seen; hypothesis refuted

The hypothesis of independent assortment
Actual results; hypothesis supported

allele that causes PRA, *n*, is recessive to allele *N*, which is necessary for normal vision. Thus, only dogs of genotype *nn* become blind from PRA. In the top of this figure, blanks in the genotypes are used where a particular phenotype may result from multiple genotypes. For example, a black Lab may have either genotype *BB* or *Bb*, which we abbreviate as *B_*.)

The lower part of Figure 9.5B shows what happens when we mate two heterozygous Labs, both of genotype *BbNn*. The F₂ phenotypic ratio will be nine black dogs with normal eyes to three black with PRA to three chocolate with normal eyes to one chocolate with PRA. These 9:3:3:1 results are analogous to the results in Figure 9.5A and demonstrate that the alleles for the *B* and *N* genes are inherited independently.

? Predict the phenotypes of offspring obtained by mating a black Lab homozygous for both coat color and normal eyes with a chocolate Lab that is blind from PRA.

● All offspring would be black with normal eyes (BBNN × bbnn → BbNn).

Phenotypes	Black coat, normal vision	Black coat, blind (PRA)	Chocolate coat, normal vision	Chocolate coat, blind (PRA)
Genotypes	B_N_	B_nn	bbN_	bbnn

Mating of double heterozygotes (black coat, normal vision)

BbNn × BbNn

Phenotypic ratio of the offspring	9 Black coat, normal vision	3 Black coat, blind (PRA)	3 Chocolate coat, normal vision	1 Chocolate coat, blind (PRA)

▲ **Figure 9.5B** Independent assortment of two genes in Labrador retrievers

Try This Rewrite the cross shown in this figure using a Punnett square, like the one used in the previous figure. You should get the same results!

9.6 Geneticists can use a testcross to determine unknown genotypes

Suppose you have a chocolate Lab. Referring to Figure 9.5B, you can tell that its genotype must be *bb*. But what if you had a black Lab? It could have one of two possible genotypes—*BB* or *Bb*—and there is no way to tell simply by looking at the dog. To determine your dog's genotype, you could perform a **testcross**, a mating between an individual of unknown genotype (your black Lab) and a homozygous recessive (*bb*) individual—in this case, a chocolate Lab.

Figure 9.6 shows the offspring that could result from such a mating. If, as shown on the bottom left, the black-coated parent's genotype is *BB*, all the offspring would be black because a cross between genotypes *BB* and *bb* can produce only *Bb* offspring. On the other hand, if the black parent is *Bb*, as shown on the bottom right, we would expect both black (*Bb*) and chocolate (*bb*) offspring. Thus, the appearance of the offspring reveals the original black dog's genotype.

To understand the results of any genetic cross, you need to understand the rules of probability, our next topic.

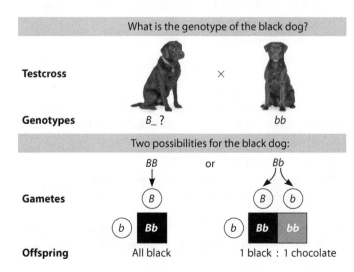

What is the genotype of the black dog?

Testcross			
Genotypes	B_?	×	bb

Two possibilities for the black dog:

	BB	or	Bb
Gametes	B		B b

	Bb		Bb	bb
Offspring	All black		1 black : 1 chocolate	

▲ **Figure 9.6** Using a testcross to determine genotype

? You use a testcross to determine the genotype of a Lab with normal eyes. Half of the offspring are normal and half develop PRA. What is the genotype of the normal parent?

● Heterozygous (Nn)

9.7 Mendel's laws reflect the rules of probability

Mendel's strong background in mathematics served him well in his studies of inheritance. He understood, for instance, that the segregation of allele pairs during gamete formation and the re-forming of pairs at fertilization obey the rules of probability—the same rules that apply to the tossing of coins, the rolling of dice, and the drawing of cards. Mendel also appreciated the statistical nature of inheritance. He knew that he needed to obtain large samples—to count many offspring from his crosses—before he could begin to interpret inheritance patterns.

Let's see how the rules of probability apply to inheritance. The probability scale ranges from 0 to 1. An event that is certain to occur has a probability of 1, whereas an event that is certain *not* to occur has a probability of 0. For example, a tossed coin has a $\frac{1}{2}$ chance of landing heads and a $\frac{1}{2}$ chance of landing tails. These two possibilities add up to 1; the probabilities of all possible outcomes for an event to occur must always add up to 1. In another example, in a standard deck of 52 playing cards, the chance of drawing a jack of diamonds is $\frac{1}{52}$ and the chance of drawing any card other than the jack of diamonds is $\frac{51}{52}$, which together add up to 1.

An important lesson we can learn from coin tossing is that for each and every toss of the coin, the probability of heads is $\frac{1}{2}$. Even if heads has landed five times in a row, the probability of the next toss coming up heads is still $\frac{1}{2}$. In other words, the outcome of any particular toss is unaffected by what has happened on previous attempts. Each toss is an independent event. If two coins are tossed simultaneously, the outcome for each coin is an independent event, unaffected by the other coin. What is the chance that both coins will land heads up when tossed together? The probability of such a dual event is the product of the separate probabilities of the independent events; for the coins, $\frac{1}{2} \times \frac{1}{2} = \frac{1}{4}$. This statistical principle is called the **rule of multiplication**, and it holds true for independent events in genetics as well as coin tosses.

Figure 9.7 offers a visual analogy of a cross between F$_1$ Labrador retrievers that have the *Bb* genotype for coat color. The genetic cross is portrayed by the tossing of two coins that stand in for the two gametes (a dime for the egg and a penny for the sperm); the heads side of each coin stands for the dominant *B* allele and the tails side of each coin the recessive *b* allele. What is the probability that a particular F$_2$ dog will have the *bb* genotype? To produce a *bb* offspring, both egg and sperm must carry the *b* allele. The probability that an egg will have the *b* allele is $\frac{1}{2}$, and the probability that a sperm will have the *b* allele is also $\frac{1}{2}$. By the rule of multiplication, the probability that the two *b* alleles will come together at fertilization is $\frac{1}{2} \times \frac{1}{2} = \frac{1}{4}$. This is exactly the answer given by the Punnett square in Figure 9.7. If we know the genotypes of the parents, we can predict the probability for any genotype among the offspring.

Now consider the probability that an F$_2$ Lab will be heterozygous for the coat-color gene. As Figure 9.7 shows, there are two ways in which F$_1$ gametes can combine to produce a heterozygous offspring. The dominant (*B*) allele can come from the egg and the recessive (*b*) allele from the sperm, or

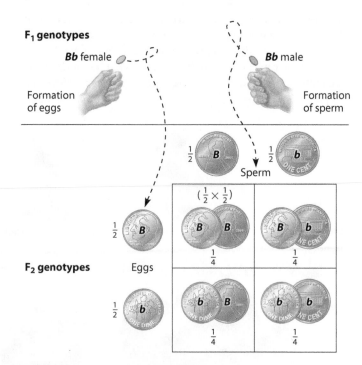

▲ **Figure 9.7** Segregation and fertilization as chance events

vice versa. The probability that an event can occur in two or more alternative ways can be determined from the sum of the separate probabilities of the alternatives; this is known as the **rule of addition**. Using this rule, we can calculate the probability of an F$_2$ heterozygote as $\frac{1}{4} + \frac{1}{4} = \frac{1}{2}$.

By applying the rules of probability to segregation and independent assortment, we can solve some rather complex genetics problems. For instance, we can predict the results of trihybrid crosses, in which three different characters are involved. Consider a cross between two organisms that both have the genotype *AaBbCc*. What is the probability that an offspring from this cross will be a recessive homozygote for all three genes (*aabbcc*)? Because each allele pair assorts independently, we can treat this trihybrid cross as three separate monohybrid crosses:

Aa × *Aa*: Probability of *aa* offspring $= \frac{1}{4}$

Bb × *Bb*: Probability of *bb* offspring $= \frac{1}{4}$

Cc × *Cc*: Probability of *cc* offspring $= \frac{1}{4}$

Because the segregation of each allele pair is an independent event, we use the rule of multiplication to calculate the probability that the offspring will be *aabbcc*:

$$\tfrac{1}{4}aa \times \tfrac{1}{4}\,bb \times \tfrac{1}{4}cc = \tfrac{1}{64}$$

We could reach the same conclusion by constructing a 64-section Punnett square, but that would take a lot of space!

> **?** A plant of genotype *AABbCC* is crossed with an *AaBbCc* plant. What is the probability of an offspring having the genotype *AABBCC*?

$\bullet$ $\frac{1}{16}$ (that is, $\frac{1}{2} \times \frac{1}{4} \times \frac{1}{2}$)

9.8 Genetic traits in humans can be tracked through family pedigrees

Although Mendel developed his laws of inheritance while working with peas, these principles apply to the inheritance of many human traits just as well. How are human traits studied? We obviously cannot perform testcrosses on people, so geneticists must analyze the results of matings that have already occurred. First, a geneticist collects information about a family's history for a trait. This information is assembled into a family tree, called a **pedigree**, that describes the traits of parents and children across generations. Here, you can see a pedigree that traces the incidence of straight hairline versus a "widow's peak" (pointed) hairline through three generations of a hypothetical family. Notice that Mendel's laws and simple logic enable us to deduce the genotypes for nearly every person in the pedigree.

READING A PEDIGREE

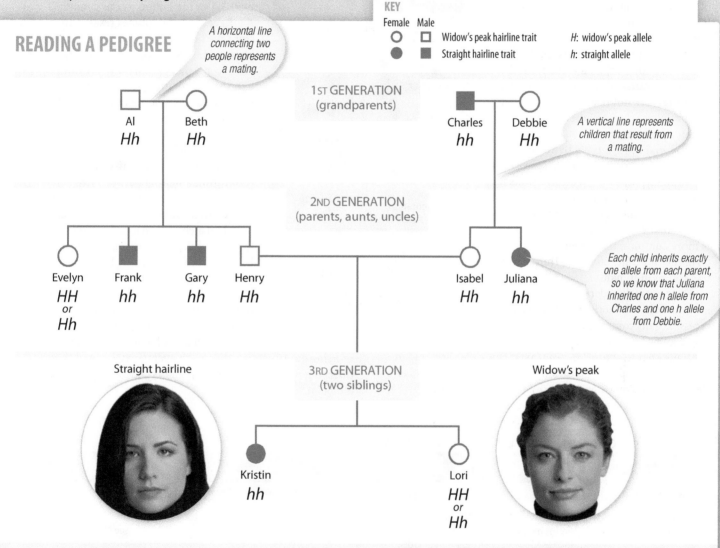

KEY

Female Male

○ □ Widow's peak hairline trait   H: widow's peak allele

● ■ Straight hairline trait   h: straight allele

A horizontal line connecting two people represents a mating.

A vertical line represents children that result from a mating.

1ST GENERATION (grandparents)

Al *Hh*   Beth *Hh*   Charles *hh*   Debbie *Hh*

2ND GENERATION (parents, aunts, uncles)

Evelyn *HH or Hh*   Frank *hh*   Gary *hh*   Henry *Hh*   Isabel *Hh*   Juliana *hh*

Each child inherits exactly one allele from each parent, so we know that Juliana inherited one h allele from Charles and one h allele from Debbie.

3RD GENERATION (two siblings)

Straight hairline

Kristin *hh*   Lori *HH or Hh*

Widow's peak

▶ Kristin has a straight hairline but neither of her parents (Henry and Isabel) do. This is only possible if the trait is recessive. We therefore know that Kristin and every other individual with a straight hairline must be homozygous recessive *hh*.

▶ Henry and Isabel must each have a copy of the *h* allele, because they each passed one on to daughter Kristin. And because they both have widow's peaks, they must each be heterozygous (*Hh*).

▶ Grandparents Al and Beth must both be *Hh* because they both had widow's peaks, but two of their sons (Frank and Gary) had straight hairlines and must therefore be *hh*.

▶ We cannot deduce the genotype of every member of the pedigree. Lori must have at least one *H* allele (since she has a widow's peak), but she could be either *HH* or *Hh*. We cannot distinguish between these two possibilities using the available data.

? If Lori had a child, which phenotype would allow her to deduce her own genotype for certain?

● If her child had a straight hairline (*hh*), then Lori would know that she herself must be *Hh*.

9.9 Many inherited traits in humans are controlled by a single gene

CONNECTION

In the previous module, you studied an example of a human character (widow's peak) controlled by simple dominant-recessive inheritance of one gene. **Figure 9.9A** shows two more examples. (The genetic underpinnings of many other human characters, such as eye and hair color, are more complex and as yet poorly understood.) A trait being dominant does not mean that it is "normal" or more common than a recessive trait; **wild-type traits**—those seen most often in nature—are not necessarily specified by dominant alleles. Rather, dominance means that a heterozygote (*Aa*) displays the dominant phenotype. By contrast, the phenotype of a recessive allele is seen only in a homozygote (*aa*). Recessive traits may in fact be more common in the population than dominant ones. For example, the absence of freckles (a dominant trait) is more common than their presence. The term mutant trait refers to a trait that is less common in nature.

The genetic disorders listed in **Table 9.9** are known to be inherited as dominant or recessive traits controlled by a single gene. These human disorders show simple inheritance patterns like the traits Mendel studied in pea plants. The genes discussed in this module are all located on autosomes, chromosomes other than the sex chromosomes X and Y (see Module 8.11).

Dominant Traits	Recessive Traits
Freckles	No freckles
Normal pigmentation	Albinism

Key
- ☐ Wild-type (more common) trait
- ☐ Mutant (less common) trait

▲ **Figure 9.9A** Examples of single-gene inherited traits in humans

Recessive Disorders Thousands of human genetic disorders—ranging in severity from relatively mild, such as albinism, to invariably fatal, such as cystic fibrosis—are inherited as recessive traits. Remember that the dominant phenotype results from either the homozygous genotype *AA* or the heterozygous genotype *Aa*. Recessive phenotypes result only from the homozygous genotype *aa*. Most people who have recessive disorders are born to normal parents who are both heterozygotes—that is, those parents who are **carriers** of the recessive allele for the disorder but are phenotypically normal.

Using Mendel's laws, we can predict the fraction of affected offspring likely to result from a mating between two carriers (**Figure 9.9B**). Suppose two people who are heterozygous carriers for albinism (*Aa*) had a child. What is the probability that this child would display albinism? Each child of two carriers has a $\frac{1}{4}$ chance of inheriting two recessive alleles. To put it another way, we can say that about one-fourth of the children from such a mating are predicted to display albinism. We can also say that a child with normal pigmentation has a $\frac{2}{3}$ chance of being an *Aa* carrier; that is, on average, two out of three offspring with the pigmented phenotype will be carriers for albinism.

TABLE 9.9 | SOME AUTOSOMAL DISORDERS IN HUMANS

Disorder	Major Symptoms	Incidence	Comments
Recessive Disorders			
Albinism	Lack of pigment in the skin, hair, and eyes	1/22,000	Prone to skin cancer
Cystic fibrosis	Excess mucus in the lungs, digestive tract, liver; increased susceptibility to infections; death in early childhood unless treated	1/2,500 Caucasians	See Module 9.9
Phenylketonuria (PKU)	Accumulation of phenylalanine in blood; lack of normal skin pigment; developmental disabilities	1/10,000 in United States and Europe	See Module 9.10
Sickle-cell disease	Sickled red blood cells; damage to many tissues	1/400 African Americans	See Module 9.13
Tay-Sachs disease	Lipid accumulation in brain cells; mental deficiency; blindness; death in childhood	1/3,600 Jews from central Europe	See Module 4.10
Dominant Disorders			
Achondroplasia	Dwarfism	1/25,000	See Module 9.9
Huntington's disease	Developmental disabilities and uncontrollable movements; strikes in middle age	1/25,000	See Module 9.9
Hypercholesterolemia	Excess cholesterol in the blood; heart disease	1/500 are heterozygous	See Module 9.11

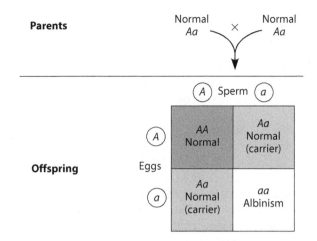

Parents

Normal
Aa × Normal *Aa*

Offspring

Sperm (A) (a)

Eggs

	(A)	(a)
(A)	*AA* Normal	*Aa* Normal (carrier)
(a)	*Aa* Normal (carrier)	*aa* Albinism

▲ **Figure 9.9B** Offspring produced by parents who are both carriers for albinism, a recessive disorder

The most common lethal genetic disease in the United States is cystic fibrosis (CF). Affecting about 30,000 Americans, the recessive CF allele is carried by about one in 31 Americans. A person with two copies of this allele has cystic fibrosis, which is characterized by an excessive secretion of very thick mucus from the lungs and other organs. This mucus can interfere with breathing, digestion, and liver function and makes the person vulnerable to recurrent bacterial infections. Although there is no cure for CF, strict adherence to a daily health regimen—including gentle pounding on the chest and back to clear the airway, inhaled antibiotics, and a special diet—can have a profound impact on the health of the affected person. CF was once invariably fatal in childhood, but tremendous advances in treatment have raised the median survival age of Americans with CF to 37.

Cystic fibrosis is most common in Caucasians. In fact, most genetic disorders are not evenly distributed across all ethnic groups. Such uneven distribution is the result of prolonged geographic isolation of certain populations. Isolation (as with settlers of a new island, for example) can lead to matings between close blood relatives. People with recent common ancestors are more likely to carry the same recessive alleles than are unrelated people. Therefore, matings between close relatives may cause the frequency of a rare allele (and the disease it causes) to increase within that community. Geneticists have observed increased incidence of harmful recessive traits among many types of inbred animals. For example, the detrimental effects of inbreeding are seen in some endangered species that recovered from small populations (see Module 13.11). With the increased mobility in most human populations today, it is relatively unlikely that two people who carry a rare, harmful allele will meet and mate.

Dominant Disorders Although most harmful alleles are recessive, a number of human disorders are caused by dominant alleles. Some are harmless conditions, such as extra fingers and toes (called polydactyly) or webbed fingers and toes.

A more serious dominant disorder is achondroplasia, a form of dwarfism in which the head and torso of the body develop normally but the arms and legs are short (**Figure 9.9C**). The homozygous dominant genotype (*AA*) causes death of the embryo; therefore, only heterozygotes (*Aa*) have this disorder. (This also means that a person with achondroplasia has a 50% chance of passing the condition on to any children.) Therefore, all those who do not have achondroplasia, more than 99.99% of the population, are homozygous for the recessive allele (*aa*). This example makes it clear that a dominant allele is not necessarily more common in a population than a corresponding recessive allele.

Dominant alleles that cause lethal diseases are much less common than recessive alleles that cause lethal diseases. One reason is that the dominant lethal allele cannot be carried by heterozygotes without affecting them. Many lethal dominant alleles result from mutations in a sperm or egg that subsequently kill the embryo. And if the afflicted individual is born but does not survive long enough to reproduce, he or she will not pass on the lethal allele to future generations. This is in contrast to lethal recessive mutations, which are perpetuated from generation to generation by healthy heterozygous carriers.

A lethal dominant allele can escape elimination, however, if it does not cause death until a relatively advanced age. One such example is the allele that causes **Huntington's disease**, a degenerative disorder of the nervous system that usually does not appear until middle age. Once the deterioration of the nervous system begins, it is irreversible and inevitably fatal. Because the allele for Huntington's disease is dominant, any child born to a parent with the allele has a 50% chance of inheriting the allele and the disorder. This example makes it clear that a dominant allele is not necessarily "better" than a corresponding recessive allele.

Until relatively recently, the onset of symptoms was the only way to know if a person had inherited the Huntington's allele. This is no longer the case. A genetic test is now available that can detect the presence of the Huntington's allele in an individual's genome. This is one of several genetic tests currently available. We'll explore the topic of personal genetic screening in the next module.

▲ **Figure 9.9C** Dr. Michael C. Ain, a specialist in the repair of bone defects caused by achondroplasia and related disorders

? Peter is a 30-year-old man whose father died of Huntington's disease. Neither Peter's mother nor a much older sister shows any signs of Huntington's. What is the probability that Peter has inherited Huntington's disease?

● Since his father had the disease, there is a $\frac{1}{2}$ chance that Peter received the gene. (The genotype of his sister is irrelevant.)

9.10 New technologies can provide insight into one's genetic legacy

Some prospective parents are aware that they have an increased risk of having a baby with a genetic disorder. For example, many pregnant women over age 35 know that they have a heightened risk of bearing children with Down syndrome (see Module 8.20), and some couples are aware that certain genetic diseases run in their families. These prospective parents may want to learn more about their own and their baby's genetic makeup. Modern technologies offer ways to obtain such information.

Genetic Testing Because most children with recessive disorders are born to healthy parents, the genetic risk for many diseases is determined by whether the prospective parents are carriers of the recessive allele. For an increasing number of genetic disorders, including Tay-Sachs disease, sickle-cell disease, and one form of cystic fibrosis, tests are available that can distinguish between individuals who have no disease-causing alleles and those who are heterozygous carriers. Other parents may know that a dominant but late-appearing disease, such as Huntington's disease, runs in their family.

Such people may benefit from genetic tests for dominant alleles. Information from genetic testing (also called genetic screening) can inform decisions about family planning.

Fetal Testing Several technologies are available for detecting genetic conditions in a fetus. Genetic testing before birth requires the collection of fetal cells. In **amniocentesis**, performed between weeks 14 and 20 of pregnancy, a physician carefully inserts a needle through the abdomen and into the mother's uterus while watching an ultrasound imager to guide the needle away from the fetus (**Figure 9.10A**, left). The physician extracts about 10 milliliters (2 teaspoons) of the amniotic fluid that bathes the developing fetus. Tests for genetic disorders can be performed on fetal cells that have been isolated from the fluid. These cells are usually cultured in the laboratory for several weeks. By then, enough dividing cells can be harvested to allow karyotyping (see Module 8.19) that will detect chromosomal abnormalities such as Down syndrome. Biochemical tests can also be performed on the cultured cells, revealing conditions such as Tay-Sachs disease.

▲ **Figure 9.10A** Testing a fetus for genetic disorders

In another procedure, **chorionic villus sampling (CVS)**, a physician extracts a tiny sample of chorionic villus tissue from the placenta, the organ that carries nourishment and wastes between the fetus and the mother. The tissue can be obtained using a narrow, flexible tube inserted through the mother's vagina and cervix into the uterus (Figure 9.10A, right). Results of karyotyping and some biochemical tests can be available within 24 hours. The speed of CVS is an advantage over amniocentesis. Another advantage is that CVS can be performed as early as the 8th week of pregnancy.

Unfortunately, both amniocentesis and CVS pose some risk of complications, such as maternal bleeding, miscarriage, or premature birth. Complication rates for amniocentesis and CVS are about 1% and 2%, respectively. Because of the risks, these procedures are usually reserved for situations in which the possibility of a genetic disease is significantly higher than average. Newer genetic screening procedures involve isolating tiny amounts of fetal cells or DNA released into the mother's bloodstream. Although few reliable tests are yet available using this method, this promising and complication-free technology may soon replace more invasive procedures.

Blood tests on the mother at 15 to 20 weeks of pregnancy can help identify fetuses at risk for certain birth defects—and thus candidates for further testing that may require more invasive procedures (such as amniocentesis). The most widely used blood test measures the mother's blood level of alpha-fetoprotein (AFP), a protein produced by the fetus. High levels of AFP may indicate a neural tube defect in the fetus. (The neural tube is an embryonic structure that develops into the brain and spinal cord.) Low levels of AFP may indicate Down syndrome. For a more complete risk profile, a woman's doctor may order a "triple screen test," which measures AFP as well as two other hormones produced by the placenta. Abnormal levels of these substances in the maternal blood may also point to a risk of Down syndrome.

Fetal Imaging

Other techniques enable a physician to examine a fetus directly for anatomical deformities. The most common procedure is **ultrasound imaging**, which uses sound waves to produce a picture of the fetus. **Figure 9.10B** shows an ultrasound scanner, which emits high-frequency sounds, beyond the range of hearing. When the sound waves bounce off the fetus, the echoes produce an image on the monitor. The inset image in Figure 9.10B shows a fetus at about 20 weeks. Traditional ultrasound imaging is noninvasive—no foreign objects are inserted into the mother's body—and has no known risk. Transvaginal ultrasound imaging—during which a probe is placed in the woman's vagina—can be used to provide clear images in early pregnancy. In another imaging method, fetoscopy, a needle-thin tube containing a fiber-optic viewing scope is inserted into the uterus. Fetoscopy can provide highly detailed images of the fetus but, unlike ultrasound, carries risk of complications.

Newborn Screening

Some genetic disorders can be detected at birth by simple tests that are now routinely performed in most hospitals in the United States. One common screening program is for phenylketonuria (PKU), a

▲ **Figure 9.10B**   Traditional ultrasound scanning of a fetus

recessively inherited disorder that occurs in about one out of every 10,000 births in the United States. Children with this disease cannot properly break down the naturally occurring amino acid phenylalanine, and an accumulation of phenylalanine may lead to developmental disabilities. However, if the deficiency is detected in the newborn, a special diet low in phenylalanine can usually prevent symptoms. Unfortunately, few other genetic disorders are currently treatable.

Ethical Considerations

As new technologies such as fetal imaging and testing become more widespread, geneticists are working to make sure that they do not cause more problems than they solve. Consider the tests for identifying carriers of recessive diseases. Such information may enable people with family histories of genetic disorders to make informed decisions about having children. But these new methods for genetic screening pose problems, too. If confidentiality is breached, will carriers be stigmatized? For example, will they be denied health or life insurance, even though they themselves are healthy? Geneticists stress that patients seeking genetic testing should receive counseling both before and after to clarify their family history, to explain the test, and to help them cope with the results. But with a wealth of genetic information increasingly available, a full discussion of the meaning of the results might be time-consuming and costly, raising the question of who should pay for such counseling.

Couples at risk for conceiving children with genetic disorders may now learn a great deal about their unborn children. In particular, CVS gives parents a chance to become informed very early in pregnancy. What is to be done with such information? If fetal tests reveal a serious disorder, the parents must choose between terminating the pregnancy and preparing themselves for a baby with severe problems. Identifying a genetic disease early can give families time to prepare—emotionally, medically, and financially. The dilemmas posed by human genetics reinforce one of this book's central themes: the immense social implications of biology.

> **?**   What is the primary benefit of genetic screening by CVS? What is the primary risk?
>
> ● CVS allows genetic screening to be performed very early in pregnancy and provides quick results, but it carries a risk of miscarriage.

▷ Variations on Mendel's Laws

9.11 Incomplete dominance results in intermediate phenotypes

Mendel's two laws explain inheritance in terms of discrete factors—genes—that are passed along from generation to generation according to simple rules of probability. These laws are valid for all sexually reproducing organisms, including garden peas, Labradors, and human beings. But just as the basic rules of musical harmony cannot account for all the rich sounds of a symphony, Mendel's laws stop short of explaining some patterns of genetic inheritance. In fact, for most sexually reproducing organisms, cases where Mendel's laws can strictly account for the patterns of inheritance are relatively rare. More often, the observed inheritance patterns are more complex, as we will see in this and the next four modules.

The F_1 offspring of Mendel's pea crosses always looked like one of the two parental varieties. In this situation—called **complete dominance**—the dominant allele has the same phenotypic effect whether present in one or two copies. But for some characters, the appearance of F_1 hybrids falls between the phenotypes of the two parental varieties, an effect called **incomplete dominance**. For instance, when red snapdragons are crossed with white snapdragons, all the F_1 hybrids have pink flowers (**Figure 9.11A**). This third phenotype results from flowers of the heterozygote having less red pigment than the red homozygotes.

As the Punnett square at the bottom of Figure 9.11A shows, the F_2 offspring appear in a phenotypic ratio of one red to two pink to one white, as the red and white alleles segregate during gamete formation in the pink F_1 hybrids. In incomplete dominance, the phenotypes of heterozygotes differ from the two homozygous varieties, and the genotypic ratio and the phenotypic ratio are both 1:2:1 in the F_2 generation.

We also see examples of incomplete dominance in humans. One case involves a recessive allele (h) that can cause hypercholesterolemia, dangerously high levels of cholesterol in the blood. Normal individuals are homozygous dominant (HH). Heterozygotes (Hh; about one in 500 people) have blood cholesterol levels about twice normal. They are unusually prone to atherosclerosis, the blockage of arteries by cholesterol buildup in artery walls, and they may have heart attacks from blocked heart arteries by their mid-30s. This form of the disease can often be controlled through changes in diet and by taking statins, a class of medications that can significantly lower blood cholesterol. Hypercholesterolemia is even more serious in homozygous recessive individuals (hh; about one in a million people). Homozygotes have about five times the normal amount of blood cholesterol and may have heart attacks as early as age 2. Homozygous hypercholesterolemia is harder to treat; options include high doses of statin drugs, organ surgeries or transplants, or physically filtering lipids from the blood.

Figure 9.11B illustrates the molecular basis for hypercholesterolemia. The dominant allele (H), which normal individuals carry in duplicate (HH), specifies a cell-surface receptor protein called an LDL receptor. Low-density lipoprotein (LDL, sometimes called "bad cholesterol") is transported in the blood. In certain cells, the LDL receptors mop up excess LDL particles from the blood and promote their breakdown. This process helps prevent the accumulation of cholesterol in arteries. Heterozygotes (Hh) have only half the normal

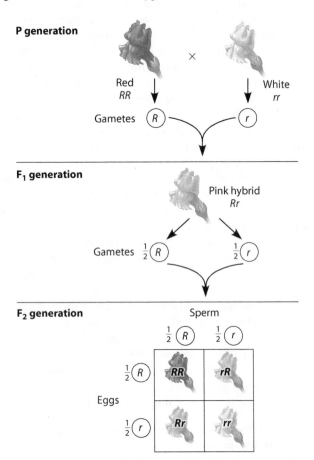

▲ Figure 9.11A   Incomplete dominance in snapdragon flower color

▲ Figure 9.11B   Incomplete dominance in human hypercholesterolemia

number of LDL receptors, and homozygous recessives (*hh*) have none. A lack of receptors prevents the cells from removing much of the excess cholesterol from the blood. The resulting buildup of LDL in the blood can be lethal.

? Why doesn't the cross shown in Figure 9.11A support the blending hypothesis (see Module 9.1)?

● Although two of the F₂ offspring show a "blended" phenotype (pink flowers), the other two do not, and the white and red alleles are not lost to future generations.

9.12 Many genes have more than two alleles in the population

So far, we have discussed inheritance patterns involving only two alleles per gene (*H* versus *h*, for example). But most genes can be found in populations in more than two versions, known as multiple alleles. Although each individual carries, at most, two different alleles for a particular gene, in cases of multiple alleles, more than two possible alleles exist in the population.

For instance, the **ABO blood group** phenotype in humans involves three alleles of a single gene. Various combinations of three alleles—called I^A, I^B, and *i*—produce four phenotypes: A person's blood type may be A, B, AB, or O (**Figure 9.12**). These letters refer to two carbohydrates, designated A and B, that may be found on the surface of red blood cells. A person's red blood cells may be coated with carbohydrate A (in which case they are said to have type A blood), carbohydrate B (type B), both carbohydrates (type AB), or neither carbohydrate (type O). (In case you are wondering, the "positive" and "negative" notations on blood types—referred to as the Rh blood group system—are due to inheritance of a separate, unrelated gene.)

Matching compatible blood types is critical for safe blood transfusions. If a donor's blood cells have a carbohydrate (A or B) that is foreign to the recipient, then the recipient's immune system produces proteins called antibodies (see Module 24.9) that bind specifically to the foreign carbohydrates and cause the donor blood cells to clump together, potentially killing the recipient. The clumping reaction is also the basis of a blood-typing test performed in the laboratory. In Figure 9.12, notice that AB individuals can receive blood from anyone without fear of clumping, making them "universal recipients," while donated type O blood never causes clumping, making those with type O blood "universal donors."

The four blood groups result from various combinations of the three different alleles: I^A (for an enzyme referred to as I, which adds carbohydrate A to red blood cells), I^B (which adds carbohydrate B), and *i* (which adds neither A nor B carbohydrate). Each person inherits one of these alleles from each parent. Because there are three alleles, there are six possible genotypes, as illustrated in the figure. Both the I^A and I^B alleles are dominant to the *i* allele. Thus, I^AI^A and I^Ai people have type A blood, and I^BI^B and I^Bi people have type B. Recessive homozygotes, *ii*, have type O blood, with neither carbohydrate. The I^A and I^B alleles are **codominant**: Both alleles are expressed in heterozygous individuals (I^AI^B), who have type AB blood. Be careful to distinguish codominance (the expression of both alleles) from incomplete dominance (the expression of one intermediate trait).

? Maria has type O blood, and her sister has type AB blood. The girls know that both of their maternal grandparents are type A. What are the genotypes of the girls' parents?

● Their mother is I^Ai; their father is I^BI^A.

Blood Group (Phenotype)	Genotypes	Carbohydrates Present on Red Blood Cells	Antibodies Present in Blood	Reaction When Blood from Groups Below Is Mixed with Antibodies from Groups at Left			
				O	A	B	AB
A	I^AI^A or I^Ai	Carbohydrate A	Anti-B				
B	I^BI^B or I^Bi	Carbohydrate B	Anti-A				
AB	I^AI^B	Carbohydrate A and Carbohydrate B	None				
O	*ii*	Neither	Anti-A Anti-B				

No reaction   Clumping reaction

▲ Figure 9.12   Multiple alleles for the ABO blood groups

9.13 A single gene may affect many phenotypic characters

All of our genetic examples to this point have been cases in which each gene specifies only one hereditary character. In many cases, however, one gene influences multiple characters, a property called **pleiotropy**.

An example of pleiotropy in humans is **sickle-cell disease** (sometimes called sickle-cell anemia). The direct effect of the sickle-cell allele is to make red blood cells produce abnormal hemoglobin proteins. These molecules tend to link together and crystallize, especially when the oxygen content of the blood is lower than usual because of high altitude, overexertion, or respiratory ailments. As the hemoglobin crystallizes, the normally disk-shaped red blood cells deform to a sickle shape with jagged edges (Figure 9.13A). Sickled cells are destroyed rapidly by the body, and their destruction may seriously lower the individual's red cell count, causing anemia and general weakening of the body. Also, because of their angular shape, sickled cells do not flow smoothly in the blood and tend to accumulate and clog tiny blood vessels. Blood flow to body parts is reduced, resulting in periodic fever, weakness, severe pain, and damage to various organs, including the heart, brain, and kidneys. The overall result is a disorder characterized by the cascade of symptoms shown in Figure 9.13B. Blood transfusions and drug treatment may relieve some of the symptoms, but there is no cure; sickle-cell disease kills about 100,000 people each year.

In most cases, only people who are homozygous for the sickle-cell allele have sickle-cell disease. Heterozygotes, who have one sickle-cell allele and one normal allele, are usually healthy—hence, the disease is considered recessive. However, in rare cases, heterozygotes may experience some effects of the disease when oxygen in the blood is severely reduced, such as at very high altitudes. Thus, at the organismal level, a heterozygote displays incomplete dominance for the sickle-cell trait, with a phenotype between the homozygous dominant and homozygous recessive phenotypes. At the molecular level, however, the two alleles are actually codominant; the blood cells of heterozygotes contain both normal and abnormal (sickle-cell) hemoglobins. A simple blood test can distinguish homozygotes from heterozygotes.

Sickle-cell disease is the most common inherited disorder among people of African descent, striking one in 400 African Americans. About one in ten African Americans is a heterozygous carrier. Among Americans of other ancestry, the sickle-cell allele is extremely rare.

One in ten is an unusually high frequency of carriers for an allele with such harmful effects in homozygotes. We might expect that the frequency of the sickle-cell allele in the population would be much lower because many homozygotes die before passing their genes to the next generation. The high frequency appears to be a vestige of the ancestral roots of African Americans. Sickle-cell disease is most common in tropical Africa, where the deadly disease malaria is also prevalent. The parasite that causes malaria spends part of its life cycle inside red blood cells. When it enters those of a person with the sickle-cell allele, it triggers sickling. The body destroys most of the sickled cells, killing the parasite with them. Consequently, sickle-cell carriers have increased resistance to malaria, and in many parts of Africa, they live longer and have more offspring than noncarriers who are exposed to malaria. In this way, malaria has kept the frequency of the sickle-cell allele relatively high in much of the African continent. To put it in evolutionary terms, as long as the environment harbors malaria, individuals with one sickle-cell allele will have a selective advantage.

? **Why is the sickle-cell trait considered codominant at the molecular level?**

● Codominance means that both traits are expressed; a carrier for the sickle-cell allele produces both normal and abnormal hemoglobin.

An individual homozygous for the sickle-cell allele

↓

Produces sickle-cell (abnormal) hemoglobin

↓

The abnormal hemoglobin crystallizes, causing red blood cells to become sickle-shaped

SEM 1,045×

The multiple effects of sickled cells

Damage to organs	Other effects
Kidney failure	Pain and fever
Heart failure	Joint problems
Spleen damage	Physical weakness
Brain damage (impaired mental function, paralysis)	Anemia
	Pneumonia and other infections

▲ Figure 9.13B Sickle-cell disease, an example of pleiotropy

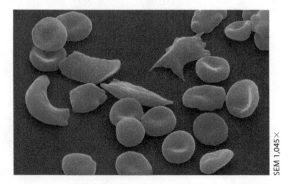

SEM 1,045×

▲ Figure 9.13A In this micrograph, you can see several jagged sickled cells in the midst of normal red blood cells.

9.14 A single character may be influenced by many genes

Mendel studied genetic characters that could be classified on an either-or basis, such as purple or white flower color. However, many characters, such as human skin color and height, vary in a population along a continuum. Many such features result from **polygenic inheritance**, the additive effects of two or more genes on a single phenotypic character. (This is the opposite of pleiotropy, in which one gene affects several characters.)

Let's consider a hypothetical example. Assume that the continuous variation in human skin color is controlled by three genes that are inherited separately, like Mendel's pea genes. (Actually, this character is probably affected by a great many genes, but for our purposes we'll simplify.) The "dark-skin" allele for each gene (*A*, *B*, or *C*) contributes one "unit" of darkness to the phenotype and is incompletely dominant to the other allele (*a*, *b*, or *c*). An *AABBCC* person would be very dark, whereas an *aabbcc* individual would be very light. An *AaBbCc* person would have skin of an intermediate shade. Because the alleles have an additive effect, the genotype *AaBbCc* would produce the same skin color as any other genotype with just three dark-skin alleles, such as *AABbcc*, because both of these individuals have three "units" of darkness.

The Punnett square in **Figure 9.14** shows all possible genotypes from a mating of two triple heterozygotes (*AaBbCc*). The row of squares below the Punnett square shows the seven skin pigmentation phenotypes that would theoretically result from this mating. The seven bars in the graph at the bottom of the figure depict the relative numbers of each of the phenotypes in the F_2 generation. This hypothetical example shows how inheritance of three genes could lead to a wide variety of pigmentation phenotypes. As we will see in the next module, in actual human populations, skin color has even more variations than shown in the figure.

Up to this point in the chapter, we have presented four types of inheritance patterns that are extensions of Mendel's laws of inheritance: incomplete dominance, codominance, pleiotropy, and polygenic inheritance. It is important to realize that these patterns are extensions of Mendel's model, rather than exceptions to it. From Mendel's pea garden experiments came data supporting the idea that genes are transmitted according to the same rules of chance that govern the tossing of coins. This basic idea of genes as discrete units of inheritance holds true for all inheritance patterns, even the patterns that are more complex than the ones originally considered by Mendel. In the next module, we consider another important source of deviation from Mendel's standard model: the effect of the environment.

? An *AaBbcc* individual would be indistinguishable in phenotype from which of the following individuals: *AAbbcc*, *aaBBcc*, *AabbCc*, *Aabbcc*, or *aaBbCc*?

All except Aabbcc

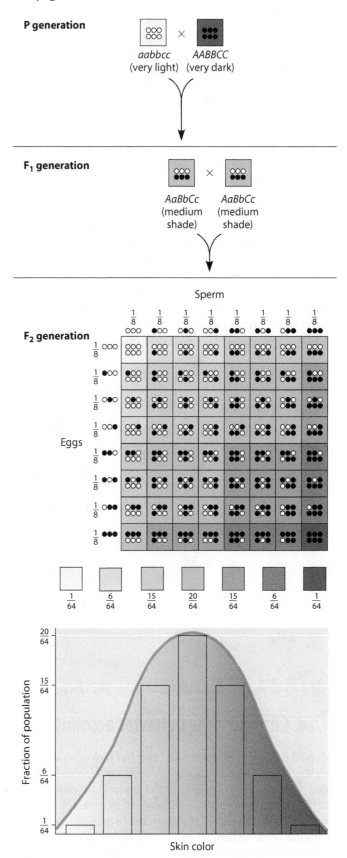

▲ **Figure 9.14** A model for polygenic inheritance of skin color

9.15 The environment affects many characters

In the previous module, we saw how a set of three hypothetical human skin-color genes could produce seven different phenotypes for skin color. But, of course, if we examine a real human population for skin color, we would see more shades than just seven. The true range might be similar to the entire spectrum of color under the bell-shaped curve in Figure 9.14. In fact, no matter how carefully we characterize the genes for skin color, a purely genetic description will always be incomplete. This is because skin color is also influenced by environmental factors, such as exposure to the sun **(Figure 9.15A)**.

Many characters result from a combination of heredity and environment. For humans, nutrition influences height; exercise alters build; sun-tanning darkens the skin; experience improves performance on intelligence tests; and social and cultural forces greatly affect appearance. As geneticists learn more and more about our genes, it is becoming clear that many human characters—such as risk of heart disease and cancer and susceptibility to alcoholism and schizophrenia—are influenced by both genes and environment.

Whether human characters are more influenced by genes or by the environment—nature or nurture—is a very hotly contested debate. For some characters, such as the ABO blood group, a given genotype mandates a very specific phenotype, and the environment plays no role whatsoever. In contrast, how many red blood cells are circulating in your body is significantly influenced by environmental factors such as the altitude of your environment and your overall health.

It is important to realize that the individual features of any organism arise from a combination of genetic and environmental factors. Simply spending time with identical twins will convince anyone that environment, and not just genes, affects a person's traits **(Figure 9.15B)**. Next, we turn to a discussion of the cellular basis of heredity: the behavior of chromosomes.

> **?** If most characters result from a combination of environment and heredity, why was Mendel able to ignore environmental influences in his pea plants?

● The characters he chose for study were all entirely genetically determined and all his test subjects were raised in a similar environment.

▲ **Figure 9.15A** The effect of genes and sun exposure on the skin of one of this book's authors and his family

▲ **Figure 9.15B** Varying phenotypes due to environmental factors in genetically identical twins

▷ The Chromosomal Basis of Inheritance

9.16 Chromosome behavior accounts for Mendel's laws

Mendel published his results in 1866, but biologists did not understand the significance of his work until long after he died. Cell biologists worked out the processes of mitosis and meiosis by the late 1800s (see Chapter 8 to review these processes). Then, around 1902, researchers began to notice parallels between the behavior of chromosomes and the behavior of Mendel's "heritable factors" (what we now call genes). By combining this new understanding of mitosis and meiosis with an increasing understanding of genes, one of biology's most important concepts was formulated: The **chromosome theory of inheritance** holds that genes occupy specific loci (positions) on chromosomes, and it is the chromosomes that undergo segregation and independent assortment during meiosis. Thus, it is the behavior of chromosomes during meiosis and fertilization that accounts for inheritance patterns.

We can see the chromosomal basis of Mendel's laws by following the fates of two genes during meiosis and fertilization in pea plants. In **Figure 9.16**, the genes for seed shape (alleles

R and r) and seed color (Y and y) are shown as black bars on different chromosomes. Notice that the Punnett square is repeated from Figure 9.5A; we will now follow the chromosomes to see how they account for the results of the dihybrid cross shown in the Punnett square. We start with the F_1 generation, in which all plants have the $RrYy$ genotype. To simplify the diagram, we show only two of the seven pairs of pea chromosomes and three of the stages of meiosis.

To see the chromosomal basis of the law of segregation (which states that pairs of alleles separate from each other during gamete formation via meiosis; see Module 9.3), let's follow just the homologous pair of long chromosomes, the ones carrying R and r, taking either the left or the right branch from the F_1 cell. Whichever arrangement the chromosomes assume at metaphase I, the two alleles segregate as the homologous chromosomes separate in anaphase I. And at the end of meiosis II, a single long chromosome ends up in each of the gametes. Fertilization then randomly recombines the two alleles, resulting in F_2 offspring that are $\frac{1}{4}$ RR, $\frac{1}{2}$ Rr,

and $\frac{1}{4}$ rr. The ratio of round to wrinkled phenotypes is thus 3:1 (12 round to 4 wrinkled), the ratio Mendel observed, as shown in the Punnett square in the figure.

To see the chromosomal basis of the law of independent assortment (which states that each pair of alleles sorts independently of other pairs of alleles during gamete formation; see Module 9.5), follow both the long and short (nonhomologous) chromosomes through the figure. Two alternative arrangements of tetrads can occur at metaphase I. The nonhomologous chromosomes (and their genes) assort independently, leading to four gamete genotypes. Random fertilization leads to the 9:3:3:1 phenotypic ratio in the F_2 generation.

> **?** Which of Mendel's laws have their physical basis in the following phases of meiosis: (a) the orientation of homologous chromosome pairs in metaphase I; (b) the separation of homologs in anaphase I?

(a) The law of independent assortment; (b) the law of segregation

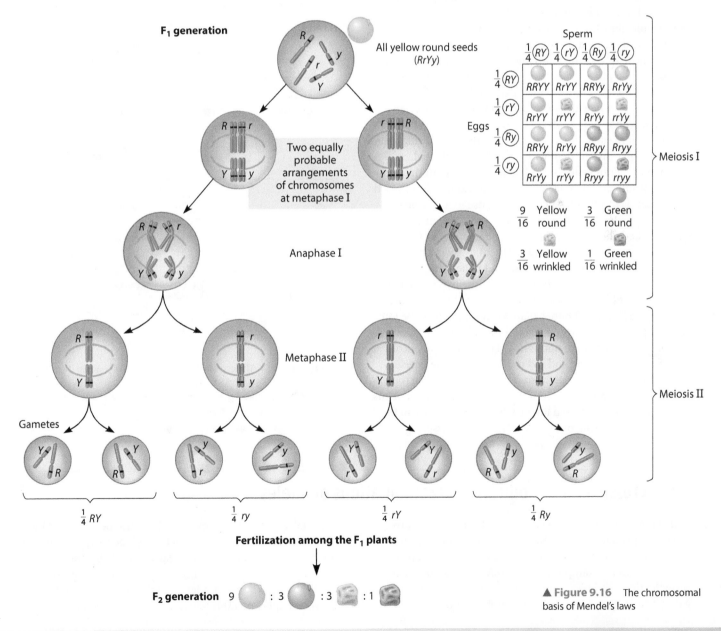

▲ Figure 9.16 The chromosomal basis of Mendel's laws

9.17 Genes on the same chromosome tend to be inherited together

SCIENTIFIC THINKING

In 1908, British biologists William Bateson and Reginald Punnett (originator of the Punnett square) observed an inheritance pattern that seemed inconsistent with Mendelian laws. Bateson and Punnett were working with two characters in sweet peas: flower color and pollen shape. They crossed doubly heterozygous plants (*PpLl*) that exhibited the dominant traits: purple flowers (expression of the *P* allele) and long pollen grains (expression of the *L* allele). The corresponding recessive traits are red flowers (in *pp* plants) and round pollen (in *ll* plants).

The top part of **Figure 9.17** illustrates Bateson and Punnett's experiment. When they looked at just one of the two characters (that is, either cross *Pp* × *Pp* or cross *Ll* × *Ll*), they recorded a phenotypic ratio of approximately 3:1 for the offspring, in agreement with Mendel's law of segregation. However, when the biologists combined their data for the two characters, they did not see the 9:3:3:1 ratio predicted by Mendel's law of independent assortment. Instead, as shown in the table, they found a disproportionately large number of plants with just two of the predicted phenotypes: purple long (almost 75% of the total) and red round (about 14%). The other two phenotypes (purple round and red long) were found in far fewer numbers than expected. It is often the case in science that a new discovery begins with a "failure," an experiment with results contrary to those expected. When scientists explore such unexpected results, the investigation may lead to deeper insight than was originally anticipated.

The number of genes in a cell is far greater than the number of chromosomes; in fact, each chromosome has hundreds or thousands of genes. Genes located close together on the same chromosome tend to be inherited together and are called **linked genes**. Linked genes generally do not follow Mendel's law of independent assortment.

Sweet-pea genes for flower color and pollen shape are located on the same chromosome. Thus, meiosis in the heterozygous (*PpLl*) sweet-pea plant yields mostly two genotypes of gametes (*PL* and *pl*) rather than equal numbers of the four types of gametes that would result if the flower-color and pollen-shape genes were not linked. The large numbers of plants with purple long and red round traits in the Bateson-Punnett experiment resulted from fertilization among the *PL* and *pl* gametes. But what about the smaller numbers of plants with purple round and red long traits? As you will see in the next module, crossing over accounts for these offspring.

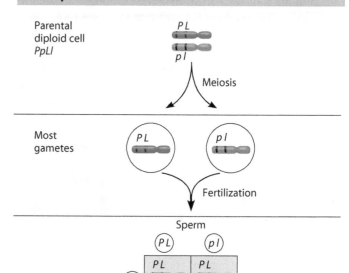

The Experiment

Purple flower

PpLl × *PpLl*

Long pollen

Phenotypes	Observed offspring	Prediction (9:3:3:1)
Purple long	284	215
Purple round	21	71
Red long	21	71
Red round	55	24

The Explanation: Linked Genes

Parental diploid cell *PpLl*

P L
p l

Meiosis

Most gametes

P L   *p l*

Fertilization

Sperm

PL   *pl*

Most offspring   Eggs

PL

pl

3 purple long : 1 red round
Not accounted for: purple round and red long

▲ Figure 9.17 The experiment revealing linked genes in the sweet pea

? **Why do linked genes tend to be inherited together and not sort independently?**

Because they are located close together on the same chromosome

9.18 Crossing over produces new combinations of alleles

During meiosis, crossing over between homologous chromosomes produces new combinations of alleles in gametes (as we saw in Module 8.17). Using the experiment shown in Figure 9.17 as an example, **Figure 9.18A** reviews this process, showing that two linked genes can give rise to four different gamete genotypes. Gametes with genotypes *PL* and *pl* carry

parental-type chromosomes that have not been altered by crossing over. In contrast, gametes with genotypes *Pl* and *pL* are recombinant gametes. The exchange of chromosome segments during crossing over has produced new combinations of alleles. We can now understand the results of the Bateson-Punnett experiment presented in the previous module: The

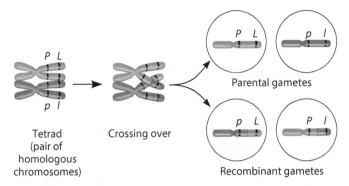

▲ Figure 9.18A Review: the production of recombinant gametes

small fraction of offspring with recombinant phenotypes (purple round and red long) must have resulted from fertilization involving recombinant gametes. The discovery of how crossing over creates gamete diversity confirmed the relationship between chromosome behavior and heredity. Some of the most important early studies of crossing over were performed in the laboratory of American embryologist Thomas Hunt Morgan in the early 1900s. Morgan and his colleagues used the fruit fly *Drosophila melanogaster* in many of their experiments (Figure 9.18B). *Drosophila* is a good research animal for genetic studies because it can be bred easily and inexpensively, producing each new generation in two weeks.

▲ Figure 9.18B *Drosophila melanogaster*

Figure 9.18C shows one of Morgan's experiments. This cross involves a wild-type fruit fly—recall from Module 9.8 that "wild-type" refers to the traits most common in nature, in this case, gray body and long wings—and a fly with a black body and vestigial wings. (Used here, the term *vestigial* describes the undeveloped, shrunken appearance of the wings and should not be confused with the evolutionary use of the word *vestigial*.) Morgan knew the genotypes of these flies from previous studies. Here we use the following gene symbols: G = gray body (dominant), g = black body (recessive), L = long wings (dominant), l = vestigial wings (recessive).

In mating a heterozygous gray fly with long wings (genotype $GgLl$) with a black fly with vestigial wings (genotype $ggll$), Morgan performed a testcross (see Module 9.6). If the genes were not linked, then independent assortment would produce offspring in a phenotypic ratio of 1:1:1:1 ($\frac{1}{4}$ gray body, long wings; $\frac{1}{4}$ black body, vestigial wings; $\frac{1}{4}$ gray body, vestigial wings; and $\frac{1}{4}$ black body, long wings). But because these genes are linked, Morgan obtained the results shown in the top part of Figure 9.18C: Most of the offspring had parental phenotypes, but 17% of the offspring flies were recombinants. The percentage of recombinant offspring among the total is called the **recombination frequency**.

The lower part of Figure 9.18C explains Morgan's results in terms of crossing over. A crossover between chromatids

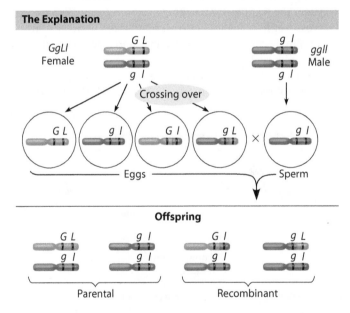

The Experiment

Gray body, long wings (wild type)

GgLl

Female

×

Black body, vestigial wings

ggll

Male

Offspring

Gray long	Black vestigial	Gray vestigial	Black long
965	944	206	185

Parental phenotypes — Recombinant phenotypes

$$\text{Recombination frequency} = \frac{391 \text{ recombinants}}{2{,}300 \text{ total offspring}} = 0.17 \text{ or } 17\%$$

The Explanation

GgLl Female   G L / g l

ggll Male   g l / g l

Crossing over

Eggs: G L, g l, G l, g L   ×   Sperm: g l

Offspring

G L / g l	g l / g l	G l / g l	g L / g l
Parental		Recombinant	

▲ Figure 9.18C A fruit fly experiment demonstrating the role of crossing over in inheritance

From T. H. Morgan and C. J. Lynch, The linkage of two factors in *Drosophila* that are not sex-linked, *Biological Bulletin* 23: 174–82 (1912).

of homologous chromosomes in parent *GgLl* broke linkages between the *G* and *L* alleles and between the *g* and *l* alleles, forming the recombinant chromosomes *Gl* and *gL*. Later steps in meiosis distributed the recombinant chromosomes to gametes, and random fertilization produced the four kinds of offspring Morgan observed.

> **?** Return to the data in Figure 9.17. What is the recombination frequency between the flower-color and pollen-length genes?
>
> 11% (42/381)

9.19 Geneticists use crossover data to map genes

While working with *Drosophila*, Alfred H. Sturtevant, one of Morgan's students, developed a way to use crossover data to map gene loci. This technique is based on the assumption that the chance of crossing over is approximately equal at all points along a chromosome. Sturtevant hypothesized that the farther apart two genes are on a chromosome, the more points there are between them where crossing over can occur. (This assumption is not entirely accurate, but it is good enough to provide useful data.) With this principle in mind, Sturtevant began using recombination data from fruit fly crosses to assign relative positions of the genes on the chromosomes—that is, to map genes.

Figure 9.19A represents a part of the chromosome that carries the linked genes for black body (*g*) and vestigial wings (*l*) that we described in Module 9.18. This same chromosome also carries a gene that has a recessive allele (we'll call it *c*) determining cinnabar eye color, a brighter red than the wild-type color. Figure 9.19A shows the actual crossover (recombination) frequencies between these alleles, taken two at a time: 17% between the *g* and *l* alleles, 9% between *g* and *c*, and 9.5% between *c* and *l*. Sturtevant reasoned that these values represent the relative distances between the genes. Because the crossover frequencies between *g* and *c* and between *l* and *c* are approximately half that between *g* and *l*, gene *c* must lie roughly midway between *g* and *l*. Thus, the sequence of these genes on one of the fruit fly chromosomes must be *g-c-l*. Such a diagram of relative gene locations is called a **linkage map**.

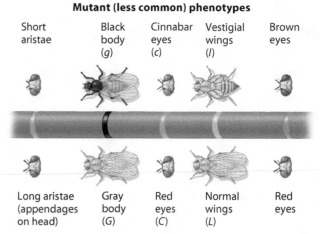

Mutant (less common) phenotypes

Short aristae | Black body (*g*) | Cinnabar eyes (*c*) | Vestigial wings (*l*) | Brown eyes

Long aristae (appendages on head) | Gray body (*G*) | Red eyes (*C*) | Normal wings (*L*) | Red eyes

Wild-type (more common) phenotypes

▲ **Figure 9.19B** A partial linkage map of a fruit fly chromosome

Although based on some approximations, Sturtevant's method of mapping genes helped establish the relative positions of many other fruit fly genes. Eventually, enough data were accumulated to reveal that *Drosophila* has four groups of genes, corresponding to its four pairs of homologous chromosomes. **Figure 9.19B** is a genetic map showing just five of the gene loci on part of one chromosome: the loci labeled *g*, *c*, and *l* and two other traits, aristae and brown eyes.

The linkage-mapping method has proved valuable in establishing the relative positions of many genes in many organisms. The real beauty of the technique is that a wealth of information about genes can be learned simply by breeding and observing the organisms; no fancy equipment is required.

? You design *Drosophila* crosses to provide recombination data for a gene not included in Figure 9.19A. The gene has recombination frequencies of 3% with the vestigial-wing (*l*) locus and 7% with the cinnabar-eye (*c*) locus. Where is it located on the chromosome?

● The gene is located between the vestigial and cinnabar loci, a bit closer to the vestigial-wing locus (because the vestigial-wing locus has a lower recombination frequency).

Section of chromosome carrying linked genes

g   *c*   *l*

←—— 17% ——→
←— 9% —→ ←— 9.5% —→
Recombination frequencies

▲ **Figure 9.19A** Mapping genes from crossover data

▷ Sex Chromosomes and Sex-Linked Genes

9.20 Chromosomes determine sex in many species

Many animals, including fruit flies and all mammals, have a pair of **sex chromosomes**, designated X and Y, that determine an individual's sex (**Figure 9.20A**). Among humans, individuals with one X chromosome and one Y chromosome are males; XX individuals are females. In addition, human males and females both have 44 autosomes (nonsex chromosomes). After meiosis, each gamete contains one sex chromosome and a haploid set of autosomes (22 in humans). All eggs

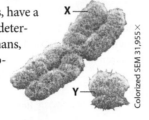

X

Y

Colorized SEM 31,955×

▲ **Figure 9.20A** The human sex chromosomes

contain a single X chromosome. Of the sperm cells, half contain an X chromosome and half contain a Y chromosome. An offspring's sex depends on whether the sperm cell that fertilizes the egg bears an X chromosome or a Y chromosome (**Figure 9.20B**).

The genetic basis of sex determination in humans is not yet completely understood, but one gene on the Y chromosome plays a crucial role.

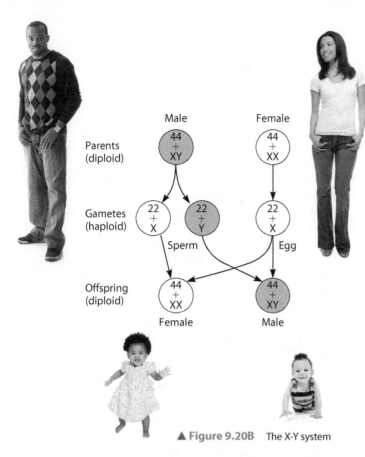

Parents (diploid)
Male: 44 + XY
Female: 44 + XX

Gametes (haploid)
22 + X / 22 + Y (Sperm)
22 + X (Egg)

Offspring (diploid)
44 + XX (Female)
44 + XY (Male)

▲ **Figure 9.20B** The X-Y system

an X-O system, in which O stands for the absence of a sex chromosome. Females have two X chromosomes (XX); males have only one sex chromosome (XO). Males produce two classes of sperm: Half bear an X and half lack a sex chromosome. In this case, as in humans, sperm cells determine the sex of the offspring at fertilization.

In contrast to the X-Y and X-O systems, eggs determine sex in certain fishes, butterflies, and birds. The sex chromosomes in these animals are designated Z and W. Males have the genotype ZZ; females are ZW. In this system, sex is determined by whether the egg carries a Z or a W.

Some organisms lack sex chromosomes altogether. In most ants and bees, sex is determined by chromosome number rather than by sex chromosomes. Females develop from fertilized eggs and thus are diploid. Males develop from unfertilized eggs—they are fatherless—and are haploid.

Most animals have two separate sexes; that is, individuals are either male or female. Many plant species have sperm-bearing and egg-bearing flowers found on different individuals. Some plant species, such as date palms, have the X-Y system of sex determination; others, such as the wild strawberry, have the Z-W system. However, most plant species and some animal species have individuals that produce both sperm and eggs. In such species, all individuals have the same complement of chromosomes.

In Module 9.15, we discussed the role that environment plays in determining many characters. Among some animals, environment can even determine sex. For some species of reptiles, the temperature at which eggs are incubated during a specific period of embryonic development determines whether that embryo will develop into a male or female. For example, if green sea turtle hatchlings incubate above 30°C (86°F), nearly all the resulting turtles will be males. (Some worry that global climate change might therefore affect the makeup of turtle populations.) Such temperature-dependent sex determination is an extreme example of the environment affecting the phenotype of an individual.

This gene is called *SRY* (for sex-determining region of Y) and triggers testis development. In the absence of *SRY*, ovaries develop rather than testes. *SRY* codes for proteins that regulate other genes on the Y chromosome. These genes in turn produce proteins necessary for normal testis development.

The X-Y system is only one of several sex-determining systems (**Table 9.20** summarizes three other systems). For example, grasshoppers, roaches, and some other insects have

TABLE 9.20	THREE SYSTEMS OF SEX DETERMINATION	Genetic Makeup	
System	**Example Organism**	**Males**	**Females**
X-O		22 + X	22 + XX
Z-W		76 + ZZ	76 + ZW
Chromosome number		16	32

? King Henry VIII of England was quick to blame his wives for bearing him only daughters. Explain how, from a genetic point of view, his thinking was wrong.

● The male sperm bears either an X or Y, thereby determining the sex of the offspring; his wives' eggs always carried an X.

9.21 Sex-linked genes exhibit a unique pattern of inheritance

Besides bearing genes that determine sex, the sex chromosomes also contain genes for characters unrelated to femaleness or maleness. A gene located on either sex chromosome is called a **sex-linked gene**. Because the human X chromosome contains many more genes than the Y, the vast majority of sex-linked genes are on the X chromosome. Be careful not to confuse the term *sex-linked gene*, which refers to a gene on a sex chromosome, with the term *linked genes*, which refers to genes on the same chromosome that tend to be inherited together.

The figures in this module illustrate inheritance patterns for white eye color in the fruit fly, an X-linked recessive trait. Wild-type fruit flies have red eyes; white eyes are very rare (Figure 9.21A). We use the uppercase letter R for the dominant, wild-type, red-eye allele and r for the recessive white-eye allele. Because these alleles are carried on the X chromosome, we show them as superscripts to the letter X. Thus, red-eyed male fruit flies have the genotype $X^R Y$; white-eyed males are $X^r Y$. The Y chromosome does not have a gene locus for eye color; therefore, the male's phenotype results entirely from his single X-linked gene. In the female, $X^R X^R$ and $X^R X^r$ flies have red eyes, and $X^r X^r$ flies have white eyes.

A white-eyed male ($X^r Y$) will transmit his X^r to all of his female offspring but to none of his male offspring. This is because his female offspring, in order to be female, must inherit his X chromosome, but his male offspring must inherit his Y chromosome.

As shown in Figure 9.21B, when the female parent is a dominant homozygote ($X^R X^R$) and the male parent is $X^r Y$, all the offspring have red eyes, but the female offspring are all carriers of the allele for white eyes ($X^R X^r$). When those offspring are bred to each other, the classic 3:1 phenotypic ratio of red eyes to white eyes appears among the offspring (Figure 9.21C). However, there is a twist: The white-eyed trait shows up only in males. All the females have red eyes, whereas half the males have red eyes and half have white eyes. All females inherit at least one dominant allele (from their male parent); half of them are homozygous dominant, whereas the other half are heterozygous carriers, like their female parent. Among the males, half of them inherit the recessive allele their mother was carrying, producing the white-eye phenotype.

Because the white-eye allele is recessive, a female will have white eyes only if she receives that allele on both X chromosomes. For example, if a heterozygous female mates with a white-eyed male, there is a 50% chance that each offspring will have white eyes (resulting from genotype $X^r X^r$ or $X^r Y$), regardless of sex (Figure 9.21D). Female offspring with red eyes are heterozygotes, whereas red-eyed male offspring completely lack the recessive allele.

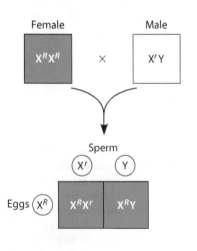

▲ **Figure 9.21A** Fruit fly eye color determined by sex-linked gene

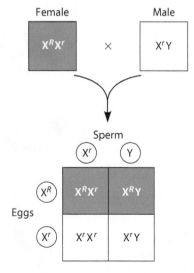

? A white-eyed female *Drosophila* is mated with a red-eyed (wild-type) male. What result do you predict for the numerous offspring?

● All female offspring will be red-eyed but heterozygous ($X^R X^r$); all male offspring will be white-eyed ($X^r Y$).

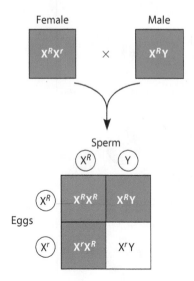

Female $X^R X^R$ × **Male** $X^r Y$

Sperm: X^r Y

Eggs X^R | $X^R X^r$ | $X^R Y$

R = red-eye allele
r = white-eye allele

▲ **Figure 9.21B** A homozygous, red-eyed female crossed with a white-eyed male

Female $X^R X^r$ × **Male** $X^R Y$

Sperm: X^R Y

Eggs
X^R | $X^R X^R$ | $X^R Y$
X^r | $X^r X^R$ | $X^r Y$

▲ **Figure 9.21C** A heterozygous female crossed with a red-eyed male

Female $X^R X^r$ × **Male** $X^r Y$

Sperm: X^r Y

Eggs
X^R | $X^R X^r$ | $X^R Y$
X^r | $X^r X^r$ | $X^r Y$

▲ **Figure 9.21D** A heterozygous female crossed with a white-eyed male

9.22 Human sex-linked disorders affect mostly males

A number of human conditions result from sex-linked recessive alleles located on the X chromosome. If a man inherits only one X-linked recessive allele—from his mother—the allele will be expressed. In contrast, a woman has to inherit two such alleles—one from each parent—to exhibit the trait. Thus, recessive X-linked traits are expressed much more frequently in men than in women.

Hemophilia is an X-linked recessive trait with a well-documented history. Hemophiliacs bleed excessively when injured because they lack one or more of the proteins required for blood clotting. A high incidence of hemophilia plagued the royal families of Europe. Queen Victoria (1819–1901) of England was a carrier of the hemophilia allele. She passed it on to one of her sons and two of her daughters. Through marriage, her daughters then introduced the disease into the families of Prussia, Russia, and Spain. The pedigree in **Figure 9.22** traces the disease through one branch of the royal family. As you can see, Alexandra, like her mother and grandmother, was a carrier, and Alexis had the disease.

Another human X-linked recessive disorder is Duchenne muscular dystrophy, a condition characterized by a progressive weakening of the muscles and loss of coordination. The first symptoms appear in early childhood, when the child begins to have difficulty standing up. Eventually, muscle tissue becomes severely wasted, the individual becomes wheelchair-bound, and normal breathing becomes difficult. Affected individuals rarely live past their early 20s. Researchers have

▲ **Figure 9.22** Hemophilia in the royal family of Russia

Try This Alexis must have had an X^h chromosome (because he had hemophilia). Use your finger to trace back this mutant chromosome through three generations of his ancestors.

traced the disorder to a recessive mutation in a gene on the X chromosome that codes for a muscle protein.

? Neither Tom nor Sue has hemophilia, but their first son does. If the couple has a second child, what is the probability that he or she will also have the disease?

● $\frac{1}{4}$ ($\frac{1}{2}$ chance of a male child × $\frac{1}{2}$ chance that he will inherit the mutant X)

9.23 The Y chromosome provides clues about human male evolution

As you learned in the chapter-opening story about Tibetans, our genes often bear evidence of recent human evolution. The Y chromosome can be particularly useful for tracing our evolutionary past because, barring mutations, the human Y chromosome passes essentially intact from father to son. By analyzing Y DNA, researchers can learn about the ancestry of human males.

In 2003, geneticists discovered that about 8% of males currently living in central Asia have Y chromosomes of striking genetic similarity. Further analysis traced their common genetic heritage to a single man living about 1,000 years ago. In combination with historical records, the data led to the speculation that the Mongolian ruler Genghis Khan **(Figure 9.23)** may be responsible for the spread of the telltale chromosome to nearly 16 million men living today. A similar study of Irish men suggested that nearly 10% of them were descendants of Niall of the Nine Hostages, a warlord who lived during the 5th century.

▲ **Figure 9.23** Genghis Khan

Another study of Y DNA seemed to confirm the claim by the Lemba people of southern Africa that they are descended from ancient Jews. Sequences of Y DNA distinctive of a particular Jewish priestly caste are found at high frequencies among the Lemba.

Are humans evolving?

The discovery of the sex chromosomes and their pattern of inheritance was one of many breakthroughs in understanding how genes are passed from one generation to the next. During the first half of the 20th century, geneticists rediscovered Mendel's work, reinterpreted his laws in light of chromosomal behavior during meiosis, and firmly established the chromosome theory of inheritance. This work set the stage for discoveries in molecular genetics, an area we explore in the next three chapters.

? Why is the Y chromosome particularly useful in tracing recent human heritage?

● Because it is passed directly from father to son, forming an unbroken chain of male lineage

For practice quizzes, BioFlix animations, MP3 tutorials, video tutors and more study tools designed for this textbook, go to

MasteringBiology®

Reviewing the Concepts

Mendel's Laws (9.1–9.10)

9.1 The study of genetics has ancient roots.

9.2 The science of genetics began in an abbey garden. The science of genetics began with Gregor Mendel's quantitative experiments. Mendel crossed pea plants and traced traits from generation to generation. He hypothesized that there are alternative versions of genes (alleles), the units that determine heritable traits.

9.3 Mendel's law of segregation describes the inheritance of a single character. Mendel's law of segregation predicts that each set of alleles will separate as gametes are formed.

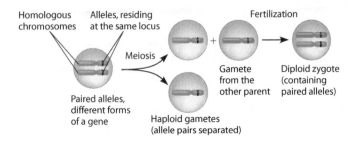

9.4 Homologous chromosomes bear the alleles for each character. When the two alleles of a gene in a diploid individual are different, the dominant allele determines the inherited trait, whereas the recessive allele has no effect.

9.5 The law of independent assortment is revealed by tracking two characters at once. Mendel's law of independent assortment states that the alleles of a pair segregate independently of other allele pairs during gamete formation.

9.6 Geneticists can use a testcross to determine unknown genotypes. The offspring of a testcross, a mating between an individual of unknown genotype and a homozygous recessive individual, can reveal the unknown's genotype.

9.7 Mendel's laws reflect the rules of probability. The rule of multiplication calculates the probability of two independent events both occurring. The rule of addition calculates the probability of an event that can occur in alternative ways.

9.8 Genetic traits in humans can be tracked through family pedigrees. The inheritance of many human traits follows Mendel's laws. Family pedigrees can help determine individual genotypes.

9.9 Many inherited disorders in humans are controlled by a single gene.

9.10 New technologies can provide insight into one's genetic legacy. Carrier screening, fetal testing, fetal imaging, and newborn screening can provide information for reproductive decisions but may create ethical dilemmas.

Variations on Mendel's Laws (9.11–9.15)

9.11 Incomplete dominance results in intermediate phenotypes. Mendel's laws are valid for all sexually reproducing species, but genotype often does not dictate phenotype in the simple way Mendel's laws describe.

9.12 Many genes have more than two alleles in the population. For example, the ABO blood group phenotype in humans is controlled by three alleles that produce a total of four phenotypes.

9.13 A single gene may affect many phenotypic characters.

9.14 A single character may be influenced by many genes.

9.15 The environment affects many characters. Many traits are affected, in varying degrees, by both genetic and environmental factors.

The Chromosomal Basis of Inheritance (9.16–9.19)

9.16 Chromosome behavior accounts for Mendel's laws. Genes are located on chromosomes, whose behavior during meiosis and fertilization accounts for inheritance patterns.

9.17 Genes on the same chromosome tend to be inherited together. Such genes are said to be linked; they display non-Mendelian inheritance patterns.

9.18 Crossing over produces new combinations of alleles. Crossing over can separate linked alleles, producing gametes with recombinant chromosomes.

9.19 Geneticists use crossover data to map genes. Recombination frequencies can be used to map the relative positions of genes on chromosomes.

Sex Chromosomes and Sex-Linked Genes (9.20–9.23)

9.20 Chromosomes determine sex in many species. In mammals, a male has XY sex chromosomes, and a female has XX. The Y chromosome has genes for the development of testes, whereas an absence of the Y allows ovaries to develop. Other systems of sex determination exist in other animals and plants.

9.21 Sex-linked genes exhibit a unique pattern of inheritance. All genes on the sex chromosomes are said to be sex-linked. However, the X chromosome carries many genes unrelated to sex.

9.22 Human sex-linked disorders affect mostly males. Most sex-linked (X-linked) human disorders are due to recessive alleles and are seen mostly in males. A male receiving a single X-linked recessive allele from his mother will have the disorder; a female must receive the allele from both parents to be affected.

9.23 The Y chromosome provides clues about human male evolution. Because they are passed on intact from father to son, Y chromosomes can provide data about recent human evolutionary history.

Connecting the Concepts

1. Complete this concept map to help you review some key concepts of genetics.

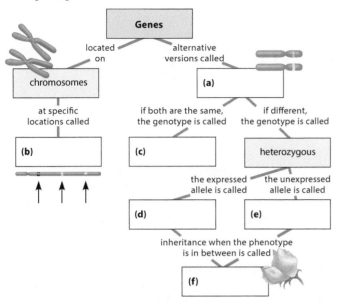

Genes
located on → **chromosomes**
alternative versions called → **(a)**

chromosomes — at specific locations called → **(b)**

(a) — if both are the same, the genotype is called → **(c)**
(a) — if different, the genotype is called → **heterozygous**

heterozygous — the expressed allele is called → **(d)**
heterozygous — the unexpressed allele is called → **(e)**

inheritance when the phenotype is in between is called → **(f)**

Testing Your Knowledge

Level 1: Knowledge/Comprehension

2. Whether an allele is dominant or recessive depends on
   a. how common the allele is, relative to other alleles.
   b. whether it is inherited from the mother or the father.
   c. whether it or another allele determines the phenotype when both are present.
   d. whether or not it is linked to other genes.

3. Edward was found to be heterozygous (*Ss*) for sickle-cell trait. The alleles represented by the letters *S* and *s* are
   a. linked.
   b. on homologous chromosomes.
   c. both present in each of Edward's sperm cells.
   d. on the same chromosome but far apart.

Level 2: Application/Analysis

4. Two fruit flies with eyes of the usual red color are crossed, and their offspring are as follows: 77 red-eyed males, 71 ruby-eyed males, 152 red-eyed females. The allele for ruby eyes is
   a. autosomal (carried on an autosome) and dominant.
   b. autosomal and recessive.
   c. sex-linked and dominant.
   d. sex-linked and recessive.

5. A man with type B blood and a woman who has type A blood could have children of which of the following phenotypes?
   a. A or B only
   b. AB only
   c. AB or O
   d. A, B, AB, or O

6. Tim and Jan both have freckles (see Module 9.9), but their son Mike does not. Show with a Punnett square how this is possible. If Tim and Jan have two more children, what is the probability that both will have freckles?

7. Both Tim and Jan (problem 6) have a widow's peak (see Module 9.8), but Mike has a straight hairline. What are their genotypes? What is the probability that Tim and Jan's next child will have freckles and a straight hairline?

8. In rabbits, black hair depends on a dominant allele, *B*, and brown hair on a recessive allele, *b*. Short hair is due to a dominant allele, *S*, and long hair to a recessive allele, *s*. If a true-breeding black short-haired male is mated with a brown long-haired female, describe their offspring. What will be the genotypes of the offspring? If two of these F_1 rabbits are mated, what phenotypes would you expect among their offspring? In what proportions?

9. A fruit fly with a gray body and red eyes (genotype *BbPp*) is mated with a fly having a black body and purple eyes (genotype *bbpp*). What ratio of offspring would you expect if the body-color and eye-color genes are on different chromosomes (unlinked)? When this mating is actually carried out, most of the offspring look like the parents, but 3% have a gray body and purple eyes, and 3% have a black body and red eyes. Are these genes linked or unlinked? What is the recombination frequency?

10. A series of matings shows that the recombination frequency between the black-body gene (problem 9) and the gene for dumpy (shortened) wings is 36%. The recombination frequency between purple eyes and dumpy wings is 41%. What is the sequence of these three genes on the chromosome?

11. A couple are both phenotypically normal, but their son suffers from hemophilia, a sex-linked recessive disorder. What fraction of their children are likely to suffer from hemophilia? What fraction are likely to be carriers?

Level 3: Synthesis/Evaluation

12. Why do more men than women have colorblindness?

13. In fruit flies, the genes for wing shape and body stripes are linked. In a fly whose genotype is *WwSs*, *W* is linked to *S*, and *w* is linked to *s*. Show how this fly can produce gametes containing four different combinations of alleles. Which are parental-type gametes? Which are recombinant gametes? How are the recombinants produced?

14. Adult height in humans is at least partially hereditary; tall parents tend to have tall children. But humans come in a range of sizes, not just tall and short. Which extension of Mendel's model accounts for the hereditary variation in human height?

15. Heather was surprised to discover she suffered from red-green colorblindness. She told her biology professor, who said, "Your father is colorblind, too, right?" How did her professor know this? Why did her professor not say the same thing to the colorblind males in the class?

16. In 1981, a stray black cat with unusual rounded, curled-back ears was adopted by a family in Lakewood, California. Suppose you owned the first curl cat and wanted to breed it to develop a true-breeding variety. Describe tests that would determine whether the curl gene is dominant or recessive and whether it is autosomal or sex-linked. Explain why you think your tests would be conclusive. Describe a test to determine that a cat is true-breeding.

17. **SCIENTIFIC THINKING** The breakthrough that led Bateson and Punnett to recognize the existence of linked genes (Module 9.17) was the appearance of unexpected results after they crossed double heterozygous pea plants (*PpLl*) with each other. Imagine that you have a group of Labrador retrievers that are all heterozygous for both coat color and blindness (*BbNn*). If you used this group of dogs to produce 160 puppies, how many puppies of each phenotype do you expect to get if the genes are not linked? How would the results differ if the genes are in fact linked?

Answers to all questions can be found in Appendix 4.

10 Molecular Biology of the Gene

? *Why are viral diseases such a constant threat?*

The electron micrograph below shows the 2009 H1N1 influenza virus, an infectious microbe that first appeared in a cluster of flu cases diagnosed in and near Mexico City. Once the threat had been identified, the city was virtually shut down in an effort to contain the outbreak. Despite these efforts, the new viral strain spread so quickly that within months the World Health Organization (WHO) declared H1N1 a pandemic (global epidemic). A vaccine against the 2009 H1N1 strain was rushed into production and became available in the fall of that year. By the time the WHO declared the pandemic over in August 2010, the disease had reached 207 countries, infecting more than 600,000 and killing an estimated 20,000 people.

The 2009 H1N1 influenza virus is just one example in a long, bleak history of human viral diseases. The flu virus, like all viruses, consists of a relatively simple structure of protein and nucleic acid (RNA in this case). Viruses share some of the characteristics of living organisms, but are generally not considered alive because they are not cellular and cannot reproduce on their own. So how can such a simple pathogen evade the best efforts of the world's scientists? The key to the elusiveness of many viruses lies in their tendency to evolve rapidly. The 2009 H1N1 strain, for example, arose through genetic reshuffling of multiple flu viruses, including ones that infect humans, birds, and pigs.

Combating any virus requires a detailed understanding of molecular biology, the study of DNA and how it serves as the basis of heredity. In fact, we owe our first glimpses of the functions of DNA, the molecule that controls hereditary traits, to the study of viruses. In this chapter, we'll explore the structure of DNA, how it replicates, and how it controls the cell by directing RNA and protein synthesis. We'll conclude by discussing the genetics of viruses and bacteria.

The Structure of the Genetic Material
(10.1–10.3)

A series of experiments established DNA as the molecule of heredity.

DNA Replication
(10.4–10.5)

Each DNA strand can serve as a template for another.

The Flow of Genetic Information from DNA to RNA to Protein
(10.6–10.16)

Genotype controls phenotype through the production of proteins.

The Genetics of Viruses and Bacteria
(10.17–10.23)

Viruses and bacteria are useful model systems for the study of molecular biology.

10.1 Experiments showed that DNA is the genetic material

SCIENTIFIC THINKING

Today, scientists routinely manipulate DNA in the laboratory and use it to change the heritable characteristics of cells. Early in the 20th century, however, the molecular basis for inheritance was a mystery. Biologists did know that genes were located on chromosomes. The two chemical components of chromosomes—DNA and protein—were therefore the leading candidates to be the genetic material. Until the 1940s, the case for proteins seemed stronger because proteins appeared to be more structurally complex: Proteins were known to be made from 20 different amino acid building blocks, whereas DNA was known to be made from just four kinds of nucleotides. It seemed logical that the more complex molecule would serve as the hereditary material. Biologists finally established the role of DNA in heredity through experiments with bacteria and the viruses that infect them. This breakthrough ushered in the field of **molecular biology**, the study of heredity at the molecular level.

We can trace the discovery of the genetic role of DNA to 1928. British medical officer Frederick Griffith was studying two strains (varieties) of a bacterium: a harmless strain and a pathogenic (disease-causing) strain that causes pneumonia. Griffith was surprised to find that when he killed the pathogenic bacteria and then mixed the bacterial remains with living harmless bacteria, some living bacterial cells became pathogenic. Furthermore, all of the descendants of the transformed bacteria inherited the newly acquired ability to cause disease. Clearly, some chemical component of the dead bacteria caused a heritable change in live bacteria.

Griffith's work set the stage for a race to discover the identity of the chemical basis of heredity. In 1952, American biologists Alfred Hershey and Martha Chase performed a very convincing set of experiments that showed DNA to be the genetic material of T2, a virus that infects the bacterium *Escherichia coli* (*E. coli*), a microbe normally found in the intestines of mammals (including humans). Viruses that exclusively infect bacteria are called **bacteriophages** ("bacteria-eaters"), or **phages** for short.

Hershey and Chase knew that T2 could reprogram its host cell to produce new phages, but they did not know what component of the virus conferred this capability. At the time, it was known that the structure of phage T2 consists solely of two types of molecules (**Figure 10.1A**): DNA (blue in the figure) and protein (gold). The researchers took advantage of this fact to devise an elegantly simple experiment that determined which of these molecules the phage transferred to *E. coli* during infection.

The Hershey and Chase experiment illustrates a point that arises repeatedly in the history of science: the importance of carefully designing an experiment and choosing the correct model organism to study. Like Mendel's garden peas (Module 9.2) and Morgan's fruit flies (Module 9.18), bacteriophage T2 had just the right properties (in this case, a simple

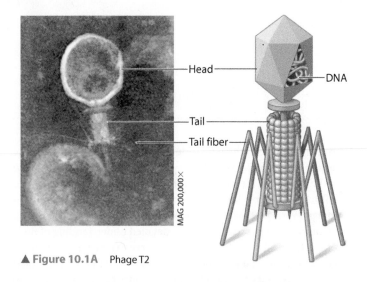

Head
DNA
Tail
Tail fiber
MAG 200,000×

▲ **Figure 10.1A**   Phage T2

structure consisting of just two contrasting elements) to allow for the design of a simple but conclusive experiment.

To begin, Hershey and Chase grew T2 with *E. coli* in a solution containing radioactive sulfur (shown in bright yellow in **Figure 10.1B**). Protein contains sulfur but DNA does not, so as new phages were made, the radioactive sulfur atoms were incorporated only into the proteins of the bacteriophage. The researchers grew a second batch of phages in a solution containing radioactive phosphorus (green). Because nearly all the phage's phosphorus is in DNA, this labeled only the phage DNA.

Armed with the two batches of labeled T2, Hershey and Chase were ready to perform the experiment outlined in Figure 10.1B. They allowed the two batches of T2 to infect separate samples of nonradioactive bacteria. Shortly after the onset of infection, they agitated the cultures in an ordinary kitchen blender to shake loose any parts of the phages that remained outside the bacterial cells. Then, they collected the mixtures in tubes and spun the tubes in a centrifuge. The cells were deposited as a solid pellet at the bottom of the centrifuge tubes, but phages and parts of phages—because they were lighter—remained suspended in the liquid. The researchers then measured the radioactivity in the pellet and in the liquid.

Hershey and Chase found that when the bacteria had been infected with T2 phages containing labeled protein, as in batch 1, the radioactivity ended up mainly in the solution within the centrifuge tube, which contained phages but not bacteria. This result suggested that the phage protein did not enter the cells. But when the bacteria had been infected with phages whose DNA was tagged, as in batch 2, most of the radioactivity was in the pellet of bacterial cells at the bottom of the centrifuge tube. Furthermore, when these bacteria were returned to a liquid growth medium, they soon lysed, or broke open, releasing new phages that contained some radioactive phosphorus in their DNA in their proteins.

Batch 1: Radioactive protein labeled in yellow

Batch 2: Radioactive DNA labeled in green

| Hershey and Chase mixed radioactively labeled phages with bacteria. The phages infected the bacterial cells. | They agitated the cultures in a blender to separate the phages outside of the bacteria from the cells and their contents. | They centrifuged the mixture so that the bacteria formed a pellet at the bottom of the test tube. | Finally, they measured the radioactivity in the pellet and in the liquid. |

▲ **Figure 10.1B** The Hershey-Chase experiment

Figure 10.1C outlines our current understanding of the replication cycle of phage T2. After the virus ❶ attaches to the host bacterial cell, it ❷ injects its DNA into the host. Notice that virtually all of the viral protein (yellow) is left outside (which is why the radioactive protein did not show up in the host cells during the experiment shown at the top of Figure 10.1B). Once injected, the viral DNA causes the bacterial cells to ❸ produce new phage proteins and DNA molecules—indeed, complete new phages—which soon ❹ cause the cell to lyse, releasing the newly produced phages, which may then attach to other host bacterial cells. As Hershey and Chase discovered, it is the viral DNA that contains the instructions for making phages.

Once DNA was shown to be the molecule of heredity, understanding its structure became the most important quest in biology. In the next two modules, we'll review the structure of DNA and discuss how it was discovered.

? **What convinced Hershey and Chase that DNA, rather than protein, is the genetic material of phage T2?**

● Radioactively labeled phage DNA, but not labeled protein, entered the host cell during infection and directed the synthesis of new viruses.

❶ A phage attaches itself to a bacterial cell.

❷ The phage injects its DNA into the bacterium.

❸ The phage DNA directs the host cell to make more phage DNA and proteins; new phages assemble.

❹ The cell lyses and releases the new phages.

▲ **Figure 10.1C** A phage replication cycle

10.2 DNA and RNA are polymers of nucleotides

By the time Hershey and Chase performed their experiments, much was already known about DNA. Scientists had identified all its atoms and knew how they were bonded to one another. What was not understood was the specific three-dimensional arrangement of atoms that gave DNA its unique properties—the capacity to store genetic information, copy it, and pass it from generation to generation. However, only one year after Hershey and Chase published their results, scientists figured out the structure of DNA and the basic strategy of how it works. We will examine that momentous discovery in Module 10.3, but first, let's look at the underlying chemical structure of DNA and its chemical cousin, RNA.

DNA and RNA are nucleic acids, consisting of long chains (polymers) of chemical units (monomers) called **nucleotides** (see Module 3.16). **Figure 10.2A** shows four representations of various parts of the same molecule. At left is a view of a DNA double helix. One of the strands is opened up (center) to show two different views of an individual DNA **polynucleotide**, a nucleotide polymer (chain). The view on the far right zooms

in to a single nucleotide from the chain. Each type of DNA nucleotide has a different nitrogen-containing base: adenine (A), cytosine (C), thymine (T), or guanine (G). Because nucleotides can occur in a polynucleotide in any sequence and because polynucleotides can be very long, the number of possible polynucleotides is enormous. The chain shown in this figure has the sequence ACTGG, only one of many possible arrangements of the four types of nucleotides that make up DNA.

Looking more closely at our polynucleotide, we see in the center of Figure 10.2A that each nucleotide consists of three components: a nitrogenous base (in DNA: A, C, T, or G), a sugar (shown in blue), and a phosphate group (shown in yellow). The nucleotides are joined to one another by covalent bonds between the sugar of one nucleotide and the phosphate of the next, which forms a **sugar-phosphate backbone** with a repeating pattern of sugar-phosphate-sugar-phosphate. The nitrogenous bases are arranged like ribs that project from the backbone.

Examining a single nucleotide in even more detail (on the right in Figure 10.2A), you can see the chemical structure of its three components. The phosphate group has a phosphorus atom (P) at its center and is the source of the word *acid* in *nucleic acid*. The sugar has five carbon atoms, shown in red here for emphasis—four in its ring and one extending above the ring. The ring also includes an oxygen atom. The sugar is called deoxyribose because, compared with the sugar

▲ **Figure 10.2A**   Breaking down the structure of DNA

Try This   Use your finger to trace each part of the nucleotide—sugar, phosphate, and base—in all four parts of this figure.

Thymine (T) Cytosine (C)

Pyrimidines

Adenine (A) Guanine (G)

Purines

▲ **Figure 10.2B** The nitrogenous bases of DNA

ribose, it is missing an oxygen atom. Notice that the C atom in the lower right corner of the ring is bonded to an H atom instead of to an —OH group, as it is in ribose; see Figure 10.2C. Hence, DNA is "deoxy"—which means "without an oxygen"—compared to RNA.

The full name for **DNA** is **deoxyribonucleic acid**, with *nucleic* referring to DNA's location in the nuclei of eukaryotic cells. Each nitrogenous base (thymine, in our example at the right in Figure 10.2A) has a single or double ring consisting of nitrogen and carbon atoms with various functional groups attached (**Figure 10.2B**). Recall that a functional group is a chemical group that affects a molecule's function by participating in specific chemical reactions (see Module 3.2). In the case of DNA, the main role of the functional groups is to determine which other kind of bases each base can form hydrogen bonds with. For example, the NH_2 group hanging off cytosine is capable of forming a hydrogen bond to the C=O group hanging off guanine, but not with the NH_2 group protruding from adenine. The chemical groups of the bases are therefore responsible for DNA's most important property, which you will learn more about in the next module. In contrast to the acidic phosphate group, nitrogenous bases are basic—hence their name.

The four nucleotides found in DNA differ only in the structure of their nitrogenous bases. At this point, the structural details are not as important as the fact that the bases are of two types. **Thymine (T)** and **cytosine (C)** are single-ring structures called pyrimidines. **Adenine (A)** and **guanine (G)** are larger, double-ring structures called purines. The

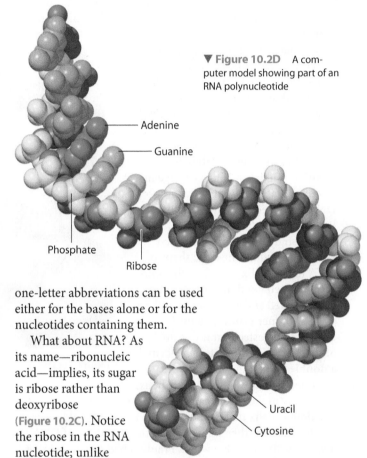

▼ **Figure 10.2D** A computer model showing part of an RNA polynucleotide

— Adenine

— Guanine

Phosphate

Ribose

Uracil

Cytosine

one-letter abbreviations can be used either for the bases alone or for the nucleotides containing them.

What about RNA? As its name—ribonucleic acid—implies, its sugar is ribose rather than deoxyribose (**Figure 10.2C**). Notice the ribose in the RNA nucleotide; unlike deoxyribose, the sugar ring has an —OH group attached to the C atom at its lower-right corner. Another difference between RNA and DNA is that instead of thymine, RNA has a nitrogenous base called **uracil (U)**. (You can see the structure of uracil in Figure 10.2C; it is very similar to thymine.) Except for the presence of ribose and uracil, an RNA polynucleotide chain is identical to a DNA polynucleotide chain. **Figure 10.2D** is a computer graphic of a piece of RNA polynucleotide about 20 nucleotides long. In this three-dimensional view, each sphere represents an atom; notice that the color scheme is the same as in the other figures in this module. The yellow phosphate groups and blue ribose sugars make it easy to spot the sugar-phosphate backbone. In the next module, we'll see how two DNA polynucleotides join together in a molecule of DNA.

Phosphate group

Nitrogenous base (can be A, G, C, or U)

Uracil (U)

Sugar (ribose)

▲ **Figure 10.2C** An RNA nucleotide

? **Compare and contrast DNA and RNA polynucleotides.**

● Both are polymers of nucleotides consisting of a sugar, a nitrogenous base, and a phosphate. In RNA, the sugar is ribose; in DNA, it is deoxyribose. Both RNA and DNA have the bases A, G, and C, but DNA has a T and RNA has a U.

10.3 DNA is a double-stranded helix

After the 1952 Hershey-Chase experiment convinced most biologists that DNA was the material that stored genetic information, a race was on to determine how the structure of this molecule could account for its role in heredity. By that time, the arrangement of covalent bonds in a nucleic acid polymer was well established, and researchers focused on discovering the three-dimensional shape of DNA. First to the finish line were two scientists who were relatively unknown at the time—American James D. Watson and Englishman Francis Crick.

The partnership that solved the puzzle of DNA structure began soon after Watson, a 23-year-old newly minted Ph.D., journeyed to Cambridge University in England, where the more senior Crick was studying protein structure with a technique called X-ray crystallography. While visiting the laboratory of Maurice Wilkins at King's College in London, Watson saw an X-ray image of DNA produced by Wilkins's colleague, Rosalind Franklin (Figure 10.3A). A careful study of the image enabled Watson to deduce the basic shape of DNA to be a helix (spiral) with a uniform diameter and the nitrogenous bases located above one another like a stack of dinner plates. The thickness of the helix suggested that it was made up of two polynucleotide strands, forming a **double helix**. But how were the nucleotides arranged in the double helix?

▲ Figure 10.3A   Rosalind Franklin and her X-ray image of DNA

Watson and Crick began trying to construct a wire model of a double helix that would conform both to Franklin's data and to what was then known about the chemistry of DNA (Figure 10.3B). They knew that Franklin had concluded that the sugar-phosphate backbones must be on the outside of the double helix, forcing the nitrogenous bases to swivel to the interior of the molecule. But how were the bases arranged in the interior of the double helix?

At first, Watson and Crick imagined that the bases paired like with like—for example, A with A and C with C. But that kind of pairing did not fit the X-ray data, which suggested that the DNA molecule has a uniform diameter. An A-A pair, with two double-ring bases, would be almost twice as wide as a C-C pair, made of two single-ring bases. It soon became apparent that a double-ringed base (purine) on one strand must always be paired with a single-ringed base (pyrimidine) on the opposite strand to produce a molecule of uniform thickness. After considerable trial and error, Watson and Crick realized that the chemical structures of the bases dictated the pairings even more specifically. As discussed in the previous module, each base has protruding functional groups that can best form hydrogen bonds with just one appropriate partner (to review the hydrogen bond, see Module 2.8). Adenine can best form hydrogen bonds with thymine, and guanine with cytosine. In the biologist's shorthand, A pairs with T, and G pairs with C. A is also said to be "complementary" to T and G to C.

Watson and Crick's pairing scheme both fit what was known about the physical attributes and chemical bonding of DNA and explained some data obtained several years earlier by American biochemist Erwin Chargaff. Chargaff had discovered that the amount of adenine in the DNA of any one species was equal to the amount of thymine and that the amount of guanine was equal to that of cytosine. Chargaff's rules, as they are called, are explained by the fact that A on one of DNA's polynucleotide chains always pairs with T on the other polynucleotide chain, and G on one chain pairs only with C on the other chain.

You can picture the model of the DNA double helix proposed by Watson and Crick as a rope ladder with wooden rungs, with the ladder twisting into a spiral (Figure 10.3C). The side ropes represent the sugar-phosphate backbones, and the rungs represent pairs of nitrogenous bases joined by hydrogen bonds.

Figure 10.3D shows three representations of the double helix. The shapes of the base symbols in the ribbonlike diagram on the left indicate the bases' complementarity; notice that the shape of any kind of base matches only one other kind of base. In the center of the diagram is an atomic-level version showing four base pairs, with the helix untwisted and the hydrogen bonds specified by dotted

▲ Figure 10.3B   Watson and Crick in 1953 with their model of the DNA double helix

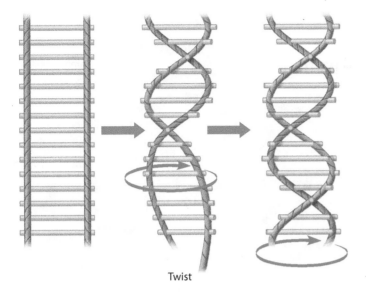

Twist

▲ **Figure 10.3C**   A rope ladder analogy for the double helix

lines. Notice that a C-G base pair has functional groups that form three hydrogen bonds, whereas an A-T base pair has functional groups that form two hydrogen bonds. This difference means that C-G base pairs are somewhat stronger than A-T base pairs. You can see that the two sugar-phosphate backbones of the double helix are oriented in opposite directions. (Notice that the sugars on the two strands are upside down with respect to each other.) On the right is a computer graphic showing most of the atoms of part of a double helix. The atoms that compose the deoxyribose sugars are shown

as blue, phosphate groups as yellow, and nitrogenous bases as shades of green and orange.

Although the Watson-Crick base-pairing rules dictate the side-by-side combinations of nitrogenous bases that form the rungs of the double helix, they place no restrictions on the sequence of nucleotides along the length of a DNA strand. In fact, the sequence of bases can vary in countless ways, and each gene has a unique order of nucleotides, or base sequence.

In April 1953, Watson and Crick rocked the scientific world with a succinct paper explaining their molecular model for DNA in the British scientific journal *Nature.* In 1962, Watson, Crick, and Wilkins received the Nobel Prize for their work. (Sadly, Rosalind Franklin died in 1958 at the age of 38 and was thus ineligible for the prize.) Few milestones in the history of biology have had as broad an impact as the discovery of the double helix, with its A-T and C-G base pairing.

The Watson-Crick model gave new meaning to the words *genes* and *chromosomes*—and to the chromosome theory of inheritance (see Module 9.16). With a complete picture of DNA, we can see that the genetic information in a chromosome must be encoded in the nucleotide sequence of the molecule. One powerful aspect of the Watson-Crick model is that the structure of DNA suggests a molecular explanation for genetic inheritance, as we will see in the next module.

> **?** Along one strand of a double helix is the nucleotide sequence GGCATAGGT. What is the complementary sequence for the other DNA strand?

● CCGTATCCA

Ribbon model   Partial chemical structure   Computer model

Hydrogen bond

Base pair

▲ **Figure 10.3D**   Three representations of DNA

▷ DNA Replication

10.4 DNA replication depends on specific base pairing

One of biology's overarching themes—the relationship between structure and function—is evident in the double helix. The idea that there is specific pairing of bases in DNA was the flash of inspiration that led Watson and Crick to the correct structure of the DNA molecule. At the same time, they saw the functional significance of the base-pairing rules.

The logic behind the Watson-Crick proposal for how DNA is copied—by specific pairing of complementary bases—is quite simple. You can see this by covering one of the strands in the parental DNA molecule in **Figure 10.4A**. You can determine the sequence of bases in the covered strand by applying the base-pairing rules to the unmasked strand: A pairs with T (and T with A), and G pairs with C (and C with G).

Watson and Crick predicted that a cell applies the same rules when copying its genes during each turn of the cell cycle (Module 8.3). As shown in Figure 10.4A, the two strands of parental DNA (blue) separate. Each strand becomes a template for the assembly of a complementary strand from a supply of free nucleotides (gray) available within the nucleus. The nucleotides line up one at a time along the template strand in accordance with the base-pairing rules. Enzymes link the nucleotides to form the new DNA strands. The completed new molecules, identical to the parental molecule, are known as daughter DNA (although no gender should be inferred).

Watson and Crick's model predicts that when a double helix replicates, each of the two daughter molecules will have one old strand from the parental molecule and one newly created strand. This model for DNA replication is known as the **semiconservative model** because half of the parental molecule is maintained (conserved) in each daughter molecule. The semiconservative model of replication was confirmed by experiments performed in the 1950s.

Although the general mechanism of DNA replication is conceptually simple, the actual process is complex, requiring

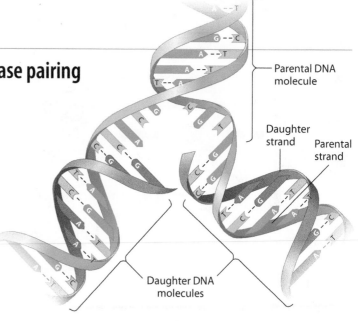

Parental DNA molecule

Daughter strand

Parental strand

Daughter DNA molecules

▲ **Figure 10.4B**   The untwisting and replication of DNA

the coordination of more than a dozen enzymes and other proteins. Some of the complexity arises from the need for the helical DNA molecule to untwist as it replicates and for the two new strands to be made roughly simultaneously (**Figure 10.4B**). Another challenge is the speed of the process. *E. coli*, with about 4.6 million DNA base pairs, can copy its entire genome in less than an hour. Human cells, with more than 6 billion base pairs in 46 chromosomes, require only a few hours. Despite this speed, the process is amazingly accurate; typically, only about one DNA nucleotide per several billion is incorrectly paired. In the next module, we take a closer look at the mechanisms of DNA replication that allow it to proceed with such speed and accuracy.

?   **How does complementary base pairing make possible the replication of DNA?**

● When the two strands of the double helix separate, free nucleotides can base-pair along each strand, leading to the synthesis of new complementary strands.

▶ **Figure 10.4A**
A template model for
DNA replication

A parental molecule
of DNA

Free nucleotides

The parental strands separate
and serve as templates

Two identical daughter
molecules of DNA are formed

10.5 DNA replication proceeds in two directions at many sites simultaneously

Replication of a DNA molecule begins at particular sites called origins of replication, short stretches of DNA having a specific sequence of nucleotides. Proteins that initiate DNA replication

attach to the DNA at the origin of replication, separating the two strands of the double helix (**Figure 10.5A**). Replication then proceeds in both directions, creating replication

Parental DNA molecule

Origin of replication

Parental strand
Daughter strand

"Bubble"

Two daughter DNA molecules

▲ **Figure 10.5A** Multiple replication bubbles in DNA

"bubbles." The parental DNA strands (blue) open up as daughter strands (gray) elongate on both sides of each bubble. The DNA molecule of a eukaryotic chromosome has many origins where replication can start simultaneously. Thus, hundreds or thousands of bubbles can be present at once, shortening the total time needed for replication. Eventually, all the bubbles fuse, yielding two completed, double-stranded daughter DNA molecules (see the bottom of Figure 10.5A).

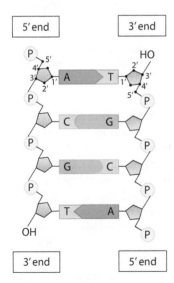

5' end   3' end

3' end   5' end

▲ **Figure 10.5B** The opposite orientations of DNA strands

Try This On each polynucleotide strand, identify one complete nucleotide by drawing a circle around it. Notice that in one strand, the phosphate is on top, and on the other strand, it's on the bottom.

Figure 10.5B shows the molecular building blocks of a tiny segment of DNA. Notice that the sugar-phosphate backbones run in opposite directions. As a result, each strand has a 3' ("three-prime") end and a 5' ("five-prime") end. The primed numbers refer to the carbon atoms of the nucleotide sugars. At one end of each DNA strand, the sugar's 3' carbon atom is attached to an —OH group; at the other end, the sugar's 5' carbon is attached to a phosphate group.

The opposite orientation of the strands is important in DNA replication. The enzymes that link DNA nucleotides to a growing daughter strand, called **DNA polymerases**, add

nucleotides only to the 3' end of the strand, never to the 5' end. Thus, a daughter DNA strand can only grow in the 5' → 3' direction. You see the consequences of this enzyme specificity in **Figure 10.5C**, where the forked structure represents one side of a replication bubble. One of the daughter strands (shown in gray) can be synthesized in one continuous piece by a DNA polymerase working toward the forking point of the parental DNA. However, to make the other daughter strand, polymerase molecules must work outward from the forking point. The only way this can be accomplished is if the new strand is synthesized in short pieces as the fork opens up. These pieces are called Okazaki fragments, after the Japanese husband and wife team of molecular biologists who discovered them. Another enzyme, called **DNA ligase**, then links, or ligates, the pieces together into a single DNA strand.

In addition to their roles in adding nucleotides to a DNA chain, DNA polymerases carry out a proof-reading step that quickly removes nucleotides that have base-paired incorrectly during replication. DNA polymerases and DNA ligase are also involved in re-pairing DNA damaged by harmful radiation, such as ultraviolet light and X-rays, or toxic chemicals in the environment, such as those found in tobacco smoke.

DNA replication ensures that all the somatic cells in a multicellular organism carry the same genetic information. It is also the means by which genetic instructions are copied for the next generation of the organism. In the next module, we begin to pursue the connection between DNA instructions and an organism's phenotypic traits.

? **What is the function of DNA polymerase in DNA replication?**

● As free nucleotides base-pair to a parental DNA strand, the enzyme covalently bonds them to the 3' end of a growing daughter strand.

DNA polymerase molecule

Parental DNA

Replication fork

This daughter strand is synthesized continuously

This daughter strand is synthesized in pieces

DNA ligase

Overall direction of replication

▲ **Figure 10.5C** How daughter DNA strands are synthesized

10.6 Genes control phenotypic traits through the expression of proteins

We can now define genotype and phenotype in terms of the structure and function of DNA. An organism's genotype, its genetic makeup, is the heritable information contained in the sequence of nucleotide bases in DNA. The phenotype is the organism's physical traits. So what is the molecular connection between genotype and phenotype?

The answer is that the DNA inherited by an organism specifies traits by dictating the synthesis of proteins. In other words, proteins are the links between genotype and phenotype. However, a gene does not build a protein directly. Rather, a gene dispatches instructions in the form of RNA, which in turn programs protein synthesis. This fundamental concept in biology is summarized in **Figure 10.6A**. The molecular "chain of command" is from DNA in the nucleus of the cell to RNA to protein synthesis in the cytoplasm. The two main stages are **transcription**, the synthesis of RNA under the direction of DNA, and **translation**, the synthesis of protein under the direction of RNA.

The relationship between genes and proteins was first proposed in 1909, when English physician Archibald Garrod suggested that genes dictate phenotypes through enzymes, proteins that catalyze chemical reactions. Garrod hypothesized that an inherited disease reflects a person's inability to make a particular enzyme. He gave as one example the hereditary condition called alkaptonuria, in which the urine is dark because it contains a chemical called alkapton. Garrod reasoned that most people have an enzyme that breaks down alkapton, whereas people with alkaptonuria inherited an inability to make the enzyme. Garrod's hypothesis was ahead of its time, but research conducted decades later supported his hypothesis. In the intervening years, biochemists accumulated evidence that cells make and break down biologically important molecules via metabolic pathways, as in the synthesis of an amino acid or the breakdown of a sugar. Each step in a metabolic pathway is catalyzed by a specific enzyme

(as we described in Unit I; see Module 5.15, for example). Therefore, individuals lacking one of the enzymes for a pathway are unable to complete it.

The major breakthrough in demonstrating the relationship between genes and enzymes came in the 1940s from the work of American geneticists George Beadle and Edward Tatum with the bread mold *Neurospora crassa* (**Figure 10.6B**). Beadle and Tatum studied strains of the mold that were unable to grow on a simple growth medium. Each of these so-called nutritional mutants turned out to lack an enzyme in a metabolic pathway that synthesized some molecule the mold needed, such as an amino acid. Beadle and Tatum also showed that each mutant was defective in a single gene. Accordingly, they hypothesized that the function of an individual gene is to dictate the production of a specific enzyme.

The "one gene–one enzyme hypothesis" has since been modified. First, it was extended beyond enzymes to include *all* types of proteins. For example, keratin (the structural protein of hair) and the hormone insulin are two examples of proteins that are not enzymes. In addition, many proteins are made from two or more polypeptide chains, with each polypeptide specified by its own gene. For example, hemoglobin, the oxygen-transporting protein in your red blood cells, is built from two kinds of polypeptides, encoded by two different genes. Thus, Beadle and Tatum's hypothesis is now stated as follows: The function of a gene is to dictate the production of a polypeptide.

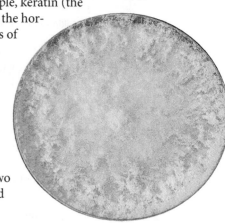

▲ **Figure 10.6B** The bread mold *Neurospora crassa* growing in a culture dish

Even this description is not entirely accurate, in that the RNA transcribed from some genes is not translated but nonetheless has important functions (you'll learn about two such kinds of RNA in Modules 10.11 and 10.12). In addition, many eukaryotic genes code for a set of polypeptides (rather than just one) by a process called alternative splicing (discussed in Module 11.4). The more biologists learn about the ways that genes act in cells, the more complicated the picture—and the very concept of a gene—becomes. This topic continues to be an active area of research within the biology community. But for now, we'll focus on genes that do code for polypeptides. The nature of that code is our next topic.

▲ **Figure 10.6A** The flow of genetic information in a eukaryotic cell

? **What are the functions of transcription and translation?**

● Transcription is the transfer of information from DNA to RNA. Translation is the use of the information in RNA to make a polypeptide.

10.7 Genetic information written in codons is translated into amino acid sequences

Genes provide the instructions for making specific proteins. But a gene does not build a protein itself. As you have learned, the bridge between DNA and protein synthesis is the nucleic acid RNA: DNA is transcribed into RNA, which is then translated into protein. Put another way, information within the cell flows as DNA → RNA → protein. This can be stated as: "DNA makes RNA makes protein."

Transcription and translation are linguistic terms, and it is useful to think of nucleic acids and proteins as having languages. To understand how genetic information passes from genotype to phenotype, we need to see how the chemical language of DNA is translated into the different chemical language of proteins.

What exactly is the language of nucleic acids? Both DNA and RNA are polymers made of nucleotide monomers strung together in specific sequences that convey information, much as specific sequences of letters convey information in written language. In DNA, there are four types of nucleotides, which differ in their nitrogenous bases (A, T, C, and G). The same is true for RNA, although it has the base U instead of T.

Figure 10.7 focuses on a small region of one gene (gene 3, shown in light blue) on a DNA molecule. DNA's language is written as a linear sequence of nucleotide bases on a polynucleotide, a sequence such as the one you see on the enlarged DNA segment in the figure. Specific sequences of bases, each with a beginning and an end, make up the genes on a DNA strand. A typical gene consists of hundreds or thousands of nucleotides in a specific sequence.

The pink strand underneath the enlarged DNA segment represents the results of transcription: an RNA molecule. The process is called transcription because the nucleic acid language of DNA has been rewritten (transcribed) as a sequence of bases on RNA. Notice that the language is still that of nucleic acids, although the nucleotide bases on the RNA molecule are complementary to those on the DNA strand. As we will see in Module 10.9, this is because the RNA was synthesized using the DNA as a template.

The purple chain at the bottom of Figure 10.7 represents the results of translation, the conversion of the nucleic acid language to the polypeptide language. Like nucleic acids, polypeptides are polymers, but the monomers that compose them are the 20 different kinds of amino acids. Again, the language is written in a linear sequence, and the sequence of nucleotides of the RNA molecule dictates the sequence of amino acids of the polypeptide. The RNA acts as a messenger carrying genetic information from DNA.

During translation, there is a change in language from the nucleotide sequence of the RNA to the amino acid sequence of the polypeptide. How is this translation achieved? Recall that there are only four different kinds of nucleotides in DNA (A, G, C, T) and in RNA (A, G, C, U). In translation, these four nucleotides must somehow specify all 20 amino acids. Consider if each single nucleotide base were to specify one amino acid. In this case, only four of the 20 amino acids could be accounted for, one for each type of base. What if the language consisted of two-letter code words? If we read the bases of a gene two at a time—AG, for example, could specify one amino acid, whereas AT could designate a different amino acid—then only 16 arrangements would be possible (4^2), which is still not enough to specify all 20 amino acids. However, if the base code in DNA consists of a triplet, with each arrangement of three consecutive bases specifying an amino acid—AGT specifies one amino acid, for example, while AGA specifies a different one—then there can be 64 (that is, 4^3) possible code words, more than enough to specify the 20 amino acids. Thus, triplets of bases are the smallest "words" of uniform length that can specify all the amino acids (see the brackets below the strand of RNA in Figure 10.7). Indeed, the 64 triplets allow for more than one to represent an amino acid. For example, the base triplets AAT and AAC could both code for the same amino acid.

Experiments have verified that the flow of information from gene to protein is based on a **triplet code**: The genetic instructions for the amino acid sequence of a polypeptide chain are written in DNA and RNA as a series of nonoverlapping three-base "words" called **codons**. Notice in the figure that three-base codons in the DNA are transcribed into complementary three-base codons in the RNA, and then the RNA codons are translated into amino acids that form a polypeptide. We turn to the codons themselves in the next module.

DNA molecule

Gene 1

Gene 2

Gene 3

DNA

A A A C C G G C A A A A

Transcription

RNA

U U U G G C C G U U U U

Translation

Codon

Polypeptide

Amino acid

? What is the minimum number of nucleotides necessary to code for 100 amino acids?

▲ **Figure 10.7** Transcription and translation of codons

10.8 The genetic code dictates how codons are translated into amino acids

During the 1960s, molecular biologists used a series of elegant experiments to crack the **genetic code**, the amino acid translations of each of the nucleotide triplets. The first codon was deciphered in 1961 by American biochemist Marshall Nirenberg. He synthesized an artificial RNA molecule by linking together identical RNA nucleotides having uracil as their only base. No matter where this message started or stopped, it could contain only one type of triplet codon: UUU. Nirenberg added this "poly-U" to a test-tube mixture containing ribosomes and the other ingredients required for polypeptide synthesis. His artificial system translated the poly-U into a polypeptide containing a single kind of amino acid, phenylalanine (Phe). Thus, Nirenberg learned that the RNA codon UUU specifies the amino acid phenylalanine. By variations on this method, the amino acids specified by all the codons were soon determined.

As shown in **Figure 10.8A**, 61 of the 64 triplets code for amino acids. The triplet AUG (green box in the figure) has a dual function: It codes for the amino acid methionine (Met) and also can provide a signal for the start of a polypeptide chain. Three codons (UAA, UGA, and UAG, shown in red) do not designate amino acids but serve as stop codons that mark the end of translation.

Notice in Figure 10.8A that there is redundancy in the code but no ambiguity. For example, although codons UUU and UUC both specify phenylalanine (redundancy), neither of them ever represents any other amino acid (no ambiguity). The codons in the figure are the triplets found in RNA. They

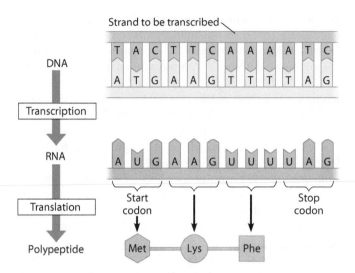

▲ **Figure 10.8B** Deciphering the genetic information in DNA

have a straightforward, complementary relationship to the codons in DNA, with UUU in the RNA matching AAA in the DNA, for example. The nucleotides making up the codons occur in a linear order along the DNA and RNA, with no gaps separating the codons.

As an exercise in translating the genetic code, consider the 12-nucleotide segment of DNA in **Figure 10.8B**. Let's read this as a series of triplets. Using the base-pairing rules (with U in RNA instead of T), we see that the RNA codon corresponding to the first transcribed DNA triplet, TAC, is AUG. As you can see in Figure 10.8A, AUG specifies, "Place Met as the first amino acid in the polypeptide." The second DNA triplet, TTC, dictates RNA codon AAG, which designates lysine (Lys) as the second amino acid. We continue until we reach a stop codon (UAG in this example).

The genetic code is nearly universal, shared by organisms from the simplest bacteria to the most complex plants and animals. Such universality is key to modern DNA technologies because it allows scientists to mix and match genes from various species (**Figure 10.8C**; see Chapter 12). A language shared by all living things must have evolved early enough in the history of life to be present in the common ancestors of all modern organisms. A shared genetic vocabulary is a reminder of the evolutionary kinship that connects all life on Earth.

▲ **Figure 10.8C** The cat on the left was engineered to express a protein that fluoresces red when exposed to UV light

Figure 10.8A — The genetic code

Second base of RNA codon

First base of RNA codon	U	C	A	G	Third base of RNA codon
U	UUU UUC — Phe / UUA UUG — Leu	UCU UCC UCA UCG — Ser	UAU UAC — Tyr / UAA Stop / UAG Stop	UGU UGC — Cys / UGA Stop / UGG Trp	U C A G
C	CUU CUC CUA CUG — Leu	CCU CCC CCA CCG — Pro	CAU CAC — His / CAA CAG — Gln	CGU CGC CGA CGG — Arg	U C A G
A	AUU AUC AUA — Ile / AUG Met or start	ACU ACC ACA ACG — Thr	AAU AAC — Asn / AAA AAG — Lys	AGU AGC — Ser / AGA AGG — Arg	U C A G
G	GUU GUC GUA GUG — Val	GCU GCC GCA GCG — Ala	GAU GAC — Asp / GAA GAG — Glu	GGU GGC GGA GGG — Gly	U C A G

▲ **Figure 10.8A** The genetic code used to translate RNA codons to amino acids

Try This Identify the DNA triplet that produces an RNA start codon, and identify the three DNA triplets that produce an RNA stop codon.

? Translate the RNA sequence CCAUUUACG into the corresponding amino acid sequence.

Pro-Phe-Thr

10.9 Transcription produces genetic messages in the form of RNA

In eukaryotic cells, transcription, the transfer of genetic information from DNA to RNA, occurs in the nucleus. Here we focus on transcription in prokaryotic cells, which is a simpler process than in eukaryotes.

After separation of the two DNA strands, one strand serves as a template for a new RNA molecule; the other DNA strand is unused. The transcription enzyme **RNA polymerase** moves along the gene, forming a new RNA strand by following the base-pairing rules—but remember that in RNA, uracil replaces thymine. A specific nucleotide sequence called a **promoter** acts as a binding site for RNA polymerase and determines where transcription starts and on which strand. RNA polymerase adds RNA nucleotides until it reaches a sequence of DNA bases called the **terminator**, which signals the end of the gene.

TRANSCRIPTION OF A GENE

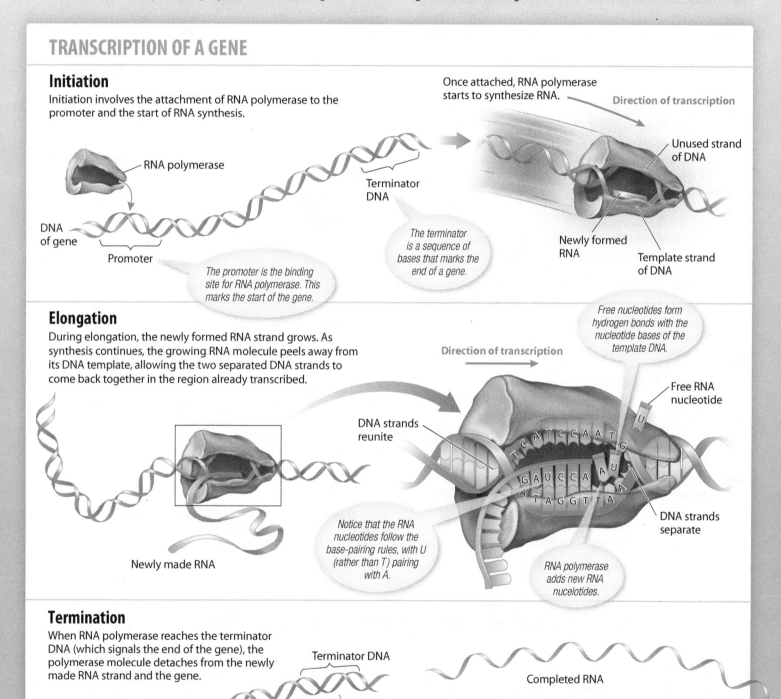

Initiation

Initiation involves the attachment of RNA polymerase to the promoter and the start of RNA synthesis.

RNA polymerase

DNA of gene

Promoter

The promoter is the binding site for RNA polymerase. This marks the start of the gene.

Terminator DNA

The terminator is a sequence of bases that marks the end of a gene.

Once attached, RNA polymerase starts to synthesize RNA.

Direction of transcription

Unused strand of DNA

Newly formed RNA

Template strand of DNA

Elongation

During elongation, the newly formed RNA strand grows. As synthesis continues, the growing RNA molecule peels away from its DNA template, allowing the two separated DNA strands to come back together in the region already transcribed.

Newly made RNA

Notice that the RNA nucleotides follow the base-pairing rules, with U (rather than T) pairing with A.

Direction of transcription

Free nucleotides form hydrogen bonds with the nucleotide bases of the template DNA.

Free RNA nucleotide

DNA strands reunite

DNA strands separate

RNA polymerase adds new RNA nucleotides.

Termination

When RNA polymerase reaches the terminator DNA (which signals the end of the gene), the polymerase molecule detaches from the newly made RNA strand and the gene.

Terminator DNA

Completed RNA

RNA polymerase detaches

? How does RNA polymerase recognize the start and end of the gene?

● Special DNA sequences mark the start (promoter) and end (terminator) of a gene.

10.10 Eukaryotic RNA is processed before leaving the nucleus as mRNA

The kind of RNA that encodes amino acid sequences is called **messenger RNA (mRNA)** because it conveys genetic messages from DNA to the translation machinery of the cell. Messenger RNA is transcribed from DNA, and the information in the mRNA is then translated into polypeptides. In prokaryotic cells, which lack nuclei, transcription and translation occur in the same place: the cytoplasm. In eukaryotic cells, however, mRNA molecules must exit the nucleus via the nuclear pores and enter the cytoplasm, where the machinery for polypeptide synthesis is located.

Before leaving the nucleus as mRNA, eukaryotic transcripts are modified, or processed, in several ways (**Figure 10.10**). One kind of RNA processing is the addition of extra nucleotides to the ends of the RNA transcript. These additions include a small cap (a modified form of a G nucleotide) at the 5′ end and a long tail (a chain of 50 to 250 A nucleotides) at the 3′ end. The cap and tail (yellow in the figure) facilitate the export of the mRNA from the nucleus, protect the mRNA from degradation by cellular enzymes, and help ribosomes bind to the mRNA. The cap and tail themselves are not translated into protein.

Another type of RNA processing is made necessary in eukaryotes by noncoding stretches of nucleotides that interrupt the nucleotides that actually code for amino acids. It is as if nonsense words were randomly interspersed in a story. Most genes of plants and animals include such internal noncoding regions, which are called **introns** ("intervening sequences"). The coding regions—the parts of a gene that are expressed— are called **exons**. As Figure 10.10 shows, both exons (shown in a darker color) and introns (in a lighter color) are transcribed from DNA into RNA. However, before the RNA leaves the nucleus, the introns are removed, and the exons are joined to produce an mRNA molecule with a continuous coding sequence. (The short noncoding regions just inside the cap and tail are considered parts of the first and last exons.) This cutting-and-pasting process is called **RNA splicing**. In most cases, RNA splicing is catalyzed by a complex of proteins and small RNA molecules. RNA splicing also provides a means to produce multiple polypeptides from a single gene (as we will see in the next chapter; see Module 11.4). In fact, RNA splicing is believed to play a significant role in humans in allowing our approximately 21,000 genes to produce many

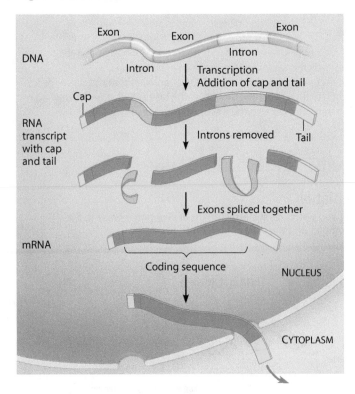

▲ **Figure 10.10** The production of eukaryotic mRNA

thousands more polypeptides. This is accomplished by varying the exons that are included in the final mRNA.

As we have discussed, translation is a conversion between different languages—from the nucleic acid language to the protein language—and it involves more elaborate machinery than transcription. The first important ingredient required for translation is the processed mRNA. Once it is present, the machinery used to translate mRNA requires enzymes and sources of chemical energy, such as ATP. In addition, translation requires two heavy-duty components: ribosomes and a kind of RNA called transfer RNA, the subject of the next module.

> ? **Explain why most eukaryotic genes are longer than the mRNA that leaves the nucleus.**
>
> ● These genes have introns, noncoding sequences of nucleotides that are spliced out of the initial RNA transcript to produce mRNA.

10.11 Transfer RNA molecules serve as interpreters during translation

Translation of any language into another language requires an interpreter, someone or something that can recognize the words of one language and convert them to another. Translation of a genetic message carried in mRNA into the amino acid language of proteins also requires an interpreter. To convert the three-letter "words" of nucleic acids (codons) to the amino acid "words" of proteins, a cell uses a molecular interpreter, a special type of RNA called **transfer RNA (tRNA)**.

A cell that is producing proteins has in its cytoplasm a supply of amino acids, either obtained from food or manufactured by the cell. But amino acids themselves cannot recognize the codons in the mRNA. It is up to the cell's molecular interpreters, tRNA molecules, to match amino acids to the appropriate codons to form the new polypeptide. To perform this task, tRNA molecules must carry out two functions: (1) picking up the appropriate amino acids and (2) recognizing

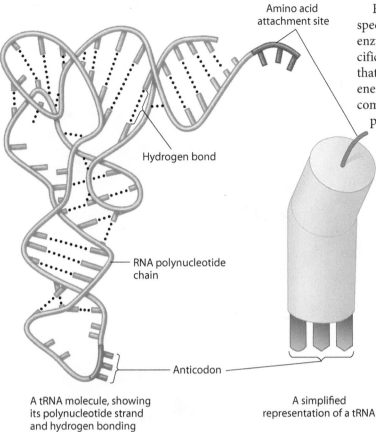

Amino acid
attachment site

Hydrogen bond

RNA polynucleotide
chain

Anticodon

A tRNA molecule, showing
its polynucleotide strand
and hydrogen bonding

A simplified
representation of a tRNA

▲ **Figure 10.11A**   The structure of tRNA

Each amino acid is joined to the correct tRNA by a specific enzyme. There is a family of 20 versions of these enzymes, one enzyme for each amino acid. Each enzyme specifically binds one type of amino acid to all tRNA molecules that code for that amino acid, using a molecule of ATP as energy to drive the reaction. The resulting amino acid–tRNA complex can then furnish its amino acid to a growing polypeptide chain, a process that we describe in Module 10.12.

The computer graphic in **Figure 10.11B** shows a tRNA molecule (green) and an ATP molecule (yellow) bound to the enzyme molecule (blue). (To help you see the two distinct molecules, the tRNA molecule is shown with a stick representation, while the enzyme is shown as space-filling spheres.) In this figure, you can see the proportional sizes of these three molecules. The amino acid that would attach to the tRNA is not shown; it would be less than half the size of the ATP.

Once an amino acid is attached to its appropriate tRNA, it can be incorporated into a growing polypeptide chain. This is accomplished within ribosomes, the cellular structures directly responsible for the synthesis of protein. We examine ribosomes in the next module.

?   **What is an anticodon, and what is its function?**

● It is the base triplet of a tRNA molecule that couples the tRNA to a complementary codon in the mRNA. This is a key step in translating mRNA to polypeptide.

the appropriate codons in the mRNA. The unique structure of tRNA molecules enables them to perform both tasks.

Figure 10.11A shows two representations of a tRNA molecule. The structure on the left shows the backbone and bases, with hydrogen bonds between bases shown as dotted lines. The structure on the right is a simplified schematic that emphasizes the most important parts of the structure. Notice from the structure on the left that a tRNA molecule is made of a single strand of RNA—one polynucleotide chain—consisting of about 80 nucleotides. By twisting and folding upon itself, tRNA forms several double-stranded regions in which short stretches of RNA base-pair with other stretches via hydrogen bonds. A single-stranded loop at one end of the folded molecule contains a special triplet of bases called an **anticodon**. The anticodon triplet is complementary to a codon triplet on mRNA. During translation, the anticodon on the tRNA recognizes a particular codon on the mRNA by using base-pairing rules. At the other end of the tRNA molecule is a site where one specific kind of amino acid attaches.

In the modules that follow, we represent tRNA with the simplified shape shown on the right in Figure 10.11A. This shape emphasizes the two parts of the molecule—the anticodon and the amino acid attachment site—that give tRNA its ability to match a particular nucleic acid word (a codon in mRNA) with its corresponding protein word (an amino acid). Although all tRNA molecules are similar, there is a slightly different variety of tRNA for each amino acid.

tRNA   Enzyme

ATP

▲ **Figure 10.11B**   A molecule of tRNA (green) binding to an enzyme molecule (blue)

10.12 Ribosomes build polypeptides

We have now looked at many of the components a cell needs to carry out translation: instructions in the form of mRNA molecules, tRNA to interpret the instructions, a supply of amino acids and enzymes (for attaching amino acids to tRNA), and ATP for energy. The final components are the **ribosomes**, structures in the cytoplasm that coordinate the functioning of mRNA and tRNA and catalyze the synthesis of polypeptides (Figure 10.12). A ribosome consists of two subunits—a large subunit and a small subunit—each made up of proteins and a kind of RNA called **ribosomal RNA (rRNA)**.

The ribosomes of bacteria and eukaryotes are very similar in function, but those of eukaryotes are slightly larger and different in composition. The differences are medically significant. Certain antibiotic drugs can inactivate bacterial ribosomes while leaving eukaryotic ribosomes unaffected. These drugs, such as tetracycline and streptomycin, are used to combat bacterial infections.

The simplified drawings on the right side of Figure 10.12 indicate how tRNA anticodons and mRNA codons fit together on ribosomes. A fully assembled ribosome has a binding site for mRNA on the small subunit and binding sites (referred to as the P site and the A site) for tRNA on the large subunit. The subunits of the ribosome act like a vise, holding the tRNA and mRNA molecules close together, allowing the amino acids carried by the tRNA molecules to be connected into a polypeptide chain. In the next two modules, we examine the steps of translation in detail.

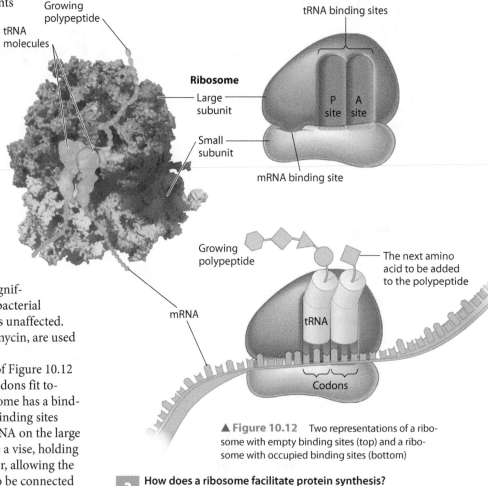

▲ **Figure 10.12**   Two representations of a ribosome with empty binding sites (top) and a ribosome with occupied binding sites (bottom)

? **How does a ribosome facilitate protein synthesis?**

● A ribosome holds mRNA and tRNAs together and connects amino acids from the tRNAs to the growing polypeptide chain.

10.13 An initiation codon marks the start of an mRNA message

Translation can be divided into the same three phases as transcription: initiation, elongation, and termination. The process of initiation brings together the mRNA, a tRNA bearing the first amino acid, and the two subunits of a ribosome.

As shown in Figure 10.13A, an mRNA molecule is longer than the genetic message it carries. The light pink nucleotides at either end of the molecule are not part of the message but help the mRNA to bind to the ribosome. The initiation process establishes exactly where translation will begin, ensuring that the mRNA codons are translated into the correct sequence of amino acids.

Initiation occurs in two steps (Figure 10.13B). ❶ An mRNA molecule binds to a small ribosomal subunit. A special initiator tRNA base-pairs with the specific codon, called the **start codon**, where translation is to begin on the mRNA molecule. The initiator tRNA carries the amino acid methionine (Met); its anticodon, UAC, base-pairs with the start codon, AUG. ❷ Next, a large ribosomal subunit binds to the small one, creating a functional ribosome. The initiator tRNA fits into one of the two tRNA binding

Cap

Start of genetic message

End

Tail

▲ **Figure 10.13A**   A molecule of eukaryotic mRNA

sites on the ribosome. This site, called the **P site**, will hold the growing polypeptide. The other tRNA binding site, called the **A site**, is shown vacant and ready for the next amino-acid-bearing tRNA.

? **What would happen if a genetic mutation in a gene changed a start codon to some other codon?**

● The messenger RNA transcribed from the mutated gene would be nonfunctional because ribosomes could not initiate translation correctly.

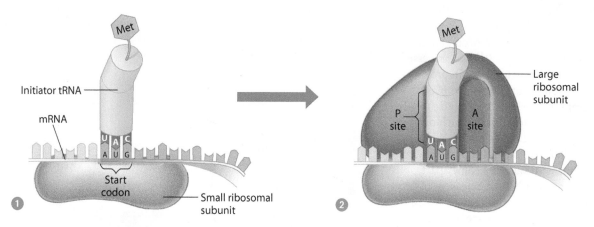

▲ **Figure 10.13B**   The initiation of translation

10.14 Elongation adds amino acids to the polypeptide chain until a stop codon terminates translation

Once initiation is complete, amino acids are added one by one to the previous amino acid. Each addition occurs in a three-step elongation process (**Figure 10.14**). ❶ The antico-don of an incoming tRNA molecule, carrying its amino acid, pairs with the mRNA codon in the A site of the ribosome. ❷ The polypeptide separates from the tRNA in the P site and attaches by a new peptide bond to the amino acid carried by the tRNA in the A site. The ribosome catalyzes formation of the peptide bond, adding one more amino acid to the growing polypeptide chain. ❸ Then, the P site tRNA (which is now lacking an amino acid) leaves the ribo-some, and the ribosome translocates (moves) the remaining tRNA (which holds the growing polypeptide) from the A site to the P site. The codon and anticodon remain hydrogen-bonded, and the mRNA and tRNA move as a unit. This movement brings into the A site the next mRNA codon to be translated, and the process can start again with step 1.

Elongation continues until a **stop codon** reaches the ribo-some's A site. As discussed earlier, stop codons—UAA, UAG, and UGA—do not code for amino acids but instead act as signals to stop translation. This is the termination stage of translation. The completed polypeptide is freed from the last tRNA, and the ribosome splits back into its separate subunits.

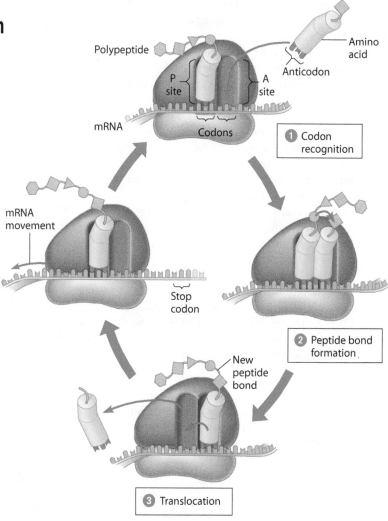

? **What would happen if a codon in the middle of an mRNA mutated from UUA to UAA?**

● Translation would stop prematurely, because a stop codon was introduced.

▲ **Figure 10.14**   Polypeptide elongation; the small green arrows indi-cate movement

10.15 Review: The flow of genetic information in the cell is DNA → RNA → protein

Figure 10.15 summarizes the flow of genetic information from DNA to RNA to protein. ❶ In transcription (DNA → RNA), the mRNA is synthesized on a DNA template. In eukaryotic cells, transcription occurs in the nucleus, and the messenger RNA is processed before it travels to the cytoplasm. In prokaryotes, transcription occurs in the cytoplasm.

❷–❺ Translation (RNA → protein) can be divided into four steps, all of which occur in the cytoplasm in eukaryotic cells. When the polypeptide is complete at the end of step 5, the two ribosomal subunits come apart, and the tRNA and mRNA are released (not shown in this figure). Translation is rapid; a single ribosome can make an average-sized polypeptide in less than a minute. Typically, an mRNA molecule is translated simultaneously by a number of ribosomes. Once the start codon emerges from the first ribosome, a second ribosome can attach to it; thus, several ribosomes may trail along on the same mRNA molecule.

As it is made, a polypeptide coils and folds, assuming a three-dimensional shape, its tertiary structure. Several polypeptides may come together, forming a protein with quaternary structure (see Module 3.14).

What is the overall significance of transcription and translation? These are the main processes whereby genes control the structures and activities of cells—or, more broadly, the way the genotype produces the phenotype. The chain of command originates with the information in a gene, a specific linear sequence of nucleotides in DNA. The gene serves as a template, dictating transcription of a complementary sequence of nucleotides in mRNA. In turn, mRNA dictates the linear sequence of amino acids in a polypeptide. Finally, the proteins that form from the polypeptides determine the appearance and the capabilities of the cell and organism.

? **Which of the following molecules or structures does not participate directly in translation: ribosomes, transfer RNA, messenger RNA, DNA?**

● DNA

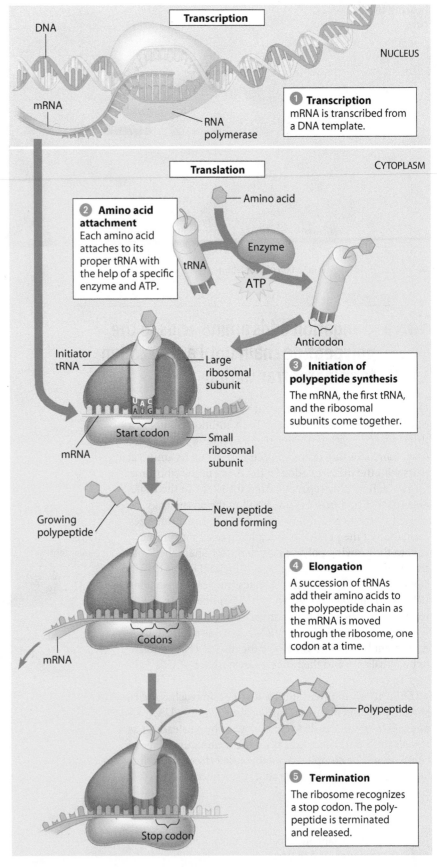

▲ Figure 10.15   A summary of transcription and translation

10.16 Mutations can affect genes

Many inherited traits can be understood in molecular terms. For instance, sickle-cell disease can be traced to a change in a single amino acid in one of the polypeptides in the hemoglobin protein (see Module 9.13). This difference is caused by a single nucleotide difference in the DNA coding for that polypeptide (Figure 10.16A). In the double helix, one nucleotide *pair* is changed.

Any change in the nucleotide sequence of a cell's DNA is called a **mutation**. Mutations can involve large regions of a chromosome or just a single nucleotide pair, as in sickle-cell disease.

Mutations within a gene can be divided into two general categories: nucleotide substitutions and nucleotide insertions or deletions (Figure 10.16B). A nucleotide substitution is the replacement of one nucleotide and its base-pairing partner with another pair of nucleotides. For example, in the second row in Figure 10.16B, A replaces G in the fourth codon of the mRNA. What effect can a substitution have? Because the genetic code is redundant, some substitution mutations have no effect at all. For example, if a mutation causes an mRNA codon to change from GAA to GAG, no change in the protein product would result because GAA and GAG both code for the same amino acid (Glu; see Figure 10.8A). Such a change is called a **silent mutation**.

In contrast, a **missense mutation** changes one amino acid to another one. For example, if a mutation causes an mRNA codon to change from GGC to AGC, as in the second row of Figure 10.16B, the resulting protein will have a serine (Ser) instead of a glycine (Gly) at this position. Some missense mutations have little or no effect on the resulting protein, but others, as in the case of sickle-cell disease, prevent the protein from performing its normal function.

Some substitutions, called **nonsense mutations**, change an amino acid codon into a stop codon. For example, if an AGA (Arg) codon is changed to a UGA (stop) codon, the result will be a prematurely terminated protein, which probably will not function properly.

Mutations involving the insertion or deletion of one or more nucleotides in a gene, called **frameshift mutations**, often have disastrous effects. Because mRNA is read as a series of nucleotide triplets (codons) during translation, adding or subtracting nucleotides may alter the reading frame (triplet grouping) of the genetic message. All the nucleotides

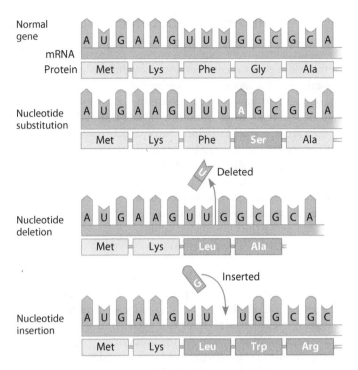

▲ **Figure 10.16B** Types of mutations and their effects

after the insertion or deletion will be regrouped into different codons (Figure 10.16B, bottom two rows). Consider this example in the English language: The red cat ate the big rat. Deleting the second letter produces an entirely nonsensical message: Ter edc ata tet heb igr at. Frameshift mutations will most likely produce a nonfunctional polypeptide.

The production of mutations, called **mutagenesis**, can occur in a number of ways. Spontaneous mutations result from errors during DNA replication or recombination. Other mutations are caused by physical or chemical agents called **mutagens**. High-energy radiation, such as X-rays or ultraviolet light, is a physical mutagen. One class of chemical mutagens consists of chemicals that are similar to normal DNA bases but pair incorrectly or are otherwise disruptive when incorporated into DNA. For example, the anti-AIDS drug AZT works because its structure is similar enough to thymine that viral polymerases incorporate it into newly synthesized DNA but different enough that the drug blocks further replication.

Occasionally, a mutation leads to a protein that enhances the success of the mutant organism and its descendants. Much more often, mutations are harmful to an organism. Mutations are, however, an important source of the rich diversity of genes in the living world, a diversity that makes evolution by natural selection possible. And within the laboratory, mutations are essential tools for geneticists, creating the different alleles needed for genetic research.

? **How could a single nucleotide substitution result in a shortened protein product?**

● A substitution that changed an amino acid codon into a stop codon would produce a prematurely terminated polypeptide.

▲ **Figure 10.16A** The molecular basis of sickle-cell disease

10.17 Viral DNA may become part of the host chromosome

As we discussed in Module 10.1, bacteria and viruses served as models in experiments that uncovered the molecular details of heredity. Now let's take a closer look at viruses, focusing on the relationship between viral structure and the processes of nucleic acid replication, transcription, and translation.

In a sense, a **virus** is an infectious particle consisting of little more than "genes in a box": a bit of nucleic acid wrapped in a protein coat called a **capsid** and, in some cases, a membrane envelope. Viruses are parasites that can replicate (reproduce) only inside cells. In fact, the host cell provides most of the components necessary for replicating, transcribing, and translating the viral nucleic acid.

In Figure 10.1C, we described the replication cycle of phage T2. This sort of cycle is called a **lytic cycle** because it results in the lysis (breaking open) of the host cell and the release of the viruses that were produced within the cell. Some phages can also replicate by an alternative route called the lysogenic cycle. During a **lysogenic cycle**, viral DNA replication occurs without destroying the host cell.

Figure 10.17 illustrates the two kinds of cycles for a phage called lambda that infects *E. coli*. Both cycles begin when the phage DNA ❶ enters the bacterium and ❷ forms a loop. The DNA then embarks on one of the two pathways. In the lytic cycle (left), ❸ lambda's DNA immediately turns the cell into a virus-producing factory, and ❹ the cell soon lyses

and releases its viral products, which may then infect another cell.

In the lysogenic cycle, ❺ viral DNA is inserted by genetic recombination into the bacterial chromosome. Once inserted, the phage DNA is referred to as a **prophage**, and most of its genes are inactive. ❻ Every time the *E. coli* cell prepares to divide, it replicates the phage DNA along with its own chromosome and passes the copies on to daughter cells. A single infected bacterium can thereby quickly give rise to a large population of bacterial cells that all carry a prophage. The lysogenic cycle enables viruses to spread without killing the host cells on which they depend. The prophages may remain in the bacterial cells indefinitely. Occasionally, however, an environmental signal—typically, one that indicates an unfavorable turn in the environment, such as an increase in radiation, drought, or certain toxic chemicals—triggers a switchover from the lysogenic cycle to the lytic cycle. This causes the viral DNA to be excised from the bacterial chromosome, eventually leading to death of the host cell.

Sometimes, the few prophage genes active in a lysogenic bacterium can cause medical problems. For example, the bacteria that cause diphtheria, botulism, and scarlet fever would be harmless to people if it were not for the prophage genes they carry. Certain of these genes direct the bacteria to produce the toxins responsible for making people ill. In the next module, we will explore viruses that infect animals and plants.

> **?** Describe one way a virus can perpetuate its genes without destroying its host cell. What is this type of replication cycle called?

● Some viruses can insert their DNA into a chromosome of the host cell, which replicates the viral genes when it replicates its own DNA prior to cell division. This is called the lysogenic cycle.

Phage

Attaches to cell

Phage DNA

Bacterial chromosome

❶ The phage injects its DNA

Newly released phage may infect another cell

❹ The cell lyses, releasing phages

❷ The phage DNA circularizes

Environmental stress

Many cell divisions

Lytic cycle

Lysogenic cycle

Phages assemble

OR

Prophage

❻ The lysogenic bacterium replicates normally, copying the prophage at each cell division

▲ Figure 10.17
Two types of phage replication cycles

❸ New phage DNA and proteins are synthesized

❺ Phage DNA inserts into the bacterial chromosome by recombination

10.18 Many viruses cause disease in animals and plants

CONNECTION

Viruses can cause disease in both animals and plants. A typical animal virus has a membranous outer envelope and projecting spikes of glycoprotein (protein molecules with attached sugars). The envelope helps the virus enter and leave the host cell. Many animal viruses have RNA rather than DNA as their genetic material. Examples of RNA viruses include those that cause the common cold, measles, mumps, polio, and AIDS. Examples of diseases caused by DNA viruses include hepatitis, chicken pox, and herpes infections.

Figure 10.18 shows the replication cycle of a typical enveloped RNA virus: the mumps virus. Once a common childhood disease characterized by fever and painful swelling of the salivary glands, mumps has become quite rare in industrialized nations thanks to widespread vaccination. When the mumps virus contacts a susceptible cell, the glycoprotein

spikes attach to receptor proteins on the cell's plasma membrane. The viral envelope fuses with the cell's membrane, allowing the protein-coated RNA to ① enter the cytoplasm. ② Enzymes (not shown) then remove the protein coat. ③ An enzyme that entered the cell as part of the virus uses the virus's RNA genome as a template for making complementary strands of RNA (shown in pink). The new strands have two functions: ④ They serve as mRNA for the synthesis of new viral proteins, and they serve as templates for synthesizing new viral genome RNA. ⑤ The new coat proteins assemble around the new viral RNA. ⑥ Finally, the viruses leave the cell by cloaking themselves in the host cell's plasma membrane. Thus, the virus obtains its envelope from the host cell, leaving the cell without necessarily lysing it.

Not all animal viruses replicate in the cytoplasm. For example, herpesviruses—which cause chicken pox, shingles, cold sores, and genital herpes—are enveloped DNA viruses that replicate in the host cell's nucleus; they acquire their envelopes from the cell's nuclear membranes. While inside the nuclei of certain nerve cells, herpesvirus DNA may remain permanently dormant, without destroying these cells. From time to time, physical stress, such as a cold or sunburn, or emotional stress may stimulate the herpesvirus DNA to begin production of the virus, which then infects cells at the body's surface and causes unpleasant symptoms.

The amount of damage a virus causes our body depends partly on how quickly our immune system responds to fight the infection and partly on the ability of the infected tissue to repair itself. We usually recover completely from colds because our respiratory tract tissue can efficiently replace damaged cells by mitosis. In contrast, the poliovirus attacks nerve cells, which are not usually replaceable. The damage to such cells, unfortunately, is permanent. In such cases, we try to prevent the disease with vaccines (see Module 24.3).

Plants, like animals, are susceptible to viral infections. Viruses that infect plants can stunt plant growth and diminish crop yields. Most known plant viruses are RNA viruses. To infect a plant, a virus must first get past the plant's outer protective layer of cells (the epidermis). Once a virus enters a plant cell and begins replicating, it can spread throughout the entire plant through plasmodesmata, the cytoplasmic connections that penetrate the walls between adjacent plant cells (see Figure 4.21). Plant viruses may spread to other plants by insects, herbivores, humans, or farming tools. As with animal viruses, there are no cures for most viral diseases of plants. Agricultural scientists focus instead on preventing infections and on breeding resistant varieties of crop plants.

▲ Figure 10.18   The replication cycle of an enveloped RNA virus

? **Explain how some viruses replicate without having DNA.**

● The genetic material of these viruses is RNA, which is replicated inside the host cell by special enzymes encoded by the virus. The viral genome (or its complement) serves as mRNA for the synthesis of viral proteins.

10.19 Emerging viruses threaten human health

EVOLUTION CONNECTION

Emerging viruses are ones that seem to burst on to the scene, becoming apparent to the medical community quite suddenly. There are many familiar examples, such as the 2009 H1N1 influenza virus (discussed in the chapter introduction). Another example is **HIV** (human immunodeficiency virus), the virus that causes **AIDS** (acquired immunodeficiency syndrome). HIV appeared in New York and California in the early 1980s, seemingly out of nowhere. Yet another example is the deadly Ebola virus, recognized initially in 1976 in central Africa; it is one of several emerging viruses that cause hemorrhagic fever, an often fatal syndrome characterized by fever, vomiting, massive bleeding, and circulatory system collapse. A number of other dangerous newly recognized viruses cause encephalitis, inflammation of the brain. One example is the West Nile virus, which appeared in North America in 1999 and has since spread to all 48 contiguous U.S. states. West Nile virus is spread primarily by mosquitoes, which carry the virus in

Why are viral diseases such a constant threat?

blood sucked from one victim and can transfer it to another victim. West Nile virus cases surged in 2012, especially in Texas. Severe acute respiratory syndrome (SARS) first appeared in China in 2002. Within eight months, about 8,000 people were infected, and 10% died. Researchers quickly identified the infectious agent as a previously unknown, single-stranded RNA coronavirus, so named for its crown-like "corona" of spikes.

How do such viruses emerge suddenly, giving rise to new diseases? And why are viral diseases so hard to eradicate? Three processes contribute to the emergence of viral diseases: mutation, contact among species, and spread from isolated populations.

The mutation of existing viruses is a major source of new viral diseases. RNA viruses tend to have unusually high rates of mutation because errors in replicating their RNA genomes are not subject to the kind of proofreading and repair mechanisms that help reduce errors in DNA replication. Some mutations change existing viruses into new strains (genetic varieties) that can cause disease in individuals who have developed immunity to ancestral strains. That is why we need yearly flu vaccines: Mutations create new influenza virus strains to which previously vaccinated people have no immunity.

New viral diseases often arise from the spread of existing viruses from one host species to another. Scientists estimate that about three-quarters of new human diseases have originated in other animals. For example, in 1997, at least 18 people in Hong Kong were infected with a strain of flu virus called H5N1, which was previously seen only in birds. A mass culling of all of Hong Kong's 1.5 million domestic

Colorized TEM 180,000×

▼ **Figure 10.19** A Hong Kong health-care worker prepares to cull a chicken to help prevent the spread of the avian flu virus (shown in the inset)

birds appeared to stop that outbreak (**Figure 10.19**). Beginning in 2002, however, new cases of human infection by this bird strain began to spread to Europe and Africa. As of 2012, the disease caused by this virus, now called "avian flu," has killed more than 300 people, and more than 100 million birds either have died from the disease or have been killed to prevent the spread of infection. The H1N1 influenza strain is another example of a virus spreading from animals to humans; after circulating among pigs for many years, a mutated form began to infect humans, creating the 2009 pandemic.

The spread of a viral disease from a small, isolated human population can also lead to widespread epidemics. For instance, AIDS went unnamed and virtually unnoticed for decades before it began to spread around the world. In this case, technological and social factors—including affordable international travel, blood transfusions, sexual practices, and the abuse of intravenous drugs—allowed a previously rare human disease to become a global scourge. If we ever manage to control HIV and other emerging viruses, that success will likely develop out of our understanding of molecular biology.

? **Why doesn't a flu shot one year give us immunity to flu in subsequent years?**

● Influenza viruses evolve rapidly by frequent mutation; thus, the strains that infect us later will most likely be different from the ones to which we've been vaccinated.

10.20 The AIDS virus makes DNA on an RNA template

HIV, the virus that causes AIDS, is an RNA virus with some special properties. In outward appearance, HIV resembles the flu or mumps virus (**Figure 10.20A**). Its membranous envelope and glycoprotein spikes enable HIV to enter and leave a host cell much the way the mumps virus does (see Figure 10.18). Notice, however, that HIV contains two identical copies of its RNA instead of one. HIV also has a different mode of replication. It is a **retrovirus**, an RNA virus that reproduces by means of a DNA molecule. Retroviruses are so named because they reverse the usual DNA → RNA flow of genetic information. These viruses carry molecules of an enzyme called **reverse transcriptase**, which catalyzes reverse transcription: the synthesis of DNA on an RNA template.

Figure 10.20B illustrates what happens after HIV RNA is uncoated in the cytoplasm of a host cell. ❶ Reverse transcriptase (⚪) uses the RNA as a template to make a DNA strand and then ❷ adds a second, complementary DNA strand. ❸ The resulting double-stranded viral DNA enters the cell's nucleus and inserts itself into the chromosomal

DNA, becoming a provirus (analogous to a prophage). The host's RNA polymerase ❹ transcribes the proviral DNA into RNA, which can then be ❺ translated by ribosomes into viral proteins. ❻ New viruses assembled from these components leave the cell and can infect other cells.

HIV infects and kills white blood cells that play important roles in the body's immune system. The loss of such cells causes the body to become susceptible to other infections that it would normally be able to fight off. Such secondary infections cause the syndrome (a collection of symptoms) that can kill an AIDS patient. (We discuss AIDS in more detail when we take up the immune system in Chapter 24.)

? **Why is HIV reverse transcriptase a good target for anti-AIDS drug therapy?**

● Reverse transcriptase is unique to HIV; we do not normally copy genetic information from RNA to DNA, so disabling reverse transcriptase would not affect a human.

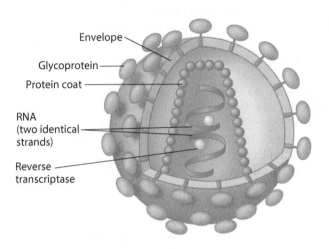

▲ Figure 10.20A   A model of HIV structure

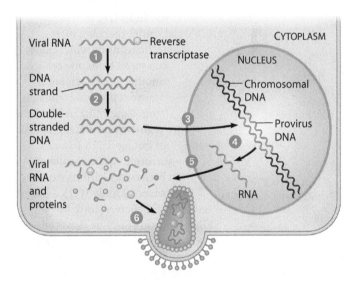

▲ Figure 10.20B   The behavior of HIV nucleic acid in a host cell

10.21 Viroids and prions are formidable pathogens in plants and animals

Viruses may be small and simple, but they are huge in comparison with another class of pathogens: viroids. **Viroids** are small, circular RNA molecules that infect plants. Unlike the nucleic acid of a virus, viroids do not encode proteins but can replicate in host plant cells, apparently using cellular enzymes. These small RNA molecules seem to interfere with regulatory systems that control plant growth. The typical signs of viroid diseases are abnormal development and stunted growth.

An important lesson to learn from viroids is that a single molecule can be an infectious agent. Viroids consist solely of nucleic acid, whose ability to be replicated is well known. Even more surprising are infectious proteins called **prions**, which cause a number of degenerative brain diseases in various animal species, including scrapie in sheep and goats, chronic wasting disease in deer and elk, mad cow disease (bovine

spongiform encephalopathy, or BSE), and Creutzfeldt-Jakob disease in humans (which is exceedingly rare).

A prion is thought to be a misfolded form of a protein normally present in brain cells. When a prion enters a cell containing the normal form of protein, the prion somehow converts the normal protein molecules to the misfolded prion versions. The abnormal proteins clump together, which may lead to loss of brain tissue (although *how* this occurs is the subject of much debate and ongoing research). There is no cure for prion diseases, and the only hope for developing effective treatments lies in understanding and preventing the process of infection.

? **What makes prions different from all other known infectious agents?**

● Prions are proteins and have no nucleic acid.

10.22 Bacteria can transfer DNA in three ways

By studying viral replication, researchers also learn about the mechanisms that regulate DNA replication and gene expression in living cells. Bacteria are equally valuable as microbial models in genetics research. As prokaryotic cells, bacteria allow researchers to investigate molecular genetics in the simplest living organisms.

Most of a bacterium's DNA is found in a single chromosome, a closed loop of DNA with associated proteins. In the diagrams here, we show the chromosome much smaller than it actually is relative to the cell. A bacterial chromosome is hundreds of times longer than its cell; it fits inside the cell because it is tightly folded.

Bacterial cells reproduce by replication of the bacterial chromosome followed by binary fission (see Module 8.2). Because binary fission is an asexual process involving only a single parent, the bacteria in a colony are genetically identical to the parental cell. But this does not mean that bacteria lack ways to produce new combinations of genes. In fact, in the bacterial world, there are three mechanisms by which genes can move from one cell to another: transformation, transduction, and conjugation. **Figure 10.22A** illustrates **transformation**, the uptake of foreign DNA from the surrounding environment.

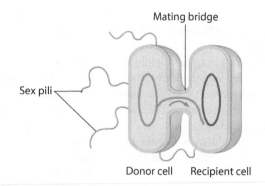

▲ **Figure 10.22C**   Conjugation

In Frederick Griffith's experiments (see Module 10.1), a harmless strain of bacteria took up pieces of DNA left over from the dead cells of a disease-causing strain. The DNA from the pathogenic bacteria carried a gene that made the cells resistant to an animal's defenses, and when the previously harmless bacteria acquired this gene and replaced its own with the pathogenic version, it caused pneumonia in infected animals.

Bacteriophages, the viruses that infect bacteria, provide the second means of bringing together genes of different bacteria. The transfer of bacterial genes by a phage is called **transduction**. During a lytic infection, when new viruses are being assembled in an infected bacterial cell, a fragment of DNA belonging to the host cell may be mistakenly packaged within the phage's coat instead of, or along with, the phage's DNA. When the phage infects a new bacterial cell, the DNA stowaway from the former host cell is injected into the new host (**Figure 10.22B**).

Figure 10.22C is an illustration of what happens at the DNA level when two bacterial cells "mate." This physical union of two bacterial cells—of the same or different species—and the

DNA transfer between them is called **conjugation**. The donor cell has hollow appendages called sex pili, one of which is attached to the recipient cell in the figure. After attachment, the pilus retracts, pulling the two cells together, much like a grappling hook. The donor then transfers DNA (light blue in the figure) to the recipient. The donor cell replicates its DNA as it transfers it, so the cell doesn't end up lacking any genes. The DNA replication is a special type that allows one copy to peel off and transfer into the recipient cell.

Once new DNA gets into a bacterial cell, by whatever mechanism, part of it may then integrate into the recipient's chromosome. As **Figure 10.22D** indicates, integration occurs by crossing over between the donor and recipient DNA molecules, a process similar to crossing over between eukaryotic chromosomes (see Module 8.17). Here we see that two crossovers result in a piece of the donated DNA replacing part of the recipient cell's original DNA. The leftover pieces of DNA are broken down and degraded, leaving the recipient bacterium with a recombinant chromosome.

As we'll see in the next module, the transfer of genetic material between bacteria has important medical consequences.

? The three modes of gene transfer between bacteria are _____, which is transfer via a virus; _____, which is the uptake of DNA from the surrounding environment; and _____, which is bacterial "mating."

transduction . . . transformation . . . conjugation

Figure 10.22A (left margin)

DNA enters cell

A fragment of DNA from another bacterial cell

Bacterial chromosome (DNA)

▲ **Figure 10.22A** Transformation

Phage

A fragment of DNA from another bacterial cell (former phage host)

▲ **Figure 10.22B** Transduction

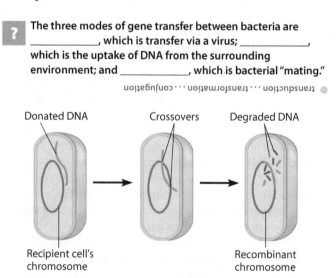

Donated DNA

Crossovers

Degraded DNA

Recipient cell's chromosome

Recombinant chromosome

▲ **Figure 10.22D**   The integration of donated DNA into the recipient cell's chromosome

10.23 Bacterial plasmids can serve as carriers for gene transfer

The ability of a donor *E. coli* cell to carry out conjugation is usually due to a specific piece of DNA called the **F factor** (F for *fertility*). The F factor carries about 25 genes for making sex pili and other requirements for conjugation; it also contains an origin of replication, where DNA replication starts.

Let's see how the F factor behaves during conjugation. In **Figure 10.23A**, the F factor (light blue) is integrated into the donor bacterium's chromosome. When this cell conjugates with a recipient cell, the donor chromosome starts replicating at the F factor's origin of replication, indicated in the figure by the blue dot on the DNA. The growing copy of the DNA peels off the chromosome and heads into the recipient cell. Thus, part of the F factor serves as the leading end of the transferred DNA, but right behind it are genes from the donor's original chromosome. The rest of the F factor stays in the donor cell. Once inside the recipient cell, the transferred donor genes can recombine with the corresponding part of the recipient chromosome by crossing over. If crossing over occurs, the recipient cell may be genetically changed, but it

Plasmids

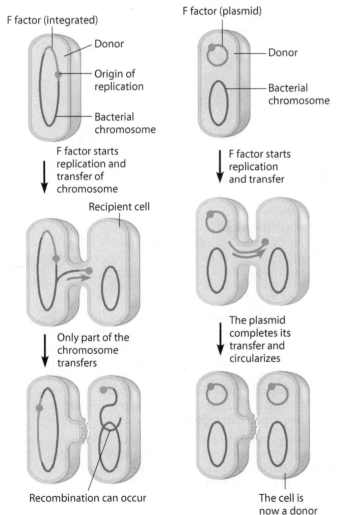

▲ **Figure 10.23C** Plasmids and part of a bacterial chromosome released from a ruptured *E. coli* cell

Colorized TEM 1,730×

4,210×

usually remains a recipient because the two cells break apart before the rest of the F factor transfers.

Alternatively, as **Figure 10.23B** shows, an F factor can exist as a **plasmid**, a small, circular DNA molecule separate from the bacterial chromosome. Every plasmid has an origin of replication, required for its replication within the cell. Some plasmids, including the F factor plasmid, can bring about conjugation and move to another cell. When the donor cell in Figure 10.23B mates with a recipient cell, the F factor replicates and at the same time transfers one whole copy of itself, in linear rather than circular form, to the recipient cell. The transferred plasmid re-forms a circle in the recipient cell, and the cell becomes a donor.

E. coli and other bacteria have many different kinds of plasmids. You can see several from one cell in **Figure 10.23C**, along with part of the bacterial chromosome, which extends in loops from the ruptured cell. Some plasmids carry genes that can affect the survival of the cell. Plasmids of one class, called **R plasmids**, pose serious problems for human medicine. Transferable R plasmids carry genes for enzymes that destroy antibiotics such as penicillin and tetracycline. Bacteria containing R plasmids are resistant (hence the designation R) to antibiotics that would otherwise kill them. The widespread use of antibiotics in medicine and agriculture has tended to kill off bacteria that lack R plasmids, whereas those with R plasmids have multiplied. As a result, an increasing number of bacteria that cause human diseases, such as food poisoning and gonorrhea, are becoming resistant to antibiotics (see Module 13.15).

We'll continue our study of molecular genetics and explore what is known about genes (see Chapter 11) and return to our discussion of plasmids (Chapter 12) in later chapters.

F factor (integrated)

Donor

Origin of replication

Bacterial chromosome

F factor starts replication and transfer of chromosome

Recipient cell

Only part of the chromosome transfers

Recombination can occur

▲ **Figure 10.23A** Transfer of chromosomal DNA by an integrated F factor

F factor (plasmid)

Donor

Bacterial chromosome

F factor starts replication and transfer

The plasmid completes its transfer and circularizes

The cell is now a donor

▲ **Figure 10.23B** Transfer of an F factor plasmid

? **Plasmids are useful tools for genetic engineering. Can you guess why?**

● Scientists can take advantage of the ability of plasmids to carry foreign genes, to replicate, and to be inherited by progeny cells.

CHAPTER 10 REVIEW

For practice quizzes, BioFlix animations, MP3 tutorials, video tutors, and more study tools designed for this textbook, go to

MasteringBiology®

Reviewing the Concepts

The Structure of the Genetic Material (10.1–10.3)

10.1 Experiments showed that DNA is the genetic material. By carefully choosing their model organism, Hershey and Chase were able to show that certain phages (bacterial viruses) reprogram host cells to produce more phages by injecting their DNA.

10.2 DNA and RNA are polymers of nucleotides.

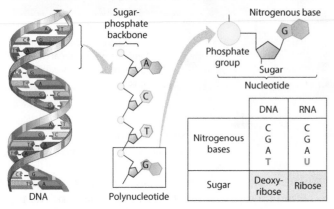

	DNA	RNA
Nitrogenous bases	C G A T	C G A U
Sugar	Deoxy-ribose	Ribose

10.3 DNA is a double-stranded helix. Watson and Crick worked out the three-dimensional structure of DNA: two polynucleotide strands wrapped around each other in a double helix. Hydrogen bonds between bases hold the strands together. Each base pairs with a complementary partner: A with T, G with C.

DNA Replication (10.4–10.5)

10.4 DNA replication depends on specific base pairing. DNA replication starts with the separation of DNA strands. Enzymes then use each strand as a template to assemble new nucleotides into a complementary strand.

10.5 DNA replication proceeds in two directions at many sites simultaneously. Using the enzyme DNA polymerase, the cell synthesizes one daughter strand as a continuous piece. The other strand is synthesized as a series of short pieces, which are then connected by the enzyme DNA ligase.

The Flow of Genetic Information from DNA to RNA to Protein (10.6–10.16)

10.6 Genes control phenotypic traits through the expression of proteins. The DNA of a gene—a linear sequence of many nucleotides—is transcribed into RNA, which is translated into a polypeptide.

10.7 Genetic information written in codons is translated into amino acid sequences. Codons are base triplets.

10.8 The genetic code dictates how codons are translated into amino acids. Nearly all organisms use an identical genetic code to convert the mRNA codons transcribed from a gene to the amino acid sequence of a polypeptide.

10.9 Transcription produces genetic messages in the form of RNA. In the nucleus, the DNA helix unzips, and RNA nucleotides line up and hydrogen-bond along one strand of the DNA, following the base-pairing rules.

10.10 Eukaryotic RNA is processed before leaving the nucleus as mRNA. Noncoding segments of RNA (introns) are spliced out, and a cap and tail are added to the ends of the mRNA.

10.11 Transfer RNA molecules serve as interpreters during translation. Translation takes place in the cytoplasm. A ribosome attaches to the mRNA and translates its message into a specific polypeptide, aided by transfer RNAs (tRNAs). Each tRNA is a folded molecule bearing a base triplet called an anticodon on one end and a specific amino acid attachment site at the other end.

10.12 Ribosomes build polypeptides. Made of rRNA and proteins, ribosomes have binding sites for tRNAs and mRNA.

10.13 An initiation codon marks the start of an mRNA message.

10.14 Elongation adds amino acids to the polypeptide chain until a stop codon terminates translation. As the mRNA moves one codon at a time relative to the ribosome, a tRNA with a complementary anticodon pairs with each codon, adding its amino acid to the growing polypeptide chain.

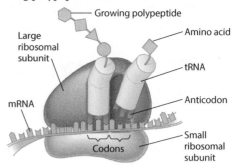

10.15 Review: The flow of genetic information in the cell is DNA → RNA → protein. The sequence of codons in DNA, via the sequence of codons in mRNA, spells out the primary structure of a polypeptide.

10.16 Mutations can affect genes. Mutations are changes in the genetic information of a cell, caused by errors in DNA replication or recombination, or by mutagens. Substituting, inserting, or deleting nucleotides alters a gene, with varying effects.

The Genetics of Viruses and Bacteria (10.17–10.23)

10.17 Viral DNA may become part of the host chromosome. Viruses are infectious particles that contain genes packaged in protein. When phage DNA enters a lytic cycle inside a bacterium, it is replicated, transcribed, and translated; the new viral DNA and protein molecules then assemble into new phages, which burst from the host cell. In the lysogenic cycle, phage DNA inserts into the host chromosome and is passed on to generations of daughter cells. Later, it may initiate phage production.

10.18 Many viruses cause disease in animals and plants. Flu viruses and most plant viruses have RNA, rather than DNA, as their genetic material. Some animal viruses steal a bit of host cell membrane as a protective envelope.

10.19 Emerging viruses threaten human health.

10.20 The AIDS virus makes DNA on an RNA template. HIV is a retrovirus: It uses RNA as a template for making DNA, which then inserts into a host chromosome.

10.21 Viroids and prions are formidable pathogens in plants and animals. Viroids are RNA molecules that can infect plants. Prions are infectious proteins that can cause brain diseases in animals.

10.22 Bacteria can transfer DNA in three ways. Bacteria can transfer genes from cell to cell by transformation, transduction, or conjugation.

10.23 Bacterial plasmids can serve as carriers for gene transfer. Plasmids are small, circular DNA molecules separate from the bacterial chromosome.

Connecting the Concepts

1. Check your understanding of the flow of genetic information through a cell by filling in the blanks.

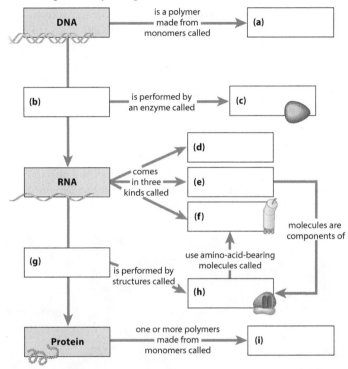

Testing Your Knowledge

Level 1: Knowledge/Comprehension

2. Which of the following correctly ranks the structures in order of size, from largest to smallest?
   a. gene-chromosome-nucleotide-codon
   b. chromosome-gene-codon-nucleotide
   c. nucleotide-chromosome-gene-codon
   d. chromosome-nucleotide-gene-codon
3. Describe the process of DNA replication: the ingredients needed, the steps in the process, and the final product.
4. What is the name of the process that produces RNA from a DNA template? What is the name of the process that produces a polypeptide from an RNA template?

Level 2: Application/Analysis

5. Scientists have discovered how to put together a bacteriophage with the protein coat of phage T2 and the DNA of phage lambda. If this composite phage were allowed to infect a bacterium, the phages produced in the host cell would have _____. (*Explain your answer.*)
   a. the protein of T2 and the DNA of lambda
   b. the protein of lambda and the DNA of T2

c. the protein and DNA of T2
d. the protein and DNA of lambda

6. A geneticist found that a particular mutation had no effect on the polypeptide encoded by a gene. This mutation probably involved
   a. deletion of one nucleotide.
   b. alteration of the start codon.
   c. insertion of one nucleotide.
   d. substitution of one nucleotide.
7. Describe the process by which the information in a eukaryotic gene is transcribed and translated into a protein. Correctly use these words in your description: tRNA, amino acid, start codon, transcription, RNA splicing, exons, introns, mRNA, gene, codon, RNA polymerase, ribosome, translation, anticodon, peptide bond, stop codon.

Level 3: Synthesis/Evaluation

8. The nucleotide sequence of a DNA codon is GTA. A messenger RNA molecule with a complementary codon is transcribed from the DNA. In the process of protein synthesis, a transfer RNA pairs with the mRNA codon. What is the nucleotide sequence of the tRNA anticodon?
   a. CAT
   b. CUT
   c. GUA
   d. CAU
9. A cell containing a single chromosome is placed in a medium containing radioactive phosphate so that any new DNA strands formed by DNA replication will be radioactive. The cell replicates its DNA and divides. Then the daughter cells (still in the radioactive medium) replicate their DNA and divide, and a total of four cells are present. Sketch the DNA molecules in all four cells, showing a normal (nonradioactive) DNA strand as a solid line and a radioactive DNA strand as a dashed line.
10. The base sequence of the gene coding for a short polypeptide is CTACGCTAGGCGATTGACT. What would be the base sequence of the mRNA transcribed from this gene? Using the genetic code in Figure 10.8A, give the amino acid sequence of the polypeptide translated from this mRNA. (*Hint*: What is the start codon?)
11. Researchers working on the Human Genome Project have determined the nucleotide sequences of human genes and in many cases identified the proteins encoded by the genes. Knowledge of the nucleotide sequences of genes might be used to develop lifesaving medicines or treatments for genetic defects. In the United States, both government agencies and biotechnology companies have applied for patents on their discoveries of genes. In Britain, the courts have ruled that a naturally occurring gene cannot be patented. Do you think individuals and companies should be able to patent genes and gene products? Before answering, consider the following: What are the purposes of a patent? How might the discoverer of a gene benefit from a patent? How might the public benefit? What might be some positive and negative results of patenting genes?
12. **SCIENTIFIC THINKING** The success of an experiment often depends on choosing an appropriate organism to study. For example, Gregor Mendel was able to deduce the fundamental principles in genetics in part because of his choice of the pea plant. What properties of bacteriophage T2 allowed Hershey and Chase (Module 10.1) to identify DNA as the genetic materials in their famous experiment?

Answers to all questions can be found in Appendix 4.

11 How Genes Are Controlled

? *Can life be rebooted?*

E ven in a world in which cloning has become routine, the case of the baby banteng stands out. The Java banteng (*Bos javanicus*), shown below, is an endangered species of cattle native to Indonesia. Hunting and habitat destruction have reduced their wild population to just a few thousand.

Scientists obtained banteng skin tissue from "The Frozen Zoo," a facility in San Diego, California, where samples from rare or endangered animals are stored for conservation. Researchers inserted nuclei from these frozen skin cells into nucleus-free eggs from domestic beef cattle. The resulting embryos were implanted into surrogate domestic cows. Months later, two bantengs were born via Caesarian section, but one had to be euthanized within days. The other banteng survived, and as of 2013, remains a healthy inhabitant of the San Diego Zoo.

Although cloning mammals is now commonplace, one startling fact about the banteng makes this case unique: *The banteng that was cloned had died more than 20 years earlier.* Not only did this undertaking make the banteng the first successfully cloned endangered animal, it also demonstrated for the first time that well-preserved animals that have been dead for decades may be cloned using

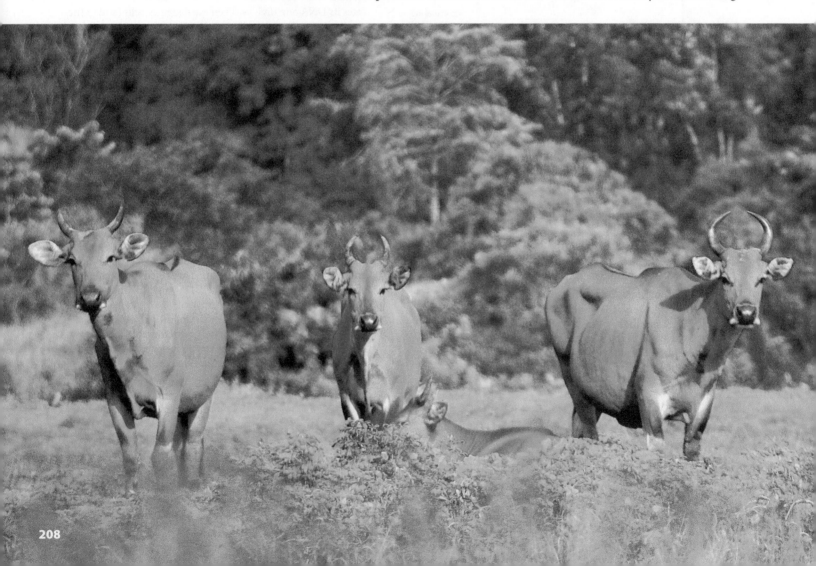

closely related animals as surrogates. Biologists hope that such efforts may increase the populations of threatened species or even recently extinct species.

How can a single cell be "rebooted" to develop into an entire organism? To be successful, the starting cell must contain a complete set of genes capable of directing the production of all the cell types in an organism. The development of different types of cells must therefore depend on turning on and off different genes in different cells—the control of gene expression.

We begin this chapter with examples of how and where cells may alter their patterns of gene expression. Next we look at the methods and applications of plant and animal cloning. Finally, we discuss cancer, a disease that can be caused by changes in gene expression.

BIG IDEAS

Control of Gene Expression
(11.1–11.11)

Cells can turn genes on and off through a variety of mechanisms.

Cloning of Plants and Animals
(11.12–11.14)

Cloning demonstrates that many body cells retain their full genetic potential.

The Genetic Basis of Cancer
(11.15–11.18)

Changes in genes that control gene expression can lead to out-of-control cell growth.

▷ Control of Gene Expression

11.1 Proteins interacting with DNA turn prokaryotic genes on or off in response to environmental changes

Picture an *Escherichia coli* (*E. coli*) bacterium living in your intestine (**Figure 11.1A**). Its environment changes continuously, depending on your dietary whims. For example, if you eat a sweet roll for breakfast, the bacterium will be bathed in sugars and broken-down fats. Later, if you have a salad for lunch, the *E. coli*'s environment will change drastically. How can a bacterium cope with such a constantly shifting flow of resources?

The answer is that **gene regulation**—the turning on and off of genes—can help organisms respond to environmental changes. What does it mean to turn a gene on or off? Genes determine the nucleotide sequences of specific messenger RNA (mRNA) molecules (as we saw in Chapter 10), and mRNA in turn determines the sequences of amino acids in protein molecules (DNA → RNA → protein). Thus, a gene that is turned on is being transcribed into mRNA, and that message is being translated into specific protein molecules. The overall process by which genetic information flows from genes to proteins—that is, from genotype to phenotype—is called **gene expression**. The control of gene expression makes it possible for cells to produce specific kinds of proteins when and where they are needed.

Let's think back to our example of a bacterium living in your digestive system. It's no coincidence that we used *E. coli* as our example. Our earliest understanding of gene control came from studies of this bacterium by French biologists François Jacob and Jacques Monod. *E. coli* has a remarkable ability to change its metabolic activities in response to changes in its environment. For example, *E. coli* produces enzymes needed to metabolize a specific nutrient only when that nutrient is available. Bacterial cells that can conserve resources and energy have an advantage over cells that are unable to do so. Thus, natural selection has favored bacteria that express only the genes whose products are needed by the cell. Let's look at how the regulation of gene transcription helps *E. coli* efficiently use available resources.

The *lac* Operon   Imagine the bacterium in your intestine soon after you drink a glass of milk. One of the main nutrients in milk is the disaccharide sugar lactose. When lactose is plentiful in the intestine, *E. coli* makes the enzymes necessary to absorb the sugar and use it as an energy source. Conversely, when lactose is not plentiful, *E. coli* does not waste its energy producing these enzymes.

Recall that most enzymes are proteins; their production is an outcome of gene expression. *E. coli* can make

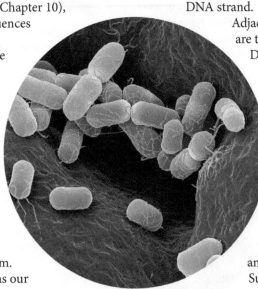

▲ **Figure 11.1A**   Cells of *E. coli* bacteria

lactose-utilization enzymes because it has genes that code for these enzymes. **Figure 11.1B** presents a model (first proposed in 1961 by Jacob and Monod) to explain how an *E. coli* cell can turn genes coding for lactose-utilization enzymes off or on, depending on whether lactose is available.

E. coli uses three enzymes to take up and start metabolizing lactose, and the genes coding for these three enzymes are regulated as a single unit. The DNA at the top of Figure 11.1B represents a small segment of the bacterium's chromosome. Notice that the three genes that code for the lactose-utilization enzymes (light blue) are situated next to each other along the DNA strand.

Adjacent to the group of lactose enzyme genes are two control sequences, short sections of DNA that help control the expression of these genes. One control sequence is a **promoter**, a site where the transcription enzyme, RNA polymerase, attaches and initiates transcription—in this case, transcription of all three lactose enzyme genes (as depicted in the bottom panel of Figure 11.1B). Between the promoter and the enzyme genes, a DNA control sequence called an **operator** acts as a switch. The operator determines whether RNA polymerase can attach to the promoter and start transcribing the genes.

Such a cluster of genes with related functions, along with the control sequences—in this instance, the entire stretch of DNA required for enzyme production—is called an **operon**; with rare exceptions, operons exist only in prokaryotes. The key advantage to the grouping of related genes into operons is that a single "on-off" switch can control the whole cluster. The operon discussed here is called the *lac* operon, short for lactose operon. When an *E. coli* bacterium encounters lactose, all the enzymes needed for its metabolism are made at once because the operon's genes are all controlled by a single switch, the operator. But what determines whether the operator switch is on or off?

The top panel of Figure 11.1B shows the *lac* operon in "off" mode, its status when there is no lactose in the cell's environment. Transcription is turned off because a protein called a **repressor** ( ) binds to the operator (▬) and physically blocks the attachment of RNA polymerase (◖) to the promoter (▬). On the left side of the figure, you can see where the repressor comes from. A gene called a **regulatory gene** (dark blue), located outside the operon, codes for the repressor. The regulatory gene is expressed continually, so the cell always has a small supply of repressor molecules.

Operon turned off (lactose is absent):

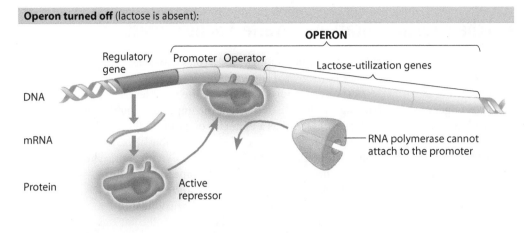

Operon turned on (lactose inactivates the repressor):

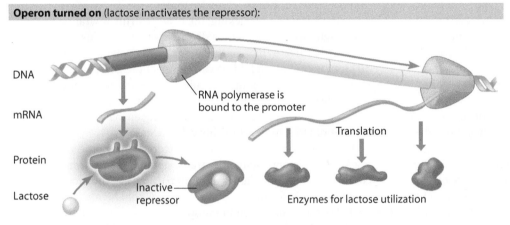

▲ **Figure 11.1B** The *lac* operon

Try This Compare the structure and function of the *lac* repressor protein when lactose is absent (top) and present (bottom).

How can an operon be turned on if its repressor is always present? As the bottom panel of Figure 11.1B indicates, lactose (⚪) interferes with the attachment of the *lac* repressor to the operator by binding to the repressor and changing its shape. With its new shape (⬮), the repressor cannot bind to the operator, and the operator switch remains on. RNA polymerase is then able to bind to the promoter (because it is no longer being blocked) and from there transcribes the genes of the operon. The resulting mRNA carries coding sequences for all three enzymes needed for lactose metabolism. The cell can translate the message in this single mRNA into three separate polypeptides because the mRNA has multiple codons signaling the start and stop of translation.

The *lac* operon is so efficient that the addition of lactose to a bacterium's environment results in a thousandfold increase in lactose utilization enzymes in just 15 minutes. The newly produced mRNA and protein molecules will remain intact for only a short time before cellular enzymes break them down. When the synthesis of mRNA and protein stops because lactose is no longer present, the existing molecules are quickly degraded.

Other Kinds of Operons The *lac* operon is an example of an inducible operon (**Figure 11.1C**, left), one that is usually turned off but can be stimulated (induced) by a molecule—in this case, by lactose. Such operons usually operate as part of a pathway that breaks down a nutrient to simpler molecules. By producing the digestive enzymes only when the nutrient is available, the cell avoids wasting resources. A second type of operon, represented here by the *trp* operon, is called a repressible operon, because it is normally turned on but can be inhibited (repressed) when a specific molecule is present in abundance. In our example, the molecule is tryptophan (Trp), an amino acid essential for protein synthesis. *E. coli* can make tryptophan from scratch, using enzymes encoded in the *trp* operon. But *E. coli* will stop making tryptophan and simply absorb it from the surroundings whenever possible. When *E. coli* is bathed in tryptophan in the intestines (as occurs when you eat foods such as milk and poultry), the tryptophan binds to the repressor of the *trp* operon. This activates the *trp* repressor, enabling it to switch off the operon. Thus, this type of operon allows bacteria to stop making certain essential molecules when the molecules are already present in the environment, saving materials and energy for the cells.

Another type of operon control involves **activators**, proteins that turn operons *on* by binding to DNA and stimulating gene transcription. Activator proteins act by making it easier for RNA polymerase to bind to the promoter, rather than by blocking RNA polymerase, as repressors do. Activators help control a wide variety of operons.

Armed with a variety of operons regulated by repressors and activators, *E. coli* and other prokaryotes can thrive in frequently changing environments. Next we examine how more complex eukaryotes regulate their genes.

? A certain mutation in *E. coli* impairs the ability of the *lac* repressor to bind to the *lac* operator. How would this affect the cell?

● The cell would wastefully produce the enzymes for lactose metabolism continuously, even when lactose is not present.

lac operon (inducible)	*trp* operon (repressible)
DNA · Promoter Operator Gene · Active repressor	Active repressor · Tryptophan
Inactive repressor · Lactose	Inactive repressor

▲ **Figure 11.1C** Two types of repressor-controlled operons

11.2 Chromosome structure and chemical modifications can affect gene expression

The cells of all organisms, whether prokaryotes or eukaryotes, must be able to turn genes on and off in response to signals from their external and internal environments. All multicellular eukaryotes also require an additional level of gene control: During the repeated cell divisions that lead from a zygote to an adult in a multicellular organism, individual cells must undergo **differentiation**—that is, they must become specialized in structure and function, with each type of cell fulfilling a distinct role. Your body, for example, contains hundreds of different types of cells. What makes a kidney cell different from, say, a bone cell?

To perform its specialized role, each cell type must maintain a specific program of gene expression in which some genes are expressed and others are not. Almost all the cells in an organism contain an identical genome, yet the subset of genes expressed in each cell type is unique, reflecting its specific function. Each adult human cell expresses only a small fraction of its total genes at any given time. And even one particular cell type can change its pattern of gene expression over time in response to developmental signals or other changes in the environment.

The differences between cell types, therefore, are not due to different genes being present but instead due to selective gene expression. In this module, we begin our exploration of gene regulation in eukaryotes by looking at the structure of chromosomes.

DNA Packing   The DNA of each human chromosome is thousands of times longer than the diameter of the nucleus. All of this DNA can fit within the nucleus because of an elaborate, multilevel system of packing, coiling, and folding. A crucial aspect of DNA packing is the association of the DNA with small proteins called **histones**. In fact, histone proteins account for about half the mass of eukaryotic chromosomes. (Prokaryotes have analogous proteins, but lack the degree of DNA packing seen in eukaryotes.)

Figure 11.2A shows a model for the main levels of DNA packing. At the left, notice that the unpacked double-helical molecule of DNA has a diameter of 2 nm. At the first level of packing, histones attach to the DNA double helix. In the electron micrograph near the top left of the figure, notice how the DNA-histone complex has the appearance of beads on a string. Each "bead," called a **nucleosome**, consists of DNA wound around a protein core of eight histone molecules. Short stretches of DNA, called linkers, are the "strings" that join consecutive "beads" of nucleosomes.

At the next level of packing, the beaded string is wrapped into a tight helical fiber with a diameter of 30 nm. This fiber coils further into a thick supercoil with a diameter of about 300 nm. Looping and folding can compact the DNA even more, as you can see in the metaphase chromosome on the right side of the figure. Figure 11.2A gives an overview of how successive levels of coiling and folding enable a huge amount of DNA to fit into a tiny cell nucleus.

DNA packing tends to block gene expression by preventing RNA polymerase and other transcription proteins from contacting the DNA. Higher levels of packing can therefore inactivate genes for the long term. Genes within highly compacted chromatin, as seen in mitotic chromosomes—such as the duplicated chromosome shown on the right side of the figure—and in varying regions of interphase chromosomes are generally not expressed at all.

Chemical Modifications and Epigenetic Inheritance   Eukaryotic chromosomes can be chemically modified in ways that help regulate gene expression. For example, the addition of methyl (CH_3) groups to some of the amino acids in histone proteins can cause the chromosomes to become more

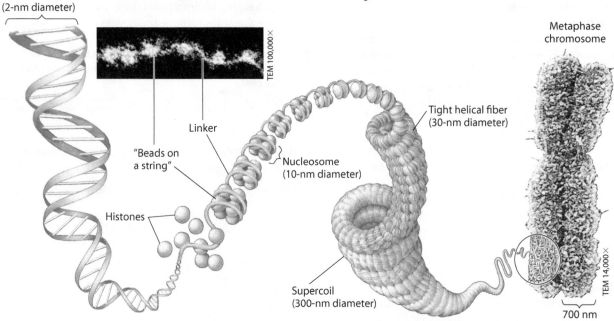

DNA double helix
(2-nm diameter)

TEM 100,000×

Linker

"Beads on
a string"

Histones

Nucleosome
(10-nm diameter)

Tight helical fiber
(30-nm diameter)

Supercoil
(300-nm diameter)

Metaphase
chromosome

TEM 14,000×

700 nm

▲ Figure 11.2A   DNA packing in a eukaryotic chromosome

compact, leading to reduced transcription. Conversely, adding acetyl groups (—COCH$_3$) opens up the chromatin structure, promoting transcription.

DNA can also be chemically modified. For example, certain enzymes add a methyl group to DNA bases, usually cytosine, without changing the actual sequence of the bases. Individual genes are usually more heavily methylated in cells in which they are not expressed, and removing the extra methyl groups can turn on some of these genes. Thus, DNA methylation appears to play a role in turning genes off. At least in some species, DNA methylation seems to be essential for the long-term inactivation of genes. Such modifications are a normal and necessary mechanism for the regulation of gene expression, and improper methylation can lead to problems for the organism. For example, insufficient DNA methylation can lead to abnormal embryonic development in many species.

Once methylated, genes usually stay that way through successive cell divisions in a given individual. During replication, when a methylated stretch of DNA is duplicated, enzymes methylate the corresponding daughter strands to match. Methylation patterns are therefore passed on, allowing cells that form specialized tissues to keep a chemical record of what occurred during embryonic development. Thus, modifications to DNA and histones can be passed along to future generations of cells—that is, they can be inherited. Inheritance of traits transmitted by mechanisms not directly involving the nucleotide sequence is called **epigenetic inheritance**. Whereas mutations in the DNA are permanent changes, modifications to the chromatin, which do not affect the sequence of DNA itself, can be reversed by processes that are not yet fully understood.

Researchers are amassing more evidence for the importance of epigenetic information in the regulation of gene expression. Epigenetic variations might help explain differences in identical twins. For example, it is often the case that one identical twin acquires a genetically influenced disease, such as schizophrenia, but the other does not, despite their identical genomes. Researchers suspect that epigenetics may be behind such differences. Alterations in normal patterns of DNA methylation are seen in some cancers, where they are associated with inappropriate gene expression. Evidently, enzymes that modify chromatin structure are integral parts of the eukaryotic cell's machinery for regulating transcription.

X Inactivation Gene regulation sometimes occurs at the whole chromosome level. For example, female mammals (including humans) inherit two X chromosomes, whereas males inherit only one. So why don't females make twice as much of the proteins encoded by genes on the X chromosome compared to the amounts in males? It turns out that in female mammals, one X chromosome in each somatic (body) cell is chemically modified and highly compacted, rendering it almost entirely inactive. Inactivation of an X chromosome involves modification of the DNA (by, for example, methylation) and the histone proteins that help compact it. A specific gene on the X chromosomes ensures that only one of them will be inactivated. This **X chromosome inactivation** is initiated early in embryonic development, when one of the two X chromosomes in each cell is inactivated at random. As a result, the cells of females and males have the same effective dose (one copy) of these genes. The inactive X in each cell of a female condenses into a compact object called a **Barr body**.

Which X chromosome is inactivated is a matter of chance in each embryonic cell, but once an X chromosome is inactivated, all descendant cells have the same copy turned off—an example of epigenetic inheritance. Consequently, females consist of a mosaic of two types of cells: those with the active X derived from the father and those with the active X derived from the mother. If a female is heterozygous for a gene on the X chromosome (a sex-linked gene; see Module 9.21), about half her cells will express one allele, while the others will express the alternate allele.

A striking example of this mosaic phenomenon is the tortoiseshell cat, which has orange and black patches of fur (Figure 11.2B). The relevant fur-color gene is on the X chromosome, and the tortoiseshell phenotype requires the presence of two different alleles, one for orange fur and one for black fur. Normally, only females can have both alleles because only they have two X chromosomes. If a female is heterozygous for the tortoiseshell gene, she will have the tortoiseshell phenotype. Orange patches are formed by populations of cells in which the X chromosome with the orange allele is active; black patches have cells in which the X chromosome with the black allele is active.

In this module, we have seen how the physical structure of chromosomes can affect which genes are expressed in a cell. In the next module, we discuss mechanisms for regulating genes in active, unpacked chromosomes.

? In your body, a nerve cell has a very different structure and performs very different functions than a skin cell. Because the two cell types have the same genes, how can the cells be so different?

Early Embryo

X chromosomes

Cell division and random X chromosome inactivation

Allele for orange fur   Allele for black fur

Adult

Two cell populations

Active X
Inactive X
Orange fur

Inactive X
Active X
Black fur

▲ **Figure 11.2B**   A tortoiseshell pattern on a female cat, a result of X chromosome inactivation

● Each cell type must be expressing certain genes that are present in, but not expressed in, the other cell type.

11.3 Complex assemblies of proteins control eukaryotic transcription

The process of packing and unpacking of chromosomal DNA provides a coarse adjustment for eukaryotic gene expression by making a region of DNA either more or less available for transcription, the synthesis of RNA. The fine-tuning begins with the initiation of transcription. In both prokaryotes and eukaryotes, the initiation of transcription (whether transcription starts or not) is the most important stage for regulating gene expression.

Like prokaryotes (see Module 11.1), eukaryotes use regulatory proteins—activators and repressors—that bind to specific segments of DNA and either promote or block the binding of RNA polymerase, turning the transcription of genes on or off. However, most eukaryotic genes have individual promoters and other control sequences and are not clustered together as in operons.

The current model for the initiation of eukaryotic transcription features an intricate array of regulatory proteins that interact with DNA and with one another to turn genes on or off. In eukaryotes, activator proteins seem to be more important than repressors. A typical animal or plant cell needs to turn on (transcribe) only a small percentage of its genes, those required for the cell's specialized structure and function. Therefore, in multicellular eukaryotes, the "default" state for most genes seems to be "off." Important exceptions include housekeeping genes, those continually active in virtually all cells for routine activities such as glycolysis, which may be in an "on" state by default.

To function, eukaryotic RNA polymerase requires the assistance of proteins called **transcription factors**. In the model depicted in **Figure 11.3**, the first step in initiating gene transcription is the binding of activator proteins ( ) to DNA control sequences called **enhancers** ( ). In contrast to the operators found within prokaryotic operons, enhancers are usually located far away on the chromosome from the gene they help regulate. Next, a DNA-bending protein brings the bound activators closer to the promoter. Once the DNA is bent, the bound activators interact with other transcription factor proteins ( ), which then bind as a complex at the gene's promoter ( ). This large assembly of proteins facilitates the correct attachment of RNA polymerase to the promoter and the initiation of transcription. Only when the complete complex of proteins has assembled can the polymerase begin to move along the gene, producing an RNA strand. As shown in the figure, multiple enhancers and activators may be involved in turning on a single gene.

▲ **Figure 11.3**　A model for the turning on of a eukaryotic gene

Try This　Explain how enhancer sequences can promote transcription of a gene that is located far away on the DNA molecule.

Genes coding for the enzymes of a metabolic pathway are often scattered across different chromosomes. How can a eukaryotic cell turn on or off all functionally related genes at the same time? The key to coordinated gene expression in eukaryotes is often the association of a specific combination of control sequences with every gene of a particular metabolic pathway. Copies of the activators that recognize these control sequences bind to them all at once (because they are all identical), promoting simultaneous transcription of the genes, no matter where they are in the genome. In the next module, we consider another method of gene regulation that is unique to eukaryotes.

> **?**　What must occur before RNA polymerase can bind to a promoter and transcribe a specific eukaryotic gene?

● Transcription factors must bind to enhancers to facilitate the attachment of RNA polymerase to the promoter.

11.4 Eukaryotic RNA may be spliced in more than one way

Although regulation of transcription is the most important step in gene regulation in most cells, transcription alone does not equal gene expression. Several other points along the path from DNA to protein can be regulated. Within a eukaryotic cell, for example, RNA transcripts are processed into mRNA before moving to the cytoplasm for translation by the ribosomes. RNA processing includes the addition of a cap and a tail, as well as the removal of any introns—noncoding DNA segments that interrupt the genetic message—and the splicing together of the remaining exons (see Module 10.10).

Some scientists hypothesize that the splicing process may help control the flow of mRNA from nucleus to cytoplasm because until splicing is completed, the RNA is attached to the molecules of the splicing machinery and cannot pass through the nuclear pores. Moreover, in some cases, the cell can carry out splicing in more than one way, generating different mRNA molecules from the same RNA transcript. Notice in **Figure 11.4**, for example, that one mRNA molecule ends up with the green exon and the other with the brown exon. With this sort of **alternative RNA splicing**, an organism can produce more than one type of polypeptide from a single gene.

One interesting example of two-way splicing is found in the *Drosophila* fruit fly, where the differences between males and females are largely due to different patterns of RNA splicing. In addition, researchers have found a gene in *Drosophila* that, through the alternate splicing of many exons, produces more than 17,500 proteins, each of which is found in the membrane of a different nerve cell where it acts as an identification marker. In humans, more than 90% of protein-coding genes appear to undergo alternate splicing.

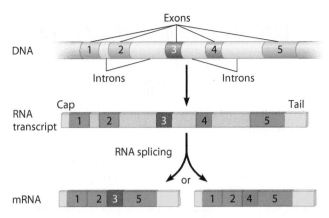

▲ **Figure 11.4**   The production of two different mRNAs from the same gene

?   **How is it possible that just under 21,000 human genes can produce more than 100,000 polypeptides?**

● Through alternate splicing: Each kind of polypeptide is encoded by an mRNA molecule containing a different combination of exons.

11.5 Small RNAs play multiple roles in controlling gene expression

Genome research has revealed that only 1.5% of the human genome—and a similarly small percentage of the genomes of many other multicellular eukaryotes—codes for proteins. Another very small fraction of DNA consists of genes for ribosomal RNA and transfer RNA. Until recently, most of the remaining DNA was thought to be untranscribed and therefore considered to be lacking any genetic information. However, a flood of recent data has contradicted this view. It turns out that a significant amount of the genome is transcribed into functioning but non–protein-coding RNAs, including a variety of small RNAs. Although many questions about the functions of these RNAs remain unanswered, researchers are uncovering more evidence of their biological roles every day.

In 1993, researchers discovered small RNA molecules, called **microRNAs (miRNAs)**, that can bind to complementary sequences on mRNA molecules (**Figure 11.5**). Each miRNA, typically about 22 nucleotides long, ❶ forms a complex with one or more proteins. The miRNA-protein complex can ❷ bind to any mRNA molecule with 7 to 8 nucleotides of complementary sequence. ❸ Then the complex either degrades the target mRNA or blocks its translation. It has been estimated that miRNAs may regulate the expression of at least one-half of all human genes, a striking figure given that miRNAs were unknown 20 years ago.

Researchers can take advantage of miRNA to artificially control gene expression. For example, injecting miRNA into a cell can turn off expression of a gene with a sequence that matches the miRNA, a procedure called **RNA interference (RNAi)**. The RNAi pathway may have evolved as a natural defense against infection by certain viruses with RNA genomes (see Chapter 10). In 2006, two American researchers were awarded a Nobel Prize for their discovery and categorization of RNA interference.

Biologists are excited about these recent discoveries, which hint at a large, diverse population of RNA molecules in the cell that play crucial roles in regulating gene expression—and have gone largely unnoticed until very recently. Our new understanding may lead to important clinical applications. For example, in 2009, researchers discovered a particular miRNA that is essential for the proper functioning of the pancreas. Without it, insulin-producing beta cells die, which can lead to diabetes.

?   **If a gene has the sequence AATTCGCG, what would be the sequence of an miRNA that turns off the gene?**

● The gene will be transcribed as the mRNA sequence UUAAGCGC; an miRNA of sequence AAUUCGCG would bind to and disable this mRNA.

▲ **Figure 11.5**   Mechanisms of RNA interference

11.6 Later stages of gene expression are also subject to regulation

Even after a eukaryotic mRNA is fully processed and transported to the cytoplasm, there are several additional opportunities for regulation. Such control points include mRNA breakdown, initiation of translation, protein activation, and protein breakdown.

Breakdown of mRNA   Molecules of mRNA do not remain intact forever. Enzymes in the cytoplasm eventually break them down, and the timing of this event is an important factor regulating the amounts of various proteins that are produced in the cell. Long-lived mRNAs can be translated into many more protein molecules than short-lived ones. Prokaryotic mRNAs have very short lifetimes; they are typically degraded by enzymes within a few minutes after their synthesis. This is one reason bacteria can change their protein production so quickly in response to environmental changes. In contrast, the mRNAs of eukaryotes have lifetimes from hours to weeks.

A striking example of long-lived mRNA is found in vertebrate red blood cells, which manufacture large quantities of the protein hemoglobin. In most species of vertebrates, the mRNAs for hemoglobin are unusually stable. They probably last as long as the red blood cells that contain them—about a month or a bit longer in reptiles, amphibians, and fishes—and are translated again and again. Mammals are an exception. When their red blood cells mature, they lose their ribosomes (along with their other organelles) and thus cease to make new hemoglobin. However, mammalian hemoglobin itself lasts about as long as the red blood cells last: around four months.

Initiation of Translation   The process of translating an mRNA into a polypeptide also offers opportunities for regulation. Among the molecules involved in translation are a great many proteins that control the start of polypeptide synthesis. Red blood cells, for instance, have an inhibitory protein that prevents translation of hemoglobin mRNA unless the cell has a supply of heme, the iron-containing chemical group essential for hemoglobin function. (It is the iron atom of the heme group to which oxygen molecules actually attach.) By controlling the start of protein synthesis, cells can avoid wasting energy if the needed components are currently unavailable.

Protein Activation   After translation is complete, some polypeptides require alterations before they become functional. Post-translational control mechanisms in eukaryotes often involve the cleavage (cutting) of a polypeptide to yield a smaller final product that is the active protein, able to carry out a specific function in the organism. In **Figure 11.6**, we see the example of the protein hormone insulin. Insulin is synthesized in the cells of the pancreas as one long polypeptide that has no hormonal activity. After translation is completed, the polypeptide folds up, and covalent bonds form between the sulfur (S) atoms of sulfur-containing amino acids (see Figure 3.12A, which shows S—S bonds in another protein). Two H atoms are lost as each S—S bond forms, linking together parts of the polypeptide in a specific way. Finally, a large center portion is cut away, leaving two shorter chains held together by the sulfur linkages. This combination of two shorter polypeptides is the form of insulin that functions as a hormone. By controlling the timing of such protein modifications, the rate of insulin synthesis can be fine-tuned.

Protein Breakdown   The final control mechanism operating after translation is the selective breakdown of proteins. Although mammalian hemoglobin may last as long as the red blood cell housing it, the lifetimes of many other proteins are closely regulated. Some of the proteins that trigger metabolic changes in cells are broken down within a few minutes or hours. This regulation allows a cell to adjust the kinds and amounts of its proteins in response to changes in its environment. It also enables the cell to maintain its proteins in prime working order. Indeed, when proteins are damaged, they are usually broken down right away and replaced by new ones that function properly.

Over the last five modules, you have learned about several ways that eukaryotes can control gene expression. The next module summarizes all of these processes.

> **?** Review Figure 11.6. If the enzyme responsible for cleaving inactive insulin is deactivated, what effect will this have on the form and function of insulin?
>
> The final molecule will have a shape different from that of active insulin and therefore will not be able to function as a hormone.

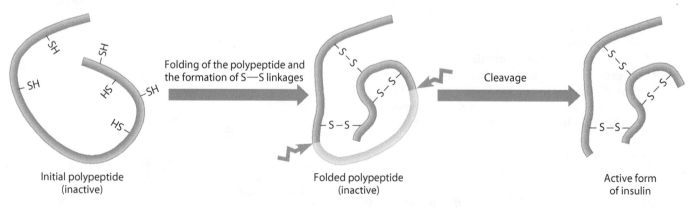

Initial polypeptide (inactive) → Folding of the polypeptide and the formation of S—S linkages → Folded polypeptide (inactive) → Cleavage → Active form of insulin

▲ **Figure 11.6**   Protein activation: the role of polypeptide cleavage in producing the active insulin protein

11.7 Multiple mechanisms regulate gene expression in eukaryotes

This summary of eukaryotic gene expression highlights the multiple control points where the process can be turned on or off, speeded up, or slowed down. Although many control points are shown, only a few of them may be important for any particular protein.

Picture the pipes that carry water from a reservoir to your faucet. At various points, valves control the flow. Similarly, genetic information flows from a chromosome—a reservoir of genetic information—through several control points (shown as valves and described in the blue ovals) to an active protein in the cell's cytoplasm.

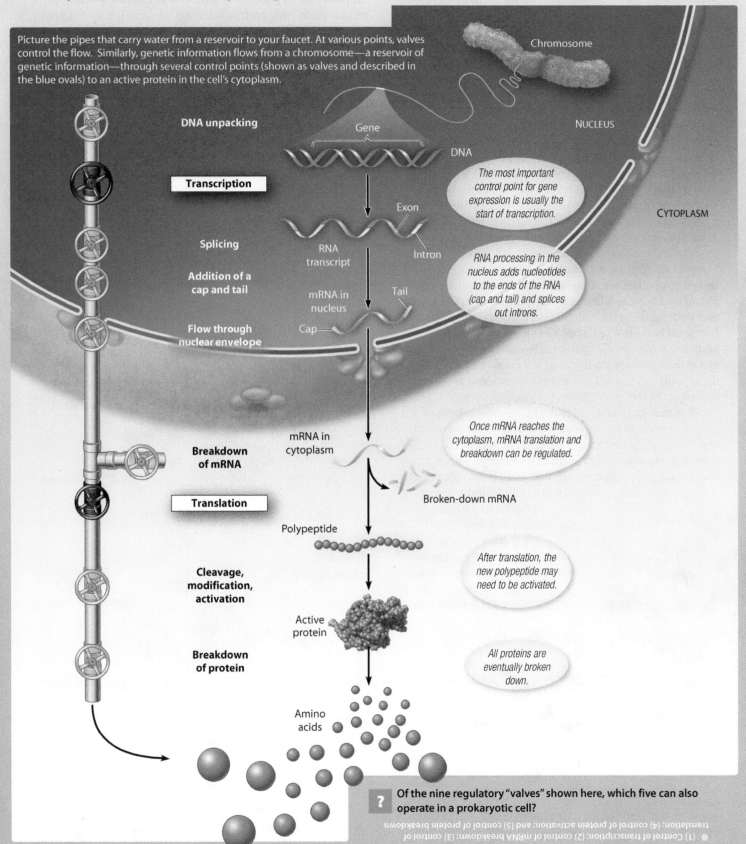

Chromosome

NUCLEUS

CYTOPLASM

DNA unpacking

Gene

DNA

Transcription

The most important control point for gene expression is usually the start of transcription.

Exon

Splicing

RNA transcript

Intron

Addition of a cap and tail

mRNA in nucleus

Tail

RNA processing in the nucleus adds nucleotides to the ends of the RNA (cap and tail) and splices out introns.

Flow through nuclear envelope

Cap

mRNA in cytoplasm

Once mRNA reaches the cytoplasm, mRNA translation and breakdown can be regulated.

Breakdown of mRNA

Broken-down mRNA

Translation

Polypeptide

After translation, the new polypeptide may need to be activated.

Cleavage, modification, activation

Active protein

All proteins are eventually broken down.

Breakdown of protein

Amino acids

? Of the nine regulatory "valves" shown here, which five can also operate in a prokaryotic cell?

● (1) Control of transcription; (2) control of mRNA breakdown; (3) control of translation; (4) control of protein activation; and (5) control of protein breakdown

11.8 Cell signaling and waves of gene expression direct animal development

In eukaryotes, cellular differentiation results from the selective turning on and off of genes. During the life cycle of a multicellular eukaryote, cellular differentiation by selective gene expression is most vital during the development of an embryo from a zygote. Waves of gene expression, with the protein products of one set of genes activating other sets of genes, are a common mechanism of development.

Some of the first glimpses into the relationship between gene expression and embryonic development came from studies of mutants of the fruit fly *Drosophila melanogaster* (see Module 9.18). Figure 11.8A shows the heads of two fruit flies. The one on the right, a mutant, developed in a strikingly abnormal way: It has two legs where its antennae should be! Research on this and other developmental mutants has led to the identification of many of the genes that program development in the normal fly. This genetic approach has revolutionized developmental biology.

Among the earliest events in fruit fly development are those that determine which end of the egg cell will become the head and which end will become the tail. As you can see in Figure 11.8B, ❶ these events occur in the ovaries of the mother fly and involve communication between an unfertilized egg cell and cells adjacent to it in its follicle (egg chamber). The back-and-forth signaling between the cells triggers expression of certain genes in the two cell types. ❷ One important result is the localization of a specific type of mRNA (shown in pink) at the end of the egg where the fly's head will develop, thus defining the animal's head-to-tail axis. (Similar events lead to the positioning of the top-to-bottom and side-to-side axes.)

After the egg is fertilized and laid, repeated rounds of mitosis transform the zygote into an embryo. The early embryo makes proteins that diffuse through its cell layers. Cell signaling—now among the cells of the embryo—helps drive the process of development. ❸ The result is the subdivision of the embryo's body into segments. At this point the finer details of the fly take shape. Protein products of some of the axis-specifying genes and segment-forming genes activate yet another set of genes,

called homeotic genes. A **homeotic gene** is a master control gene that regulates the "batteries" of other genes that determine the anatomy of parts of the body and in this example determine which body parts will develop where in the fly. For example, one set of homeotic genes in fruit flies instructs cells in the segments of the head and thorax (midbody) to form antennae and legs, respectively. (See Module 27.14 for further discussion of homeotic genes.) ❹ The eventual outcome is an adult fly. Notice that the adult's body segments correspond to those of the embryo in step 3. It was mutation of a homeotic gene that was responsible for the abnormal fly in Figure 11.8A.

How can scientists study the expression of genes within living systems? In the next module, we'll look at how DNA technology can help elucidate gene expression in any cell.

? **What determines which end of a developing fruit fly will become the head?**

● A specific kind of mRNA localizes at the end of the unfertilized egg that will become the head.

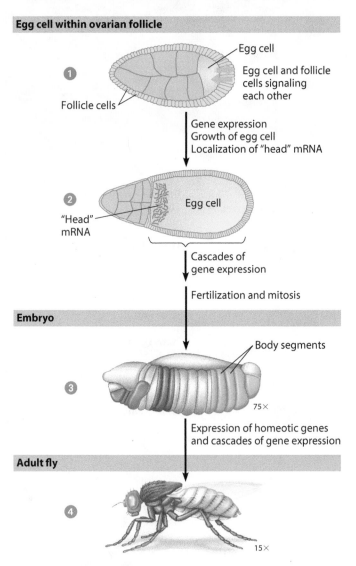

Egg cell within ovarian follicle

❶ Egg cell
Egg cell and follicle cells signaling each other
Follicle cells

Gene expression
Growth of egg cell
Localization of "head" mRNA

❷ Egg cell
"Head" mRNA

Cascades of gene expression

Fertilization and mitosis

Embryo

❸ Body segments

75×

Expression of homeotic genes and cascades of gene expression

Adult fly

❹

15×

▲ Figure 11.8B   Key steps in the early development of head-tail axis in a fruit fly

Eye

Antenna

▲ Figure 11.8A
A normal fruit fly (left) compared with a mutant fruit fly (right) with legs coming out of its head

Extra pair of legs

SEM 50×

SEM 50×

11.9 Scientists use DNA microarrays to test for the transcription of many genes at once

CONNECTION

Biologists today are working hard to learn how genes act together within a functioning organism. Now that a number of whole genomes have been sequenced (see Module 12.17), it is possible to study the expression of large groups of genes. For example, researchers can investigate which genes are transcribed in different situations, such as in different tissues or at different stages of development. They can also look for groups of genes that are expressed in a coordinated manner, with the aim of identifying networks of gene expression across an entire genome.

Genome-wide expression studies are made possible by DNA microarrays. A **DNA microarray** consists of a glass or plastic surface with tiny amounts of thousands of different kinds of single-stranded DNA fragments attached to microscopic wells in a tightly spaced array, or grid. (A DNA microarray is also called a DNA chip or gene chip by analogy to a computer chip.) Each fixed DNA fragment is obtained from a particular gene; a single microarray thus carries DNA from thousands of genes, perhaps even all the genes of an organism.

Figure 11.9 outlines how microarrays are used. ❶ A researcher collects all of the mRNA transcribed from genes in a particular type of cell at a given moment. ❷ This collection of mRNAs is mixed with reverse transcriptase (a viral enzyme that produces DNA from an RNA template; see Module 10.20) to produce a mixture of single-stranded DNA fragments. These fragments are called cDNAs (complementary DNAs) because each one is complementary to one of the mRNAs. The cDNAs are produced in the presence of nucleotides that have been modified to fluoresce (glow). The fluorescent cDNA collection thus represents all of the genes that are being actively transcribed in that particular cell at that particular time. ❸ A small amount of the fluorescently labeled cDNA mixture is added to each of the wells in the microarray. If a molecule in the cDNA mixture is

complementary to a DNA fragment at a particular location on the grid, the cDNA molecule binds to it, becoming fixed there. ❹ After unbound cDNA is rinsed away, the remaining cDNA produces a detectable glow in the microarray. The pattern of glowing spots enables the researcher to determine which genes were being transcribed in the starting cells.

DNA microarrays hold great promise in medical research. Many cancers have a variety of subtypes with different patterns of gene expression that can be identified with DNA microarrays. For example, one study showed that DNA microarray data can classify different types of leukemia into specific subtypes based on the activity of 17 genes. This information can be used to predict which of several available regimens of chemotherapy is likely to be most effective. In addition, comparing patterns of gene expression in breast cancer tumors and noncancerous breast tissue has resulted in more informed and effective treatment protocols. Some oncologists predict that DNA microarrays will usher in a new era in which medical treatment is personalized to each patient (see Module 8.10).

DNA microarrays can also reveal general profiles of gene expression over the lifetime of an organism. For example, researchers performed DNA microarray experiments on more than 90% of the genes of the nematode worm *Caenorhabditis elegans* during every stage of its life cycle. The results showed that expression of nearly 60% of the *C. elegans* genes changed dramatically during development. This study supported the model held by most developmental biologists that embryonic development of multicellular eukaryotes involves a complex and elaborate program of gene expression, rather than simply the expression of a small number of important genes.

? What can be learned from a DNA microarray?

● Which genes are active (transcribed) in a particular sample of cells

DNA microarray

Each well contains DNA from a particular gene.

Actual size (6,400 genes)

❶ mRNA is isolated.

Reverse transcriptase and fluorescent DNA nucelotides

❷ cDNA is made from mRNA.

❹ Unbound cDNA is rinsed away.

❸ cDNA is applied to the wells.

Fluorescent spot

Nonfluorescent spot

cDNA

DNA of an expressed gene

DNA of an unexpressed gene

▲ Figure 11.9   A DNA microarray

11.10 Signal transduction pathways convert messages received at the cell surface to responses within the cell

Within a multicellular organism, cells must be able to communicate messages that will coordinate gene expression. Cell-to-cell signaling via proteins or other kinds of molecules carrying messages from signaling cells to receiving (target) cells is a key mechanism in the coordination of cellular activities. In most cases, a signaling molecule acts by binding to a receptor protein in the plasma membrane and initiating a signal transduction pathway in the target cell.

A **signal transduction pathway** is a series of molecular changes that converts a signal on a target cell's surface to a specific response inside the cell (Figure 11.10). ❶ The cell sending a message secretes a signaling molecule. ❷ This molecule binds to a specific receptor protein embedded in the target cell's plasma membrane. ❸ The binding activates the first in a series of relay proteins within the target cell. Each relay molecule activates another. ❹ The last relay molecule in the series activates a transcription factor that ❺ triggers transcription of a specific gene. ❻ Translation of the mRNA produces a protein that performs the function originally called for by the signal.

Signal transduction pathways are crucial to many cellular functions. Throughout your study of biology, you'll see the importance of signal transduction pathways again and again. We encountered them when we studied the cell cycle control system (Module 8.8); we'll revisit them when we discuss cancer later in this chapter (see, for example, Module 11.17); and we'll see how they relate to hormone function in animals (Chapter 26) and plants (Chapter 33).

> **?** To turn on a gene, must a signal molecule actually enter a target cell?

No: a signal molecule can bind to a receptor protein in the outer membrane of the target cell and trigger a signal transduction pathway that activates transcription factors

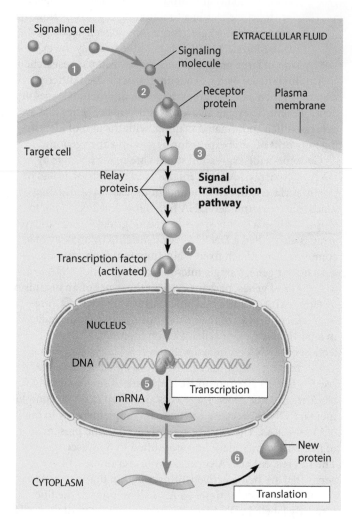

▲ Figure 11.10 A signal transduction pathway that turns on a gene

11.11 Cell-signaling systems appeared early in the evolution of life

EVOLUTION CONNECTION

As explained in Module 11.10, one cell can communicate with another by secreting molecules that bind to surface proteins on a target cell. How widespread are such signaling systems among Earth's organisms—and how ancient are these systems? To answer these questions, we can look at communication between microorganisms, because modern microbes offer clues regarding the role of cell signaling during the evolution of life on Earth.

One topic of cell "conversation" is sex—at least for the yeast *Saccharomyces cerevisiae,* which people have used for millennia to make bread, wine, and beer. Researchers have learned that cells of this yeast identify their mates by chemical signaling. There are two sexes, or mating types, called **a** and **α** (Figure 11.11). Cells of mating type **a** secrete a chemical signal called **a** factor, which can bind to specific receptor proteins on nearby **α** cells. At the same time, **α** cells secrete **α** factor, which binds to receptors on **a** cells. Without actually entering the target cells,

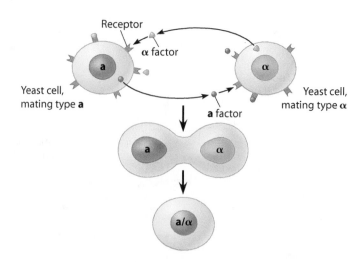

▲ Figure 11.11 Communication between mating yeast cells

the two mating factors cause the cells to grow toward each other and bring about other cellular changes. The result is the fusion, or mating, of two cells of opposite type. The resulting **a/α** cell contains all the genes of both original cells, a combination of genetic resources that provides advantages to the cell's descendants, which arise by subsequent cell divisions.

Extensive studies across different species have revealed that the molecular details of signal transduction in yeast and mammals are strikingly similar, even though the last common ancestor of these two groups of organisms lived more than a billion years ago. These similarities—and others more recently uncovered between signaling systems in bacteria and plants—suggest that early versions of the cell-signaling mechanisms used today evolved well before the first multicellular creatures appeared on Earth. Scientists think that signaling mechanisms evolved first in ancient prokaryotes and single-celled eukaryotes and then became adapted for new uses in their multicellular descendants.

? **In what sense is the joining of yeast mating types "sex"?**

⊕ The process results in the creation of a diploid cell that is a genetic blend of two parental haploid cells.

▷ Cloning of Plants and Animals

11.12 Plant cloning shows that differentiated cells may retain all of their genetic potential

One of the most important take-home lessons from this chapter is that most cells express only a small percentage of their genes. If all genes are still present but some are turned off, have the unexpressed genes become permanently disabled? Or do all genes (even the unexpressed ones) retain the potential to be expressed?

One way to approach these questions is to determine if a differentiated cell can be stimulated to generate a whole new organism. In plants, this ability is common. In fact, if you have ever grown a plant from a small cutting, you've seen evidence that a differentiated plant cell can undergo cell division and give rise to all the tissues of an adult plant. On a larger scale, the technique described in **Figure 11.12** can be used to produce hundreds or thousands of genetically identical plants from the cells of a single plant. For example, when cells from a carrot are transferred to a culture medium, a single cell can begin dividing and eventually grow into an adult plant, a genetic replica of the original. Such an organism, produced through asexual reproduction from a single parent, is called a **clone**. In this context, the term clone refers to an individual created by asexual reproduction (that is, reproduction of a single individual that does not involve fusion of sperm and egg). The fact that a mature plant cell can dedifferentiate, or reverse its differentiation, and then give rise to all the different kinds of specialized cells of a new plant shows that differentiation does not necessarily involve irreversible changes in the plant's DNA.

Plant cloning is used extensively in agriculture. Seedless plants (such as seedless grapes and watermelons) cannot reproduce sexually, leaving cloning as the sole means of mass-producing these common foods. Other plants, such as orchids, reproduce poorly in artificial settings, leaving cloning as the only commercially practical means of production. In other cases, cloning has been used to reproduce a plant with desirable traits, such as high fruit yield or resistance to disease.

But is this sort of cloning possible in animals? A good indication that differentiation need not impair an animal cell's genetic potential is the natural process of **regeneration**, the regrowth of lost body parts. When a salamander loses a leg, for example, certain cells in the leg stump dedifferentiate, divide, and then redifferentiate, giving rise to a new leg. Many animals, especially among the invertebrates (sea stars, for example), can regenerate lost parts. In a few relatively simple animals (such as some sponges), isolated differentiated cells can dedifferentiate and then develop into an entire organism (see Module 27.1). Additional evidence for the complete genetic potential of animal cells comes from cloning experiments, our next topic.

? **How does the cloning of plants from differentiated cells support the view that differentiation is based on the control of gene expression rather than on irreversible changes in the genome?**

⊕ Cloning shows that all the genes of a fully differentiated plant cell are still present.

▶ **Figure 11.12**
Growth of a carrot plant from a differentiated root cell

Root of carrot plant

Single cell

Root cells cultured in growth medium

Cell division in culture

Plantlet

Adult plant

11.13 Biologists can clone animals via nuclear transplantation

SCIENTIFIC THINKING

Animal cloning has been achieved through **nuclear transplantation** (Figure 11.13). This method involves ❶ replacing the nucleus of an egg cell or a zygote with ❷ a nucleus removed from an adult somatic cell. If properly stimulated, the recipient cell may then begin to divide. ❸ After a few days, repeated cell divisions form a blastocyst, a hollow ball of about 100 cells. ❹ If the animal being cloned is a mammal, the blastocyst is then implanted into the uterus of a surrogate mother. The cloned animal will be genetically identical to the donor of the nucleus—in other words, a clone of the donor. This type of cloning is called **reproductive cloning** because it results in the birth of a new living individual.

Can life be rebooted?

Nuclear transplantation was first performed in the 1950s using cells from frog embryos. In later decades, scientists successfully cloned mammals starting from embryonic cells. However, investigators had success only with very young embryos; they found that the older a donor nucleus, the less chance it could be used to successfully clone an animal. In fact, attempts to clone using nuclei from adult cells failed repeatedly. Something within the nucleus of adult cells was preventing them from being "rebooted" into a cell that would give rise to a new, living animal.

A major breakthrough in cloning came in 1996 when Scottish researcher Ian Wilmut and his colleagues cloned a sheep named Dolly, the first mammal successfully cloned from an adult cell. How did they achieve success? Wilmut and his team hypothesized that the significant changes that occur to chromosomes over the cell cycle require that the phases of the donor nucleus and recipient egg be matched during nuclear transplantation. To achieve synchronization, the researchers grew both nucleus-donor mammary gland cells and nucleus-recipient egg cells in a growth medium that contained only 1/20th the normal nutrients. Faced with starvation, all of the cells switched into the dormant G_0 phase of the cell cycle (see Module 8.8). The researchers then removed the nuclei from the dormant eggs, fused these empty egg cells with nuclei from dormant udder cells, and zapped them with electricity to fuse and reboot them. After several days of growth, the resulting embryos were implanted in the uteruses of surrogate sheep mothers. One of the embryos developed into Dolly.

The pioneering cloning work of Wilmut and colleagues demonstrates how scientific success is often preceded by numerous failures. After decades of failures in previous experiments, the Scottish team produced a total of 277 zygotes, of which only 29 survived to implantation, resulting in just one live birth.

Dolly demonstrated that the differentiation of animal cells is achieved by changes in gene expression, rather than by permanent changes in the genes themselves. This conclusion has numerous practical implications. Since Dolly's landmark birth, researchers have cloned many other mammals, including mice, cats, horses, cows, mules, pigs, rabbits, ferrets, and dogs. Why bother cloning animals? Scientists working in agriculture are cloning farm animals with specific sets of desirable traits in the hope of creating high-yielding herds. The pharmaceutical industry is experimenting with cloning mammals for the production of potentially valuable drugs. For example, researchers have produced pig clones that lack a gene for a protein that can cause immune system rejection in humans. Organs from such pigs may one day be used in human patients who require life-saving transplants.

Conservation biologists hope that reproductive cloning can be used to restock the populations of endangered animals. In addition to the banteng discussed in the chapter introduction, other rare animals have been cloned, including a wild mouflon (a small European sheep), a gaur (an Asian ox), and gray wolves. Despite cloning's potential for increasing the numbers of endangered animals, some conservationists object, arguing that cloning may detract from efforts to preserve natural habitats. Such critics correctly point out that cloning does not increase genetic diversity and is therefore not as beneficial to endangered species as natural reproduction.

Another important consideration when cloning animals is the health of the offspring produced. An increasing body of evidence suggests that cloned animals may be less healthy than those arising from a fertilized egg. In 2003, Dolly was euthanized after suffering complications from a lung disease usually seen only in much older sheep. She was 6 years old, while her breed has a life expectancy of 12 years. Other cloned animals have exhibited arthritis, susceptibility to obesity, pneumonia, liver failure, and premature death. Recent research suggests that the methylation of chromatin (see Module 11.2) may be responsible for health problems in cloned animals. Researchers have found that the DNA in cells from cloned embryos often has different patterns of

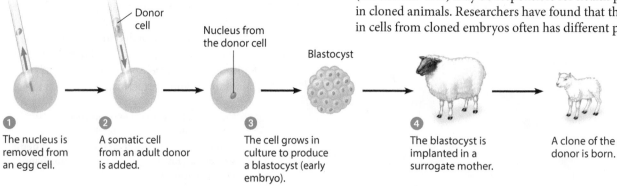

| | Donor cell | Nucleus from the donor cell | Blastocyst | | |

❶ The nucleus is removed from an egg cell.

❷ A somatic cell from an adult donor is added.

❸ The cell grows in culture to produce a blastocyst (early embryo).

❹ The blastocyst is implanted in a surrogate mother.

A clone of the donor is born.

▲ **Figure 11.13** Reproductive cloning via nuclear transplantation methylation than does the DNA in equivalent cells from normal embryos of the same species. Because DNA methylation helps regulate gene expression, misplaced methyl groups may interfere with the pattern of gene expression necessary for normal embryonic development. Researchers are investigating whether chromatin in a donor nucleus can be artificially "rejuvenated" to resemble that of a newly fertilized egg.

The successful cloning of mammals has heightened speculation that humans could be cloned. Critics point out that there are many obstacles—both practical and ethical—to human cloning. Practically, animal cloning is extremely difficult and inefficient. Only a small percentage of cloned embryos (usually less than 10%) develop normally, and those

cloned animals that do develop are less healthy than naturally born kin. Indeed, Dolly's creators have since predicted that their cloning technique will never be sufficiently efficient to attempt in humans. Ethically, the discussion about whether people should be cloned, and under what circumstances, is far from settled. Ethical questions also surround the outcomes of therapeutic cloning, our next topic.

> **?** It took three sheep to create Dolly: A blackface sheep donated the egg, a white-faced sheep donated the mammary cells from which the nucleus was taken, and a blackface sheep served as surrogate. What color face should Dolly have?

● White, reflecting the genetic makeup of the nucleus donor

11.14 Therapeutic cloning can produce stem cells with great medical potential

CONNECTION

A blastocyst, made via natural sexual reproduction or produced via nuclear transplantation (see Figure 11.13), can provide **embryonic stem cells (ES cells)**. Within the embryo, ES cells differentiate to give rise to all the specialized cell types of the body. When grown in laboratory culture, embryonic stem cells can divide indefinitely. The right conditions—such as the presence of certain growth factors—can (hypothetically) induce changes in gene expression that cause differentiation of ES cells into a particular cell type (Figure 11.14). When the goal is to produce ES cells to use in therapeutic treatments, this process is called **therapeutic cloning**.

Embryonic stem cells are not the only stem cells available to researchers. Blood collected from the umbilical cord and placenta at birth contains stem cells that are partially differentiated. In 2005, doctors reported that an infusion of umbilical cord blood stem cells from a compatible (but unrelated) donor appeared to cure some babies of Krabbe's disease, a usually fatal inherited disorder of the nervous system. To date, however, most attempts at umbilical cord blood therapy have not been successful. At present, the American Academy of Pediatrics recommends cord blood banking only for babies born into families with a known genetic risk.

The adult body also has stem cells, which serve to replace nonreproducing specialized cells as needed. Because **adult stem cells** are farther along the road to differentiation than ES cells, they can give rise to only a few related types of cells. Adult animals have only tiny numbers of stem cells, but scientists are learning to identify and isolate these cells from various tissues and, in some cases, to grow them in culture. For example, bone marrow contains several types of stem cells, including one that can generate all the different kinds of blood cells. Adult stem cells from donor bone marrow have long been used as a source of immune system cells in patients whose own immune systems have been destroyed by genetic disorders or radiation treatments for cancer. More recently, clinical trials using bone marrow stem cells have shown slight success in promoting regeneration of heart tissue in patients whose hearts have been damaged by heart attacks.

The ultimate aim of therapeutic cloning is to supply cells for the repair of damaged or diseased organs. Some people

▲ Figure 11.14 Therapeutic cloning using stem cells

speculate, for example, that ES cells may one day be used to replace cells damaged by spinal cord injuries or heart attacks. In the future, a donor nucleus from a patient could allow production of embryonic stem cells that are an exact genetic match for that patient and are thus not rejected by his or her immune system.

Opinions vary widely about the morality of therapeutic cloning using embryonic stem cells, which require destruction of the embryo upon harvesting. Because no embryonic tissue is involved in their harvest, adult stem cells are less ethically problematic in therapy than ES cells. On the other hand, many researchers hypothesize that only the more versatile ES cells are likely to lead to groundbreaking advances in human health. The study of stem cells emphasizes the importance of understanding the control of gene expression. In the next section, we'll explore another important implication of gene regulation to human health: cancer.

> **?** In nature, how do embryonic stem cells differ from adult stem cells?

● Embryonic cells give rise to all the different kinds of cells in the body. Adult stem cells generate only a few related types of cells.

11.15 Cancer results from mutations in genes that control cell division

Cancer is a set of diseases in which the control mechanisms that normally limit cellular growth have malfunctioned (see Module 8.9). Scientists have learned that such malfunction is often due to changes in gene expression.

The abnormal behavior of cancer cells was observed years before anything was known about the cell cycle, its control, or the role genes play in making cells cancerous. One of the earliest clues to the cancer puzzle was the discovery, in 1911, of a virus that causes cancer in chickens. Recall that viruses are simply molecules of DNA or RNA surrounded by protein and in some cases a membranous envelope. Viruses that cause cancer can become permanent residents in host cells by inserting their nucleic acid into the DNA of host chromosomes (see Module 10.17).

The genes that a cancer-causing virus inserts into a host cell can make the cell cancerous. Such a gene, which can cause cancer when present in a single copy in the cell, is called an **oncogene** (from the Greek *onco*, tumor). Over the last century, researchers have identified a number of viruses that harbor cancer-causing genes. One example is the human papillomavirus (HPV), which can be transmitted through sexual contact and is associated with several types of cancer, most frequently cervical cancer.

Proto-oncogenes In 1976, American molecular biologists J. Michael Bishop, Harold Varmus, and their colleagues made a startling discovery. They found that the cancer-causing chicken virus discovered in 1911 contains an oncogene that is an altered version of a normal chicken gene. Subsequent research has shown that the genomes of many animals, including humans, contain genes that can be converted to oncogenes. A normal gene that has the potential to become an oncogene is called a **proto-oncogene**. (These terms can be confusing, so

they bear repeating: a *proto-oncogene* is a normal, healthy gene that, if changed, can become a cancer-causing *oncogene*.) A cell can acquire an oncogene from a virus or from the mutation of one of its own proto-oncogenes.

Searching for their normal role, researchers found that many proto-oncogenes code for proteins that affect the cell cycle. When these proteins are functioning normally, in the right amounts at the right times, they help properly control cell division and cellular differentiation. But changes in these proteins can result in out-of-control growth.

How might a proto-oncogene—a gene that has an essential function in normal cells—become a cancer-causing oncogene? In general, an oncogene arises from a genetic change that leads to an increase either in the amount of the proto-oncogene's protein product or in the activity of each protein molecule. **Figure 11.15A** illustrates three kinds of changes in DNA that can produce oncogenes. Let's assume that the starting proto-oncogene codes for a growth factor, a protein that stimulates cell division. On the left in the figure, a mutation (shown in green) in the proto-oncogene creates an oncogene that codes for a hyperactive protein, one whose stimulating effect is stronger than normal. An error in DNA replication or recombination can generate multiple copies of the gene (as shown in the center of the figure), which are all transcribed and translated; the result is an excess of the normal stimulatory protein. On the right in the figure, the proto-oncogene has been moved from its normal location in the cell's DNA to another location. At its new site, the gene is under the control of a different promoter, one that causes it to be transcribed more often than normal; the normal protein is again made in excess. So in all three cases, normal gene expression is changed, and the cell is stimulated to divide excessively.

▶ **Figure 11.15A** Alternative ways to make oncogenes from a proto-oncogene (all leading to excessive cell growth)

▲ Figure 11.15B   The effect of a mutation in a tumor-suppressor gene

Tumor-Suppressor Genes   In addition to genes whose products normally *promote* cell division, cells contain genes whose normal products *inhibit* cell division. Such genes are called **tumor-suppressor genes** because the proteins they encode help prevent uncontrolled cell growth. Any mutation that decreases the normal activity of a tumor-suppressor protein may contribute to the onset of cancer (**Figure 11.15B**).

Scientists have also discovered a class of tumor-suppressor genes that function in the repair of damaged DNA. When these genes are mutated, other cancer-causing mutations are more likely to accumulate. How do such DNA mutations lead to the progression of disease? We consider that question next.

?   **How do proto-oncogenes relate to oncogenes?**

● A proto-oncogene is a normal gene that, if mutated, can become a cancer-causing oncogene.

11.16 Multiple genetic changes underlie the development of cancer

More than 100,000 Americans will be stricken by cancer of the colon (the main part of the large intestine) this year. One of the best-understood types of human cancer, colon cancer illustrates an important principle about how cancer develops: More than one somatic mutation is needed to produce a full-fledged cancer cell. As in many cancers, the development of malignant (spreading) colon cancer is a gradual process. (See Module 8.9 to review cancer terms.)

Figure 11.16A illustrates the gradual progression from somatic mutation to cancer using colon cancer as an example. ❶ Colon cancer begins when an oncogene arises or is activated through mutation, causing unusually frequent division of apparently normal cells in the colon lining. ❷ Later, additional DNA mutations, such as the inactivation of a tumor-suppressor gene, cause the growth of a small benign tumor (a polyp) in the colon wall. ❸ Still more mutations eventually lead to formation of a malignant tumor, a tumor that has the potential to metastasize (spread). The requirement for several mutations—the actual number is usually around six—explains why cancers can take a long time to develop.

Thus, the development of a malignant tumor is paralleled by a gradual accumulation of mutations that convert proto-oncogenes to oncogenes and knock out tumor-suppressor genes.

▲ Figure 11.16B   Accumulation of mutations in a cancer cell

Multiple changes must occur at the DNA level for a cell to become fully cancerous. In **Figure 11.16B**, colors distinguish the normal cell (tan) from cells with one or more mutations leading to increased cell division and cancer (red). Once a cancer-promoting mutation occurs (the red band on the chromosome), it is passed to all the descendants of the cell carrying it.

The fact that more than one somatic mutation is generally needed to produce a full-fledged cancer cell may help explain why the incidence of cancer increases with age. If cancer results from an accumulation of mutations that occur throughout life, then the longer we live, the more likely we are to develop cancer. Researchers are steadily cataloguing mutations that cause cancer and placing them in public databases. The hope is that such data will lead to improved treatment strategies and perhaps, someday, a cure.

?   **Epithelial cells, those that line body cavities, are frequently replaced and so divide more often than most other types of body cells. Will epithelial cells become cancerous more or less frequently than other types of body cells?**

● More frequent cell divisions will result in more frequent mutation and thus a greater chance of cancer.

DNA changes:	An oncogene is activated	A tumor-suppressor gene is inactivated	A second tumor-suppressor gene is inactivated
Cellular changes:	Increased cell division	Growth of a polyp (benign tumor)	Growth of a malignant tumor
	❶	❷	❸

▲ Figure 11.16A   Stepwise development of a typical colon cancer

11.17 Faulty proteins can interfere with normal signal transduction pathways

The figures below (excluding, for the moment, the white boxes) illustrate two types of signal transduction pathways leading to the synthesis of proteins that influence the cell cycle. In **Figure 11.17A**, the pathway leads to the stimulation of cell division. The initial signal is a growth factor (●), and the target cell's ultimate response is the production of a protein that stimulates the cell to divide. By contrast, **Figure 11.17B** shows an inhibitory pathway, in which a growth-*inhibiting* factor (▼) causes the target cell to make a protein that inhibits cell division. In both cases, the newly made proteins function by interacting with components of the cell cycle control system.

Now, let's see what can happen when the target cell undergoes a cancer-causing mutation. The white box in Figure 11.17A shows the protein product of an oncogene resulting from mutation of a proto-oncogene called *ras*. The normal product of *ras* is a relay protein. Ordinarily, a stimulatory pathway like this will not operate unless the growth factor is available. However, an oncogene protein that is a hyperactive version of a protein in the pathway may trigger the pathway even in the absence of a growth factor. In this example, the oncogene protein is a hyperactive version of the *ras* relay protein that issues signals on its own.

The white box in Figure 11.17B indicates how a mutant tumor-suppressor protein can affect cell division. In this case, the mutation affects a gene called *p53*, which codes for an essential transcription factor. This mutation leads to the production of a faulty transcription factor, one that the signal transduction pathway cannot activate. As a result, the gene for the inhibitory protein at the bottom of the figure remains turned off, and excessive cell division may occur.

Mutations of the *ras* and *p53* genes have been implicated in many kinds of cancer. In fact, mutations in *ras* occur in about 30% of human cancers, and mutations in *p53* occur in more than 50%. As we see next, carcinogens are responsible for many mutations that lead to cancer.

> **?** Contrast the action of an oncogene with that of a cancer-causing mutation in a tumor-suppressor gene.

● An oncogene encodes an abnormal protein that stimulates cell division via a signal transduction pathway; a mutant tumor-suppressor gene encodes a defective protein unable to function in a pathway that normally inhibits cell division.

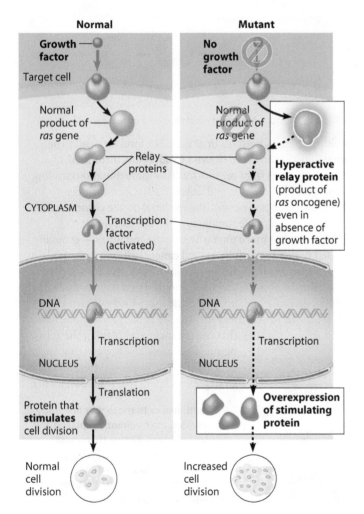

▲ **Figure 11.17A** A stimulatory signal transduction pathway and the effect of an oncogene protein

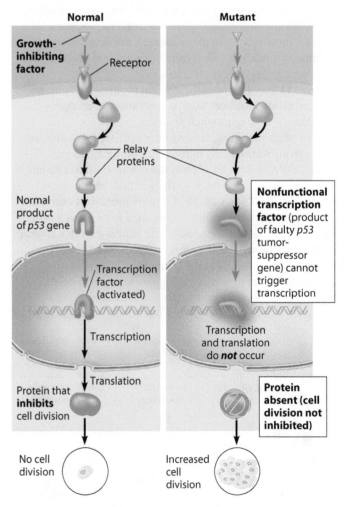

▲ **Figure 11.17B** An inhibitory signal transduction pathway and the effect of a faulty tumor-suppressor protein

11.18 Lifestyle choices can reduce the risk of cancer

CONNECTION

Cancer is the second-leading cause of death (after heart disease) in most industrialized nations. Death rates due to certain forms of cancer—including stomach, cervical, and uterine cancers—have decreased in recent years, but the overall cancer death rate is on the rise, currently increasing at about 1% per decade. Table 11.18 lists the most common cancers in the United States and associated risk factors for each.

The fact that multiple genetic changes are required to produce a cancer cell helps explain the observation that cancers can run in families. An individual inheriting an oncogene or a mutant allele of a tumor-suppressor gene is one step closer to accumulating the necessary mutations for cancer to develop than an individual without any such mutations.

But the majority of cancers are not associated with a mutation that is passed from parent to offspring; they arise from new mutations caused by environmental factors. Agents that alter DNA and make cells cancerous are called **carcinogens**. Most mutagens, substances that cause mutations, are carcinogens. Two of the most potent mutagens are X-rays and ultraviolet radiation in sunlight. X-rays are a significant cause of leukemia and brain cancer. Exposure to UV radiation from the sun is known to cause skin cancer, including a deadly type called melanoma.

The one substance known to cause more cases and types of cancer than any other single agent is tobacco. More people die of lung cancer (nearly 160,000 Americans in 2013) than any other form of cancer. Most tobacco-related cancers come from smoking, but the passive inhalation of secondhand smoke is also a risk. As Table 11.18 indicates, tobacco use, sometimes in combination with alcohol consumption, causes a number of other types of cancer in addition to lung cancer. In nearly all cases, cigarettes are the main culprit, but smokeless tobacco products, such as snuff and chewing tobacco, are linked to cancer of the mouth and throat.

How do carcinogens cause cancer? In many cases, the genetic changes that cause cancer result from decades of exposure to the mutagenic effects of carcinogens. Carcinogens can also produce their effect by promoting cell division. Generally, the higher the rate of cell division, the greater the chance for mutations resulting from errors in DNA replication or recombination. Some carcinogens seem to have both effects. For instance, the hormones linked to breast and uterine cancers promote cell division and may also cause mutations that lead to cancer. In other cases, several different agents, such as viruses and one or more carcinogens, may together produce cancer.

Avoiding carcinogens is not the whole story, because there is growing evidence that some food choices significantly reduce the risk of some cancers. For instance, eating 20–30 grams (g) of plant fiber daily—roughly equal to the amount of fiber in four slices of whole-grain bread, 1 cup of bran flakes, one apple, and $\frac{1}{2}$ cup of carrots combined—and at the same time reducing animal fat intake may help prevent colon cancer. There is also evidence that other substances in fruits and vegetables, including vitamins C and E and certain

TABLE 11.18 | CANCER IN THE UNITED STATES

Cancer	Risk Factors	New Cases 2013 (est.)
Prostate	African heritage; possibly dietary fat	239,000
Breast	Estrogen	235,000
Lung	Tobacco smoke	228,000
Colon, rectum	High dietary fat; tobacco smoke; alcohol	143,000
Lymphomas	Viruses (for some types)	79,000
Melanoma of the skin	Ultraviolet light	77,000
Urinary bladder	Tobacco smoke	73,000
Kidney	Tobacco smoke	65,000
Uterus	Estrogen	62,000
Leukemias	X-rays; benzene; virus (for one type)	49,000
Pancreas	Tobacco smoke; obesity	45,000
Oral cavity	Tobacco in various forms; alcohol	41,000
Liver	Alcohol; hepatitis viruses	31,000
Brain and nerve	Trauma; X-rays	23,000
Ovary	Obesity; many ovulation cycles	22,000
Stomach	Table salt; tobacco smoke	22,000
Cervix	Sexually transmitted viruses; tobacco smoke	12,000
Total, including all other types		1,660,000

compounds related to vitamin A, may offer protection against a variety of cancers. Cabbage and its relatives, such as broccoli and cauliflower (see Figure 13.2), are thought to be especially rich in substances that help prevent cancer, although the identities of these substances are not yet established.

The battle against cancer is being waged on many fronts, and there is reason for optimism. It is especially encouraging that we can help reduce our risk of acquiring—and increase our chance of surviving—some of the most common forms of cancer by the choices we make in our daily life. Not smoking, exercising adequately, avoiding overexposure to the sun, and eating a high-fiber, low-fat diet can all help prevent cancer. Furthermore, seven types of cancer can be easily detected: cancers of the skin and oral cavity (via physical exam), breast (via self-exams and mammograms for higher-risk women), prostate (via rectal exam), cervix (via Pap smear), testes (via self-exam), and colon (via colonoscopy). Regular visits to the doctor can help identify tumors early, thereby significantly increasing the possibility of successful treatment.

? Which of the most common cancers listed in Table 11.18 affect primarily males? Which affect primarily females?

● Males: prostate; females: breast, uterus, cervix

For practice quizzes, BioFlix animations, MP3 tutorials, video tutors, and more study tools designed for this textbook, go to

MasteringBiology®

Reviewing the Concepts

Control of Gene Expression (11.1–11.11)

11.1 Proteins interacting with DNA turn prokaryotic genes on or off in response to environmental changes. In prokaryotes, genes for related enzymes are often controlled together in units called operons. Regulatory proteins bind to control sequences in the DNA and turn operons on or off in response to environmental changes.

A typical operon

Regulatory gene — Encodes a repressor that in active form attaches to an operator

Promoter — RNA polymerase binding site

Operator — Switches the operon on or off

Gene 1, Gene 2, Gene 3 — Code for proteins

DNA

11.2 Chromosome structure and chemical modifications can affect gene expression. In multicellular eukaryotes, different types of cells make different proteins because different combinations of genes are active in each type. A chromosome contains DNA wound around clusters of histone proteins, forming a string of bead-like nucleosomes. DNA packing tends to block gene expression by preventing access of transcription proteins to the DNA. One example of DNA packing is X chromosome inactivation in the cells of female mammals. Chemical modification of DNA bases or histone proteins can result in epigenetic inheritance.

11.3 Complex assemblies of proteins control eukaryotic transcription. A variety of regulatory proteins interact with DNA and with each other to turn the transcription of eukaryotic genes on or off.

11.4 Eukaryotic RNA may be spliced in more than one way. After transcription, alternative RNA splicing may generate two or more types of mRNA from the same transcript.

11.5 Small RNAs play multiple roles in controlling gene expression. MicroRNAs, bound to proteins, can prevent gene expression by forming complexes with mRNA molecules.

11.6 Later stages of gene expression are also subject to regulation. The lifetime of an mRNA molecule helps determine how much protein is made, as do factors involved in translation. A protein may need to be activated in some way, and eventually the cell will break it down.

11.7 Multiple mechanisms regulate gene expression in eukaryotes. Gene expression can be regulated multiple ways within both the nucleus and cytoplasm.

11.8 Cell signaling and waves of gene expression direct animal development. A series of RNAs and proteins produced in the embryo control the development of an animal from a fertilized egg.

11.9 Scientists use DNA microarrays to test for the transcription of many genes at once. Scientists can use a DNA microarray to gather data about which genes are turned on or off in a particular cell. A glass slide containing DNA fragments from thousands of genes can be used to test which of those genes are being expressed in a particular cell type.

11.10 Signal transduction pathways convert messages received at the cell surface to responses within the cell.

11.11 Cell-signaling systems appeared early in the evolution of life. Similarities among organisms suggest that signal transduction pathways evolved early in the history of life on Earth.

Cloning of Plants and Animals (11.12–11.14)

11.12 Plant cloning shows that differentiated cells may retain all of their genetic potential. A clone is an individual created by asexual reproduction and thus genetically identical to a single parent.

11.13 Biologists can clone animals via nuclear transplantation. Inserting DNA from a donor cell into a nucleus-free host egg can result in an early embryo that is a clone of the DNA donor. Implanting a blastocyst into a surrogate mother can lead to the birth of a cloned mammal.

Egg cell or zygote with nucleus removed — Nucleus from a donor cell — An early embryo resulting from nuclear transplantation — Surrogate mother — Clone of the donor

11.14 Therapeutic cloning can produce stem cells with great medical potential. The goal of therapeutic cloning is to produce embryonic stem cells. Such cells may eventually be used for a variety of therapeutic purposes. Like embryonic stem cells, adult stem cells can both perpetuate themselves in culture and give rise to differentiated cells. Unlike embryonic stem cells, adult stem cells normally give rise to only a limited range of cell types.

Egg cell or zygote with nucleus removed — Nucleus from a donor cell — An early embryo resulting from nuclear transplantation — Embryonic stem cells in culture — Specialized cells

The Genetic Basis of Cancer (11.15–11.18)

11.15 Cancer results from mutations in genes that control cell division. Cancer cells, which divide uncontrollably, result from mutations in genes whose protein products affect the cell cycle. A mutation can change a proto-oncogene, a normal gene that helps control cell division, into an oncogene, which causes cells to divide excessively. Mutations that inactivate tumor-suppressor genes have similar effects.

11.16 Multiple genetic changes underlie the development of cancer. Cancers result from a series of genetic changes.

11.17 Faulty proteins can interfere with normal signal transduction pathways. Many proto-oncogenes and tumor-suppressor genes code for proteins active in signal transduction pathways regulating cell division.

11.18 Lifestyle choices can reduce the risk of cancer. Reducing exposure to carcinogens, which induce cancer-causing mutations, and making other lifestyle choices can help reduce cancer risk.

Connecting the Concepts

1. Complete the following concept map to test your knowledge of gene regulation.

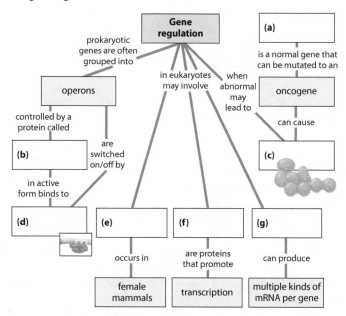

Testing Your Knowledge

Level 1: Knowledge/Comprehension

2. Which of the following methods of gene regulation do eukaryotes and prokaryotes have in common?
   a. elaborate packing of DNA in chromosomes
   b. activator and repressor proteins, which attach to DNA
   c. the addition of a cap and tail to mRNA after transcription
   d. *lac* and *trp* operons

3. A homeotic gene does which of the following?
   a. It serves as the ultimate control for prokaryotic operons.
   b. It regulates the expression of groups of other genes during development.
   c. It represses the histone proteins in eukaryotic chromosomes.
   d. It helps splice mRNA after transcription.

4. Which of the following is a valid difference between embryonic stem cells and the stem cells found in adult tissues?
   a. In laboratory culture, only adult stem cells are immortal.
   b. In nature, only embryonic stem cells give rise to all the different types of cells in the organism.
   c. Only adult stem cells can differentiate in culture.
   d. Embryonic stem cells are generally more difficult to grow in culture than adult stem cells.

Level 2: Application/Analysis

5. The control of gene expression is more complex in multicellular eukaryotes than in prokaryotes because _____. (*Explain your answer.*)
   a. eukaryotic cells are much smaller
   b. in a multicellular eukaryote, different cells are specialized for different functions
   c. prokaryotes are restricted to stable environments
   d. eukaryotes have fewer genes, so each gene must do several jobs

6. Your bone cells, muscle cells, and skin cells look different because
   a. each cell contains different kinds of genes.
   b. they are present in different organs.
   c. different genes are active in each kind of cell.
   d. they contain different numbers of genes.

7. All your cells contain proto-oncogenes, which can change into cancer-causing oncogenes. Why do cells possess such potential time bombs?
   a. Viruses infect cells with proto-oncogenes.
   b. Proto-oncogenes are genetic "junk" with no known function.
   c. Proto-oncogenes are unavoidable environmental carcinogens.
   d. Proto-oncogenes normally control cell division.

8. You obtain an egg cell from the ovary of a white mouse and remove the nucleus from it. You then obtain a nucleus from a liver cell from an adult black mouse. You use the methods of nuclear transplantation to insert the nucleus into the empty egg. After some prompting, the new zygote divides into an early embryo, which you then implant into the uterus of a brown mouse. A few weeks later, a litter of mice is born. What color will they be? Why?

9. Mutations can alter the function of the *lac* operon (see Module 11.1). Predict how the following mutations would affect the function of the operon in the presence and absence of lactose:
   a. Mutation of regulatory gene; repressor cannot bind to lactose.
   b. Mutation of operator; repressor will not bind to operator.
   c. Mutation of regulatory gene; repressor will not bind to operator.
   d. Mutation of promoter; RNA polymerase will not attach to promoter.

Level 3: Synthesis/Evaluation

10. A mutation in a single gene may cause a major change in the body of a fruit fly, such as an extra pair of legs or wings. Yet it probably takes the combined action of hundreds or thousands of genes to produce a wing or leg. How can a change in just one gene cause such a big change in the body?

11. A chemical called dioxin is produced as a by-product of some chemical manufacturing processes. This substance was present in Agent Orange, a defoliant sprayed on vegetation during the Vietnam War. There has been a continuing controversy over its effects on soldiers exposed to it during the war. Animal tests have suggested that dioxin can be lethal and can cause birth defects, cancer, organ damage, and immune system suppression. But its effects on humans are unclear, and even animal tests are inconclusive. Researchers have discovered that dioxin enters a cell and binds to a protein that in turn attaches to the cell's DNA. How might this mechanism help explain the variety of dioxin's effects? How might you determine whether a particular individual became ill as a result of exposure to dioxin?

12. **SCIENTIFIC THINKING** Each scientist works as part of a broader community of scientists, building on the work of others. Scientific advances often depend on the application of new technologies and/or on new techniques applied to an existing problem. What improvements to existing cloning methods did Wilmut make that allowed him to successfully clone Dolly the sheep from an adult cell?

Answers to all questions can be found in Appendix 4.

12 | DNA Technology and Genomics

Papaya fruit, shown in the photograph below, are sweet and loaded with vitamin C. They are borne on a rapidly growing treelike plant (*Carica papaya*) that grows only in tropical climates. In Hawaii, papaya is both a dietary staple and a valuable export crop.

Although thriving today, Hawaii's papaya industry seemed doomed just a few decades ago. A deadly pathogen called the papaya ringspot virus (PRV) had spread throughout the islands and appeared poised to completely eradicate the papaya plant population. But scientists from the University of Hawaii were able to rescue the industry by creating new, genetically engineered PRV-resistant strains of papaya. Today, the papaya industry is once again vibrant—and the vast majority of Hawaii's papayas are genetically modified organisms (GMOs).

Are genetically modified organisms safe?

However, not everyone is happy about the circumstances surrounding the recovery of the Hawaiian papaya industry. Although genetically modified papayas are approved for consumption in the United States (as are many other GMO fruits and vegetables), some critics have raised safety concerns—for the people who eat them and for the environment. On three occasions over a three-year

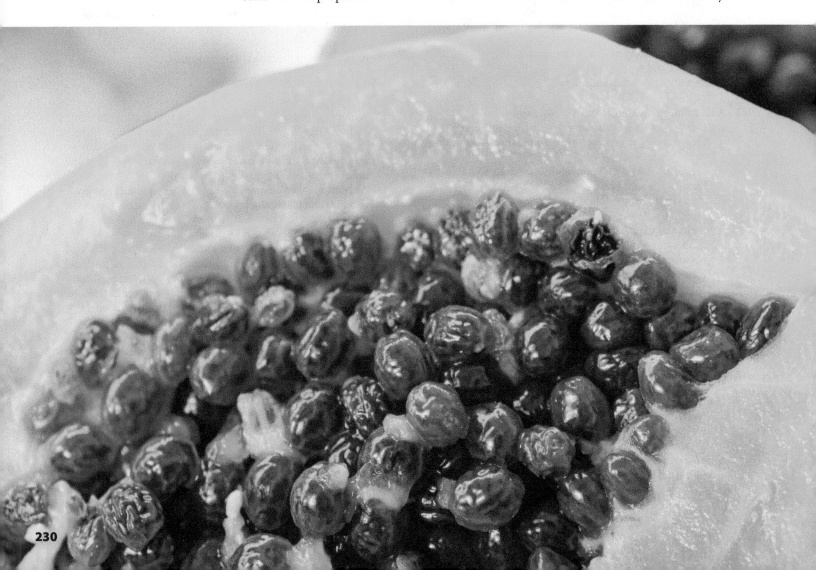

span, thousands of papaya trees on the big island of Hawaii were hacked down under the cover of darkness, presumably as a protest against GMO crops. Although few would condone such criminal behavior, should we in fact be concerned about the safety of GMO crops? This question continues to foster considerable debate and disagreement.

In addition to GMOs in our diet, DNA technologies affect our lives in many other ways: Gene cloning is used to produce medical and industrial products, DNA profiling has changed the field of forensic science, new technologies produce valuable data for biological research, and DNA can even be used to investigate historical questions. In this chapter, we'll discuss each of these applications. We'll also consider the specific techniques used, how they are applied, and some of the social, legal, and ethical issues that are raised by the new technologies.

BIG IDEAS

Gene Cloning
(12.1–12.5)

A variety of laboratory techniques can be used to copy and combine DNA molecules.

Genetically Modified Organisms
(12.6–12.10)

Transgenic cells, plants, and animals are used in agriculture and medicine.

DNA Profiling
(12.11–12.16)

Genetic markers can be used to definitively match a DNA sample to an individual.

Genomics
(12.17–12.21)

The study of complete DNA sets helps us learn about evolutionary history.

▷ Gene Cloning

12.1 Genes can be cloned in recombinant plasmids

Although it may seem like a modern field, **biotechnology**, the manipulation of organisms or their components to make useful products, actually dates back to the dawn of civilization. Consider such ancient practices as the use of yeast to make beer, wine, and bread and the selective breeding of livestock, dogs, and other animals. But when people use the term *biotechnology* today, they are usually referring to **DNA technology**, modern laboratory techniques for studying and manipulating genetic material. Using these methods, scientists can, for instance, modify specific genes and move them between organisms as different as *Escherichia coli* bacteria, papaya, and fish.

In the 1970s, the field of biotechnology exploded with the invention of methods for making recombinant DNA in a test tube. **Recombinant DNA** is formed when scientists combine pieces of DNA from two different sources—often different species—*in vitro* (in a test tube) to form a single DNA molecule. Today, recombinant DNA technology is widely used for **genetic engineering**, the direct manipulation of genes for practical purposes. Scientists have genetically engineered bacteria to mass-produce a variety of useful chemicals, from cancer drugs to pesticides. Scientists have also transferred genes from bacteria into plants and from one animal species into another **(Figure 12.1A)**.

To manipulate genes in the laboratory, biologists often use bacterial **plasmids**, small, circular DNA molecules that replicate (duplicate) separately from the much larger bacterial chromosome (see Module 10.23). Plasmids typically carry only a few genes and are passed from one generation of bacteria to the next. Because plasmids are easily manipulated to carry virtually any genes, they are key tools for **gene cloning**, the production of many identical copies of a gene-carrying piece of DNA. Gene-cloning methods are central to the production of useful products via genetic engineering.

Consider a typical genetic engineering challenge: A molecular biologist at a pharmaceutical company has identified a gene that codes for a valuable product, a hypothetical substance called protein V. The biologist wants to manufacture the protein on a large scale. The biggest challenge in such an effort is of the "needle in a haystack" variety: The gene of interest is one relatively tiny segment embedded in a much longer DNA molecule. **Figure 12.1B** illustrates how the techniques of gene cloning can be used to find the desired gene and copy it.

To begin, the biologist isolates two kinds of DNA: ➊ a bacterial plasmid (usually from the bacterium *E. coli*) that

will serve as the **vector**, or gene carrier, and ➋ the DNA from another organism that includes the gene that codes for protein V (gene *V*) along with other, unwanted genes. The DNA containing gene *V* could come from a variety of sources, such as a different bacterium, a plant, a nonhuman animal, or even human tissue cells growing in laboratory culture.

➌ The researcher treats both the plasmid and the gene *V* source DNA with an enzyme that cuts DNA. An enzyme is chosen that cleaves the plasmid in only one place. ➍ The source DNA, which is usually much longer in sequence than the plasmid, may be cut into many fragments, one of which carries gene *V*. The figure shows the processing of just one DNA fragment and one plasmid, but actually, millions of plasmids and DNA fragments, most of which do not contain gene *V*, are treated simultaneously. ➎ The cut DNA from both sources—the plasmid and target gene—are mixed. The single-stranded ends of the plasmid base-pair with the complementary ends of the target DNA fragment (see Module 10.4 if you need a refresher on the DNA base-pairing rules). ➏ The enzyme **DNA ligase** joins the two DNA molecules by way of covalent bonds. This enzyme, which the cell normally uses in DNA replication (see Module 10.5), is a "DNA pasting" enzyme that catalyzes the formation of covalent bonds between adjacent nucleotides, joining the strands. The result is a recombinant DNA plasmid containing gene *V*, as well as many other recombinant DNA plasmids carrying other genes not shown here.

▲ Figure 12.1A   Glowing angelfish produced by transferring a gene originally obtained from a jelly (cnidarian)

➐ The recombinant plasmid containing the targeted gene is mixed with bacteria. Under the right conditions, a bacterium takes up the plasmid DNA by transformation (see Module 10.22). ➑ The recombinant bacterium then reproduces to form a **clone** of cells, each carrying a copy of gene *V*. (In this context, the term *clone* refers to a group of identical cells descended from a single ancestral cell.) This step is the actual gene cloning. In our example, the biologist will eventually grow a cell clone large enough to produce protein *V* in marketable quantities.

➒ Gene cloning can be used to produce a variety of desirable products. Copies of the gene itself can be the immediate product, to be used in additional genetic engineering projects. For example, a pest-resistance gene present in one plant species might be cloned and transferred into plants of another species. Other times, the protein product of the cloned gene is harvested and used. For example, an enzyme that creates a faded look in blue jeans can be harvested in large quantities from bacteria carrying the cloned gene (in

E. coli bacterium

Plasmid

Bacterial chromosome

1 A plasmid is isolated.

①
②
③
④
⑤
⑥

A cell with DNA containing the gene of interest

2 The cell's DNA is isolated.

DNA

3 The plasmid is cut with an enzyme.

Gene of interest (gene V)

4 The cell's DNA is cut with the same enzyme.

Gene of interest

5 The targeted fragment and plasmid DNA are combined.

6 DNA ligase is added, which joins the two DNA molecules.

Recombinant DNA plasmid

Gene of interest

7 The recombinant plasmid is taken up by a bacterium through transformation.

Recombinant bacterium

8 The bacterium reproduces.

Clone of cells

Genes may be inserted into other organisms.

9

Harvested proteins may be used directly.

Examples of gene use

A gene for pest resistance is inserted into plants.

A gene is used to alter bacteria for cleaning up toxic waste.

Examples of protein use

A protein is used to make "stone-washed" blue jeans.

A protein is used to dissolve blood clots in heart attack therapy.

▲ Figure 12.1B   An overview of gene cloning

Try This   Examine the shapes of the cut regions of the plasmid and the gene of interest, paying particular attention to the complementary shapes of the pieces that allow them to bond together.

other words, no stones are harmed in the making of stone-washed jeans!).

In the next four modules, we discuss the methods outlined in Figure 12.1B. You may find it useful to turn back to this summary figure as each technique is discussed.

? In the example shown in Figure 12.1, what is the vector?

● A plasmid isolated from an E. coli bacterium

12.2 Enzymes are used to "cut and paste" DNA

To understand how DNA is manipulated in the laboratory, you need to learn how enzymes cut and paste DNA. The cutting tools are bacterial enzymes called **restriction enzymes**. Biologists have identified hundreds of different restriction enzymes, each of which recognizes a particular short DNA sequence, which is called a **restriction site**. After a restriction enzyme binds to its restriction site, it cuts both strands of the DNA at precise points within the sequence—like a pair of highly specific molecular scissors—yielding pieces of DNA called

restriction fragments. All copies of a particular DNA molecule always yield the same set of DNA fragments when exposed to the same restriction enzyme. Once cut, fragments of DNA can be pasted together by the enzyme **DNA ligase**. The techniques outlined here form the basis of many genetic engineering procedures that involve combining DNA from different sources.

DNA

Restriction site

GAATTC
CTTAAG

A restriction site is usually 4–8 nucleotide pairs long.

The restriction enzyme shown here, called EcoRI, is found naturally in *E. coli* bacteria. EcoRI recognizes the DNA sequence GAATTC and always cuts it the same way—between the bases A and G—producing restriction fragments.

Restriction enzyme

G
CTTAA

AATTC
G

In bacteria, restriction enzymes play a defensive role, chopping up foreign DNA; the cell's own DNA is protected by the addition of methyl groups.

A piece of DNA from another source (the gene of interest) is cut by the same restriction enzyme and added to the first DNA. Both molecules of DNA are cut unevenly, yielding "sticky ends," single-stranded extensions from the double-stranded fragments.

Sticky end

Gene of interest

AATTC
G

G
CTTAA

Sticky end

The sticky ends from the two different DNA molecules are complementary to one another because they were cut by the same enzyme.

The complementary ends on the two different fragments stick together by base pairing.

GAATTC
CTTAAG

GAATTC
CTTAAG

Sticky ends are the key to joining restriction fragments from different sources: Hydrogen bonds (not shown) form base pairs that hold the two strands together.

DNA ligase

The temporary union between the DNA fragments is made permanent by DNA ligase, which creates new covalent bonds that join the sugar-phosphate backbones of the DNA strands.

Recombinant DNA

? **What are "sticky ends"?**

Answer: Single-stranded regions whose unpaired bases can hydrogen-bond to the complementary sticky ends of other fragments created by the same restriction enzyme

12.3 Cloned genes can be stored in genomic libraries

Each bacterial clone created using the procedure described in Figure 12.1B consists of identical cells with plasmids carrying one particular fragment of target DNA. A collection of cloned DNA fragments that includes an organism's entire genome is

▼ **Figure 12.3** Genomic libraries

A genome is cut up with a restriction enzyme

or

Recombinant plasmid

Recombinant phage DNA

Bacterial clone

Phage clone

Plasmid library

Phage library

called a **genomic library**. On the left side of Figure 12.3, the red, yellow, and green DNA segments represent three of the thousands of different library "books" that are "shelved" in plasmids inside bacterial cells. A typical cloned DNA fragment is big enough to carry one or a few genes, and together, the fragments include the entire genome of the organism from which the DNA was derived.

Bacteriophages (also called phages)—viruses that infect bacteria—can also serve as vectors when cloning genes (Figure 12.3, right). When a phage is used as a vector, the DNA fragments are inserted into phage DNA molecules. The recombinant phage DNA can then be introduced into a bacterial cell through the normal infection process. Inside the cell, phage DNA is replicated, producing new phage particles carrying the foreign DNA. In the next module, we look at another source of DNA for cloning: eukaryotic mRNA.

? **In what sense does a genomic library have multiple copies of each "book"?**

● Each "book"—a piece of DNA from the genome that was the source of the library—is present in every recombinant bacterium or phage in a clone.

12.4 Reverse transcriptase can help make genes for cloning

Rather than starting with an entire eukaryotic genome, a researcher can focus on the genes expressed in a particular kind of cell by using its mRNA as the starting material for cloning (**Figure 12.4**). ① The chosen cells transcribe their genes within the nucleus and ② process the transcripts, removing introns and splicing exons together, producing mRNA. ③ The researcher isolates the mRNA in a test tube. ④ Single-stranded DNA transcripts are made from the mRNA using **reverse transcriptase**, a viral enzyme that can synthesize DNA from

an RNA template (gold in the figure; see Module 10.20). ⑤ Another enzyme is added to break down the mRNA, and ⑥ DNA polymerase (the enzyme that replicates DNA; see Module 10.5) is used to synthesize a second DNA strand.

The DNA that results from such a procedure, called **complementary DNA (cDNA)**, represents only the subset of genes that had been transcribed into mRNA in the starting cells. Among other purposes, such a cDNA library is useful for studying the genes responsible for the specialized functions of a particular cell type, such as brain or liver cells.

? **Why is a cDNA gene made using reverse transcriptase often shorter than the natural form of the gene?**

● Because cDNAs are made from spliced mRNAs, which lack introns

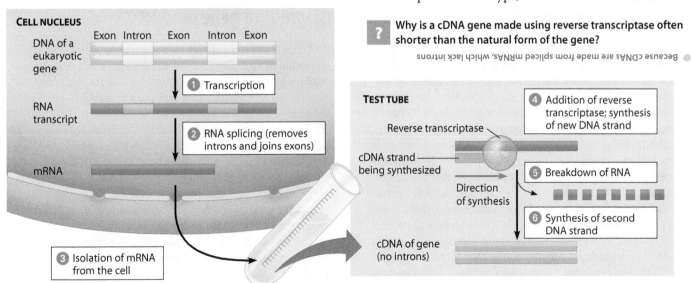

CELL NUCLEUS

DNA of a eukaryotic gene

Exon Intron Exon Intron Exon

① Transcription

RNA transcript

② RNA splicing (removes introns and joins exons)

mRNA

③ Isolation of mRNA from the cell

TEST TUBE

Reverse transcriptase

cDNA strand being synthesized

Direction of synthesis

④ Addition of reverse transcriptase; synthesis of new DNA strand

⑤ Breakdown of RNA

⑥ Synthesis of second DNA strand

cDNA of gene (no introns)

▲ **Figure 12.4** Making complimentary DNA (cDNA) from eukaryotic mRNA

12.5 Nucleic acid probes identify clones carrying specific genes

Often, the most difficult task in gene cloning is finding the right "books" in a genomic library—that is, identifying only the clones that contain a desired gene from among all those created. For example, a researcher might want to pull out just the clone of bacteria carrying what is depicted as the red gene in Figure 12.3. If bacterial clones containing a specific gene actually translate the gene into protein, they can be identified by testing for the protein product. However, not every desired gene produces detectable proteins. In such cases, researchers can also test directly for the gene itself.

Methods for detecting a gene directly depend on base pairing between the gene and a complementary sequence on another nucleic acid molecule, either DNA or RNA. When at least part of the nucleotide sequence of a gene is known, this information can be used to a researcher's advantage. For example, if we know that a gene contains the sequence TAGGCT, a biochemist can synthesize a short single strand of DNA with the complementary sequence (ATCCGA) and label it with a radioactive isotope or fluorescent tag. This labeled, complementary molecule is called a **nucleic acid probe** because it is used to find a specific gene or other nucleotide sequence within a mass of DNA. (In actual practice, probe molecules are considerably longer than six nucleotides.)

Figure 12.5 shows how a probe works. The DNA sample to be tested is treated with heat or chemicals to separate the DNA strands. When the radioactive DNA probe is added to these strands, it tags the correct molecules—that is, it finds the correct books in the genomic library—by hydrogen-bonding to the complementary sequence in the gene of interest. Such a probe can be simultaneously applied to many bacterial clones to screen all of them at once for a desired gene.

▲ Figure 12.5 How a DNA probe tags a gene by base pairing

In one technique, a piece of filter paper is pressed against bacterial colonies (clones) growing on a petri dish. The filter paper picks up cells from each colony. A chemical treatment is used to break open the cells and separate the DNA strands. The DNA strands are then soaked in probe solution. Any bacterial colonies carrying the gene of interest will be tagged on the filter paper, marking them for easy identification. Once the researcher identifies a colony carrying the desired gene, the cells can be grown further, and the gene of interest, or its protein product, can be collected in large amounts.

> **?** How does a probe consisting of radioactive DNA or RNA enable a researcher to find the bacterial clones carrying a particular gene?

The probe molecules bind to and label DNA only from the cells containing the gene of interest, which has a complementary DNA sequence.

▷ Genetically Modified Organisms

12.6 Recombinant cells and organisms can mass-produce gene products

Recombinant cells and organisms constructed by DNA technology are used to manufacture many useful products, chiefly proteins (**Table 12.6**, on the facing page). By transferring the gene for a desired protein into a bacterium, yeast, or other kind of cell that is easy to grow in culture, a genetic engineer can produce large quantities of proteins that are otherwise difficult to obtain. Bacteria—most commonly *E. coli*—are often the best organisms for manufacturing a protein product. Major advantages of bacteria include the plasmids and phages available for use as gene-cloning vectors and the fact that bacteria can be grown rapidly and cheaply in large tanks. Furthermore, bacteria can be engineered to produce large amounts of particular proteins and, in some cases, to secrete the proteins directly into their growth medium, simplifying the task of collecting and purifying the products. Bacteria are used for a wide variety of purposes, from producing valuable human drugs to enzymes used in making cheese and processed fruit juice.

Despite the advantages of using bacteria, it is sometimes desirable or necessary to use eukaryotic cells to produce a protein product. Often, the first-choice eukaryotic organism for protein production is the same yeast used in making bread and beer, *Saccharomyces cerevisiae*. As bakers and brewers have recognized for centuries, yeast cells are easy to grow. And like *E. coli*, yeast cells can take up foreign DNA and integrate it into their genomes. Yeast cells are often better than bacteria at synthesizing and secreting eukaryotic proteins, such as the hepatitis B vaccine. *S. cerevisiae* is currently used to produce a number of proteins. In certain cases, the same product—for example, interferons used in cancer research—can be made using either yeast or bacteria. In other cases, such as the hepatitis B vaccine, yeast alone is used.

The cells of choice for making some gene products come from mammals. Many proteins that mammalian cells

TABLE 12.6	SOME PROTEIN PRODUCTS OF RECOMBINANT DNA TECHNOLOGY	

Product	Made by	Use
Human insulin	E. coli	Treatment for diabetes
Human growth hormone (HGH)	E. coli	Treatment for growth defects
Epidermal growth factor (EGF)	E. coli	Treatment for burns, ulcers
Interleukin-2 (IL-2)	E. coli	Possible treatment for cancer
Bovine growth hormone (BGH)	E. coli	Improving weight gain in cattle
Cellulase	E. coli	Breaking down cellulose for animal feeds
Taxol	E. coli	Treatment for ovarian cancer
Interferons (alpha and gamma)	S. cerevisiae, E. coli	Possible treatment for cancer and viral infections
Hepatitis B vaccine	S. cerevisiae	Prevention of viral hepatitis
Erythropoietin (EPO)	Mammalian cells	Treatment for anemia
Factor VIII	Mammalian cells	Treatment for hemophilia
Tissue plasminogen activator (TPA)	Mammalian cells	Treatment for heart attacks and some strokes

▲ **Figure 12.6A** A goat carrying a gene for a human blood protein that is secreted in the milk

normally secrete are glycoproteins, proteins with chains of sugars attached. Because only mammalian cells can attach the sugars correctly, mammalian cells must be used for making these products. For example, recombinant mammalian cells growing in laboratory cultures are currently used to produce human erythropoietin (EPO), a hormone that stimulates the production of red blood cells. EPO can save lives as a treatment for anemia. However, EPO is also abused by some athletes who seek the advantage of artificially high levels of oxygen-carrying red blood cells (called "blood doping"; see Module 23.13). EPO is one of several drugs bicyclist Lance Armstrong and his teammates have admitted to abusing during his historic string of victories in the Tour de France bicycle race. After years of denial, Armstrong admitted his abuse of EPO (and other performance-enhancing substances) in 2012, leading to a lifetime ban from sanctioned athletic competition.

Recently, pharmaceutical researchers have been exploring the mass production of gene products by whole animals or plants rather than cultured cells. Genetic engineers have used recombinant DNA technology to insert genes for desired human proteins into other mammals, where the protein encoded by the recombinant gene may be secreted in the animal's milk. For example, a gene for antithrombin—a human protein that helps prevent inappropriate blood clotting—has been inserted into the genome of a goat (**Figure 12.6A**); isolated from the milk, the protein reduces the risk of life-threatening blood clots during surgery or childbirth. The sheep in **Figure 12.6B** have been genetically modified to produce a human protein called AAT; this protein can be supplied to patients to treat a hereditary form of emphysema. Other

mammals have been modified to serve as models for human diseases or to improve the health of livestock.

However, genetically engineered animals are difficult and costly to produce. Typically, a biotechnology company starts by injecting the desired DNA into a large number of embryos, which are then implanted into surrogate mothers. With luck, one or a few recombinant animals may result, but success rates for such procedures are very low. Once a recombinant organism is successfully produced, it may be cloned. The result can be a genetically identical herd—a grazing pharmaceutical "factory" of "pharm" animals that produce otherwise rare biological substances for medical use.

We continue an exploration of the medical applications of DNA technology in the next module.

? Why can't all human proteins be synthesized in E. coli?

● Because bacteria cannot correctly produce many eukaryotic (and mammalian) proteins, such as ones that require the attachment of sugar groups

▲ **Figure 12.6B** Sheep that have been genetically modified to produce a useful human protein

12.7 DNA technology has changed the pharmaceutical industry and medicine

CONNECTION

DNA technology, and gene cloning in particular, is widely used to produce medicines and to diagnose diseases.

Therapeutic Hormones Consider the first two products in Table 12.6 on the previous page—human insulin and human growth hormone. Insulin, normally secreted by the pancreas, is a hormone that helps regulate the levels of glucose in the blood. About 2 million Americans with diabetes depend on insulin injections. Before 1982, the main sources of this hormone were slaughtered pigs and cattle. Insulin extracted from these animals is chemically similar, but not identical, to human insulin, and it causes allergic reactions in some people. Genetic engineering has largely solved this problem by developing bacteria that synthesize and secrete the human form of insulin. In 1982, Humulin (Figure 12.7A)—human insulin produced by bacteria—became the first recombinant DNA drug approved by the U.S. Food and Drug Administration.

▲ Figure 12.7A
Human insulin produced by bacteria

Treatment with human growth hormone (HGH) is a boon to children born with a form of dwarfism caused by inadequate amounts of HGH. Because growth hormones from other animals are not effective in humans, children with HGH deficiency historically have had to rely on scarce and expensive supplies from human cadavers. In 1985, however, molecular biologists made an artificial gene for HGH by joining a human DNA fragment to a chemically synthesized piece of DNA; using this gene, they were able to produce HGH in *E. coli*. HGH from recombinant bacteria is now widely used.

Another important pharmaceutical product produced by genetic engineering is tissue plasminogen activator (TPA). If administered soon after a heart attack, this protein helps dissolve blood clots and reduces the risk of subsequent heart attacks.

Diagnosis of Disease DNA technology can also serve as a diagnostic tool. Among the hundreds of genes for human diseases that have been identified are those for sickle-cell disease, hemophilia, cystic fibrosis, and Huntington's disease. Affected individuals with such diseases often can be identified before the onset of symptoms, even before birth. It is also possible to identify symptomless carriers of potentially harmful recessive alleles (see Module 9.9). In addition, DNA technology can pinpoint infections. For example, DNA analysis can help track down and identify elusive viruses such as HIV, the virus that causes AIDS.

Vaccines DNA technology is also helping medical researchers develop vaccines. A **vaccine** is a harmless variant (mutant) or derivative of a pathogen—usually a bacterium or virus—that is used to stimulate the immune system to mount a lasting defense against that pathogen, thereby preventing disease

(see Module 24.3). For many viral diseases (such as measles, mumps, and polio), prevention by vaccination is the only medical way to prevent illness among those exposed to the virus.

Genetic engineering can be used in several ways to make vaccines. One approach is to use genetically engineered cells or organisms to produce large amounts of a protein molecule that is found on the pathogen's outside surface. This method has been used to make the vaccine against hepatitis B, a disabling and sometimes fatal liver disease. Figure 12.7B shows a tank for growing yeast cells that have been engineered to carry the gene for the hepatitis B virus's surface protein. This protein, which is made by the yeast, will be the main ingredient of the vaccine.

Another way to use DNA technology in vaccine development is to make a harmless artificial mutant of the pathogen by altering one or more of its genes. When a harmless mutant is used as a so-called live vaccine, it multiplies in the body and may trigger a strong immune response. Artificial-mutant vaccines may cause fewer side effects than vaccines that have traditionally been made from natural mutants.

Yet another method for making vaccines uses a virus related to the one that causes smallpox. Smallpox was once a dreaded human disease, but it was eradicated worldwide in the 1970s by widespread vaccination with a harmless variant of the smallpox virus. Using this harmless virus, genetic engineers could replace some smallpox genes with genes that induce immunity to other diseases. In fact, the virus could be engineered to carry genes needed to vaccinate against several diseases simultaneously. In the future, one inoculation may prevent a dozen diseases.

Genetic engineering rapidly transformed the field of medicine and continues to do so today. But this new technology affects our lives in other ways, as we'll see next.

? Human growth hormone and insulin produced by DNA technology are used in the treatment of _____ and _____, respectively.

● dwarfism . . . diabetes

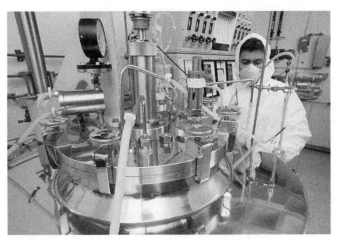

▲ Figure 12.7B Equipment used in the production of a vaccine against hepatitis B

12.8 Genetically modified organisms are transforming agriculture

CONNECTION

Since ancient times, people have selectively bred agricultural crops to make them more useful (see Chapter 31 for a discussion of plant domestication). Today, DNA technology is quickly replacing traditional breeding programs as scientists work to improve the productivity of agriculturally important plants and animals. Genetic engineers have produced many different varieties of **genetically modified organisms (GMOs)**, organisms that have acquired one or more genes by artificial means. If the new gene is from another organism, typically of another species, the recombinant organism is called a **transgenic organism**.

A common vector used to introduce new genes into plant cells is a plasmid from the soil bacterium *Agrobacterium tumefaciens* called the Ti plasmid (Figure 12.8A). ❶ With the help of a restriction enzyme and DNA ligase, the gene for the desired trait (indicated in red) is inserted into a modified version of the plasmid. ❷ Then the recombinant plasmid is put into a plant cell, where the DNA carrying the new gene integrates into one of the plant's chromosomes. ❸ Finally, the recombinant cell is cultured and grown into a plant.

With an estimated 1 billion people facing malnutrition, GMO crops may be able to help a great many hungry people by improving food production, shelf life, pest resistance, and the nutritional value of crops. The story of the Hawaiian papaya industry (see the chapter introduction) provides one dramatic example. In India, the insertion of a natural but rare salinity-resistance gene has enabled new varieties of rice to grow in water three times as salty as seawater, allowing food to be grown in drought-stricken or flooded areas. Similar research is under way in Australia to help improve wheat yields in salty soil. Golden Rice, a transgenic variety created in 2000 with a few daffodil genes, produces yellow grains containing beta-carotene, which our body uses to make vitamin A (Figure 12.8B). A newer strain (Golden Rice 2) uses corn genes to boost beta-carotene levels even higher. Golden rice could help prevent vitamin A deficiency, which causes blindness in a quarter million children each year.

In addition to agricultural applications, genetic engineers are now creating plants that make human proteins for medical use. A recently developed transgenic rice strain harbors genes for milk proteins that can be used in rehydration formulas to treat infant diarrhea, a serious problem in developing countries. Other pharmaceutical trials under way involve using modified corn to treat cystic fibrosis, and duckweed to treat hepatitis. Although these trials seem promising, no plant-made drugs intended for use by humans have been approved.

Agricultural researchers are producing transgenic animals by injecting cloned genes directly into the nuclei of fertilized eggs. Some of the cells integrate the foreign DNA into their genomes. The engineered embryos are then surgically implanted into a surrogate mother. If an embryo develops successfully, the resulting animal will contain a gene from a third "parent"— the gene donor—which may even be of another species.

▲ Figure 12.8B Golden Rice

The goals in creating a transgenic animal are often the same as the goals of traditional breeding—for instance, to make a sheep with better quality wool or a cow that will mature in less time. In 2006, researchers genetically modified pigs to carry a round-worm gene whose protein converts less healthy fatty acids to omega-3 fatty acids. Meat from the modified pigs contains four to five times as much healthy omega-3 fat as regular pork. Atlantic salmon have been genetically modified by the addition of a more active promoter of a growth hormone gene from Chinook salmon. Such fish can mature in half the time of conventional salmon and grow to twice the size. In late 2012, the FDA found that the modified salmon had no significant effect on humans or the environment, clearing an important hurdle to their sale as food. As of mid–2013, public hearings on whether to allow the salmon to become the first transgenic animal sold as food were ongoing. As we'll discuss next, some people worry that GMOs are not safe for human health or the environment.

> **?** What is the function of the Ti plasmid in the creation of transgenic plants?
>
> It is used as the vector for introducing foreign genes into a plant cell.

Agrobacterium tumefaciens

DNA containing the gene for a desired trait

Ti plasmid

Restriction site

❶ The gene is inserted into the plasmid using a restriction enzyme and DNA ligase.

Recombinant Ti plasmid

❷ The recombinant plasmid is introduced into a plant cell in culture.

Plant cell

DNA carrying the new gene within the plant chromosome

❸ The plant cell is cultured and grows into a plant.

A plant with the new trait

▲ Figure 12.8A   Using the Ti plasmid to genetically engineer plants

12.9 Genetically modified organisms raise health concerns

SCIENTIFIC THINKING

As soon as scientists realized the power of DNA technology, they began to worry about potential dangers. Early concerns focused on the possibility that recombinant DNA technology might create new pathogens. To guard against rogue microbes, scientists developed a set of guidelines including strict laboratory safety and containment procedures, the genetic crippling of transgenic organisms to ensure that they cannot survive outside the laboratory, and a prohibition on certain dangerous experiments. Today, most public concern centers on GMOs used for food.

Are genetically modified organisms safe?

Human Safety   Genetically modified organisms are used in crop production because they are more nutritious or because they are cheaper to produce. But do these advantages come at a cost to the health of people consuming GMOs? When investigating complex questions like this one, scientists often use multiple experimental methods. A 2012 animal study involved 104 pigs that were divided into two groups: The first was fed a diet containing 39% GMO corn and the other a closely related non-GMO corn. The health of the pigs was measured over the short term (31 days), the medium term (110 days), and the normal generational life span. The researchers reported no significant differences between the two groups and no traces of foreign DNA in the slaughtered pigs.

Although pigs are a good model organism for human digestion, critics argue that human data are required to draw conclusions about the safety of dietary GMOs for people. The results of one human study, conducted jointly by Chinese and American scientists, were published in 2012. Sixty-eight Chinese schoolchildren (ages 6–8) were fed Golden Rice, spinach (a natural source of beta-carotene), or a capsule containing pure beta-carotene. Over 21 days, blood samples were drawn to measure how much vitamin A the body produced from each food source. The data show that the beta-carotene in both Golden Rice and the capsules was converted to vitamin A in the body with similar efficiency, while the beta-carotene in spinach led to significantly less vitamin A (**Figure 12.9**). The results led researchers to conclude that GMO rice can indeed be effective in preventing vitamin A deficiency.

Despite its positive findings, this study caused an uproar. Chinese authorities called the study an unethical "scandal," complaining that U.S. scientists had used Chinese schoolchildren as laboratory subjects. The project leaders countered that proper permission and consent had been obtained in both China and the United States. The controversy highlights one of the difficulties in conducting research on human nutrition: Animal studies are of limited value, but human studies may be unethical. To date, no study has documented health risks in humans from GMO foods, and there is general agreement among scientists that the GMO foods on the market are safe. However, it is not yet possible to measure the long-term effects (if any) of GMOs on human health.

Environmental Safety   Advocates of a cautious approach toward GMO crops fear that transgenic plants might pass their new genes to related species in nearby wild areas, disturbing the composition of the natural ecosystem. Critics of GMO crops can point to several studies that do indeed show unintended gene transfer from engineered crops to nearby wild relatives. But GMO advocates counter that no lasting or detrimental effects from such transfers have been demonstrated, and that some GMOs (such as bacteria engineered to break down oil spills) can actively help the environment.

Labeling   Although the majority of several staple crops grown in the United States—including corn and soybeans—are genetically modified, products made from GMOs are not required to be labeled in any way. Chances are you ate a food containing GMOs today, but the lack of labeling means you probably can't say for certain. Labeling of foods containing more than trace amounts of GMOs is required in Europe, Japan, Australia, China, Russia, and other countries. Labeling advocates point out that the information would allow consumers to decide for themselves whether they wish to be exposed to GMO foods. Some biotechnology advocates, however, respond that similar demands were not made when "transgenic" crop plants produced by traditional breeding techniques were put on the market. For example, triticale (a crop used primarily in animal feed but also in some human foods) was created decades ago by combining the genomes of wheat and rye—two plants that do not interbreed in nature. Triticale is now sold worldwide without any special labeling.

Scientists and the public need to weigh the possible benefits versus risks on a case-by-case basis. The best scenario would be to proceed with caution, basing our decisions on sound scientific information rather than on either irrational fear or blind optimism.

> **?**   **Why might crop plants engineered to be resistant to weed killer pose a danger to the environment?**
>
> ● The genes for herbicide resistance could transfer to closely related weeds, which could themselves then become resistant.

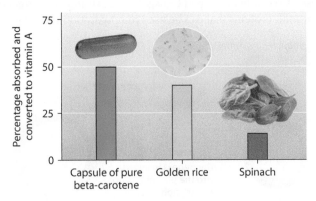

▲ **Figure 12.9**   Vitamin A production after consumption of different sources of beta-carotene

Data from G. Tang et al., Beta-carotene in Golden Rice is as good as beta-carotene in oil at providing vitamin A to children, *American Journal of Clinical Nutrition* 96(3): 658–64 (2012).

12.10 Gene therapy may someday help treat a variety of diseases

CONNECTION

So far in this chapter, we have discussed transgenic viruses, bacteria, yeast, plants, and animals. What about transgenic humans? Why would anyone want to insert genes into a living person?

One reason to tamper with the human genome is the potential of **gene therapy**—alteration of a diseased individual's genes for therapeutic purposes. In people afflicted with disorders caused by a single defective gene, it might be possible to replace or supplement the defective gene by inserting a normal allele into cells of the tissue affected by the disorder. Once there, the normal allele might be expressed, potentially offering a permanent cure after just one treatment.

For gene therapy to be permanent, the normal allele would have to be transferred to cells that multiply throughout a person's life. Bone marrow cells, which include the stem cells that give rise to all the cells of the blood and immune system, are prime candidates (**Figure 12.10**). ❶ A gene from a healthy person is cloned, converted to an RNA version, and then inserted into the RNA genome of a harmless virus. ❷ Bone marrow cells are taken from the patient and infected with the recombinant virus. ❸ The virus inserts a DNA version of its genome, including the normal human gene, into the cells' DNA. ❹ The engineered cells are then injected back into the patient. If the procedure succeeds, the cells will multiply throughout the patient's life and produce a steady supply of the missing protein, curing the patient.

The promise of gene therapy thus far exceeds actual results, but there have been some successes. From 2000 to 2011, gene therapy cured 22 children with severe combined immunodeficiency (SCID), a fatal inherited disease caused by a defective gene that prevents development of the immune system, requiring patients to live within protective "bubbles." Unless treated with a bone marrow transplant, which is effective only 60% of the time, SCID patients quickly die from infections by microbes that most of us fend off. Although the gene therapy treatment cured the patients of SCID, there were some serious side effects: Four of the treated patients developed leukemia, and one died after the inserted gene turned the blood cells cancerous.

A 2009 gene therapy trial involved a disease called Leber's congenital amaurosis (LCA). People with one form of LCA produce abnormal rhodopsin, a pigment that enables the eye to detect light. In such people, photoreceptor cells gradually die, causing progressive blindness. Researchers found that a single injection—containing a virus carrying the normal gene—into one eye of affected children improved vision in that eye, sometimes enough to allow normal functioning.

Gene therapy raises difficult ethical questions. Some critics suggest that tampering with human genes in any way will inevitably lead to eugenics, the deliberate effort to control the genetic makeup of human populations. Other observers see no fundamental difference between the transplantation of genes into somatic cells and the transplantation of organs.

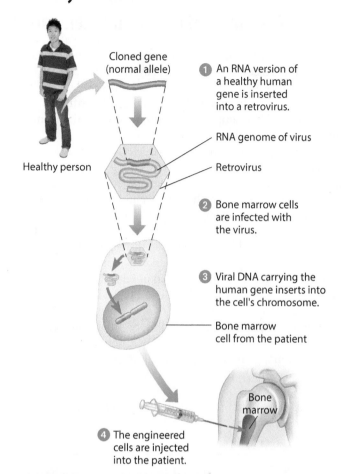

❶ An RNA version of a healthy human gene is inserted into a retrovirus.

Cloned gene (normal allele)

Healthy person

RNA genome of virus

Retrovirus

❷ Bone marrow cells are infected with the virus.

❸ Viral DNA carrying the human gene inserts into the cell's chromosome.

Bone marrow cell from the patient

Bone marrow

❹ The engineered cells are injected into the patient.

▲ **Figure 12.10** One type of gene therapy procedure

The implications of genetically manipulating gamete-forming cells or zygotes (already accomplished in lab animals) are more problematic. This possibility raises the most difficult ethical questions of all: Should we try to eliminate genetic defects in our children and their descendants? Should we interfere with evolution in this way? From a biological perspective, the elimination of unwanted alleles from the gene pool could backfire. Genetic variety is a necessary ingredient for the survival of a species as environmental conditions change with time. Genes that are damaging under some conditions may be advantageous under others (one example is the sickle-cell allele; see Module 9.13). Are we willing to risk making genetic changes that could be detrimental to our species in the future? We may have to face this question soon.

? **Why does bone marrow make a good target for gene therapy?**

● Bone marrow cells multiply throughout a person's life and contain stem cells that give rise to different kinds of blood cells.

▷ DNA Profiling

12.11 The analysis of genetic markers can produce a DNA profile

Modern DNA technology methods have rapidly transformed the field of **forensics**, the scientific analysis of evidence for crime scene investigations and other legal proceedings. The most important application to forensics is **DNA profiling**, the analysis of DNA samples to determine whether they came from the same individual.

Imagine that you have two DNA samples, perhaps one from a crime scene and one from a suspect. How do you test whether the two samples of DNA originate from the same person? You could compare the entire genomes found in the two samples, but such an approach would be extremely impractical, requiring a lot of time and money. Instead, scientists compare genetic markers, sequences in the genome that vary from person to person. A genetic marker is more likely to be a match between relatives than between unrelated individuals.

Figure 12.11 presents an overview of a typical investigation involving a DNA profile. ❶ First, DNA samples are isolated from the crime scene, suspects, victims, or other evidence. ❷ Next, selected markers from each DNA sample are amplified (copied many times), producing a large sample of DNA fragments. ❸ Finally, the amplified DNA markers are compared, providing data about which samples are from the same individual. In the next four modules, we'll explore the methods behind these steps in detail.

❶ DNA is isolated.

❷ The DNA of selected markers is amplified.

❸ The amplified DNA is compared.

▲ **Figure 12.11**   An overview of DNA profiling

> **?** According to the data presented in Figure 12.11, which suspect left DNA at the crime scene?

● Suspect 2: Notice that the number and location of the DNA markers in suspect 2's DNA and the crime scene DNA match.

12.12 The PCR method is used to amplify DNA sequences

The **polymerase chain reaction (PCR)** is a technique by which a specific segment of a DNA molecule can be targeted and quickly amplified in the laboratory. Starting with a minute sample, automated PCR can generate billions of copies of a DNA segment in just a few hours, producing enough DNA to allow a DNA profile to be constructed.

In principle, PCR is fairly simple (**Figure 12.12**). A repeated cycle brings about a chain reaction that doubles the population of identical DNA molecules during each round. The key to amplifying one particular segment of DNA and no others is the use of **primers**, short (usually 15–20 nucleotides long), chemically synthesized single-stranded DNA molecules with

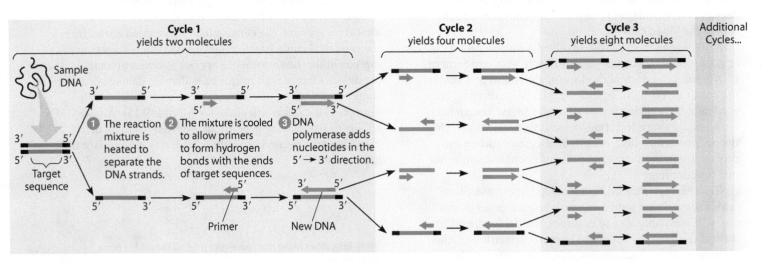

Cycle 1
yields two molecules

Cycle 2
yields four molecules

Cycle 3
yields eight molecules

Additional Cycles...

Sample DNA

Target sequence

❶ The reaction mixture is heated to separate the DNA strands.

❷ The mixture is cooled to allow primers to form hydrogen bonds with the ends of target sequences.

❸ DNA polymerase adds nucleotides in the 5′ → 3′ direction.

Primer

New DNA

▲ **Figure 12.12**   DNA amplification by PCR

Try This   If each cycle takes 15 minutes, calculate the number of copies of the original DNA molecule that will be present after 6 hours.

sequences that are complementary to sequences at each end of the target sequence. One primer is complementary to one strand at one end of the target sequence; the second primer is complementary to the other strand at the other end of the sequence. The primers thus bind to sequences that flank the target sequence, marking the start and end points for the segment of DNA being amplified.

① In the first step of each PCR cycle, the reaction mixture is heated to separate the strands of the DNA double helices. ② Next, the strands are cooled. As they cool, primer molecules hydrogen-bond to their target sequences on the DNA. ③ Then a heat-stable DNA polymerase builds new DNA strands by extending the primers in the $5' \rightarrow 3'$ direction. These three steps are repeated over and over, doubling the amount of DNA after each three-step cycle. A key prerequisite for automating PCR was the discovery of an unusual DNA polymerase, first isolated from a bacterium living in hot springs, that could withstand the heat at the start of each cycle. Without such a heat-stable polymerase, PCR would not be possible because standard DNA polymerases would denature (unfold) during the heating step of each cycle.

Only minute amounts of DNA need to be present in the starting material, and this DNA can even be in a partially degraded state. The key to the high sensitivity is the primers. Because the primers only bind the sequences associated with the target, the DNA polymerase duplicates only the desired segments of DNA. Other DNA will not be bound by primers and thus not copied by the DNA polymerase.

Devised in 1985, PCR has had a major impact on biological research and biotechnology. PCR has been used to amplify DNA from a wide variety of sources: fragments of ancient DNA from a mummified human, a 40,000-year-old frozen woolly mammoth, and a 30-million-year-old plant fossil; DNA from fingerprints or from tiny amounts of blood, tissue, or semen found at crime scenes; DNA from single embryonic cells for rapid prenatal diagnosis of genetic disorders; and DNA of viral genes from cells infected with viruses that are difficult to detect, such as HIV.

? Why does PCR amplify only one specific region of DNA rather than all of it?

The primers mark the ends, ensuring that only the DNA within the region between is amplified.

12.13 Gel electrophoresis sorts DNA molecules by size

Many DNA technology applications rely on **gel electrophoresis**, a method that separates macromolecules—usually proteins or nucleic acids—on the basis of size, electrical charge, or other physical properties. A gel is a thin rectangle of jellylike material often made from agarose, a carbohydrate polymer extracted from seaweed. Because agarose contains a tangle of cable-like threads, it can act as a molecular sieve.

Figure 12.13 outlines how gel electrophoresis can be used to separate mixtures of DNA fragments obtained from three different sources. A DNA sample from each source is placed in a separate well (hole) at one end of a gel that is suspended in liquid. A negatively charged electrode from a power supply is attached near the end of the gel containing the DNA, and a positive electrode is attached near the far end. Because all nucleic acid molecules carry negative charges on their phosphate groups (PO_4^-; see Module 10.2), the DNA molecules all travel through the gel toward the positive pole. However,

longer DNA fragments are held back by the thicket of polymer fibers within the gel, so they move more slowly than the shorter fragments. Over time, shorter molecules move farther through the gel than longer fragments. Gel electrophoresis thus separates DNA fragments by length, with shorter molecules migrating toward the bottom faster.

When the current is turned off, a series of bands is left in each "lane" of the gel. Each band is a collection of DNA fragments of the same length. The bands can be made visible by staining, by exposure onto photographic film (if the DNA is radioactively labeled), or by measuring fluorescence (if the DNA is labeled with a fluorescent dye).

? What causes DNA molecules to move toward the positive pole during electrophoresis? Why do large molecules move more slowly than smaller ones?

The negatively charged phosphate groups of the DNA are attracted to the positive pole; the gel restricts the movement of longer fragments more.

▲ **Figure 12.13** Gel electrophoresis of DNA

Try This Explain why the shortest DNA molecules end up at the bottom of the gel.

12.14 Short tandem repeat analysis is commonly used for DNA profiling

Now that we've learned about DNA amplification by PCR and gel electrophoresis, let's see how these methods can be combined in DNA profiling. To create a DNA profile, a forensic scientist gathers data about a predefined set of genetic markers. The genetic markers most often used in DNA profiling are inherited variations in the lengths of repetitive DNA segments. **Repetitive DNA** consists of nucleotide sequences that are present in multiple copies in the genome; much of the DNA that lies between genes in humans is of this type. Some regions of repetitive DNA vary considerably from one individual to the next.

The repetitive DNA used in genetic DNA profiles consists of short sequences repeated many times in a row; such a series of repeats is called a **short tandem repeat (STR)**. For example, one person might have the sequence AGAT repeated 12 times in a row at one place in the genome, the sequence GATA repeated 45 times in a row at a second place, and so on. Another person has the same sequences at the same places but with different numbers of repeats. These stretches of repetitive DNA, like any genetic marker, are more likely to be an exact match between relatives than between unrelated individuals.

STR analysis is a method of DNA profiling that compares the lengths of STR sequences at specific sites in the genome. The current standard for DNA profiling in forensic and legal systems compares the number of repeats of specific four-nucleotide DNA sequences at 13 sites scattered throughout the genome. Each of these repeat sites, which typically contain from 3 to 50 four-nucleotide repeats in a row, vary widely from person to person. In fact, some of the STRs used in the standard procedure can be found in up to 80 different variations in the human population. In the United States, the number of repeats at each site is entered into a database called CODIS (Combined DNA Index System) administered by the Federal Bureau of Investigation (FBI). Law enforcement agencies around the world can access CODIS to search for matches to DNA samples they have obtained from crime scenes or suspects.

▲ **Figure 12.14B**   DNA profiles generated from the STRs in Figure 12.14A

Consider the two samples of DNA shown in **Figure 12.14A**, where the top DNA was obtained at a crime scene and the bottom DNA from a suspect. The two segments have the same number of repeats at the first site: 7 repeats of the four-nucleotide DNA sequence AGAT (shown in orange). Notice, however, that they differ in the number of repeats at the second site: 8 repeats of GATA (shown in purple) in the crime scene DNA, compared with 13 repeats in the suspect's DNA. To create a DNA profile, a scientist uses PCR to specifically amplify the regions of DNA that include these STR sites. This can be done by using primers matching nucleotide sequences known to flank the STR sites. The resulting DNA molecules are then compared by gel electrophoresis.

Figure 12.14B shows a gel that could have resulted from the STR fragments in Figure 12.14A. The differences in the locations of the bands reflect the different lengths of the DNA fragments. (A gel from an actual DNA profile would typically contain more than just two bands in each lane.) This gel would provide evidence that the crime scene DNA did not come from the suspect. Notice that electrophoresis allows us to see similarities as well as differences between mixtures of DNA molecules. Thus, data from DNA profiling can provide evidence of either innocence or guilt.

Within the human population, so much variation exists within the 13 standard sites that a DNA profile made via STR analysis can definitely identify a single person from within the entire human population. In the next module, we'll examine several real-world examples of how this technology has been used.

? **What are STRs? What is STR analysis?**

● STRs are regions of the genome that contain varying numbers of sequential repeats of a short nucleotide sequence; STR analysis is a technique for determining whether two DNA samples have identical STRs.

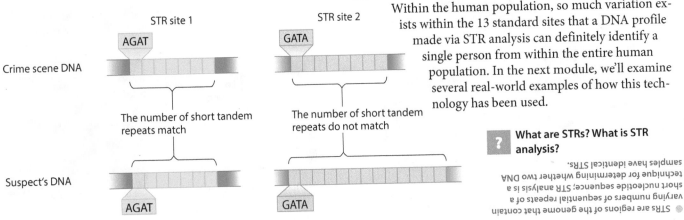

▲ **Figure 12.14A**   Two representative STR sites from crime scene DNA samples

12.15 DNA profiling has provided evidence in many forensic investigations

CONNECTION

When a violent crime is committed, body fluids or small pieces of tissue may be left at the crime scene or on the clothes of the victim or assailant. If rape has occurred, semen may be recovered from the victim. DNA profiling can match such samples to the person they came from with a high degree of certainty because the DNA sequence of every person is unique (except for identical twins). PCR amplification allows tissue samples comprising as few as 20 cells to be tested.

Since its introduction in 1986, DNA profiling has become a standard tool of forensics and has provided crucial evidence in many famous cases. DNA profiling first gained wide public attention during the O. J. Simpson murder trial, when DNA analysis proved that blood in Simpson's car belonged to the victims and that blood at the crime scene belonged to Simpson. (The jury in this case did not find the DNA evidence alone to be sufficient, and Simpson was found not guilty.) During the investigation that led to his impeachment, President Bill Clinton repeatedly denied that he had sexual relations with Monica Lewinsky—until DNA profiling proved that his semen was on her dress.

DNA evidence can prove innocence as well as guilt. Lawyers at the Innocence Project, a nonprofit organization dedicated to overturning wrongful convictions, have used DNA technology and legal work to exonerate more than 300 convicted criminals since 1989, including 17 who were on death row (**Figure 12.15A**). In more than a third of these cases, DNA profiling also identified the true perpetrators.

▲ Figure 12.15A   Earl Washington, a convicted murderer who was freed after 17 years in prison thanks to an STR analysis that proved his innocence

DNA profiling can also be used to identify victims. The largest such effort in history occurred after the terrorist attack on the World Trade Center on September 11, 2001. Forensic scientists, under the coordination of the Office of the Chief Medical Examiner of New York City, worked for years to identify more than 20,000 samples of victims' remains. DNA profiles of tissue samples from the disaster site were matched to DNA profiles from tissue known to be from the victims. If no sample of a victim's DNA was available, blood samples from close relatives were used to confirm identity through near matches. More than half of the identified victims at the World Trade Center site were recognized solely by DNA evidence, providing closure to many grieving families.

The use of DNA profiling extends beyond crimes. For instance, a comparison of the DNA of a child and the purported father can conclusively settle a question of paternity. Sometimes, paternity is of historical interest: DNA profiling proved that Thomas Jefferson or a close male relative of Jefferson's fathered a child with his slave Sally Hemings. Going back much further, one of the strangest cases of DNA

▲ Figure 12.15B   Cheddar Man and one of his modern-day descendants

profiling is that of Cheddar Man, a 9,000-year-old skeleton found in a cave near Cheddar, England (**Figure 12.15B**). DNA was extracted from his tooth and analyzed. The DNA profile showed that Cheddar Man was a direct ancestor—through approximately 300 generations—of a present-day schoolteacher who lived only a half mile from the cave!

Just how reliable is DNA profiling? When the standard CODIS set of 13 STR sites (see Module 12.14) is used, the probability of finding the same DNA profile in randomly selected, unrelated individuals is less than one in 10 billion. Put another way, a standard DNA profile can provide a statistical match of a particular DNA sample to just one living human. For this reason, DNA analyses are now accepted as compelling evidence by legal experts and scientists alike. In fact, DNA analysis on stored forensic samples has provided the evidence needed to solve many "cold cases" in recent years.

DNA analysis has also been used to probe the origin of non-human materials. For example, examination of DNA can prove the origin of food, as with a U.S. Fish and Wildlife Service program that tests caviar to determine if the fish eggs originate from the species claimed on the label. In addition, DNA profiling can help protect endangered species by conclusively providing the origin of contraband animal products, allowing for increased vigilance in endangered regions. Animals can also be the subject of research, as with a 2005 study that determined that DNA extracted from a 27,000-year-old Siberian mammoth was 98.6% identical to DNA from modern African elephants.

Although DNA profiling has provided definitive evidence in many investigations, the method is far from foolproof. Problems can arise from insufficient data, human error, or flawed evidence. Although the science behind DNA profiling is irrefutable, the human element remains a possible confounding factor.

? **In what way is DNA profiling valuable for determining innocence as well as guilt?**

● A DNA profile can prove with near certainty that a sample of DNA does or does not come from a particular individual. DNA profiling therefore can provide evidence in support of guilt or innocence.

12.16 RFLPs can be used to detect differences in DNA sequences

Recall that a genetic marker is a DNA sequence that varies in a population. Like different alleles of a gene, the DNA sequence at a specific place on a chromosome may exhibit small nucleotide differences, or polymorphisms (from the Greek for "many forms"). Geneticists have cataloged many single-base-pair variations in the genome. Such a variation found in at least 1% of the population is called a **single nucleotide polymorphism** (**SNP**, pronounced "snip"). SNPs occur on average about once in 100 to 300 base pairs in the human genome, both in the coding sequences of genes and in noncoding sequences between genes. Scientists have identified several million SNP sites, and more are discovered each year.

SNPs may alter a restriction site—the sequence recognized by a restriction enzyme. Such alterations change the lengths of the restriction fragments formed by that enzyme when it cuts the DNA. A sequence variation of this type is called a **restriction fragment length polymorphism** (**RFLP**, pronounced "rif-lip"). Thus, RFLPs can serve as genetic markers for particular loci in the genome. RFLPs have many uses. For example, disease-causing alleles can be diagnosed with reasonable accuracy if a closely linked RFLP marker has been found. Alleles for a number of genetic diseases were first detected by means of RFLPs in this indirect way.

Restriction fragment analysis involves two of the methods you have learned about: DNA fragments produced by restriction enzymes (Module 12.2) are sorted by gel electrophoresis (Module 12.13). The number of restriction fragments and their sizes reflect the specific sequence of nucleotides in the starting DNA.

At the top of **Figure 12.16**, you can see corresponding segments of DNA from two DNA samples prepared from human tissue. Notice that the DNA sequences differ by a single base pair (highlighted in yellow). In this case, the restriction enzyme cuts DNA between two cytosine (C) bases in the sequence CCGG and in its complement, GGCC. Because DNA from the first sample has two recognition sequences for the restriction enzyme, it is cleaved in two places, yielding three restriction fragments (labeled *w*, *x*, and *y*). DNA from the second sample, however, has only one recognition sequence and yields only two restriction fragments (*z* and *y*). Notice that the lengths of restriction fragments, as well as the number of fragments, differ, depending on the exact sequence of bases in the DNA.

To detect the differences between the collections of restriction fragments, we need to separate the restriction fragments in the two mixtures and compare their lengths. This process, called RFLP analysis, is accomplished through gel electrophoresis. As shown in the bottom of the figure, the three kinds of restriction fragments from sample 1 separate into three bands in the gel, whereas those from sample 2 separate into only two bands. Notice that the shortest fragment from sample 1 (*y*) produces a band at the same location as the identical short fragment from the sample 2. So you can see that electrophoresis allows us to see similarities as well as differences between mixtures of restriction fragments—and similarities

► **Figure 12.16** RFLP analysis

as well as differences between the base sequences in DNA from two individuals. The restriction fragment analysis in Figure 12.16 clearly shows that the two DNA samples differ in sequence. Although RFLP analysis is rarely used today for identification, this method was vital in some of the earliest discoveries of disease-causing genes. For example, the gene for Huntington's disease was found after researchers used RFLPs to track a genetic marker that was closely associated with the disorder.

? You use a restriction enzyme to cut a DNA molecule that has three copies of the enzyme's recognition sequence clustered near one end. When you separate the restriction fragments by gel electrophoresis, how do you expect the bands to look?

● There should be three bands near the positive pole at the bottom of the gel (small fragments) and one band near the negative pole at the top of the gel (large fragment).

▷ Genomics

12.17 Genomics is the scientific study of whole genomes

By the 1980s, biologists were using RFLPs to map important genes in humans and some other organisms. But it didn't take long for biologists to think on a larger scale. In 1995, a team of scientists determined the nucleotide sequence of the entire genome of *Haemophilus influenzae*, a bacterium that can cause several human diseases, including pneumonia and meningitis. **Genomics**, the study of complete sets of genes (genomes) and their interactions, was born.

Since 1995, researchers have used the tools and techniques of DNA technology to develop more and more detailed maps of the genomes of a number of species. The first targets of genomics research were bacteria, which have relatively little DNA. The *H. influenza* genome, for example, contains only 1.8 million nucleotides and 1,709 genes. But soon, the attention of genomics researchers turned toward more complex organisms with much larger genomes. As of 2013, the genomes of nearly 7,000 species have been completed, and thousands more are in progress. Table 12.17 lists some of the completed genomes; for diploids, the size refers to the haploid genome. The majority of genomes under study are from prokaryotes, including *E. coli* and several thousand other bacteria (some of medical importance), and more than 200 Archaea. Over 300 eukaryotic species have been sequenced, including vertebrates, invertebrates, fungi, and plants.

Baker's yeast (*Saccharomyces cerevisiae*) was the first eukaryote to have its full sequence determined, and the roundworm *Caenorhabditis elegans* was the first multicellular organism. Other sequenced animals include the fruit fly (*Drosophila melanogaster*) and the laboratory mouse (*Mus musculus*), both model organisms for genetics research. Plants, such as one type of mustard (*Arabidopsis thaliana*,

an important research organism) and rice (*Oryza sativa*, one of the world's most economically important crops), have also been completed. Other recently completed eukaryotic genomes include sorghum (another important commercial crop), the honeybee, dog, wallaby (a marsupial), turkey, and bottlenose dolphin.

In 2005, researchers completed the genome sequence for our closest living relative on the evolutionary tree of life, the chimpanzee (*Pan troglodytes*). Comparisons with human DNA revealed that we share 96% of our genome with our closest animal relative. As you will see in Module 12.21, genomic scientists are currently finding and studying the important differences, shedding scientific light on the age-old question of what makes us human.

Why map so many genomes? Not only are all genomes of interest in their own right, but comparative analysis provides invaluable insights into the evolutionary relationships among organisms. Also, having maps of a variety of genomes helps scientists interpret the human genome. For example, when scientists find a nucleotide sequence in the human genome similar to a yeast gene whose function is known, they have a valuable clue to the function of the human sequence. In fact, the roles of several human disease-causing genes were determined by studying their yeast counterparts. Indeed, many genes of disparate organisms are being found to be astonishingly similar: Some researchers joke that fruit flies can even be thought of as "little people with wings."

? **Does a larger genome always correlate with more genes?**

● No. Compare, for example, the genomes of rice and mice.

TABLE 12.17 | SOME IMPORTANT COMPLETED GENOMES

Organism	Year Completed	Size of Haploid Genome (in Base Pairs)	Approximate Number of Genes
Haemophilus influenzae (bacterium)	1995	1.8 million	1,700
Saccharomyces cerevisiae (yeast)	1996	12 million	6,300
Escherichia coli (bacterium)	1997	4.6 million	4,400
Caenorhabditis elegans (nematode)	1998	100 million	20,100
Drosophila melanogaster (fruit fly)	2000	165 million	14,000
Arabidopsis thaliana (mustard plant)	2000	120 million	27,000
Mus musculus (mouse)	2001	2.6 billion	22,000
Oryza sativa (rice)	2002	430 million	42,000
Homo sapiens (humans)	2003	3.0 billion	21,000
Rattus norvegicus (lab rat)	2004	2.8 billion	25,000
Pan troglodytes (chimpanzee)	2005	3.1 billion	22,000
Macaca mulatta (macaque)	2007	2.9 billion	22,000
Macropus eugenii (wallaby)	2012	2.9 billion	18,000

12.18 The Human Genome Project revealed that most of the human genome does not consist of genes

The **Human Genome Project (HGP)** was a massive, long-term scientific endeavor with the goals of determining the nucleotide sequence of all DNA in the human genome and identifying the location and sequence of every gene. The HGP began in 1990 and was completed in 2003. More than 99% of the human genome has been determined to 99.999% accuracy. (There remain a few hundred gaps of unknown sequences within the human genome that remain elusive.) The DNA sequences determined by the HGP and related projects have been deposited in a publicly available database called GenBank.

The chromosomes in the human genome—22 autosomes plus the X and Y sex chromosomes—contain approximately 3 billion nucleotide pairs of DNA. To get a sense of this much DNA, imagine that its nucleotide sequence is printed in letters (A, T, C, and G) like the letters in this book. At this size, the sequence would fill a stack of books 18 stories high! The biggest surprise from the HGP is the small number of human genes. The current estimate is just below 21,000 genes—very close to the number found in a microscopic worm. How, then, do we account for human complexity? Part of the answer may lie in alternative RNA splicing (see Module 11.4); scientists think that a typical human gene specifies several different polypeptides.

In humans, as in most complex eukaryotes, only a small amount of our total DNA (about 1.5%) is contained in genes that code for proteins, tRNAs, or rRNAs (**Figure 12.18**). Most multicellular eukaryotes have a huge amount of noncoding DNA; about 98.5% of human DNA is of this type. About one-quarter of our DNA consists of introns and gene control sequences such as promoters, enhancers, and microRNAs (see Chapter 11). The remaining noncoding DNA had been dubbed "junk DNA," a tongue-in-cheek way of saying that scientists don't fully understand its functions, but it is now generally accepted that much of this DNA probably plays some role. This stands in sharp contrast to a typical prokaryotic genome, in which the vast majority of DNA serves an obvious function; the human genome contains roughly 10,000 times more noncoding DNA than the *E. coli* genome.

Much of the DNA between genes consists of repetitive DNA, nucleotide sequences present in many copies in the genome. The repeated units of some of this DNA are short, such as the STRs used in DNA profiling (see Module 12.14). Stretches of DNA with thousands of short repetitions are also prominent at the centromeres and ends of chromosomes—called **telomeres**—suggesting that this DNA plays a role in chromosome structure.

In the second main type of repetitive DNA, each repeated unit is hundreds of nucleotides long, and the copies are scattered around the genome. Most of these sequences seem to be associated with **transposable elements** ("jumping genes"), DNA segments that can move or be copied from one location to another in a chromosome and even between chromosomes.

The potential benefits of having a complete map of the human genome are enormous. For instance, hundreds of disease-associated genes have been identified. One example is the gene that is mutated in an inherited type of Parkinson's disease, a debilitating brain disorder that causes tremors of increasing severity. Until recently, Parkinson's disease was not known to have a hereditary component. But data from the Human Genome Project mapped a small number of cases of Parkinson's disease to a specific gene. Interestingly, an altered version of the protein encoded by this gene has also been tied to Alzheimer's disease, suggesting a previously unknown link between these two brain disorders. Moreover, the same gene is also found in rats, where it plays a role in the sense of smell, and in zebra finches, where it is thought to be involved in song learning. Cross-species comparisons such as these may uncover clues about the role played by the normal version of the protein in the human brain. And such knowledge could eventually lead to treatment for the half million Americans with Parkinson's disease.

One interesting question about the Human Genome Project is, Whose genome was sequenced? The first human genome to be sequenced was actually a reference genome compiled from a group of individuals. At nearly the same time, a private biotechnology company sequenced the genome of the company's president. These representative sequences will serve as standards so that comparisons of individual differences and similarities can be made. Starting in 2007, the genomes of a number of other individuals—the first was James Watson, codiscoverer of the structure of DNA—have also been sequenced. These sequences are part of a larger effort to collect information on all of the genetic variations that affect human characteristics. As the amount of sequence data multiplies, the small differences that account for individual variation within our species will come to light.

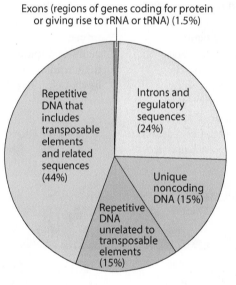

Exons (regions of genes coding for protein or giving rise to rRNA or tRNA) (1.5%)

Repetitive DNA that includes transposable elements and related sequences (44%)

Introns and regulatory sequences (24%)

Unique noncoding DNA (15%)

Repetitive DNA unrelated to transposable elements (15%)

▲ **Figure 12.18** Composition of the human genome

? The haploid human genome consists of about _____ base pairs and _____ genes spread over _____ different chromosomes (provide three numbers).

● 3 billion . . . 21,000 . . . 24 (22 autosomes plus 2 sex chromosomes)

12.19 The whole-genome shotgun method of sequencing a genome can provide a wealth of data quickly

Sequencing an entire genome is a complex task that requires careful work. The Human Genome Project proceeded through three stages that provided progressively more detailed views of the human genome. First, geneticists combined pedigree analyses of large families to map more than 5,000 genetic markers (mostly RFLPs) spaced throughout all of the chromosomes. The resulting low-resolution linkage map (see Module 9.19) provided a framework for mapping other markers and for arranging later, more detailed maps of particular regions. Next, researchers determined the number of base pairs between the markers in the linkage map. These data helped them construct a physical map of the human genome. Finally came the most arduous part of the project: determining the nucleotide sequences of the set of DNA fragments that had been mapped. Advances in automated DNA sequencing were crucial to this endeavor.

This three-stage approach is logical and thorough. However, in 1992, molecular biologist J. Craig Venter proposed an alternative strategy called the **whole-genome shotgun method** and set up the company Celera Genomics to implement it. His idea was essentially to skip the genetic and physical mapping stages and start directly with the sequencing step. In the whole-genome shotgun method, an entire genome is chopped by restriction enzymes into fragments that are cloned and sequenced in just one stage **(Figure 12.19)**. High-performance computers running specialized mapping software can assemble the millions of overlapping short sequences into a single continuous sequence for every chromosome—an entire genome.

Today, the whole-genome shotgun approach is the method of choice for genomic researchers because it is fast and relatively inexpensive. However, recent research has revealed some limitations of this method, such as difficulties with repetitive sequences, suggesting that a hybrid approach that

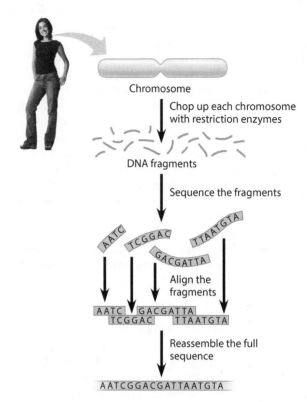

▲ **Figure 12.19**   The whole-genome shotgun method

combines whole-genome shotgunning with physical or genetic maps may prove to be the most useful method.

> **?** What are the primary advantages of the whole-genome shotgun method?
>
> ● It is faster and cheaper than the three-stage method of genome sequencing.

12.20 Proteomics is the scientific study of the full set of proteins encoded by a genome

The successes in the field of genomics have encouraged scientists to begin similar systematic studies of the full protein sets (proteomes) encoded by genomes, an approach called **proteomics**. The number of different proteins in humans far exceeds the number of different genes—about 100,000 proteins versus about 21,000 genes. And because proteins, not genes, actually carry out most of the activities of the cell, scientists must study when and where proteins are produced in an organism and how they interact to understand the functioning of cells and organisms. Given the huge number of proteins and the myriad ways that their production can be controlled, assembling and analyzing proteomes pose many experimental challenges. Ongoing advances are beginning to provide the tools to meet those challenges.

Genomics and proteomics are enabling biologists to approach the study of life from an increasingly holistic (whole-system) perspective. Biologists are now compiling catalogs of genes and proteins—that is, listings of all the "parts" that contribute to the operation of cells, tissues, and organisms. As such catalogs become complete, researchers are shifting their attention from the individual parts to how these parts function together in biological systems.

> **?** If every protein is encoded by a gene, how can humans have many more proteins than genes?
>
> ● The RNA transcribed from one gene may be spliced several different ways to produce different mRNAs that are translated into different proteins (see Module 11.4).

12.21 Genomes hold clues to human evolution

EVOLUTION CONNECTION

Scientists are accumulating genomic sequence data at an astonishing pace. As of 2013, the publicly accessible GenBank included DNA sequences totaling 150 billion base pairs, and this total is doubling every 18 months. Geneticists can now compare genome sequences from many species, allowing hypotheses about evolutionary relationships between those species to be tested. The more similar in sequence the same gene is in two species, the more closely related those species are in their evolutionary history.

The small number of genetic differences between closely related species makes it easier to correlate phenotypic differences between the species with particular genetic differences. The completion of the chimpanzee genome in 2005 has allowed us to compare our genome with that of our primate cousins. Such an analysis revealed that these two genomes differ by 1.2% in single-base substitutions. Researchers were surprised when they found a further 2.7% difference due to insertions or deletions of larger regions in the genome of one or the other species, with many of the insertions being duplications or other repetitive DNA. In fact, a third of the human duplications are not present in the chimpanzee genome, and some of these duplications contain regions associated with human diseases. All of these observations provide clues to the forces that might have swept the two genomes along different paths, but we don't have a complete understanding yet.

What about specific genes and types of genes that differ between humans and chimpanzees? Using evolutionary analyses, biologists have identified a number of genes that have evolved faster in humans. Among them are genes involved in defense against malaria and tuberculosis and a gene regulating brain size. One gene that changed rapidly in the human lineage is *FOXP2*, a gene implicated in speech and vocalization. Differences between the *FOXP2* gene in humans and chimpanzees may play a role in the ability of humans, but not chimpanzees, to communicate by speech.

Neanderthals (*Homo neanderthalensis*) were humans' closest relatives (**Figure 12.21**). First appearing at least 300,000 years ago, Neanderthals lived in Europe and Asia until suddenly going extinct a mere 30,000 years ago. Modern humans (*Homo sapiens*) first appeared in Africa around 200,000 years

ago and spread into Europe and Asia around 50,000 years ago (see Module 19.14)—meaning that modern humans and Neanderthals most likely comingled for some time.

A 2009 rough draft of a 60%-complete Neanderthal genome has, for the first time, allowed detailed genomic comparisons between two species in the genus *Homo*. Using 38,000-year-old thigh bone fossils of two *Homo neanderthalensis* females discovered in a Croatian cave, genomic analysis confirmed Neanderthals as a separate species and as our closest relatives (much closer than chimpanzees). Further comparisons, completed in 2010, suggested that Neanderthals and some *H. sapiens* probably did interbreed. Analysis of the sequence of the *FOXP2* gene showed that Neanderthals had the same allele as modern humans, hinting that Neanderthals may have had the ability to speak. Other genetic analyses of less complete Neanderthal genomes revealed one male to have an unusual allele for a pigment gene that would have given him pale skin and red hair. And, interestingly, analysis of the lactase gene suggests that Neanderthals, like the majority of modern humans, were lactose intolerant as adults (see Chapter 3).

Comparisons with Neanderthals and chimpanzees are part of a larger effort to learn more about the human genome. Other research efforts are extending genomic studies to many more species. These studies will advance our understanding of all aspects of biology, including health, ecology, and evolution. In fact, comparisons of the completed genome sequences of bacteria, archaea, and eukaryotes supported the theory that these are the three fundamental domains of life —a topic we discuss further in the next unit.

▲ Figure 12.21 Reconstruction of a Neanderthal female, based on a 36,000-year-old skull

? How can cross-species comparisons of the nucleotide sequences of a gene provide insight into evolution?

Similarities in gene sequences correlate with evolutionary relatedness; greater genetic similarities reflect a more recent shared ancestry.

CHAPTER 12 REVIEW

For practice quizzes, BioFlix animations, MP3 tutorials, video tutors, and more study tools designed for this textbook, go to

MasteringBiology®

Reviewing the Concepts

Gene Cloning (12.1–12.5)

12.1 Genes can be cloned in recombinant plasmids. Gene cloning is one application of biotechnology, the manipulation of organisms or their components to make useful products. Researchers can manipulate bacterial plasmids so that they contain genes from other organisms. These recombinant DNA plasmids can then be inserted into bacteria. If the recombinant bacteria multiply into a clone, the foreign genes are also duplicated and copies of the gene or its protein product can be harvested.

12.2 Enzymes are used to "cut and paste" DNA. Restriction enzymes cut DNA at specific sequences, forming restriction fragments. DNA ligase "pastes" DNA fragments together.

12.3 Cloned genes can be stored in genomic libraries. Genomic libraries, sets of DNA fragments containing all of an organism's genes, can be constructed and stored for use in DNA technology applications.

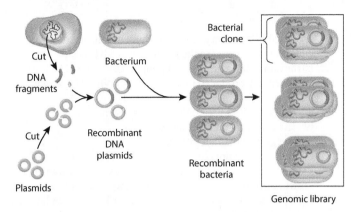

Genomic library

12.4 Reverse transcriptase can help make genes for cloning. cDNA libraries contain only the genes that are transcribed by a particular type of cell.

12.5 Nucleic acid probes identify clones carrying specific genes. A short, single-stranded molecule of labeled DNA or RNA can tag a desired gene in a library.

Genetically Modified Organisms (12.6–12.10)

12.6 Recombinant cells and organisms can mass-produce gene products. Bacteria, yeast, cell cultures, and whole animals can be used to make products for medical and other uses.

12.7 DNA technology has changed the pharmaceutical industry and medicine. Researchers use gene cloning to produce hormones, diagnose diseases, and produce vaccines.

12.8 Genetically modified organisms are transforming agriculture. A number of important crop plants are genetically modified.

12.9 Genetically modified organisms raise health concerns. Genetic engineering involves potential risks to human health and the environment.

12.10 Gene therapy may someday help treat a variety of diseases.

DNA Profiling (12.11–12.16)

12.11 The analysis of genetic markers can produce a DNA profile. DNA technology—methods for studying and manipulating genetic material—has revolutionized the field of forensics. DNA profiling can determine whether two samples of DNA come from the same individual.

12.12 The PCR method is used to amplify DNA sequences. The polymerase chain reaction (PCR) can be used to amplify a DNA sample. The use of specific primers that flank the desired sequence ensures that only a particular subset of the DNA sample will be copied.

12.13 Gel electrophoresis sorts DNA molecules by size.

A mixture of DNA fragments

A "band" is a collection of DNA fragments of one particular length

Longer fragments move slower

Shorter fragments move faster

Power source

DNA is attracted to + pole due to PO_4^- groups

12.14 Short tandem repeat analysis is commonly used for DNA profiling. Short tandem repeats (STRs) are stretches of DNA that contain short nucleotide sequences repeated many times in a row. DNA profiling by STR analysis involves amplifying 13 STRs.

12.15 DNA profiling has provided evidence in many forensic investigations. The applications of DNA profiling include helping to solve crimes, establishing paternity, and identify victims.

12.16 RFLPs can be used to detect differences in DNA sequences. Restriction fragment length polymorphisms (RFLPs) reflect differences in the sequences of DNA samples.

Genomics (12.17–12.21)

12.17 Genomics is the scientific study of whole genomes. Genomics researchers have sequenced many prokaryotic and eukaryotic genomes. Besides being of interest in their own right, nonhuman genomes can be compared with the human genome.

12.18 The Human Genome Project revealed that most of the human genome does not consist of genes. Data from the Human Genome Project (HGP) revealed that the human genome contains just under 21,000 genes and a huge amount of noncoding DNA, much of which consists of repetitive nucleotide sequences.

12.19 The whole-genome shotgun method of sequencing a genome can provide a wealth of data quickly. The HGP used genetic and physical mapping of chromosomes followed by DNA sequencing. Modern genomic analysis often uses the faster whole-genome shotgun method.

12.20 Proteomics is the scientific study of the full set of proteins encoded by a genome.

12.21 Genomes hold clues to human evolution.

Connecting the Concepts

1. Imagine you have found a small quantity of DNA. Fill in the following diagram, which outlines a series of DNA technology experiments you could perform to study this DNA.

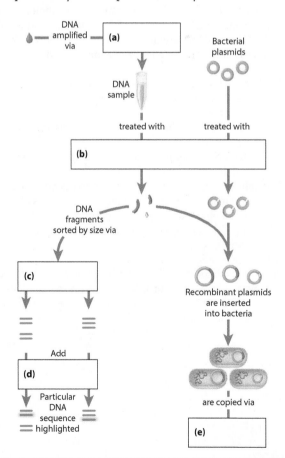

DNA amplified via **(a)**

DNA sample

Bacterial plasmids

treated with   treated with

(b)

DNA fragments sorted by size via

(c)

Add

(d)

Particular DNA sequence highlighted

Recombinant plasmids are inserted into bacteria

are copied via

(e)

Testing Your Knowledge

Level 1: Knowledge/Comprehension

2. Which of the following would be considered a transgenic organism?
   a. a bacterium that has received genes via conjugation
   b. a human given a corrected human blood-clotting gene
   c. a fern grown in cell culture from a single fern root cell
   d. a rat with rabbit hemoglobin genes

3. The DNA profiles used as evidence in a murder trial look something like supermarket bar codes. The pattern of bars in a DNA profile shows
   a. the order of bases in a particular gene.
   b. the presence of various-sized fragments of DNA.
   c. the presence of dominant or recessive alleles for particular traits.
   d. the order of genes along particular chromosomes.

4. A paleontologist has recovered a tiny bit of organic material from the 400-year-old preserved skin of an extinct dodo. She would like to compare DNA from the sample with DNA from living birds. Which of the following would be most useful for increasing the amount of DNA available for testing?
   a. restriction fragment analysis
   b. polymerase chain reaction
   c. molecular probe analysis
   d. electrophoresis

5. How many genes are there in a human sperm cell?
   a. 23
   b. 46
   c. about 21,000
   d. about 3 billion

Level 2: Application/Analysis

6. When a typical restriction enzyme cuts a DNA molecule, the cuts are uneven, giving the DNA fragments single-stranded ends. These ends are useful in recombinant DNA work because
   a. they enable a cell to recognize fragments produced by the enzyme.
   b. they serve as starting points for DNA replication.
   c. the fragments will bond to other fragments with complementary ends.
   d. they enable researchers to use the fragments as molecular probes.

7. Why does DNA profiling rely on comparing specific genetic markers rather than the entire genome?

8. Recombinant DNA techniques are used to custom-build bacteria for two main purposes: to obtain multiple copies of certain genes and to obtain useful proteins produced by certain genes. Give an example of each of these applications in medicine and agriculture.

9. A biochemist hopes to find a gene in human liver cells that codes for an important blood-clotting protein. She knows that the nucleotide sequence of a small part of the blood-clotting gene is CTGGACTGACA. Briefly outline a possible method she might use to isolate the desired gene.

Level 3: Synthesis/Evaluation

10. A biologist isolated a gene from a human cell, inserted it into a plasmid, and inserted the plasmid into a bacterium. The bacterium made a new protein, but it was nothing like the protein normally produced in a human cell. Why? (*Explain your answer.*)
    a. The bacterium had undergone transformation.
    b. The gene did not have sticky ends.
    c. The gene contained introns.
    d. The gene did not come from a genomic library.

11. Explain how you might engineer *E. coli* to produce human growth hormone (HGH) using the following: *E. coli* containing a plasmid, DNA carrying the gene for HGH, DNA ligase, a restriction enzyme, equipment for manipulating and growing bacteria, a method for extracting and purifying the hormone, and an appropriate DNA probe. (Assume that the human HGH gene lacks introns.)

12. What is left for genetic researchers to do now that the Human Genome Project has determined nearly complete nucleotide sequences for all of the human chromosomes? Explain.

13. Today, it is fairly easy to make transgenic plants and animals. What are some important safety and ethical issues raised by this use of recombinant DNA technology? What are some of the possible dangers of introducing genetically engineered organisms into the environment? What are some reasons for and against leaving decisions in these areas to scientists? To business owners and executives? What are some reasons for and against more public involvement? How might these decisions affect you? How do you think these decisions should be made?

14. In the not-too-distant future, gene therapy may be an option for the treatment and cure of some inherited disorders. What do you think are the most serious ethical issues that must be dealt with before human gene therapy is used on a large scale? Why do you think these issues are important?

15. The possibility of extensive genetic testing raises questions about how personal genetic information should be used. For example, should employers or potential employers have access to such information? Why or why not? Should the information be available to insurance companies? Why or why not? Is there any reason for the government to keep genetic files? Is there any obligation to warn relatives who might share a defective gene? Might some people avoid being tested for fear of being labeled genetic outcasts? Or might they be compelled to be tested against their wishes? Can you think of other reasons to proceed with caution?

16. **SCIENTIFIC THINKING** Scientists investigate hypotheses using a variety of methods, depending on the circumstances behind the research. Human nutrition studies (such as those studying whether GMO foods have any health effects) are particularly problematic. Can you design a hypothetical human nutrition study to test whether GMO corn is less healthy than traditional corn? Can you identify real-world problems that may interfere with your design and confound your results?

Answers to all questions can be found in Appendix 4.

Metric Conversion Table

Measurement	Unit and Abbreviation	Metric Equivalent	Approximate Metric-to-English Conversion Factor	Approximate English-to-Metric Conversion Factor
Length	1 kilometer (km)	= 1,000 (10^3) meters	1 km = 0.6 mile	1 mile = 1.6 km
	1 meter (m)	= 100 (10^2) centimeters	1 m = 1.1 yards	1 yard = 0.9 m
		= 1,000 millimeters	1 m = 3.3 feet	1 foot = 0.3 m
			1 m = 39.4 inches	
	1 centimeter (cm)	= 0.01 (10^{-2}) meter	1 cm = 0.4 inch	1 foot = 30.5 cm
				1 inch = 2.5 cm
	1 millimeter (mm)	= 0.001 (10^{-3}) meter	1 mm = 0.04 inch	
	1 micrometer (μm)	= 10^{-6} meter (10^{-3} mm)		
	1 nanometer (nm)	= 10^{-9} meter (10^{-3} μm)		
	1 angstrom (Å)	= 10^{-10} meter (10^{-4} μm)		
Area	1 hectare (ha)	= 10,000 square meters	1 ha = 2.5 acres	1 acre = 0.4 ha
	1 square meter (m^2)	= 10,000 square centimeters	1 m^2 = 1.2 square yards	1 square yard = 0.8 m^2
			1 m^2 = 10.8 square feet	1 square foot = 0.09 m^2
	1 square centimeter (cm^2)	= 100 square millimeters	1 cm^2 = 0.16 square inch	1 square inch = 6.5 cm^2
Mass	1 metric ton (t)	= 1,000 kilograms	1 t = 1.1 tons	1 ton = 0.91 t
	1 kilogram (kg)	= 1,000 grams	1 kg = 2.2 pounds	1 pound = 0.45 kg
	1 gram (g)	= 1,000 milligrams	1 g = 0.04 ounce	1 ounce = 28.35 g
			1 g = 15.4 grains	
	1 milligram (mg)	= 10^{-3} gram	1 mg = 0.02 grain	
	1 microgram (μg)	= 10^{-6} gram		
Volume (Solids)	1 cubic meter (m^3)	= 1,000,000 cubic centimeters	1 m^3 = 1.3 cubic yards	1 cubic yard = 0.8 m^3
			1 m^3 = 35.3 cubic feet	1 cubic foot = 0.03 m^3
	1 cubic centimeter (cm³ or cc)	= 10^{-6} cubic meter	1 cm^3 = 0.06 cubic inch	1 cubic inch = 16.4 cm^3
	1 cubic millimeter (mm^3)	= 10^{-9} cubic meter (10^{-3} cubic centimeter)		
Volume (Liquids and Gases)	1 kiloliter (kL or kl)	= 1,000 liters	1 kL = 264.2 gallons	
	1 liter (L or l)	= 1,000 milliliters	1 L = 0.26 gallon	1 gallon = 3.79 L
			1 L = 1.06 quarts	1 quart = 0.95 L
	1 milliliter (mL or ml)	= 10^{-3} liter	1 mL = 0.03 fluid ounce	1 quart = 946 mL
		= 1 cubic centimeter	1 mL = ¼ teaspoon	1 pint = 473 mL
			1 mL = 15–16 drops	1 fluid ounce = 29.6 mL
				1 teaspoon = 5 mL
	1 microliter (μL or μl)	= 10^{-6} liter (10^{-3} milliliter)		
Time	1 second (s)	= ¹⁄₆₀ minute		
	1 millisecond (ms)	= 10^{-3} second		
Temperature	Degrees Celsius (°C)		°F = $\frac{9}{5}$ °C + 32	°C = $\frac{5}{9}$ (°F − 32)

APPENDIX 2 The Periodic Table

Atomic number (number of protons) → 6 — Atomic mass (number of protons plus number of neutrons averaged over all isotopes)
Element symbol → C
12.01

Metals   Metalloids   Nonmetals

Representative elements

Groups: Elements in a vertical column have the same number of electrons in their valence (outer) shell and thus have similar chemical properties.

Periods: Each horizontal row contains elements with the same total number of electron shells. Across each period, elements are ordered by increasing atomic number.

Transition elements

*Lanthanides
†Actinides

Name (Symbol)	Atomic Number	Name (Symbol)	Atomic Number	Name (Symbol)	Atomic Number	Name (Symbol)	Atomic Number	Name (Symbol)	Atomic Number
Actinium (Ac)	89	Copernicium (Cn)	112	Iodine (I)	53	Osmium (Os)	76	Silicon (Si)	14
Aluminum (Al)	13	Copper (Cu)	29	Iridium (Ir)	77	Oxygen (O)	8	Silver (Ag)	47
Americium (Am)	95	Curium (Cm)	96	Iron (Fe)	26	Palladium (Pd)	46	Sodium (Na)	11
Antimony (Sb)	51	Darmstadtium (Ds)	110	Krypton (Kr)	36	Phosphorus (P)	15	Strontium (Sr)	38
Argon (Ar)	18	Dubnium (Db)	105	Lanthanum (La)	57	Platinum (Pt)	78	Sulphur (S)	16
Arsenic (As)	33	Dysprosium (Dy)	66	Lawrencium (Lr)	103	Plutonium (Pu)	94	Tantalum (Ta)	73
Astatine (At)	85	Einsteinium (Es)	99	Lead (Pb)	82	Polonium (Po)	84	Technetium (Tc)	43
Barium (Ba)	56	Erbium (Er)	68	Lithium (Li)	3	Potassium (K)	19	Tellurium (Te)	52
Berkelium (Bk)	97	Europium (Eu)	63	Livermorium (Lv)	116	Praseodymium (Pr)	59	Terbium (Tb)	65
Beryllium (Be)	4	Fermium (Fm)	100	Lutetium (Lu)	71	Promethium (Pm)	61	Thallium (Tl)	81
Bismuth (Bi)	83	Flerovium (Fl)	114	Magnesium (Mg)	12	Protactinium (Pa)	91	Thorium (Th)	90
Bohrium (Bh)	107	Fluorine (F)	9	Manganese (Mn)	25	Radium (Ra)	88	Thulium (Tm)	69
Boron (B)	5	Francium (Fr)	87	Meitnerium (Mt)	109	Radon (Rn)	86	Tin (Sn)	50
Bromine (Br)	35	Gadolinium (Gd)	64	Mendelevium (Md)	101	Rhenium (Re)	75	Titanium (Ti)	22
Cadmium (Cd)	48	Gallium (Ga)	31	Mercury (Hg)	80	Rhodium (Rh)	45	Tungsten (W)	74
Calcium (Ca)	20	Germanium (Ge)	32	Molybdenum (Mo)	42	Roentgenium (Rg)	111	Uranium (U)	92
Californium (Cf)	98	Gold (Au)	79	Neodymium (Nd)	60	Rubidium (Rb)	37	Vanadium (V)	23
Carbon (C)	6	Hafnium (Hf)	72	Neon (Ne)	10	Ruthenium (Ru)	44	Xenon (Xe)	54
Cerium (Ce)	58	Hassium (Hs)	108	Neptunium (Np)	93	Rutherfordium (Rf)	104	Ytterbium (Yb)	70
Cesium (Cs)	55	Helium (He)	2	Nickel (Ni)	28	Samarium (Sm)	62	Yttrium (Y)	39
Chlorine (Cl)	17	Holmium (Ho)	67	Niobium (Nb)	41	Scandium (Sc)	21	Zinc (Zn)	30
Chromium (Cr)	24	Hydrogen (H)	1	Nitrogen (N)	7	Seaborgium (Sg)	106	Zirconium (Zr)	40
Cobalt (Co)	27	Indium (In)	49	Nobelium (No)	102	Selenium (Se)	34		

The Amino Acids of Proteins

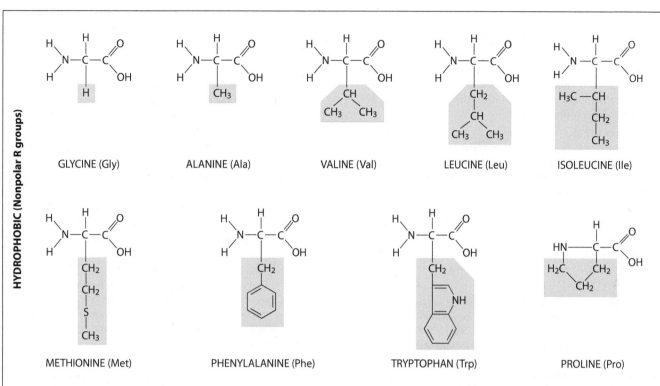

HYDROPHOBIC (Nonpolar R groups)

GLYCINE (Gly)   ALANINE (Ala)   VALINE (Val)   LEUCINE (Leu)   ISOLEUCINE (Ile)

METHIONINE (Met)   PHENYLALANINE (Phe)   TRYPTOPHAN (Trp)   PROLINE (Pro)

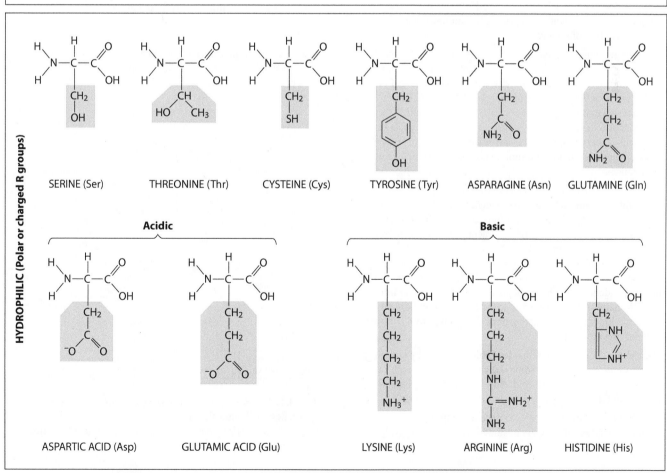

HYDROPHILIC (Polar or charged R groups)

SERINE (Ser)   THREONINE (Thr)   CYSTEINE (Cys)   TYROSINE (Tyr)   ASPARAGINE (Asn)   GLUTAMINE (Gln)

Acidic   **Basic**

ASPARTIC ACID (Asp)   GLUTAMIC ACID (Glu)   LYSINE (Lys)   ARGININE (Arg)   HISTIDINE (His)

APPENDIX 3

Chapter Review Answers

Chapter 1

1. a. life; b. evolution; c. natural selection; d. unity of life; e. three domains (or numerous kingdoms; 1.8 million species)

2. b 3. c 4. b 5. b 6. d 7. a 8. d (You may have been tempted to choose b, the molecular level. However, protists may have chemical communication or interactions with other protists. No protists, however, have organs.) 9. d

10. Both energy and chemicals are passed through an ecosystem from producers to consumers to decomposers. But energy enters an ecosystem as sunlight and leaves as heat. Chemicals are recycled from the soil or atmosphere through plants, consumers, and decomposers and returned to the air, soil, and water.

11. Darwin described how natural selection operates in populations whose individuals have varied traits that are inherited. When natural selection favors the reproductive success of certain individuals in a population more than others, the proportions of heritable variations change over the generations, gradually adapting a population to its environment.

12. In pursuit of answers to questions about nature, a scientist uses a logical thought process involving these key elements: observations about natural phenomena, questions derived from observations, hypotheses posed as tentative explanations of observations, logical predictions of the outcome of tests if the hypotheses are correct, and actual tests of hypotheses. Scientific research is not a rigid method because a scientist must adapt these processes to the set of conditions particular to each study. Intuition, chance, and luck are also part of science.

13. Technology is the application of scientific knowledge. For example, the use of solar power to run a calculator or heat a home is an application of our knowledge, derived by the scientific process, of the nature of light as a type of energy and how light energy can be converted to other forms of energy. Another example is the use of DNA to insert new genes into crop plants. This process, often called genetic engineering, stems from decades of scientific research on the structure and function of DNA from many kinds of organisms.

14. The vertical scale of biology refers to the hierarchy of biological organization: from molecules to organelles, cells, tissues, organs, organ systems, organisms, populations, communities, ecosystems, and the biosphere. At each level, emergent properties arise from the interaction and organization of component parts. The horizontal scale of biology refers to the incredible diversity of living organisms, past and present, including the 1.8 million species that have been identified so far. Biologists divide these species into three domains—Bacteria, Archaea, and Eukarya—and organize them into kingdoms and other groups that attempt to reflect evolutionary relationships.

15. Natural selection screens (edits) heritable variations by favoring the reproductive success of some individuals over others. It can only select from the variations that are present in the population; it does not create new genes or variations.

16. a. Hypothesis: Giving rewards to mice will improve their learning. Prediction: If mice are rewarded with food, they will learn to run a maze faster.

b. The control group was the mice that were not rewarded. Without them, it would be impossible to know if the mice that were rewarded decreased their time running the maze only because of practice.

c. Both groups of mice should not have run the maze before and should be about the same age. Both experiments should be run at the same time of day and under the same conditions.

d. Yes, the results support the hypothesis because the data show that the rewarded mice began to run the maze faster by day 3 and improved their performance (ran faster than the control mice) each day thereafter.

17. The researcher needed to determine the percent of total attacks in each habitat that occurred on dark models. It may be that there were simply more predators in the inland habitat than in the beach habitat. The experiment needed proper data analysis.

18. If these cell division control genes are involved in producing the larger tomato, they may have similar effects if transferred to other fruits or vegetables. Cancer is a result of uncontrolled cell division. One could see if there are similarities between the tomato genes and any human genes that could be related to human development or disease. The control of cell division is a fundamental process in growth, repair, and asexual reproduction—all important topics in biology.

19. Virtually any news report or magazine contains stories that are about biology or at least have biological connections. How about biological connections in advertisements?

Chapter 2

1. a. protons; b. neutrons; c. electrons; d. different isotopes; e. covalent bonds; f. ionic bonds; g. polar covalent bonds; h. hydrogen bonding

2.

3. b 4. b 5. d 6. c 7. b (Sulfur has 6 electrons in its valence shell. It reaches a full outer shell of 8 by sharing one pair of electrons with each of two hydrogen atoms. Each H then has a full valence shell of 2.)

8. Iodine (part of a thyroid hormone) and iron (part of hemoglobin in blood) are both trace elements, required in minute quantities. Calcium and phosphorus (components of bones and teeth) are needed by the body in much greater quantities.

9. The atoms of each element have a characteristic number of protons in their nuclei, which is referred to as the atomic number and is 6 for carbon. The mass number is an indication of the approximate mass of an atom and is equal to the number of protons and neutrons in the nucleus. Carbon-12 has 6 neutrons (and 6 protons, of course), so its mass number is 12. The valence usually equals the number of electrons needed to fill an atom's outer shell (the number of unpaired electrons). Carbon's valence or bonding capacity of 4 indicates that it will form 4 covalent bonds. Thus, an atom's valence is most related to its chemical behavior.

10. In nonpolar covalent bonds, electrons are equally shared between two atoms. Polar covalent bonds form when a more electronegative atom pulls the shared electrons closer to it, producing a partial negative charge associated with that portion of the molecule and a partial positive charge associated with the atom from which the electrons are pulled. In the formation of ions, an electron is completely pulled away from one atom and transferred to another, creating negatively and positively charged ions. These oppositely charged ions may be attracted to each other in an ionic bond.

11. Fluorine needs 1 electron for a full outer shell of 8, and if potassium loses 1 electron, its outer shell will have 8. Potassium will lose an electron (becoming a + ion), and fluorine will pick it up (becoming a − ion). The ions can form an ionic bond.

12. The elements in a row all have the same number of electron shells. In a column, all the elements have the same number of electrons in their outer shell. Elements in the same column should have similar chemical properties because they have the same valence or bonding capacity and thus would make the same number of covalent bonds. Or if they have only 1 or 2 electrons, or if they have 7 electrons in their outer shell, atoms of these elements would tend to lose or gain electrons, forming ions and participating in ionic bonds.

13. The results indicate that both a lower pH and higher temperature negatively affected the growth of coral polyps and that the reduction in growth was much greater when both pH and temperature were varied at the same time. Because rising atmospheric levels of CO_2 are predicted to continue to acidify the oceans and raise ocean temperatures, it is beneficial to see how these two factors may interact.

14. When water is heated, much of the heat is absorbed in breaking hydrogen bonds before the water molecules increase their motion and the temperature increases. Conversely, when water is cooled, many hydrogen bonds are formed, which releases a significant amount of heat. This release of heat can provide some protection against freezing of the plants' leaves, thus protecting the cells from damage.

15. These extreme environments may be similar to those found on other planets. The fact that life may have evolved and continues to flourish in such extreme environments here on Earth suggests that some form of life may have evolved on other planets. In addition to seeking evidence for the past or current presence of water on Mars or other planets, scientists now know to search in environments that previously would have been thought incapable of supporting life.

Chapter 3

1. a. glucose; b. energy storage; c. cellulose; d. fats; e. cell membrane component; f. steroids; g. amino group; h. carboxyl group; i. R group; j. enzyme; k. structural protein; l. movement; m. membrane transport protein; n. defense; o. phosphate group; p. nitrogenous base; q. ribose or deoxyribose; r. DNA; s. code for proteins

2. d (The second kind of molecule is a polymer of the first.) 3. c 4. c 5. d 6. a 7. a 8. d 9. a

10. Circle NH_2, an amino group; COOH, a carboxyl group; and OH, a hydroxyl group on the R group. This is an amino acid, a monomer of proteins. The OH group makes it a polar amino acid.

11. Amino acids with hydrophobic R groups are most likely to be found clustered together in the interior of a protein, sheltered from the surrounding water.

12. This is a hydrolysis reaction, which consumes water. It is essentially the reverse of the diagram in Figure 3.5, except that fructose has a different shape than glucose.

13. Carbon forms four covalent bonds, either with other carbon atoms, producing chains or rings of various lengths and shapes, or with other atoms, such as characteristic chemical groups that confer specific properties on a molecule. This is the basis for the incredible diversity of organic compounds. Organisms can link a small number of monomers into different arrangements to produce a huge variety of polymers.

14. The 20 amino acids that are found in proteins can be arranged in many different sequences into chains of many different lengths. The sequences of DNA nucleotides in the genes of a cell dictate the amino acid sequences of its proteins.

15. A developing chick is growing rapidly, increasing its number of cells. To build new cells it needs large stores of cell membrane components, including cholesterol and lipids, and amino acids for building its proteins. It also requires energy to fuel all this construction, and that is available in the form of fats, as fat molecules can be broken down to yield a lot of energy.

16. a. A: at about 37°C; B: at about 78°C
    b. A: from humans (human body temperature is about 37°C); B: from thermophilic bacteria
    c. Above 40°C, the human enzyme denatures and loses its shape and thus its function. The increased thermal energy disrupts the weak bonds that maintain secondary and tertiary structure in an enzyme.

17. These results indicate that replacing either saturated or trans fats in the diet with unsaturated fats reduces the risk of coronary heart disease. The benefit is greater (risk reduced the most) when trans fats are replaced, even though the quantity of energy in the diet replaced was only 2% rather than the 5% of saturated fats replaced.

Chapter 4

1. a. rough ER; b. nucleus; c. nucleolus; d. ribosomes; e. peroxisome; f. centrosome; g. cytoskeleton; h. mitochondrion; i. plasma membrane; j. lysosome; k. Golgi apparatus; l. smooth ER. For functions, see Table 4.22. A centrosome is a microtubule-organizing center.

2. c 3. b (Small cells have a greater ratio of surface area to volume.) 4. b 5. a

6. DNA as genetic material, ribosomes, plasma membrane, and cytosol

7. Cilia may propel a cell through its environment or sweep a fluid environment past the cell.

8. d 9. b 10. a 11. c

12. Different conditions and conflicting processes can occur simultaneously within separate, membrane-enclosed compartments. Also, there is increased area for membrane-attached enzymes that carry out metabolic processes.

13. Part true, part false. All animal *and* plant cells have mitochondria; plant cells do have chloroplasts, but animal cells do not. Both organelles process energy. A mitochondrion converts chemical energy (such as sugar molecules) to another form of chemical energy (ATP). This process provides almost all eukaryotic cells with ATP needed for cellular work. A chloroplast converts light energy to chemical energy (sugar molecules). These sugar molecules may then provide a plant cell's mitochondria with a source of energy. Or they may be stored in the plant body and passed to animals that eat plants or each other.

14. The plasma membrane is a phospholipid bilayer with the hydrophilic heads facing the aqueous environment on both sides and the hydrophobic fatty acid tails mingling in the center of the membrane. Proteins are embedded in and attached to this membrane. Microfilaments form a three-dimensional network just inside the plasma membrane. The extracellular matrix outside the membrane is composed largely of glycoproteins, which may be attached to membrane proteins called integrins. Integrins can transmit information from the ECM to microfilaments on the other side of the membrane.

15. Cell 1: $S = 1,256 \ \mu m^2$; $V = 4,187 \ \mu m^3$; $S/V = 0.3$. Cell 2: $S = 5,024 \ \mu m^2$; $V = 33,493 \ \mu m^3$; $S/V = 0.15$. The smaller cell has a larger surface area relative to volume, facilitating the uptake of sufficient nutrients and oxygen and the excretion of waste.

16. An mRNA molecule is transcribed from the gene for insulin and moves into the cytosol. There it joins with a ribosome that becomes attached to the outside of the rough ER (a bound ribosome). The ribosome produces a polypeptide that is threaded into the ER compartment. The polypeptide folds up and may be modified within the ER. It is then packaged into a transport vesicle. The vesicle joins with a Golgi sac, and the protein may be further modified during its journey through the Golgi apparatus. A transport vesicle pinches off from the "shipping" face of the Golgi and fuses with the plasma membrane, secreting insulin from the cell.

17. According to the endosymbiotic theory, an ancestral eukaryotic cell engulfed (ingested) an aerobic bacterium but did not digest its potential food item. The prokaryote took up residence within the cell, and its aerobic metabolism probably contributed ATP to the host cell. Over many generations of cells, the host and endosymbiont became mutually dependent and unable to exist on their own—they became a single organism. A similar process may have occurred when one of these mitochondria-containing cells ingested but did not digest a photosynthetic prokaryote.

18. Individuals with PCD have nonfunctional cilia and flagella due to a lack of dynein motor proteins. This defect would also mean that the cilia involved in left-right pattern formation in the embryo would not be able to set up the fluid flow that initiates the normal arrangement of organs.

19. As the chromosomes moved poleward, the microtubule segments on the chromosome side of the mark shortened, while those on pole side stayed the same length. Thus chromosome movement toward the poles of this dividing cell is correlated with the shortening (depolymerizing) of the microtubules at the end where the chromosome is attached. The experiment would have to be repeated on different types of cells from different organisms to determine whether the location where a spindle fiber depolymerizes is always the same. Indeed, other experiments have shown that in some cells, the microtubules depolymerize from the pole end of the spindle fibers.

Chapter 5

1. a. active transport; b. concentration gradient; c. small nonpolar molecules; d. facilitated diffusion; e. transport proteins

2. a. enzyme; b. active site of enzyme; c. substrate; d. substrate in active site; induced fit strains substrate bonds; e. substrate converted to products; f. product molecules released

3. b 4. d 5. c (Only active transport can move solute against a concentration gradient.) 6. a 7. b

8. The work of cells falls into three main categories: chemical, transport, and mechanical. ATP provides the energy for cellular work by transferring a phosphate group to a substrate (chemical) or to a protein (transport and mechanical).

9. Energy is stored in the chemical bonds of a cell's organic molecules. The activation energy barrier prevents these molecules from spontaneously breaking down and releasing that energy. When a substrate fits into an enzyme's active site with an induced fit, its bonds may be strained and thus easier to break, or the active site may orient two substrates in such a way that facilitates the reaction.

10. Energy is neither created nor destroyed but can be transferred and transformed. Plants transform the energy of sunlight into chemical energy stored in organic molecules. Almost all organisms rely on the products of photosynthesis for the source of their energy. In every energy transfer or transformation, disorder increases as some energy is lost to the random motion of thermal energy and released as heat.

11. Cell membranes are composed of diverse proteins suspended in a fluid phospholipid bilayer. The hydrophilic heads of the phospholipids face the aqueous environment on both sides of the membrane and the fatty acid tails cluster in the hydrophobic center of the membrane The membrane forms a selectively permeable boundary between cells and their surroundings (or between organelles and the cytosol). The proteins perform the many functions of membranes, such as enzyme action, transport, attachment, and signaling.

12. Inhibitors that are toxins or poisons irreversibly inhibit key cellular enzymes. Inhibitors that are designed as drugs are beneficial, such as when they interfere with the enzymes of bacterial or viral invaders or cancer cells. Cells use feedback inhibition of enzymes in metabolic pathways as important mechanisms that conserve resources.

13. Aquaporins are water transport channels that allow for very rapid diffusion of water through a cell membrane. It would be most important for your body to reabsorb water from the urine, thus preventing dehydration, after a run on a hot day.

14. The aquaporin RNA-injected oocytes had a high rate of water permeability. (Remember from Module 5.7 that they swelled and ruptured in 3 minutes.) Treatment with mercury chloride inhibited the aquaporins, and the water permeability of the oocytes was reduced. As expected, the higher the concentration of mercury, the greater the inhibition and reduction in water permeability.

When that inhibition was reversed by treatment with the chemical ME, the channels once again functioned and water permeability increased to almost the level of the uninhibited oocytes. The control oocytes were not injected with aquaporin RNA and thus did not have aquaporins. Thus, their water permeability should be very low and not affected by the mercury treatment. Indeed, their water permeability was much lower than any of the RNA-injected oocytes.

15. a. The more enzyme present, the faster the rate of reaction, because it is more likely that enzyme and substrate molecules will meet.

b. The more substrate present, the faster the reaction, for the same reason, but only up to a point. An enzyme molecule can work only so fast; once it is saturated (working at top speed), more substrate does not increase the rate.

16. Some issues and questions to consider: Is improving crop yields of paramount importance in a world where many people can't get enough food? Does the fact that these compounds rapidly break down indicate that the risk to humans is low? How about the risks to people who work in agriculture or to other organisms, such as bees and other pollinating insects, birds, and small mammals? Might there be negative effects on ecosystems that are impossible to predict?

Chapter 6

1. a. glycolysis; b. pyruvate oxidation and citric acid cycle; c. oxidative phosphorylation; d. oxygen; e. electron transport chain; f. CO_2; g. H_2O

2. d 3. d 4. b 5. a 6. c (NAD^+ and FAD, which are recycled by electron transport, are in limited supply in a cell.) 7. b (at the same time NADH is oxidized to NAD^+)

8. Glycolysis is considered the most ancient because it occurs in all living cells and doesn't require oxygen or membrane-enclosed organelles.

9. In lactic acid fermentation (in muscle cells), pyruvate is reduced by NADH to form lactate, and NAD^+ is recycled. In alcohol fermentation, pyruvate is broken down to CO_2 and ethanol as NADH is oxidized to NAD^+. Both types of fermentation allow glycolysis to continue to produce 2 ATP per glucose by recycling NAD^+.

10. As carbohydrates are broken down in glycolysis and the oxidation of pyruvate, glycerol can be made from G3P and fatty acids can be made from acetyl CoA. Amino groups, containing N atoms, must be supplied to various intermediates of glycolysis and the citric acid cycle to produce amino acids.

11. 100 kcal per day is 700 kcal per week. According to Figure 6.4, walking 3 mph would require $\frac{700}{245}$ = about 2.8 hours; swimming, 1.7 hours; running, 0.7 hour.

12. NAD^+ and FAD are coenzymes that are not used up during the oxidation of glucose. NAD^+ and FAD are recycled when NADH and $FADH_2$ pass the electrons they are carrying to the electron transport chain. We need a small additional supply to replace those that are damaged.

13. a. No, this shows the blue color getting more intense. The reaction decolorizes the blue dye.
    b. No, this shows the dye being decolorized, but it also shows the three mixtures with different initial color intensities. The intensities should have started out the same, since all mixtures used the same concentration of dye.
    c. Correct. The mixtures all start out the same, and then the ones with more malate (reactant) decolorize faster.

14. The presence of ATP synthase enzymes in prokaryotic plasma membranes and the inner membrane of mitochondria provides support for the theory of endosymbiosis—that mitochondria evolved from an engulfed prokaryote that used aerobic respiration (see Module 4.15).

15. The percentage of body fat is the independent variable and is plotted on the x axis. The activity of brown fat is the dependent variable, and it is plotted on the y axis. Your graph should show a negative correlation between body fat percentage and activity of brown fat (the data points are higher for lower body fat percentage and decrease as the body fat percentage increases). One hypothesis is that thin individuals have more active brown fat and thus burn more calories, which contributes to their thinness (lower percentage of body fat). A second hypothesis is that the higher percentage of body fat insulated the bodies of the more overweight subjects, thus their brown fat did not have to be as active to maintain their body temperatures when exposed to cold.

16. In a person treated with uncoupling agents like DNP, the proton gradient established during electron transport is no longer tied to ATP synthesis. As a result, oxidation of glucose during cellular respiration yields very little ATP, since ATP is normally produced as H^+ ions flow back through ATP synthase in the inner mitochondrial membrane. Without large amounts of ATP available, biosynthesis cannot take place and new organic molecules cannot be synthesized. Low ATP levels would signal the body to continue breaking down its own molecules and feeding them into the cellular respiration pathway, leading to excessive weight loss and severe overheating, sweating, and dehydration. One or a combination of these factors can cause death.

17. The mitochondria of brown fat cells have protein channels that make the inner mitochondrial membrane leaky to H^+ ions, producing the same effect that the drug DNP has on mitochondria. When these channels are activated, brown fat burns fuel without producing ATP. Drugs that could activate brown fat would help a patient burn more calories. Thus, excess calories from the diet would not be converted to fat, and fat stores of the body could be reduced. If these drugs somehow affected the mitochondria of all body cells, however, the results could be as disastrous as they were with DNP.

Chapter 7

1. a. light energy; b. light reactions; c. Calvin cycle; d. O_2 released; e. electron transport chain; f. NADPH; g. ATP; h. G3P (sugar)

2. c 3. b 4. a 5. c (NADPH and ATP from the light reactions are required by the Calvin cycle.) 6. d 7. b 8. c

9. CO_2 and H_2O are the products of respiration; they are the reactants in photosynthesis. In respiration, glucose is oxidized to CO_2 as electrons are passed through an electron transfer chain from glucose to O_2, producing H_2O. In photosynthesis, H_2O is the source of electrons, which are energized by light, temporarily stored in NADPH, and used to reduce CO_2 to carbohydrate.

10. The light reactions require ADP and $NADP^+$, neither of which are recycled from ATP and NADPH when the Calvin cycle stops.

11. Plants can break down the sugar for energy in cellular respiration or use the sugar as a raw material for making other organic molecules. Excess sugar is stored as starch.

12. a. electron transport chain; b. ATP synthase; c. thylakoid space; d. stroma; e. ATP. The higher H^+ concentration is found in the intermembrane space of the mitochondrion and in the thylakoid space of the chloroplast.

13. In mitochondria: a. Electrons come from food molecules. b. Electrons have high potential energy in the bonds in organic molecules. c. Electrons are passed to oxygen, which picks up H^+ and forms water.
In chloroplasts: a. Electrons come from splitting of water. b. Light energy excites the electrons to a higher energy level. c. Electrons flow from water to the reaction-center chlorophyll in photosystem II to the reaction-center chlorophyll in photosystem I to $NADP^+$, reducing it to NADPH.
In both processes: d. Energy released by redox reactions in the electron transport chain is used to transport H^+ across a membrane. The flow of H^+ down its concentration gradient back through ATP synthase drives the phosphorylation of ADP to make ATP.

14. The hypothesis was that, because CO_2 is a raw material for photosynthesis, rising CO_2 levels would increase the growth and production of pollen by ragweed. Pollen production was positively correlated with CO_2 concentrations, and the results supported the hypothesis. Because rising CO_2 levels are associated with warmer temperatures, an experiment could also look at the effect of temperature on ragweed pollen production. One might also want to determine whether the growing season is getting longer, as this would expose hay fever sufferers to pollen for extended periods. It would also be interesting to measure whether ragweed pollen is more allergenic when grown in higher CO_2 levels, as poison ivy was shown to be. These types of experiments have been performed, and their results are as you would predict—the growing season for ragweed has gotten longer, and pollen that is more allergenic is produced in higher quantities under conditions of elevated CO_2.

15. Some issues and questions to consider: What are the risks that we take and costs we must pay if global climate change continues? How certain do we have to be that global warming is caused by human activities before we act? What can we do to reduce CO_2 emissions? Is it possible that the costs and sacrifices of reducing CO_2 emissions might actually improve our lifestyle?

Chapter 8

1.

	Mitosis	Meiosis
Number of chromosomal duplications	1	1
Number of cell divisions	1	2
Number of daughter cells produced	2	4
Number of chromosomes in the daughter cells	Diploid (2n)	Haploid (n)
How the chromosomes line up during metaphase	Singly	In tetrads (metaphase I), then singly (metaphase II)
Genetic relationship of the daughter cells to the parent cell	Genetically identical	Genetically unique
Functions performed in the human body	Growth, development, and repair	Production of gametes

2. b 3. c 4. b 5. b 6. b 7. a 8. b 9. d (A diploid cell would have an even number of chromosomes; the odd number suggests that meiosis I has been completed. Sister chromatids are together only in prophase and metaphase of meiosis II.) 10. c 11. d

12. Most of the cells are in interphase (a time of growth, DNA synthesis, metabolic activity), without recognizable compacted individual chromosomes. During prophase, chromosomes compact and thicken (e.g., the cell on the left edge, about halfway down) and the mitotic spindle forms. During metaphase, the chromosomes line up in the middle of the cell (e.g., the second cell from the top, near the top left corner). In anaphase, the chromosomes split into two groups (which you can see in two cells near the bottom right corner) as sister chromatids split. During telophase, the chromosomes reach opposite ends (e.g., at the very top, fifth cell from the right) as daughter nuclei form around the chromosomes and cytokinesis begins.

13. Mitosis without cytokinesis would result in a single cell with two nuclei. Multiple rounds of cell division like this could produce such a "megacell."

14. Various orientations of homologous chromosome pairs at metaphase I of meiosis lead to different combinations of chromosomes in gametes. Crossing over during prophase I results in an exchange of chromosome segments and new combinations of genes. Random fertilization of eggs by sperm further increases possibilities for variation in offspring.

15. In culture, normal cells usually divide only when they are in contact with a surface but not touching other cells on all sides (the cells usually grow to form only a single layer). The density-dependent inhibition of cell division apparently results from local depletion of substances called growth factors. Growth factors are proteins secreted by certain cells that stimulate other cells to divide; they act via signal transduction pathways to signal the cell cycle control system of the affected cell to proceed past its checkpoints. The cell cycle control systems of cancer cells do not function properly. Cancer cells generally do not require externally supplied growth factors to complete the cell cycle, and they divide indefinitely (in contrast to normal mammalian cells, which stop dividing after 20 to 50 generations)—two reasons why cancer cells

are relatively easy to grow in the lab. Furthermore, cancer cells can often grow without contacting a solid surface, making it possible to culture them in suspension in a liquid medium.

16. A ring of microfilaments pinches an animal cell in two, a process called cleavage. In a plant cell, membranous vesicles form a disk called the cell plate at the midline of the parent cell, cell plate membranes fuse with the plasma membrane, and a cell wall grows in the space, separating the daughter cells.

17. See Figure 8.18.

18. a. No. For this to happen, the chromosomes of the two gametes that fused would have to represent, together, a complete set of the donor's maternal chromosomes (the ones that originally came from the donor's mother) and a complete set of the donor's paternal chromosomes (from the donor's father). It is much more likely that the zygote would be missing one or more maternal chromosomes and would have an excess of paternal chromosomes, or vice versa.

    b. Correct. Consider what would have to happen to produce a zygote genetically identical to the gamete donor: The zygote would have to have a complete set of the donor's maternal chromosomes and a complete set of the donor's paternal chromosomes. The first gamete in this union could contain any mixture of maternal and paternal chromosomes, but once that first gamete was "chosen," the second one would have to have one particular combination of chromosomes—the combination that supplies whatever the first gamete did not supply. So, for example, if the first three chromosomes of the first gamete were maternal, maternal, and paternal, the first three of the second gamete would have to be paternal, paternal, and maternal. The chance that all 23 chromosome pairs would be complementary in this way is only one in 22^3 (that is, one in 8,388,608). Because of independent assortment, it is much more likely that the zygote would have an unpredictable combination of chromosomes from the donor's father and mother.

    c. No. First, the zygote could not be genetically identical to the gamete donor (see answer b). Second, the zygote could not be identical to either of the gamete donor's parents because the donor only has half the genetic material of each of his or her parents. For example, even if the zygote were formed by two gametes containing only paternal chromosomes, the combined set of chromosomes could not be identical to that of the donor's father because it would still be missing half of the father's chromosomes.

    d. No. See answer c.

19. Some possible hypotheses: The replication of the DNA of the bacterial chromosome takes less time than the replication of the DNA in a eukaryotic cell. The time required for a growing bacterium to roughly double its cytoplasm is much less than for a eukaryotic cell. Bacteria have a cell cycle control system much simpler than that of eukaryotes.

20. 1 cm³ = 1,000 mm³, so 5,000 mm³ of blood contains 5,000 × 1,000 × 5,000,000 = 25,000,000,000,000, or 2.5×10^{13}, red blood cells. The number of cells replaced each day = $2.5 \times 10^{13}/120$ = 2.1×10^{11} cells. There are 24 × 60 × 60 = 86,400 seconds in a day. Therefore, the number of cells replaced each second = 2.1 × $10^{11}/86,400$ = about 2×10^6, or 2 million. Thus, about 2 million cell divisions must occur each second to replace red blood cells that are lost.

21. Each chromosome is on its own in mitosis; chromosome replication and the separation of sister chromatids occur independently

for each horse or donkey chromosome. Therefore, mitotic divisions, starting with the zygote, are not impaired. In meiosis, however, homologous chromosomes must pair in prophase I. This process of synapsis cannot occur properly because horse and donkey chromosomes do not match in number or content.

22. There are two unusual cases presented in Table 8.10: the patient who did not have the mutation but responded to everolimus and the patient who had the mutation but did not respond to everolimus. These patients could be studied in a manner similar to the original patient by performing a genetic analysis of their tumor cells. Such an analysis might reveal other mutations that explain their results. Further experiments like the one presented in Table 8.10 might then be performed to see if these results can be generalized. Such an approach may allow refinement of the personalized cancer therapy.

Chapter 9

1. a. alleles; b. loci; c. homozygous; d. dominant; e. recessive; f. incomplete dominance

2. c 3. b 4. d (Neither parent is ruby-eyed, but some offspring are, so it is recessive. Different ratios among male and female offspring show that it is sex-linked.) 5. d

6. The trait of freckles is dominant, so Tim and Jan must both be heterozygous. There is a chance that they will produce a child with freckles and a chance that they will produce a child without freckles. The probability that the next two children will have freckles is 3/4 × 3/4 = 9/16.

7. As in problem 6, both Tim and Jan are heterozygous, and Mike is homozygous recessive. The probability of the next child having freckles is 3/4. The probability of the next child having a straight hairline is 1/4. The probability that the next child will have freckles and a straight hairline is 3/4 × 1/4 = 3/16.

8. The genotype of the black short-haired parent rabbit is BBSS. The genotype of the brown long-haired parent rabbit is bbss. The F₁ rabbits will all be black and short-haired, BbSs. The F₂ rabbits will be black short-haired, black long-haired, brown short-haired, and brown long-haired, in a proportion of 9:3:3:1.

9. If the genes are not linked, the proportions among the offspring will be 25% gray red, 25% gray purple, 25% black red, and 25% black purple. The actual percentages show that the genes are linked. The recombination frequency is 6%.

10. The recombination frequencies are black dumpy 36%, purple dumpy 41%, and black purple 6% (see problem 9). Because these recombination frequencies reflect distances between the genes, the sequence must be purple-black-dumpy (or dumpy-black-purple).

11. 1/4 will be boys suffering from hemophilia, and 1/4 will be female carriers. (The mother is a heterozygous carrier [XᴴXʰ], and the father is normal [XᴴY].)

12. Genes on the single X chromosome in males are always expressed because there are no corresponding genes on the Y chromosome to mask them. A male needs only one recessive colorblindness allele (from his mother) to show the trait; a female must inherit the allele from both parents, which is less likely.

13. The parental gametes are WS and ws. Recombinant gametes are Ws and wS, produced by crossing over.

14. Height appears to be a quantitative trait resulting from polygenic inheritance, like human skin color. See Module 9.14.

15. For a woman to be colorblind, she must inherit X chromosomes bearing the colorblindness allele from both parents. Her father has only one X chromosome, which he passes on to all his daughters, so he must be colorblind. A male need only inherit the colorblindness allele from a carrier mother; both his parents are usually phenotypically normal.

16. Start out by breeding the cat to get a population to work with. If the curl allele is recessive, two curl cats can have only curl kittens. If the allele is dominant, curl cats can have "normal" kittens. If the curl allele is sex-linked, ratios will differ in male and female offspring of some crosses. If the curl allele is autosomal, the same ratios will be seen among males and females. Once you have established that the curl allele is dominant and autosomal, you can determine if a particular curl cat is true-breeding (homozygous) by doing a testcross with a normal cat. If the curl cat is homozygous, all offspring of the testcross will be curl; if heterozygous, half of the offspring will be curl and half normal.

17. If the genes are unlinked, you expect puppies in a 9:3:3:1 ratio: 90 black normal vision, 30 black blind, 30 chocolate normal, and 10 chocolate blind. If the genes are linked, you would expect a 3:1 ratio of black normal to chocolate blind, with a small number of black blind and chocolate normal recombinant offspring.

Chapter 10

1. a. nucleotides; b. transcription; c. RNA polymerase; d. mRNA; e. rRNA; f. tRNA; g. translation; h. ribosomes; i. amino acids

2. b

3. Ingredients: Original DNA, nucleotides, several enzymes and other proteins, including DNA polymerase and DNA ligase. Steps: Original DNA strands separate at a specific site (origin of replication), free nucleotides hydrogen-bond to each strand according to base-pairing rules, and DNA polymerase covalently bonds the nucleotides to form new strands. New nucleotides are added only to the 3′ end of a growing strand. One new strand is made in one continuous piece; the other new strand is made in a series of short pieces that are then joined by DNA ligase. Product: Two identical DNA molecules, each with one old strand and one new strand.

4. transcription; translation

5. d (Only the phage DNA enters a host cell; lambda DNA determines both DNA and protein.)

6. d

7. A gene is the polynucleotide sequence with information for making one polypeptide. Each codon—a triplet of bases in DNA or RNA—codes for one amino acid. Transcription occurs when RNA polymerase produces RNA using one strand of DNA as a template. In prokaryotic cells, the RNA transcript may immediately serve as mRNA. In eukaryotic cells, the RNA is processed: A cap and tail are added, and RNA splicing removes introns and links exons together to form a continuous coding sequence. A ribosome is the site of translation, or polypeptide synthesis, and tRNA molecules serve as interpreters of the genetic code. Each folded tRNA molecule has an amino acid attached at one end and a three-base anticodon at the other end. Beginning at the start codon, mRNA is moved relative to the ribosome a codon at a time. A tRNA with a complementary anticodon pairs with each codon, adding its amino acid to the polypeptide chain. The amino acids are linked by peptide bonds. Translation stops at a stop codon, and the finished polypeptide is released. The polypeptide folds to form a functional protein, sometimes in combination with other polypeptides.

8. c

9.

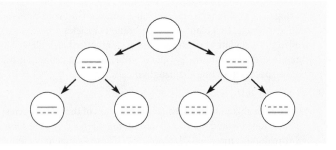

10. mRNA: GAUGCGAUCCGCUAACUGA; amino acids: Met-Arg-Ser-Ala-Asn

11. Some issues and questions to consider: Is it fair to issue a patent for a gene or gene product that occurs naturally in every human being? Or should a patent be issued only for something new that is invented rather than found? Suppose another scientist slightly modifies the gene or protein. How different does the gene or protein have to be to avoid patent infringement? Might patents encourage secrecy and interfere with the free flow of scientific information? What are the benefits to the holder of a patent? When research discoveries cannot be patented, what are the scientists' incentives for doing the research? What are the incentives for the institution or company that is providing financial support?

12. A bacteriophage is capable of easily infecting a host (bacterium) and therefore multiplying its genetic material. Most importantly, a bacteriophage has a very simple structure, allowing the outer structure (made entirely of protein) to be easily distinguished from the inner structure (made of DNA).

Chapter 11

1. a. proto-oncogene; b. repressor (or activator); c. cancer; d. operator; e. X inactivation; f. transcription factors; g. alternative RNA splicing

2. b **3.** b **4.** b **5.** b (Different genes are active in different kinds of cells.) **6.** c **7.** d

8. They will be black, because the DNA of the cell was obtained from a black mouse.

9.
  a. If the mutated repressor could still bind to the operator on the DNA, it would continuously repress the operon; enzymes for lactose utilization would not be made, whether or not lactose was present.
  b. The *lac* genes would continue to be transcribed and the enzymes made, whether or not lactose was present.
  c. Same predicted result as for b.
  d. RNA polymerase would not be able to transcribe the genes; no proteins would be made, whether or not lactose was present.

10. A mutation in a single gene can influence the actions of many other genes if the mutated gene is a control gene, such as a homeotic gene. A single control gene may encode a protein that affects (activates or represses) the expression of a number of other genes. In addition, some of the affected genes may themselves be control genes that in turn affect other batteries of genes. Cascades of gene expression are common in embryonic development.

11. The protein to which dioxin binds in the cell is probably a transcription factor that regulates multiple genes (see Module 11.3). If the binding of dioxin influences the activity of this transcription factor—either activating or inactivating it—dioxin could thereby affect multiple genes and thus have a variety of effects on the body. The differing effects in different animals might be explained by differing genetic details in the different species. It would be extremely difficult to demonstrate conclusively that dioxin exposure was the cause of illness in a particular individual, even if dioxin had been shown to be present in the person's tissues. However, if you had detailed information about how dioxin affects patterns of gene expression in humans and were able to show dioxin-specific abnormal patterns in the patient (perhaps using DNA microarrays; see Module 11.9), you might be able to establish a strong link between dioxin and the illness.

12. Wilmut was able to coordinate the cell cycle of the donor and host cells by depriving them of nutrients. When faced with starvation, both cells switched to the G_0 phase of the cell cycle. Wilmut could therefore be sure that, when placed in a growth medium with nutrients, the cell cycles within both the donor and host cell were synchronized. This allowed him to successfully clone a mammal from an adult cell for the first time.

Chapter 12

1. a. PCR; b. a restriction enzyme; c. gel electrophoresis; d. nucleic acid probe; e. cloning

2. d 3. b 4. b 5. c 6. c

7. Because it would be too expensive and time consuming to compare whole genomes. By choosing STR sites that vary considerably from person to person, investigators can get the necessary degree of specificity without sequencing the entire genome.

8. Medicine: Genes can be used to produce transgenic lab animals for AIDS research or for research related to human gene therapy. Proteins can be hormones, enzymes, blood-clotting factors, or the active ingredient of vaccines. Agriculture: Foreign genes can be inserted into plant cells or animal eggs to produce transgenic crop plants or farm animals. Animal growth hormones are examples of agriculturally useful proteins that can be made using recombinant DNA technology.

9. She could start with DNA isolated from liver cells (the entire genome) and carry out the procedure outlined in Module 12.1 to produce a collection of recombinant bacterial clones, each carrying a small piece of liver cell DNA. To find the clone with the desired gene, she could then make a probe of radioactive RNA with a nucleotide sequence complementary to part of the gene: GACCUGACUGU. This probe would bind to the gene, labeling it and identifying the clone that carries it. Alternatively, the biochemist could start with mRNA isolated from liver cells and use it as a template to make cDNA (using reverse transcriptase). Cloning this DNA rather than the entire genome would yield a smaller library of genes to be screened—only those active in liver cells. Furthermore, the genes would lack introns, making the desired gene easier to manipulate after isolation.

10. c (Bacteria lack the RNA-splicing machinery needed to delete eukaryotic introns.)

11. Isolate plasmids from a culture of *E. coli*. Cut the plasmids and the human DNA containing the HGH gene with the restriction enzyme to produce molecules with sticky ends. Join the plasmids and the fragments of human DNA with ligase. Allow *E. coli* to take up recombinant plasmids. Bacteria will then replicate plasmids and multiply, producing clones of bacterial cells. Identify a clone carrying and expressing the HGH gene using a nucleic acid probe. Grow large amounts of the bacteria and extract and purify HGH from the culture.

12. Determining the nucleotide sequences is just the first step. Once researchers have written out the DNA "book," they will have to try to figure out what it means—what the nucleotide sequences code for and how they work.

13. Some issues and questions to consider: What are some of the unknowns in recombinant DNA experiments? Do we know enough to anticipate and deal with possible unforeseen and negative consequences? Do we want this kind of power over evolution? Who should make these decisions? If scientists doing the research were to make the decisions about guidelines, what factors might shape their judgment? What might shape the judgment of business executives in the decision-making process? Does the public have a right to a voice in the direction of scientific research? Does the public know enough about biology to get involved in this decision-making process? Who represents "the public," anyway?

14. Some issues and questions to consider: What kinds of impact will gene therapy have on the individuals who are treated? On society? Who will decide what patients and diseases will be treated? What costs will be involved, and who will pay them? How do we draw the line between treating disorders and "improving" the human species?

15. Some issues and questions to consider: Should genetic testing be mandatory or voluntary? Under what circumstances? Why might employers and insurance companies be interested in genetic data? Since genetic characteristics differ among ethnic groups and between the sexes, might such information be used to discriminate? Which of these questions do you think is most important? Which issues are likely to be the most serious in the future?

16. Gather two groups of volunteers. Have one group ingest a standard amount of GMO corn in their diet and the other group ingest a standard amount of traditional corn. Monitor the health of the individuals in both groups, looking for differences. In real life, such a study would be problematic because it is difficult to control and monitor what people eat, it would require many years to search for long-term health effects, and it may run afoul of ethics standards for human testing.

APPENDIX 5 Credits

Photo Credits

COVER: Andy Rouse/Nature Picture Library

Detailed Table of Contents, pages xxiii–xxix

Uri Golman/Nature Picture Library; Herman Eisenbeiss/Science Source; Dieter Hopf/AGE Fotostock; M.I. Walker/Science Source; Peter B. Armstrong; R. Gino Santa Maria/Shutterstock; Graham Kent/Pearson Science; Dr. Yorgos Nikas/Science Source; akg-images/Newscom; NIBSC/Science Source; Eric Isselee/Shutterstock; Repligen Corporation; Peter Scoones/Science Source; David Kjaer/Nature Picture Library; Stephen Dalton/Science Source; Eric V. Grave/Science Source; Phil Dotson/Science Source; Reinhard Dirscherl/Getty Images; David Tlipling/Nature Picture Library; Eric Isselee/Shutterstock; Markus Varesvuo/Nature Picture Library; F Rauschenbach/F1 ONLINE/SuperStock; Ingram Publishing/Photolibrary Royalty Free; Chris Bjornberg/Science Source; Mike Wilkes/Nature Picture Library; Tier Images/Getty Images; D. Phillips/Science Source; Mike Kemp/RubberBall/Alamy; Dave Watts/NHPA/Science Source; Eric J. Simon; Carlyn Iverson/Science Source; MShieldsPhotos/Alamy; Eric Isselee/Shutterstock; Image Quest Marine; Roy Corral/Corbis; BERNARD CASTELEIN/Nature Picture Library; Roger Kirkpatrick/Image Quest Marine.

Unit Openers: Unit 1 SPL/Science Source. **Unit 2** Andrew Syred/Science Source. **Unit 3** Nick Garbutt/Nature Picture Library. **Unit 4** Vaughan Fleming/Science Source. **Unit 5** J & C Sohns/AGE Fotostock. **Unit 6** AVTG/Getty Images. **Unit 7** Paul Lawrence/AGE Fotostock America Inc.

Chapter 1: Chapter Opener Jared Hobbs/AGE Fotostock. **p. 1 top to bottom** ImageState Media Partners Limited; Sacha Vignieri; Sacha Vignieri; Pascal Goetgheluck/Science Source. **1.1.1** ImageState Media Partners Limited. **1.1.2** Werner Bollmann/AGE Fotostock. **1.1.3** WILDLIFE GmbH/Alamy. **1.1.4** ekawatchaow/Shutterstock. **1.1.5** Fabio Pupin/FLPA. **1.1.6** Kim Taylor and Jane Burton/DK Images. **1.1.7** Fabio Pupin/FLPA. **1.2 top to bottom** worker/Shutterstock; Universal Images Group/Super Stock; Tsolo T. Tsolo/RGB Ventures LLC dba SuperStock/Alamy; Bildagentur-online/McPhoto/Alamy. **1.3 left** Steve Gschmeissner/Science Source. **1.3 right** CNRI/Science Source. **1.4** Ron Erwin/AGE Fotostock. **1.6 top left** Eye of Science/Science Source. **1.6 top right** Eye of Science/Science Source. **1.6 center left** Dr. D. P. Wilson/Science Source. **1.6 center right** Florapix/Alamy. **1.6 bottom left** FLPA/Alamy. **1.6 bottom right** Michael & Patricia Fogden/CORBIS. **1.7A** Francois Gohier/Science Source/Science Source. **1.7B** Science Source. **1.7C top** zhaoyan/Shutterstock. **1.7C center** Uri Golman/Nature Picture Library. **1.7C bottom** Volodymyr Goinyk/Shutterstock. **1.9 left** Sacha Vignieri. **1.9 left inset** Sacha Vignieri. **1.9 right** Hopi Hoekstra, Harvard University. **1.9 right inset** Shawn P. Carey, Migration Productions. **1.10** Pascal Goetgheluck/Science Source. **p. 13** Ron Erwin/AGE Fotostock.

Chapter 2: Chapter Opener Mark Conlin/V&W/imagequestmarine.com. **2.1 left** Chip Clark. **2.1 center** Pearson Education/Pearson Science. **2.1 right** Pearson Education/Pearson Science. **2.2A** Alison Wright/Science Source. **2.2B** Anton Prado/Alamy. **2.4A** Will & Deni McIntyre/Science Source. **2.4B** Chester A. Mathis. **2.7B** Pearson Education/Pearson Science. **2.10** Herman Eisenbeiss/Science Source. **2.11** Joe Fox/Alamy. **2.12** thp73/istockphoto. **2.14 top to bottom** Jakub Semeniuk/istockphoto; VR Photos/Shutterstock; Beth Van Trees/Shutterstock. **2.15B** Reinhard Dirscherl/Alamy.

Chapter 3: Chapter Opener Kay Blaschke/Getty Images. **p. 33** Dougal Waters/Getty Images. **3.2 left** Miki Verebes/Shutterstock. **3.2 right** Herbert Kratky/istockphoto. **3.4A** Dougal Waters/Getty Images. **3.6** Kristin Piljay/Pearson Science. **3.7 clockwise from top left** Dougal Waters/Getty Images; Biophoto Associates/Science Source; Dr. Lloyd M. Beidler; Biophoto Associates/Science Source. **3.8C clockwise from top left** Stargazer/

Shutterstock; Angel Simon/Shutterstock; Alex Staroseltsev/Shutterstock; Thomas M Perkins/Shutterstock. **Table 3.9** Lilyana Vynogradova/Shutterstock. **p. 42** Anetta/Shutterstock. **3.12C** Dieter Hopf/AGE Fotostock. **3.17** Serge de Sazo/Science Source.

Chapter 4: Chapter Opener Dr. Torsten Wittmann/Science Source. **p. 51 top to bottom** M.I. Walker/Science Source; Dr. Mary Osborn. **4.1A** Michael Abbey/Science Source. **4.1B** Andrew Syred/Science Source. **4.1C** Dr. Klaus Boller/Science Source. **4.1D** M.I. Walker/Science Source. **4.3** Dr. Linda M. Stannard, University of Cape Town/Science Source. **4.5** David M. Phillips/Science Source. **4.6** Joseph F. Gennaro Jr./Science Source. **4.8A** Don W. Fawcett/Science Source. **4.9** Biophoto Associates/Science Source. **4.11A** Roland Birke/Getty Images. **4.11B** Biophoto Associates/Science Source. **4.13** Don W. Fawcett/Science Source. **4.16 left** Dr. Frank Solomon. **4.16 center** Mark Ladinsky. **4.16 right** Dr. Mary Osborn. **4.17** Dr. Alexey Khodjakov/Science Source. **4.18A** SPL/Science Source. **4.18B** Eye of Science/Science Source. **4.18C** Bjorn Afzelius.

Chapter 5: Chapter Opener B.L. de Groot. **5.2** Peter B. Armstrong. **5.16** Krista Kennell/Newscom.

Chapter 6: Chapter Opener Stephen Marks/Getty Images **p. 89 top to bottom** R. Gino Santa Maria/Shutterstock; StockLite/Shutterstock; GoodOlga/AGE Fotostock. **6.2** UpperCut Images/Alamy. **6.4** R. Gino Santa Maria/Shutterstock. **6.13C top** StockLite/Shutterstock. **6.13C bottom** Sean Lower/Marty Taylor. **6.15** Simon Smith/DK Images. **6.16** GoodOlga/AGE Fotostock.

Chapter 7: Chapter Opener John Burke/Getty Images. **p. 107 top to bottom** rodho/Shutterstock; ImageDJ/Jupiter Images. **7.1A** ODM/Shutterstock. **7.1B** Mark Conlin/Alamy. **7.1C** Susan M. Barns, Ph.D. **7.2 top to bottom** rodho/Shutterstock; Graham Kent/Pearson Science; Dr. Jeremy Burgess/Science Source. **7.3** Martin Shields/Alamy. **7.6B** llaszlo/Shutterstock. **7.7A** Christine Case. **7.11 bottom left** Dinodia/Pixtal/AGE Fotostock. **7.11 bottom right** ImageDJ/Jupiter Images. **7.13A** Prof. William H. Schlesinger. **7.14A** NASA. **7.14B** National Oceanic and Atmospheric Administration (NOAA).

Chapter 8: Chapter Opener Steve Gschmeissner/Science Source. **p. 125 top to bottom** Dr. Yorgos Nikas/Science Source; Michelle Gilders/Alamy. **8.1A** London School of Hygiene & Tropical Medicine/Science Source. **8.1B** Roger Steene/Image Quest Marine. **8.1C** Eric J. Simon. **8.1D** Bob Thomas/Getty Images. **8.1E** Dr. Yorgos Nikas/Science Source. **8.1F** Dr. Torsten Wittmann/Science Source. **8.2B** Lee D. Simon/Science Source. **8.3A** Dr. Andrew S. Bajer, University of Oregon. **8.3B** Biophoto Associates/Science Source. **8.5, p. 130 left** Conly L. Rieder, Ph.D. **8.5, p. 130 center** Conly L. Rieder, Ph.D. **8.5, p. 130 right** Conly L. Rieder, Ph.D. **8.5, p. 131 left** Conly L. Rieder, Ph.D. **8.5, p. 131 center** Conly L. Rieder, Ph.D. **8.5, p. 131 right** Conly L. Rieder, Ph.D. **8.6A** Don W. Fawcett/Science Source. **8.6B** Eldon H. Newcomb. **8.12A** Ron Chapple/Alamy. **p. 139** Ed Reschke/Getty Images. **8.16 top** F. Schussler/PhotoDisc/Getty Images, Inc. **8.16 bottom** Roxana Gonzalez/Shutterstock. **8.17A** Mark Petronczki. **8.19 left** Véronique Burger/Science Source. **8.19 right** CNRI/Science Source. **8.20A left** SPL/Science Source. **8.20A right** Lawrence Shear/Science Source. **8.22** Michelle Gilders/Alamy. **p. 151** J.L. Carson/Custom Medical Stock Photo.

Chapter 9: Chapter Opener David Pickford/Robert Harding. **p. 153 top to bottom** akg-images/Newscom; Eric J. Simon; Andrew Syred/Science Source. **9.1** bilwissedition Ltd. & Co. KG/Alamy. **9.2A** akg-images/Newscom. **9.8 left** PhotoDisc/Getty Images, Inc. **9.8 right** PhotoDisc/Getty Images, Inc. **9.9 top left** Liza McCorkle/iStockphoto. **9.9 top right** Westend61/Getty Images. **9.9 bottom left** Shell114/Shutterstock. **9.9 bottom right** David Terrazas Morales/Getty Images. **9.9C** Michael Ciesielski Photography. **9.10A** CNRI/Science Source. **9.10B top** Gusto/Science

Source. **9.10B bottom** Eric J. Simon. **9.13A** Eye of Science/Science Source. **9.13B** Eye of Science/Science Source. **9.15A** Eric J. Simon. **9.15B** Eric J. Simon. **9.18B** Graphic Science/Alamy. **9.20A** Andrew Syred/Science Source. **9.20B clockwise from top left** Jose Luis Pelaez, Inc./Getty Images; Yuri Arcurs/Shutterstock; Rubberball/Nicole Hill/Getty Images; Anatoliy Samara/Shutterstock. **Table 9.20 top** Tomasz Zachariasz/iStockphoto. **Table 9.20 center** kosam/Shutterstock. **Table 9.20 bottom** Tomasz Zachariasz/iStockphoto. **9.21A left** University of Texas MD Anderson Cancer Center. **9.21A right** University of Texas MD Anderson Cancer Center. **9.22** FPG/Getty Images.

Chapter 10: Chapter Opener Dr. Klaus Boller/Science Source. **10.1A** Biophoto Associates/Science Source. **10.3A left** Library of Congress. **10.3A right** Cold Spring Harbor Laboratory Archives. **10.3B** National Institutes of Health. **10.6B** Kevin McCluskey, PhD. **10.8C** Yonhap Choi Byung-kil/AP Images. **10.12** Joachim Frank. **p. 201** Hazel Appleton, Centre for Infections/Health Protection Agency/Science Source/Science Source. **10.19 left** NIBSC/Science Source. **10.19 right** Liu Siu Wai/Newscom. **10.23C left** Huntington Potter. **10.23C right** Huntington Potter.

Chapter 11: Chapter Opener dirtlight photography/Getty Images. **p. 209 top to bottom** Martin Oeggerli/Science Source; Robyn Mackenzie/Shutterstock. **11.1A** Martin Oeggerli/Science Source. **11.2A left** Don W. Fawcett/Science Source. **11.2A right** Biophoto Associates/Science Source. **11.2B** Eric Isselee/Shutterstock. **11.8A left** F. Rudolf Turner. **11.8A right** F. Rudolf Turner. **11.9** Alila Medical Images/Shutterstock. **11.12** Robyn Mackenzie/Shutterstock. **11.16A** GeoM/Shutterstock.

Chapter 12: Chapter Opener Efired/Shutterstock. **p. 231 top to bottom** Pichi Chuang/Thomson Reuters; Hank Morgan/Science Source; Steve Helber/AP Photo; Philippe Plailly & Atelier Daynes/Science Source. **12.1A** Pichi Chuang/Thomson Reuters. **12.1B top to bottom** Smileus/Dreamstime LLC; A.J. Sisco/UPI/Newscom; Kedrov/Shutterstock; Angel Hell/iStockphoto. **12.6A left** Brad DeCecco Photography. **12.6A right** Brad DeCecco Photography. **12.6B** Science Source. **12.7A** Eli Lilly and Company. **12.7B** Hank Morgan/Science Source. **12.8A** Vladimir Nikitin/Shutterstock. **12.8B** Patti McConville/Alamy. **12.9 left** Borys Shevchuk/Fotolia. **12.9 center** Kirill Kurashov/Shutterstock. **12.9 right** Dionisvera/Shutterstock. **12.10** Phil Date/Shutterstock. **12.13** Repligen Corporation. **12.15A** Steve Helber/AP Photo. **12.15B** Michael Stephens/Agence France Presse/Newscom. **Table 12.17 top to bottom** Olivia Meckes/Nicole Ottawa/Science Source/Science Source; Vaclav Volrab/Shutterstock; Andrew Burgess/Shutterstock; Gary Ombler/DK Images. **12.19** Rubberball/Getty Images, Inc. **12.21** Philippe Plailly & Atelier Daynes/Science Source.

Illustration and Text Credits

Chapter 2: 2.15A Adaptation of figure 5 from "Effect of Calcium Carbonate Saturation State on the Calcification Rate of an Experimental Coral Reef" by C. Langdon, et al., from *Global Biogeochemical Cycles* (June 2000): 14(2). Copyright © 2000 by American Geophysical Union. Reprinted with permission of Wiley Inc.

Chapter 4: 4.2B Figure adapted from *The World of the Cell*, 3rd ed., by Wayne M. Becker, Jane B. Reece and Wayne F. Poenie. Copyright © 1996 by Pearson Education, Inc. Adapted and electronically reproduced by permission of Pearson Education, Inc., Upper Saddle River, New Jersey.

Chapter 5: 5.7 Adaptation of Figure 2A from "Appearance of Water Channels in *Xenopus* Oocytes Expressing Red Cell CHIP28 Protein" by Gregory Preston et al., from *Science* (April 1992): 256(5055). Copyright © 1992 by AAAS. Reprinted with permission.

Chapter 7: 7.13B Adaptation of Figure 1A from "Biomass and Toxicity Responses of Poison Ivy (*Toxicodendron radicans*) to Elevated Atmospheric CO_2," by Jacqueline E. Mohan, et al., from *PNAS* (June 2006): 103(24). Copyright © 2006 by National Academy of Sciences. Reprinted with permission.

Glossary

A

A site One of two of a ribosome's binding sites for tRNA during translation. The A site holds the tRNA that carries the next amino acid in the polypeptide chain. (A stands for aminoacyl tRNA.)

abiotic factor (ā´-bī-ot´-ik) A nonliving component of an ecosystem, such as air, water, or temperature.

abiotic reservoir (ā´-bī-ot´-ik) The part of an ecosystem where a chemical, such as carbon or nitrogen, accumulates or is stockpiled outside of living organisms.

ABO blood groups Genetically determined classes of human blood that are based on the presence or absence of carbohydrates A and B on the surface of red blood cells. The ABO blood group phenotypes, also called blood types, are A, B, AB, and O.

abscisic acid (ABA) (ab-sis´-ik) A plant hormone that inhibits cell division, promotes dormancy, and interacts with gibberellins in regulating seed germination.

absorption The uptake of small nutrient molecules by an organism's own body; the third main stage of food processing, following digestion.

acetyl CoA (a-sē´-til kō´-ā´) (acetyl coenzyme A) The entry compound for the citric acid cycle in cellular respiration; formed from a two-carbon fragment of pyruvate attached to a coenzyme.

acetylcholine (a-sē´-til-kō´-lēn) A nitrogen-containing neurotransmitter. Among other effects, it slows the heart rate and makes skeletal muscles contract.

acid A substance that increases the hydrogen ion (H^+) concentration in a solution.

acrosome (ak´-ruh-som) A membrane-enclosed sac at the tip of a sperm. The acrosome contains enzymes that help the sperm penetrate an egg.

actin A globular protein that links into chains, two of which twist helically around each other, forming microfilaments in muscle cells.

action potential A change in membrane voltage that transmits a nerve signal along an axon.

activation energy The amount of energy that reactants must absorb before a chemical reaction will start.

activator A protein that switches on a gene or group of genes.

active immunity Immunity conferred by recovering from an infectious disease or by receiving a vaccine.

active site The part of an enzyme where a substrate molecule attaches; typically, a pocket or groove on the enzyme's surface.

active transport The movement of a substance across a biological membrane against its concentration gradient, aided by specific transport proteins and requiring an input of energy (often as ATP).

adaptation An inherited character that enhances an organism's ability to survive and reproduce in a particular environment.

adaptive immunity A vertebrate-specific defense that is activated only after exposure to an antigen and is mediated by lymphocytes. It exhibits specificity, memory, and self-nonself recognition. Also called acquired immunity.

adaptive radiation Period of evolutionary change in which groups of organisms form many new species whose adaptations allow them to fill new or vacant ecological roles in their communities.

adenine (A) (ad´-uh-nēn) A double-ring nitrogenous base found in DNA and RNA.

adhesion The attraction between different kinds of molecules.

adipose tissue A type of connective tissue whose cells contain fat.

adrenal cortex (uh-drē´-nul) The outer portion of an adrenal gland, controlled by ACTH from the anterior pituitary; secretes hormones called glucocorticoids and mineralocorticoids.

adrenal gland (uh-drē´-nul) One of a pair of endocrine glands, located atop each kidney in mammals, composed of an outer cortex and a central medulla.

adrenal medulla (uh-drē´-nul muh-dul´-uh) The central portion of an adrenal gland, controlled by nerve signals; secretes the fight-or-flight hormones epinephrine and norepinephrine.

adrenocorticotropic hormone (ACTH) (uh-drē´-nō-cōr´-ti-kō-trop´-ik) A protein hormone secreted by the anterior pituitary that stimulates the adrenal cortex to secrete corticosteroids.

adult stem cell A cell present in adult tissues that generates replacements for nondividing differentiated cells. Adult stem cells are capable of differentiating into multiple cell types, but they are not as developmentally flexible as embryonic stem cells.

age structure The relative number of individuals of each age in a population.

agonistic behavior (a´-gō-nis´-tik) Confrontational behavior involving a contest waged by threats, displays, or actual combat that settles disputes over limited resources, such as food or mates.

AIDS (acquired immunodeficiency syndrome) The late stages of HIV infection, characterized by a reduced number of T cells and the appearance of characteristic opportunistic infections.

alcohol fermentation Glycolysis followed by the reduction of pyruvate to ethyl alcohol, regenerating NAD^+ and releasing carbon dioxide.

alga (al´-guh) (plural, **algae**) A protist that produces its food by photosynthesis.

alimentary canal (al´-uh-men´-tuh-rē) A complete digestive tract consisting of a tube running between a mouth and an anus.

allantois (al´-an-tō´-is) In animals, an extraembryonic membrane that develops from the yolk sac. The allantois helps dispose of the embryo's nitrogenous wastes and forms part of the umbilical cord in mammals.

allele (uh-lē´-ul) An alternative version of a gene.

allergen (al´-er-jen) An antigen that causes an allergy.

allergy A disorder of the immune system caused by an abnormally high sensitivity to an antigen. Symptoms are triggered by histamines released from mast cells.

allopatric speciation The formation of new species in populations that are geographically isolated from one another.

alternation of generations A life cycle in which there is both a multicellular diploid form, the sporophyte, and a multicellular haploid form, the gametophyte; a characteristic of plants and multicellular green algae.

alternative RNA splicing A type of regulation at the RNA-processing level in which different mRNA molecules are produced from the same primary transcript, depending on which RNA segments are treated as exons and which as introns.

altruism (al´-trū-iz-um) Behavior that reduces an individual's fitness while increasing the fitness of another individual.

Alveolata (al-vē´-uh-let-uh) A clade of the SAR supergroup of protists that includes dinoflagellates, ciliates, and certain parasites.

alveolus (al-vē´-oh-lus) (plural, **alveoli**) One of the dead-end air sacs within the mammalian lung where gas exchange occurs.

Alzheimer's disease (AD) An age-related dementia (mental deterioration) characterized by confusion, memory loss, and other symptoms.

amino acid (uh-mēn´-ō) An organic molecule containing a carboxyl group and an amino group; serves as the monomer of proteins.

amino group (uh-mēn´-ō) A chemical group consisting of a nitrogen atom bonded to two hydrogen atoms.

ammonia NH_3; A small and very toxic nitrogenous waste produced by metabolism.

amniocentesis (am´-nē-ō-sen-tē´-sis) A technique for diagnosing genetic defects while a fetus is in the uterus. A sample of amniotic fluid, obtained by a needle inserted into the uterus, is analyzed for telltale chemicals and defective fetal cells.

amnion (am´-nē-on) In vertebrate animals, the extraembryonic membrane that encloses the fluid-filled amniotic sac containing the embryo.

amniote Member of a clade of tetrapods that have an amniotic egg containing specialized membranes that protect the embryo. Amniotes include mammals and birds and other reptiles.

amniotic egg (am´-nē-ot´-ik) A shelled egg in which an embryo develops within a fluid-filled amniotic sac and is nourished by yolk. Produced by reptiles (including birds) and egg-laying mammals, the amniotic egg enables them to complete their life cycles on dry land.

amoeba (uh-mē´-buh) A general term for a protist that moves and feeds by means of pseudopodia.

amoebocyte (uh-mē´-buh-sīt) An amoeba-like cell that moves by pseudopodia and is found in most animals; depending on the species, may digest and distribute food, dispose of wastes, form skeletal fibers, fight infections, and change into other cell types.

amoebozoan A member of a clade of protists in the supergroup Unikonta that includes amoebas and slime molds and is characterized by lobe-shaped pseudopodia.

amphibian Member of a clade of tetrapods that includes frogs, toads, salamanders, and caecilians.

amygdala (uh-mig´-duh-la) An integrative center of the cerebrum; functionally, the part of the limbic system that seems central in recognizing the emotional content of facial expressions and laying down emotional memories.

anabolic steroid (an´-uh-bol´-ik ster´-oyd) A synthetic variant of the male hormone testosterone that mimics some of its effects.

analogy The similarity between two species that is due to convergent evolution rather than to descent from a common ancestor with the same trait.

anaphase The fourth stage of mitosis, beginning when sister chromatids separate from each other and ending when a complete set of daughter chromosomes arrives at each of the two poles of the cell.

anatomy The study of the structures of an organism.

anchorage dependence The requirement that to divide, a cell must be attached to a solid surface.

androgen (an´-drō-jen) A steroid sex hormone secreted by the gonads that promotes the development and maintenance of the male reproductive system and male body features.

anemia (uh-nē´-me-ah) A condition in which an abnormally low amount of hemoglobin or a low number of red blood cells results in the body cells receiving too little oxygen.

angiosperm (an´-jē-ō-sperm) A flowering plant, which forms seeds inside a protective chamber called an ovary.

annelid (uh-nel´-id) A segmented worm. Annelids include earthworms, polychaetes, and leeches.

annual A plant that completes its life cycle in a single year or growing season.

antagonistic hormones Two hormones that have opposite effects.

anterior Pertaining to the front, or head, of a bilaterally symmetric animal.

anterior pituitary (puh-tū´-uh-tār-ē) An endocrine gland, adjacent to the hypothalamus and the posterior pituitary, that synthesizes several hormones, including some that control the activity of other endocrine glands.

anther A sac located at the tip of a flower's stamen; contains male sporangia in which meiosis occurs to produce spores that form the male gametophytes, or pollen grains.

anthropoid (an´-thruh-poyd) A member of a primate group made up of the apes (gibbons, orangutans, gorillas, chimpanzees, bonobos, and humans) and monkeys.

antibody (an´-tih-bod´-ē) A protein dissolved in blood plasma that attaches to a specific kind of antigen and helps counter its effects; secreted by plasma cells.

anticodon (an´-tī-kō´-don) On a tRNA molecule, a specific sequence of three nucleotides that is complementary to a codon triplet on mRNA.

antidiuretic hormone (ADH) (an´-tē-dī´-yū-ret´-ik) A hormone made by the hypothalamus and secreted by the posterior pituitary that promotes water retention by the kidneys.

antigen (an´-tuh-jen) A foreign (nonself) molecule that elicits an adaptive immune response.

antigen receptor (an´-tuh-jen) The general term for a surface protein, located on B cells and T cells, that binds to antigens and initiates the adaptive immune response.

antigen-binding site (an´-tuh-jen) A region of the antigen receptor or antibody that binds the antigenic determinant on the antigen.

antigenic determinant (an´-tuh-jen´-ik) A small region on the surface of an antigen molecule to which an antigen receptor or antibody binds; also called an epitope.

antigen-presenting cell (APC) (an´-tuh-jen) One of a family of white blood cells that ingests a foreign substance or a microbe and attaches antigenic portions of the ingested material to its own surface, thereby displaying the antigens to a helper T cell.

antihistamine (an´-tē-his´-tuh-mēn) A drug that interferes with the action of histamine, providing relief from an allergic reaction.

anus The opening through which undigested materials are expelled.

aorta (ā-or´-tuh) A large artery that conveys blood directly from the left ventricle of the heart to other arteries.

aphotic zone (ā-fō´-tik) The region of an aquatic ecosystem beneath the photic zone, where light does not penetrate enough for photosynthesis to take place.

apical dominance (ā´-pik-ul) In a plant, the hormonal inhibition of axillary buds by a terminal bud.

apical meristem (ā´-pik-ul mer´-uh-stem) A growth-producing region of cell division consisting of undifferentiated cells located at the tip of a plant root or in the terminal or axillary bud of a shoot.

apoptosis (ā-puh-tō´-sus) The timely and tidy suicide of cells; also called programmed cell death.

appendicular skeleton (ap´-en-dik´-yū-ler) Components of the skeletal system that support the fins of a fish or the arms and legs of a land vertebrate; in land vertebrates, the cartilage and bones of the shoulder girdle, pelvic girdle, forelimbs, and hind limbs. *See also* axial skeleton.

appendix (uh-pen´-dix) A small, finger-like extension of the vertebrate cecum; contains a mass of white blood cells that contribute to immunity.

aquaporin A transport protein in the plasma membrane of an animal, plant, or microorganism cell that facilitates the diffusion of water across the membrane (osmosis).

aqueous humor (ā´-kwē-us hyū´-mer) Plasma-like liquid in the space between the lens and the cornea in the vertebrate eye; helps maintain the shape of the eye, supplies nutrients and oxygen to its tissues, and disposes of its wastes.

aqueous solution (ā´-kwē-us) A solution in which water is the solvent.

arachnid A member of a major arthropod group (chelicerates) that includes spiders, scorpions, ticks, and mites.

Archaea (ar´-kē-uh) One of two prokaryotic domains of life, the other being Bacteria.

Archaeplastida One of four monophyletic supergroups proposed in a current hypothesis of the evolutionary history of eukaryotes. The other four supergroups are SAR (Stramenopila, Alveolata, and Rhizaria), Excavata, and Unikonta.

arteriole (ar-ter´-ē-ōl) A vessel that conveys blood between an artery and a capillary bed.

artery A vessel that carries blood away from the heart to other parts of the body.

arthropod (ar´-thrō-pod) A member of the most diverse phylum in the animal kingdom. Arthropods include the horseshoe crab, arachnids (for example, spiders, ticks, scorpions, and mites), crustaceans (for example, crayfish, lobsters, crabs, and barnacles), millipedes, centipedes, and insects. Arthropods are characterized by a chitinous exoskeleton, molting, jointed appendages, and a body formed of distinct groups of segments.

artificial selection The selective breeding of domesticated plants and animals to promote the occurrence of desirable traits.

ascomycete (as´-kuh-mī´-sēt) Member of a group of fungi characterized by saclike structures called asci that produce spores in sexual reproduction.

asexual reproduction The creation of genetically identical offspring by a single parent, without the participation of sperm and egg.

assisted reproductive technology Procedure that involves surgically removing eggs from a woman's ovaries, fertilizing them, and then returning them to the woman's body. *See also in vitro* fertilization.

association areas Sites of higher mental activities, making up most of the cerebral cortex.

associative learning The ability to associate one environmental feature with another. In one type of associative learning, the animal learns to link a particular stimulus with a particular outcome. Trial-and-error learning is also a type of associative learning.

astigmatism (uh-stig´-muh-tizm) Blurred vision caused by a misshapen lens or cornea.

atherosclerosis (ath´-uh-rō´-skluh-rō´-sis) A cardiovascular disease in which fatty deposits called plaques develop on the inner walls of the arteries, narrowing their inner diameters.

atom The smallest unit of matter that retains the properties of an element.

atomic mass The total mass of an atom; also called atomic weight. Given as a whole number, the atomic mass approximately equals the mass number.

atomic number The number of protons in each atom of a particular element.

ATP Adenosine triphosphate, the main energy source for cells. ATP releases energy when its phosphate bonds are hydrolyzed.

ATP synthase A cluster of several membrane proteins that function in chemiosmosis with adjacent electron transport chains, using the energy of a hydrogen ion concentration gradient to make ATP.

atrium (ā´-trē-um) (plural, **atria**) A heart chamber that receives blood from the veins.

auditory canal Part of the vertebrate outer ear that channels sound waves from the pinna or outer body surface to the eardrum.

autoimmune disorder An immunological disorder in which the immune system attacks the body's own molecules.

autonomic nervous system (ot´-ō-nom´-ik) The component of the vertebrate peripheral nervous system that regulates the internal environment; made up of sympathetic and parasympathetic subdivisions. Most actions of the autonomic nervous system are involuntary.

autosome A chromosome not directly involved in determining the sex of an organism; in mammals, for example, any chromosome other than X or Y.

autotroph (ot´-ō-trōf) An organism that makes its own food (often by photosynthesis), thereby sustaining itself without eating other organisms or their molecules. Plants, algae, and numerous bacteria are autotrophs.

auxin (ok´-sin) A plant hormone (indoleacetic acid or a related compound) that promotes seedling elongation.

AV (atrioventricular) node A region of specialized heart muscle tissue between the left and right atria where electrical impulses are delayed for about 0.1 second before spreading to both ventricles and causing them to contract.

axial skeleton (ak´-sē-ul) Components of the skeletal system that support the central trunk of the body: the skull, backbone, and rib cage in a vertebrate. *See also* appendicular skeleton.

axillary bud (ak´-sil-ār-ē) An embryonic shoot present in the angle formed by a leaf and stem.

axon (ak´-son) A neuron extension that conducts signals to another neuron or to an effector cell. A neuron has one long axon.

B

B cell A type of lymphocyte that completes its development in the bone marrow and is responsible for the humoral immune response. Effector B cells are also called plasma cells.

bacillus (buh-sil´-us) (plural, **bacilli**) A rod-shaped prokaryotic cell.

Bacteria One of two prokaryotic domains of life, the other being Archaea.

bacteriophage (bak-tēr´-ē-ō-fāj) A virus that infects bacteria; also called a phage.

balancing selection Natural selection that maintains stable frequencies of two or more phenotypic forms in a population.

ball-and-socket joint A joint that allows rotation and movement in several planes. Examples in humans are the hip and shoulder joints.

bark All the tissues external to the vascular cambium in a plant that is growing in thickness. Bark is made up of secondary phloem, cork cambium, and cork.

Barr body A dense body formed from a deactivated X chromosome found in the nuclei of female mammalian cells.

basal metabolic rate (BMR) The number of kilocalories a resting animal requires to fuel its essential body processes for a given time.

basal nuclei (bā´-sul nū´-klē-ī) Clusters of nerve cell bodies located deep within the cerebrum that are important in motor coordination.

base A substance that decreases the hydrogen ion (H^+) concentration in a solution.

basidiomycete (buh-sid´-ē-ō-mī´sēt) Member of a group of fungi characterized by club-shaped, spore-producing structures called basidia.

basilar membrane The floor of the middle canal of the inner ear.

behavior Individually, an action carried out by the muscles or glands under control of the nervous system in response to a stimulus; collectively, the sum of an animal's responses to external and internal stimuli.

behavioral ecology The study of behavior in an evolutionary context.

benign tumor An abnormal mass of cells that remains at its original site in the body.

benthic realm A seafloor or the bottom of a freshwater lake, pond, river, or stream.

biennial A plant that completes its life cycle in two years.

bilateral symmetry An arrangement of body parts such that an organism can be divided equally by a single cut passing longitudinally through it. A bilaterally symmetric organism has mirror-image right and left sides.

bilaterian Member of the clade Bilateria, animals exhibiting bilateral symmetry.

bile A mixture of substances that is produced by the liver and stored in the gallbladder. Bile emulsifies fats and aids in their digestion.

binary fission A means of asexual reproduction in which a parent organism, often a single cell, divides into two genetically identical individuals of about equal size.

binomial A two-part, latinized name of a species; for example, *Homo sapiens.*

biodiversity The variety of living things; includes genetic diversity, species diversity, and ecosystem diversity.

biodiversity hot spot A small geographic area with an exceptional concentration of endangered and threatened species, especially endemic species (those found nowhere else).

biofilm A surface-coating colony of prokaryotes that engage in metabolic cooperation.

biogeochemical cycle Any of the various chemical circuits that involve both biotic and abiotic components of an ecosystem.

biogeography The study of the past and present distribution of organisms.

biological clock An internal timekeeper that controls an organism's biological rhythms, marking time with or without environmental cues but often requiring signals from the environment to remain tuned to an appropriate period. *See also* circadian rhythm.

biological control The intentional release of a natural enemy to attack a pest population.

biological magnification The accumulation of harmful chemicals that are retained in the living tissues of consumers in food chains.

biological species concept Definition of a species as a group of populations whose members have the potential to interbreed in nature and produce viable, fertile offspring but do not produce viable, fertile offspring with members of other such populations.

biology The scientific study of life.

biomass The amount, or mass, of organic material in an ecosystem.

biome (bī-ōm) A major type of ecological association that occupies a broad geographic region of land or water and is characterized by organisms adapted to the particular environment.

bioremediation The use of living organisms to detoxify and restore polluted and degraded ecosystems.

biosphere The entire portion of Earth inhabited by life; the sum of all the planet's ecosystems.

biotechnology The manipulation of living organisms or their components to make useful products.

biotic factor (bī-o´-tik) A living component of a biological community; an organism, or a factor pertaining to one or more organisms.

bipolar disorder Depressive mental illness characterized by extreme mood swings; also called manic-depressive disorder.

birds Members of a clade of reptiles that have feathers and adaptations for flight.

bivalve A member of a group of molluscs that includes clams, mussels, scallops, and oysters.

blastocoel (blas´-tuh-sēl) In a developing animal, a central, fluid-filled cavity in a blastula.

blastocyst (blas´-tō-sist) A mammalian embryo (equivalent to an amphibian blastula) made up of a hollow ball of cells that results from cleavage and that implants in the mother's endometrium.

blastula (blas´-tyū-luh) An embryonic stage that marks the end of cleavage during animal development; a hollow ball of cells in many species.

blood A type of connective tissue with a fluid matrix called plasma in which red blood cells, white blood cells, and platelets are suspended.

blood pressure The force that blood exerts against the walls of blood vessels.

blood-brain barrier A system of capillaries in the brain that restricts passage of most substances into the brain, thereby preventing large fluctuations in the brain's environment.

body cavity A fluid-containing space between the digestive tract and the body wall.

bolus A lubricated ball of chewed food.

bone A type of connective tissue consisting of living cells held in a rigid matrix of collagen fibers embedded in calcium salts.

bottleneck effect Genetic drift resulting from a drastic reduction in population size. Typically, the surviving population is no longer genetically representative of the original population.

Bowman's capsule A cup-shaped swelling at the receiving end of a nephron in the vertebrate kidney; collects the filtrate from the blood.

brain The master control center of the nervous system, involved in regulating and controlling body activity and interpreting information from the senses transmitted through the nervous system.

brainstem A functional unit of the vertebrate brain, composed of the midbrain, the medulla oblongata, and the pons; serves mainly as a sensory filter, selecting which information reaches higher brain centers.

brassinosteroids A class of plant steroid hormones that promote cell elongation and cell division in stems and seedlings.

breathing Ventilation of the lungs through alternating inhalation and exhalation of air.

breathing control center The part of the medulla in the brain that directs the activity of organs involved in breathing.

bronchiole (bron´-kē-ōl) A fine branch of the bronchi that transports air to alveoli.

bronchus (bron´-kus) (plural, **bronchi**) One of a pair of breathing tubes that branch from the trachea into the lungs.

brown alga One of a group of marine, multicellular, autotrophic protists belonging to the stramenopile clade of the SAR supergroup; the most common and largest type of seaweed. Brown algae include the kelps.

bryophyte (brī´-uh-fīt) A plant that lacks xylem and phloem; a seedless nonvascular plant. Bryophytes include mosses, liverworts, and hornworts.

budding A means of asexual reproduction whereby a new individual develops from an outgrowth of a parent. The new individual eventually splits off and lives independently.

buffer A chemical substance that resists changes in pH by accepting hydrogen ions from or donating hydrogen ions to solutions.

bulbourethral gland (bul´-bō-yū-rē´-thrul) One of a pair of glands near the base of the penis in the human male that secrete a clear alkaline mucus.

bulk feeder An animal that eats relatively large pieces of food.

C

C₃ plant A plant that uses the Calvin cycle for the initial steps that incorporate CO_2 into organic material, forming a three-carbon compound as the first stable intermediate.

C₄ plant A plant in which the Calvin cycle is preceded by reactions that incorporate CO_2 into a four-carbon compound, which then supplies CO_2 for the Calvin cycle.

Calvin cycle The second of two stages of photosynthesis; a cyclic series of chemical reactions that occur in the stroma of a chloroplast, using the carbon in CO_2 and the ATP and NADPH produced by the light reactions to make the energy-rich sugar molecule G3P.

CAM plant A plant that uses an adaptation for photosynthesis in arid conditions in which carbon dioxide entering open stomata during the night is converted to organic acids, which release CO_2 for the Calvin cycle during the day, when stomata are closed.

cancer A disease characterized by the presence of malignant tumors (rapidly growing and spreading masses of abnormal body cells) in the body.

capillary (kap´-il-er-ē) A microscopic blood vessel that conveys blood between an arteriole and a venule; enables the exchange of nutrients and dissolved gases between the blood and interstitial fluid.

capillary bed (kap´-il-er-ē) A network of capillaries in a tissue or organ.

capsid The protein shell that encloses a viral genome.

carbohydrate (kar´-bō-hī´-drāt) Member of the class of biological molecules consisting of single-monomer sugars (monosaccharides), two-monomer sugars (disaccharides), and polymers (polysaccharides).

carbon fixation The incorporation of carbon from atmospheric CO_2 into an organic compound. During photosynthesis in a C₃ plant, carbon is fixed into a three-carbon sugar as it enters the Calvin cycle. In C₄ and CAM plants, carbon is first fixed into a four-carbon sugar.

carbonyl group (kar´-buh-nēl´) A chemical group consisting of a carbon atom linked by a double bond to an oxygen atom.

carboxyl group (kar-bok´-sil) A chemical group consisting of a carbon atom double-bonded to an oxygen atom and also bonded to a hydroxyl group.

carcinogen (kar-sin´-uh-jin) A cancer-causing agent, either high-energy radiation (such as X-rays or UV light) or a chemical.

cardiac cycle (kar´-dē-ak) The alternating contractions and relaxations of the heart.

cardiac muscle (kar´-dē-ak) A type of striated muscle that forms the contractile wall of the heart.

cardiac output (kar´-dē-ak) The volume of blood pumped per minute by each ventricle of the heart.

cardiovascular disease (kar´-dē-ō-vas´-kyū-ler) Disorders of the heart and blood vessels.

cardiovascular system (kar´-dē-ō-vas´-kyū-ler) A closed circulatory system with a heart and a branching network of arteries, capillaries, and veins.

carnivore An animal that mainly eats other animals.

carpel (kar´-pul) The female part of a flower, consisting of a stalk with an ovary at the base and a stigma, which traps pollen, at the tip.

carrier An individual who is heterozygous for a recessively inherited disorder and who therefore does not show symptoms of that disorder but who may pass on the recessive allele to offspring.

carrying capacity In a population, the number of individuals that an environment can sustain.

cartilage (kar´-ti-lij) A flexible connective tissue consisting of living cells and collagenous fibers embedded in a rubbery matrix.

Casparian strip (kas-par´-ē-un) A waxy barrier in the walls of endodermal cells in a plant root that prevents water and ions from entering the xylem without crossing one or more cell membranes.

cation exchange A process in which positively charged minerals are made available to a plant when hydrogen ions in the soil displace mineral ions from the clay particles.

cecum (sē´-kum) (plural, **ceca**) A blind outpocket at the beginning of the large intestine.

cell A basic unit of living matter separated from its environment by a plasma membrane; the fundamental structural unit of life.

cell body The part of a cell, such as a neuron, that houses the nucleus.

cell cycle An ordered sequence of events (including interphase and the mitotic phase) that extends from the time a eukaryotic cell is first formed from a dividing parent cell until its own division into two cells.

cell cycle control system A cyclically operating set of proteins that triggers and coordinates events in the eukaryotic cell cycle.

cell division The reproduction of a cell through duplication of the genome and division of the cytoplasm.

cell plate A double membrane across the midline of a dividing plant cell, between which the new cell wall forms during cytokinesis.

cell theory The theory that all living things are composed of cells and that all cells come from other cells.

cell wall A protective layer external to the plasma membrane in plant cells, bacteria, fungi, and some protists; protects the cell and helps maintain its shape.

cell-mediated immune response The branch of adaptive immunity that involves the activation of cytotoxic T cells, which defend against infected cells.

cellular metabolism (muh-tab´-uh-lizm) All the chemical activities of a cell.

cellular respiration The aerobic harvesting of energy from food molecules; the energy-releasing chemical breakdown of food molecules, such as glucose, and the storage of potential energy in a form that cells can use to perform work; involves glycolysis, the citric acid cycle, and oxidative phosphorylation (the electron transport chain and chemiosmosis).

cellular slime mold A type of protist that has unicellular amoeboid cells and aggregated reproductive bodies in its life cycle; a member of the amoebozoan clade.

cellulose (sel´-yū-lōs) A structural polysaccharide of plant cell walls composed of glucose monomers. Cellulose molecules are linked by hydrogen bonds into cable-like fibrils.

centipede A carnivorous terrestrial arthropod that has one pair of long legs for each of its numerous body segments, with the front pair modified as poison claws.

central canal The narrow cavity in the center of the spinal cord that is continuous with the fluid-filled ventricles of the brain.

central nervous system (CNS) The integration and command center of the nervous system; the brain and, in vertebrates, the spinal cord.

central vacuole In a plant cell, a large membranous sac with diverse roles in growth and the storage of chemicals and wastes.

centralization The presence of a central nervous system (CNS) distinct from a peripheral nervous system.

centromere (sen´-trō-mēr) The region of a duplicated chromosome where two sister chromatids are joined (often appearing as a narrow "waist") and where spindle microtubules attach during mitosis and meiosis. The centromere divides at the onset of anaphase during mitosis and anaphase II during meiosis.

centrosome A structure found in animal cells from which microtubules originate and that is important during cell division. A centrosome has two centrioles.

cephalization (sef´-uh-luh-zā´-shun) An evolutionary trend toward concentration of the nervous system at the head end.

cephalopod A member of a group of molluscs that includes squids, cuttlefish, octopuses, and nautiluses.

cerebellum (sār´-ruh-bel´-um) Part of the vertebrate hindbrain; mainly a planning center that interacts closely with the cerebrum in coordinating body movement.

cerebral cortex (suh-rē´-brul kor´-teks) A folded sheet of gray matter forming the surface of the cerebrum. In humans, it contains integrating centers for higher brain functions such as reasoning, speech, language, and imagination.

cerebral hemisphere (suh-rē´-brul) The right or left half of the vertebrate cerebrum.

cerebrospinal fluid (suh-rē´-brō-spī´-nul) Blood-derived fluid that surrounds, nourishes, and cushions the brain and spinal cord.

cerebrum (suh-rē´-brum) The largest, most sophisticated, and most dominant part of the vertebrate forebrain, made up of right and left cerebral hemispheres.

cervix (ser´-viks) The neck of the uterus, which opens into the vagina.

chaparral (shap´-uh-ral´) A biome dominated by spiny evergreen shrubs adapted to periodic drought and fires; found where cold ocean currents circulate offshore, creating mild, rainy winters and long, hot, dry summers.

character A heritable feature that varies among individuals within a population, such as flower color in pea plants or eye color in humans.

chelicerate (kē-lih-suh´-rāte) A lineage of arthropods that includes horseshoe crabs, scorpions, ticks, and spiders.

chemical bond An attraction between two atoms resulting from a sharing of outer-shell electrons or the presence of opposite charges on the atoms. The bonded atoms gain complete outer electron shells.

chemical cycling The use and reuse of a chemical element, such as carbon, within an ecosystem.

chemical energy Energy available in molecules for release in a chemical reaction; a form of potential energy.

chemical reaction The making and breaking of chemical bonds, leading to changes in the composition of matter.

chemiosmosis (kem´-ē-oz-mō´-sis) An energy-coupling mechanism that uses the energy of hydrogen ion (H^+) gradients across membranes to drive cellular work, such as the phosphorylation of ADP; powers most ATP synthesis in cells.

chemoautotroph An organism that obtains both energy and carbon from inorganic chemicals. A chemoautotroph makes its own organic compounds from CO_2 without using light energy.

chemoheterotroph An organism that obtains both energy and carbon from organic compounds.

chemoreceptor (kē´-mō-rē-sep´-ter) A sensory receptor that detects chemical changes within the body or a specific kind of molecule in the external environment.

chiasma (kī-az´-muh) (plural, **chiasmata**) The microscopically visible site where crossing over has occurred between chromatids of homologous chromosomes during prophase I of meiosis.

chitin (kī-tin) A structural polysaccharide found in many fungal cell walls and in the exoskeletons of arthropods.

chlamydia A member of a group of bacteria that live inside eukaryotic host cells; a common sexually transmitted disease caused by the bacterium *Chlamydia trachomatis*.

chlorophyll A green pigment located within the chloroplasts of plants and algae and in the membranes of certain prokaryotes. Chlorophyll *a* participates directly in the light reactions, which convert solar energy to chemical energy.

chloroplast (klō´-rō-plast) An organelle found in plants and algae that absorbs sunlight and uses it to drive the synthesis of organic compounds (sugars) from carbon dioxide and water.

choanocyte (kō-an´-uh-sīt) A flagellated feeding cell found in sponges. Also called a collar cell, it has a collar-like ring that traps food particles around the base of its flagellum.

cholesterol (kō-les´-tuh-rol) A steroid that is an important component of animal cell membranes and that acts as a precursor molecule for the synthesis of other steroids, such as hormones.

chondrichthyan (kon-drik´-thē-an) Cartilaginous fish; member of a clade of jawed vertebrates with skeletons made mostly of cartilage, such as sharks and rays.

chorion (kō´r-ē-on) In animals, the outermost extraembryonic membrane, which becomes the mammalian embryo's part of the placenta.

chorionic villus (kōr´-ē-on´-ik vil´-us) Outgrowth of the chorion, containing embryonic blood vessels. As part of the placenta, chorionic villi absorb nutrients and oxygen from, and pass wastes into, the mother's bloodstream.

chorionic villus sampling (CVS) A technique for diagnosing genetic defects while the fetus is in an early development stage within the uterus. A small sample of the fetal portion of the placenta is removed and analyzed.

choroid (kōr´-oyd) A thin, pigmented layer in the vertebrate eye, surrounded by the sclera. The iris is part of the choroid.

chromatin (krō´-muh-tin) The complex of DNA and proteins that makes up eukaryotic chromosomes; often used to refer to the diffuse, very extended form taken by chromosomes when a cell is not dividing.

chromosome (krō´-muh-sōm) A gene-carrying structure found in the nucleus of a eukaryotic cell and most visible during mitosis and meiosis; also, the main gene-carrying structure of a prokaryotic cell. A chromosome consists of one very long DNA molecule and associated proteins.

chromosome theory of inheritance (krō´-muh-sōm) A basic principle in biology stating that genes are located on chromosomes and that the behavior of chromosomes during meiosis accounts for inheritance patterns.

chronic traumatic encephalopathy A dementia (mental deterioration) caused by brain trauma such as sports concussions and characterized by depression, memory loss, and other symptoms.

chyme (kīm) The mixture of partially digested food and digestive juices formed in the stomach.

chytrid (kī-trid) Member of a group of fungi that are mostly aquatic and have flagellated spores. They probably represent the most primitive fungal lineage.

ciliate (sil´-ē-it) A type of protist that moves and feeds by means of cilia. Ciliates belong to the alveolate clade of the SAR supergroup.

cilium (plural, **cilia**) A short cellular appendage specialized for locomotion or moving fluid past the cell, formed from a core of nine outer doublet microtubules and two single microtubules (the "9 + 2" arrangement) covered by the cell's plasma membrane.

circadian rhythm (ser-kā´-dē-un) In an organism, a biological cycle of about 24 hours that is controlled by a biological clock, usually under the influence of environmental cues; a pattern of activity that is repeated daily. *See also* biological clock.

circulatory system The organ system that transports materials such as nutrients, O_2, and hormones to body cells and transports CO_2 and other wastes from body cells.

citric acid cycle The chemical cycle that completes the metabolic breakdown of glucose molecules begun in glycolysis by oxidizing acetyl CoA (derived from pyruvate) to carbon dioxide. The cycle occurs in the matrix of mitochondria and supplies most of the NADH molecules that carry electrons to the electron transport chains. Together with pyruvate oxidation, the second major stage of cellular respiration.

clade A group of species that includes an ancestral species and all its descendants.

cladistics (kluh-dis´-tiks) An approach to systematics in which common descent is the primary criterion used to classify organisms by placing them into groups called clades.

class In Linnaean classification, the taxonomic category above order.

cleavage (klē´-vij) (1) Cytokinesis in animal cells and in some protists, characterized by pinching in of the plasma membrane. (2) In animal development, the first major phase of embryonic development, in which rapid cell divisions without cell growth transforms the animal zygote into a ball of cells.

cleavage furrow (klē´-vij) The first sign of cytokinesis during cell division in an animal cell; a shallow groove in the cell surface near the old metaphase plate.

clitoris An organ in the female that engorges with blood and becomes erect during sexual arousal.

clonal selection (klōn´-ul) The process by which an antigen selectively binds to and activates only those lymphocytes bearing receptors specific for the antigen. The selected lymphocytes proliferate and differentiate into a clone of effector cells and a clone of memory cells specific for the stimulating antigen.

clone As a verb, to produce genetically identical copies of a cell, organism, or DNA molecule. As a noun, the collection of cells, organisms, or molecules resulting from cloning; colloquially, a single organism that is genetically identical to another because it arose from the cloning of a somatic cell.

closed circulatory system A circulatory system in which blood is confined to vessels and is kept separate from the interstitial fluid.

club fungus *See* basidiomycete.

clumped dispersion pattern A pattern in which the individuals of a population are aggregated in patches.

cnidarian (nī-dār´-ē-un) An animal characterized by cnidocytes, radial symmetry, a gastrovascular cavity, and a polyp and medusa body form. Cnidarians include the hydras, jellies, sea anemones, corals, and related animals.

cnidocyte (nī´-duh-sīt) A specialized cell for which the phylum Cnidaria is named; consists of a capsule containing a fine coiled thread, which, when discharged, functions in defense and prey capture.

coccus (kok´-us) (plural, **cocci**) A spherical prokaryotic cell.

cochlea (kok´-lē-uh) A coiled tube in the inner ear of birds and mammals that contains the hearing organ, the organ of Corti.

codominant Inheritance pattern in which a heterozygote expresses the distinct trait of both alleles.

codon (kō´-don) A three-nucleotide sequence in mRNA that specifies a particular amino acid or polypeptide termination signal; the basic unit of the genetic code.

coelom (sē´-lom) A body cavity completely lined with mesoderm.

coenzyme An organic molecule serving as a cofactor. Most vitamins function as coenzymes in important metabolic reactions.

coevolution Evolutionary change in which adaptations in one species act as a selective force on a second species, inducing adaptations that in turn act as a selective force on the first species; a series of reciprocal evolutionary adaptations in two interacting species.

cofactor A nonprotein molecule or ion that is required for the proper functioning of an enzyme. *See also* coenzyme.

cognition The process carried out by an animal's nervous system to perceive, store, integrate, and use information obtained by the animal's sensory receptors.

cohesion (kō-hē´-zhun) The sticking together of molecules of the same kind, often by hydrogen bonds.

collecting duct A tube in the vertebrate kidney that concentrates urine while conveying it to the renal pelvis.

collenchyma cell (kō-len´-kim-uh) In plants, a cell with a thick primary wall and no secondary wall, functioning mainly in supporting growing parts.

colon (kō´-lun) The largest section of the large intestine.

communication Animal behavior including transmission of, reception of, and response to signals.

community An assemblage of all the populations of organisms living close enough together for potential interactions.

companion cell In a plant, a cell connected to a sieve-tube element whose nucleus and ribosomes provide proteins for the sieve-tube element.

competitive inhibitor A substance that reduces the activity of an enzyme by entering the active site in place of the substrate. A competitive inhibitor's structure mimics that of the enzyme's substrate.

complement system A family of innate defensive blood proteins that cooperate with other components of the vertebrate defense system to protect against microbes; can enhance phagocytosis, directly lyse pathogens, and amplify the inflammatory response.

complementary DNA (cDNA) A DNA molecule made *in vitro* using mRNA as a template and the enzyme reverse transcriptase. A cDNA molecule therefore corresponds to a gene but lacks the introns present in the DNA of the genome.

complete digestive tract A digestive tube with two openings, a mouth and an anus.

complete dominance A type of inheritance in which the phenotypes of the heterozygote and dominant homozygote are indistinguishable.

complete metamorphosis (met´-uh-mōr´-fuh-sis) A type of development in certain insects in which development from larva to adult is achieved by multiple molts that are followed by a pupal stage. While encased in its pupa, the body rebuilds from clusters of embryonic cells that have been held in reserve. The adult emerges from the pupa.

compost Decomposing organic material that can be used to add nutrients to soil.

compound A substance containing two or more elements in a fixed ratio. For example, table salt (NaCl) consists of one atom of the element sodium (Na) for every atom of chlorine (Cl).

compound eye The photoreceptor in many invertebrates; made up of many tiny light detectors, each of which detects light from a tiny portion of the field of view.

concentration gradient A region along which the density of a chemical substance increases or decreases. Cells often maintain concentration gradients of ions across their membranes. When a concentration gradient exists, substances tend to move from where they are more concentrated to where they are less concentrated.

conception The fertilization of the egg by a sperm cell in humans.

condom A form of contraception; a sheath that fits over the penis to prevent the transfer of sperm to the vagina.

cone (1) In vertebrates, a photoreceptor cell in the retina stimulated by bright light and enabling color vision. (2) In conifers, a reproductive structure bearing pollen or ovules.

coniferous forest A biome characterized by conifers, cone-bearing evergreen trees.

conjugation The union (mating) of two bacterial cells or protist cells and the transfer of DNA between the two cells.

conjunctiva A thin mucous membrane that lines the inner surface of vertebrate eyelids.

connective tissue Animal tissue that functions mainly to bind and support other tissues, having a sparse population of cells scattered through an extracellular matrix, which they produce.

conservation biology A goal-oriented science that endeavors to sustain biological diversity.

continental shelf The submerged part of a continent.

contraception The deliberate prevention of pregnancy.

controlled experiment An experiment in which an experimental group is compared with a control group that varies only in the factor being tested.

convergent evolution The evolution of similar features in different evolutionary lineages, which can result from living in very similar environments.

copulation Sexual intercourse, usually necessary for internal fertilization to occur.

cork The outermost protective layer of a plant's bark, produced by the cork cambium.

cork cambium Meristematic tissue that produces cork cells during secondary growth of a plant.

cornea (kor´-nē-uh) The transparent frontal portion of the sclera, which admits light into the vertebrate eye.

corpus callosum (kor´-pus kuh-lō´-sum) The thick band of nerve fibers that connect the right and left cerebral hemispheres in placental mammals, enabling the hemispheres to process information together.

corpus luteum (kor´-pus lū´-tē-um) A small body of endocrine tissue that develops from an ovarian follicle after ovulation and secretes progesterone and estrogen during pregnancy.

cortex In plants, the ground tissue system of a root, made up mostly of parenchyma cells, which store food and absorb minerals that have passed through the epidermis.

corticosteroid A hormone synthesized and secreted by the adrenal cortex. The corticosteroids include the mineralocorticoids and glucocorticoids.

cotyledon (kot´-uh-lē´-don) The first leaf that appears on an embryo of a flowering plant; a seed leaf. Monocot embryos have one cotyledon; dicot embryos have two.

countercurrent exchange The transfer of a substance or heat between two fluids flowing in opposite directions.

countercurrent heat exchange A circulatory adaptation in which parallel blood vessels convey warm and cold blood in opposite directions, maximizing heat transfer to the cold blood.

covalent bond (ko-vā´-lent) A type of strong chemical bond in which two atoms share one or more pairs of valence electrons.

craniate A chordate with a head.

crista (kris´-tuh) (plural, **cristae**) An infolding of the inner mitochondrial membrane.

crop A pouch-like organ in a digestive tract where food is softened and may be stored temporarily.

cross A mating of two sexually reproducing individuals; often used to describe a genetics experiment involving a controlled mating (a "genetic cross").

crossing over The exchange of segments between chromatids of homologous chromosomes during synapsis in prophase I of meiosis; also, the exchange of segments between DNA molecules in prokaryotes.

crustacean A member of a major arthropod group that includes lobsters, crayfish, crabs, shrimps, and barnacles.

cuticle (kyū´-tuh-kul) (1) In animals, a tough, nonliving outer layer of the skin. (2) In plants, a waxy coating on the surface of stems and leaves that helps retain water.

cyanobacteria (sī-an´-ō-bak-tēr´-ē-uh) Photoautotrophic prokaryotes with plantlike, oxygen-generating photosynthesis.

cytokinesis (sī´-tō-kuh-nē´-sis) The division of the cytoplasm to form two separate daughter cells. Cytokinesis usually occurs in conjunction with telophase of mitosis. Mitosis and cytokinesis make up the mitotic (M) phase of the cell cycle.

cytokinin (sī´-tō-kī´-nin) One of a family of plant hormones that promotes cell division, retards aging in flowers and fruits, and may interact antagonistically with auxins in regulating plant growth and development.

cytoplasm (si´-tō-plaz´-um) The contents of a eukaryotic cell between the plasma membrane and the nucleus; consists of a semifluid medium and organelles; can also refer to the interior of a prokaryotic cell.

cytosine (C) (sī´-tuh-sin) A single-ring nitrogenous base found in DNA and RNA.

cytoskeleton A network of protein fibers in the cytoplasm of a eukaryotic cell; includes microfilaments, intermediate filaments, and microtubules.

cytosol The semifluid portion of the cytoplasm.

cytotoxic T cell (sī´-tō-tok´-sik) A type of lymphocyte that attacks body cells infected with pathogens.

D

decomposer A prokaryote or fungus that secretes enzymes that digest molecules in organic material and convert them to inorganic forms.

decomposition The breakdown of organic materials into inorganic ones.

dehydration reaction (dē-hī-drā´-shun) A chemical reaction in which two molecules become covalently bonded to each other with the removal of a water molecule.

deletion The loss of one or more nucleotides from a gene by mutation; the loss of a fragment of a chromosome.

demographic transition A shift from zero population growth in which birth rates and death rates are high to zero population growth characterized by low birth and death rates.

denaturation (dē-nā´-chur-ā´-shun) A process in which a protein unravels, losing its specific structure and hence function; can be caused by changes in pH or salt concentration or by high temperature; also refers to the separation of the two strands of the DNA double helix, caused by similar factors.

dendrite (den´-drīt) A neuron fiber that conveys signals from its tip inward, toward the rest of the neuron. A neuron typically has many short dendrites.

density-dependent factor A population-limiting factor whose intensity is linked to population density. For example, there may be a decline in birth rates or a rise in death rates in response to an increase in the number of individuals living in a designated area.

density-dependent inhibition The ceasing of cell division that occurs when cells touch one another.

density-independent factor A population-limiting factor whose intensity is unrelated to population density.

deoxyribonucleic acid (DNA) (dē-ok´-sē-rī´-bō-nū-klā´-ik) A double-stranded helical nucleic acid molecule consisting of nucleotide monomers with deoxyribose sugar and the nitrogenous bases adenine (A), cytosine (C), guanine (G), and thymine (T). Capable of replicating, DNA is an organism's genetic material. *See also* gene.

dermal tissue system The outer protective covering of plants.

desert A biome characterized by organisms adapted to sparse rainfall (less than 30 cm per year) and rapid evaporation.

desertification The conversion of semi-arid regions to desert.

determinate growth Termination of growth after reaching a certain size, as in most animals. *See also* indeterminate growth.

detritivore (duh-trī´-tuh-vor) An organism that consumes decaying organic material.

detritus (duh-trī´-tus) Dead organic matter, including animal wastes, plant litter, and the bodies of dead organisms.

deuterostome (dū-ter´-ō-stōm) A mode of animal development in which the opening formed during gastrulation becomes the anus. Animals with the deuterostome pattern of development include the echinoderms and the chordates.

diabetes mellitus (dī´-uh-bē´-tis me-lī´-tis) A human hormonal disease in which body cells cannot absorb enough glucose from the blood and become energy starved; body fats and proteins are then consumed for their energy. Type 1 (insulin-dependent) diabetes results when the pancreas does not produce insulin; type 2 (non-insulin-dependent) diabetes results when body cells fail to respond to insulin.

dialysis (dī-al´-uh-sis) Separation and disposal of metabolic wastes from the blood by mechanical means; an artificial method of performing the functions of the kidneys that can be life sustaining in the event of kidney failure.

diaphragm (dī´-uh-fram) The sheet of muscle separating the chest cavity from the abdominal cavity in mammals. Its contraction expands the chest cavity, and its relaxation reduces it.

diastole (dȳ´-as´-tō-lē) The stage of the heart cycle in which the heart muscle is relaxed, allowing the chambers to fill with blood. *See also* systole.

diatom (dī´-uh-tom) A unicellular, autotrophic protist that belongs to the stramenopile clade of the SAR supergroup. Diatoms possess a unique glassy cell wall containing silica.

dicot (dī´-kot) A term traditionally used to refer to flowering plants that have two embryonic seed leaves, or cotyledons.

differentiation The specialization in the structure and function of cells that occurs during the development of an organism; results from selective activation and deactivation of the cells' genes.

diffusion The random movement of particles that results in the net movement of a substance down its concentration gradient from a region where it is more concentrated to a region where it is less concentrated.

digestion The mechanical and chemical breakdown of food into molecules small enough for the body to absorb; the second stage of food processing in animals.

digestive system The organ system involved in ingestion and digestion of food, absorption of nutrients, and elimination of wastes.

dihybrid cross (dī´-hī´-brid) An experimental mating of individuals that are each heterozygous for both of two characters (or the self-pollination of a plant that is heterozygous for both characters).

dinoflagellate (dī´-nō-flaj´-uh-let) A member of a group of protists belonging to the alveolate clade of the SAR supergroup. Dinoflagellates are common components of marine and freshwater phytoplankton.

diploid In an organism that reproduces sexually, a cell containing two homologous sets of chromosomes, one set inherited from each parent; a 2*n* cell.

directional selection Natural selection in which individuals at one end of the phenotypic range survive and reproduce more successfully than do other individuals.

disaccharide (dī-sak´-uh-rīd) A sugar molecule consisting of two monosaccharides linked by a dehydration reaction.

dispersion pattern The manner in which individuals in a population are spaced within their area. Three types of dispersion patterns are clumped (individuals are aggregated in patches), uniform (individuals are evenly distributed), and random (unpredictable distribution).

disruptive selection Natural selection in which individuals on both extremes of a phenotypic range are favored over intermediate phenotypes.

distal tubule In the vertebrate kidney, the portion of a nephron after the loop of Henle that helps refine filtrate and empties it into a collecting duct.

disturbance In ecology, an event that changes a biological community by removing organisms from it or altering the availability of resources.

DNA *See* deoxyribonucleic acid (DNA).

DNA ligase (lī´-gās) An enzyme, essential for DNA replication, that catalyzes the covalent bonding of adjacent DNA polynucleotide strands. DNA ligase is used in genetic engineering to paste a specific piece of DNA containing a gene of interest into a bacterial plasmid or other vector.

DNA microarray A glass slide carrying thousands of different kinds of single-stranded DNA fragments arranged in an array (grid). A DNA microarray is used to detect and measure the expression of thousands of genes at one time. Tiny amounts of a large number of single-stranded DNA fragments representing different genes are fixed to the glass slide. These fragments, ideally representing all the genes of an organism, are tested for hybridization with various samples of cDNA molecules.

DNA polymerase (puh-lim´-er-ās) A large molecular complex that assembles DNA nucleotides into polynucleotides using a preexisting strand of DNA as a template.

DNA profiling A procedure that analyzes DNA samples to determine if they came from the same individual.

DNA technology Methods used to study and/or manipulate DNA, including recombinant DNA technology.

doldrums (dol´-drums) An area of calm or very light winds near the equator, caused by rising warm air.

domain A taxonomic category above the kingdom level. The three domains of life are Archaea, Bacteria, and Eukarya.

dominance hierarchy The ranking of individuals within a group, based on social interactions and usually maintained by agonistic behavior.

dominant allele (uh-lē´-ul) The allele that determines the phenotype of a gene when the individual is heterozygous for that gene.

dorsal Pertaining to the back of a bilaterally symmetric animal.

dorsal, hollow nerve cord One of the four hallmarks of chordates, a tube that forms on the dorsal side of the body, above the notochord.

double circulation A circulatory system with separate pulmonary and systemic circuits, in which blood passes through the heart after completing each circuit; ensures vigorous blood flow to all organs.

double fertilization In flowering plants, the formation of both a zygote and a cell with a triploid nucleus, which develops into the endosperm.

double helix The form of native DNA, referring to its two adjacent polynucleotide strands interwound into a spiral shape.

Down syndrome *See* trisomy 21.

duodenum (dū-ō-dē´-num) The first portion of the vertebrate small intestine after the stomach, where chyme from the stomach mixes with bile and digestive enzymes.

duplication Repetition of part of a chromosome resulting from fusion with a fragment from a homologous chromosome; can result from an error in meiosis or from mutagenesis.

E

eardrum A sheet of connective tissue separating the outer ear from the middle ear that vibrates when stimulated by sound waves and passes the waves to the middle ear.

echinoderm (uh-kī´-nō-derm) Member of a phylum of slow-moving or sessile marine animals characterized by a rough or spiny skin, a water vascular system, an endoskeleton, and radial symmetry in adults. Echinoderms include sea stars, sea urchins, and sand dollars.

ecological footprint An estimate of the amount of land and water area required to provide the resources an individual or nation consumes and to absorb the waste it generates.

ecological niche (nich) The role of a species in its community; the sum total of a species' use of the biotic and abiotic resources of its environment.

ecological species concept A definition of species in terms of ecological niche, the sum of how members of the species interact with the nonliving and living parts of their environment.

ecological succession The process of biological community change resulting from disturbance; transition in the species composition of a biological community. *See also* primary succession; secondary succession.

ecology The scientific study of how organisms interact with their environment.

ecosystem (ē´-kō-sis-tem) All the organisms in a given area, along with the nonliving (abiotic) factors with which they interact; a biological community and its physical environment.

ecotourism Travel to natural areas for tourism and recreation.

ectoderm (ek´-tō-derm) The outer layer of three embryonic cell layers in a gastrula. The ectoderm forms the skin of the gastrula and gives rise to the epidermis and nervous system in the adult.

ectopic pregnancy (ek-top´-ik) The implantation and development of an embryo outside the uterus.

ectothermic (ek´-tō-therm-ik) Referring to organisms that do not produce enough metabolic heat to have much effect on body temperature.

effector cell (1) A muscle cell or gland cell that performs the body's response to stimuli, responding to signals from the brain or other processing center of the nervous system. (2) A lymphocyte that has undergone clonal selection and is capable of mediating an acquired immune response.

egg A female gamete.

ejaculation (ih-jak´-yū-lā´-shun) Expulsion of semen from the penis.

ejaculatory duct The short section of the ejaculatory route in mammals formed by the convergence of the vas deferens and a duct from the seminal vesicle. The ejaculatory duct transports sperm from the vas deferens to the urethra.

electromagnetic receptor A sensory receptor that detects energy of different wavelengths, such as electricity, magnetism, and light.

electromagnetic spectrum The entire spectrum of electromagnetic radiation ranging in wavelength from less than a nanometer to more than a kilometer.

electron A subatomic particle with a single negative electrical charge. One or more electrons move around the nucleus of an atom.

electron microscope (EM) A microscope that uses magnets to focus an electron beam through, or onto the surface of, a specimen. An electron microscope achieves a hundredfold greater resolution than a light microscope.

electron shell A level of electrons at a characteristic average distance from the nucleus of an atom.

electron transport chain A series of electron carrier molecules that shuttle electrons during a series of redox reactions that release energy used to make ATP; located in the inner membrane of mitochondria, the thylakoid membranes of chloroplasts, and the plasma membranes of prokaryotes.

electronegativity The attraction of a given atom for the electrons of a covalent bond.

element A substance that cannot be broken down to other substances by chemical means.

elimination The passing of undigested material out of the digestive compartment; the fourth and final stage of food processing in animals.

embryo (em´-brē-ō) A developing stage of a multicellular organism. In humans, the stage in the development of offspring from the first division of the zygote until body structures begin to appear, about the 9th week of gestation.

embryo sac (em´-brē-ō) The female gametophyte contained in the ovule of a flowering plant.

embryonic stem cell (ES cell) Cell in the early animal embryo that differentiates during development to give rise to all the different kinds of specialized cells in the body.

embryophyte Another name for land plants, recognizing that land plants share the common derived trait of multicellular, dependent embryos.

emergent properties New properties that arise with each step upward in the hierarchy of life, owing to the arrangement and interactions of parts as complexity increases.

emerging virus A virus that has appeared suddenly or has recently come to the attention of medical scientists.

endemic species A species whose distribution is limited to a specific geographic area.

endergonic reaction (en´-der-gon´-ik) An energy-requiring chemical reaction, which yields products with more potential energy than the reactants.

endocrine gland (en´-dō-krin) A ductless gland that synthesizes hormone molecules and secretes them directly into the bloodstream.

endocrine system (en´-dō-krin) The organ system consisting of ductless glands that secrete hormones and the molecular receptors on or in target cells that respond to the hormones. The endocrine system cooperates with the nervous system in regulating body functions and maintaining homeostasis.

endocytosis (en´-dō-sī-tō´-sis) Cellular uptake of molecules or particles via formation of new vesicles from the plasma membrane.

endoderm (en´-dō-derm) The innermost of three embryonic cell layers in a gastrula; gives rise to the innermost linings of the digestive tract and other hollow organs in the adult.

endodermis The innermost layer (a one-cell-thick cylinder) of the cortex of a plant root; forms a selective barrier determining which substances pass from the cortex into the vascular tissue.

endomembrane system A network of membranes inside and surrounding a eukaryotic cell, related either through direct physical contact or by the transfer of membranous vesicles.

endometrium (en´-dō-mē´-trē-um) The inner lining of the uterus in mammals, richly supplied with blood vessels that provide the maternal part of the placenta and nourish the developing embryo.

endoplasmic reticulum (ER) An extensive membranous network in a eukaryotic cell, continuous with the outer nuclear membrane and composed of ribosome-studded (rough) and ribosome-free (smooth) regions. *See also* rough ER; smooth ER.

endoskeleton A hard skeleton located within the soft tissues of an animal; includes spicules of sponges, the hard plates of echinoderms, and the cartilage and bony skeletons of vertebrates.

endosperm In flowering plants, a nutrient-rich mass formed by the union of a sperm cell with two polar nuclei during double fertilization; provides nourishment to the developing embryo in the seed.

endospore A thick-coated, protective cell produced within a bacterial cell. The endospore becomes dormant and is able to survive harsh environmental conditions.

endosymbiont theory (en´-dō-sim´-bī-ont) The theory that mitochondria and chloroplasts originated as prokaryotic cells engulfed by an ancestral eukaryotic cell. The engulfed cell and its host cell then evolved into a single organism.

endothermic Referring to organisms that use heat generated by their own metabolism to maintain a warm, steady body temperature.

endotoxin A poisonous component of the outer membrane of gram-negative bacteria that is released only when the bacteria die.

energy The capacity to cause change, especially to perform work.

energy coupling In cellular metabolism, the use of energy released from an exergonic reaction to drive an endergonic reaction.

energy flow The passage of energy through the components of an ecosystem.

enhancer A eukaryotic DNA sequence that helps stimulate the transcription of a gene at some distance from it. An enhancer functions by means of a transcription factor called an activator, which binds to it and then to the rest of the transcription apparatus.

enteric division Part of the autonomic nervous system consisting of complex networks of neurons in the digestive tract, pancreas, and gallbladder.

entropy (en´-truh-pē) A measure of disorder, or randomness. *See also* second law of thermodynamics.

enzyme (en´-zīm) A macromolecule, usually a protein, that serves as a biological catalyst, changing the rate of a chemical reaction without being consumed by the reaction.

epidermis (ep´-uh-der´-mis) (1) In animals, one or more living layers of cells forming the protective covering, or outer skin. (2) In plants, the tissue system forming the protective outer covering of leaves, young stems, and young roots.

epididymis (ep´-uh-did´-uh-mus) A long coiled tube into which sperm pass from the testis and are stored until mature and ejaculated.

epigenetic inheritance The inheritance of traits transmitted by mechanisms not directly involving the nucleotide sequence of a genome, such as the chemical modification of histone proteins or DNA bases.

epiglottis A flap of elastic cartilage that protects the entrance to the trachea. Normally, the epiglottis is positioned to allow air to enter the trachea; it changes position when food is swallowed, allowing food to enter the esophagus and preventing food from entering the trachea.

epinephrine (ep´-uh-nef´-rin) An amine hormone (also called adrenaline) secreted by the adrenal medulla that prepares body organs for action (fight or flight); also serves as a neurotransmitter.

epithelial tissue (ep´-uh-thē´-lē-ul) A sheet of tightly packed cells lining organs, body cavities, and external surfaces; also called epithelium.

erythrocyte (eh-rith´-rō-sīt´) A blood cell containing hemoglobin, which transports oxygen; also called a red blood cell.

erythropoietin (EPO) (eh-rith´rō-poy´uh-tin) A hormone that stimulates the production of erythrocytes. It is secreted by the kidney when tissues of the body do not receive enough oxygen.

esophagus (eh-sof´-uh-gus) A muscular tube that conducts food by peristalsis, usually from the pharynx to the stomach.

essential amino acid An amino acid that an animal cannot synthesize itself and must obtain from food. Eight amino acids are essential for the human adult.

essential element In plants, a chemical element required for the plant to complete its life cycle (to grow from a seed and produce another generation of seeds).

essential fatty acid An unsaturated fatty acid that an animal needs but cannot make.

essential nutrient A substance that an organism must absorb in preassembled form because it cannot synthesize it from any other material. In humans, there are essential vitamins, minerals, amino acids, and fatty acids.

estrogen (es´-trō-jen) One of several chemically similar steroid hormones secreted by the gonads; maintains the female reproductive system and promotes the development of female body features.

estuary (es´-chū-ār-ē) The area where a freshwater stream or river merges with the ocean.

ethylene A gas that functions as a hormone in plants, triggering aging responses such as fruit ripening and leaf drop.

eudicot (yūdī´-kot) Member of a group that consists of the vast majority of flowering plants that have two embryonic seed leaves, or cotyledons.

Eukarya (yū-kar´-ē-uh) Domain of life that includes all eukaryotic organisms.

eukaryotic cell (yū-kar-ē-ot´-ik) A type of cell that has a membrane-enclosed nucleus and membrane-enclosed organelles. All organisms except bacteria and archaea are composed of eukaryotic cells.

eumetazoan (yū-met-uh-zō´-un) Member of the clade of "true animals," the animals with true tissues (all animals except sponges).

Eustachian tube (yū-stā´-shun) An air passage between the middle ear and throat of vertebrates that equalizes air pressure on either side of the eardrum.

eutherian (yū-thēr´-ē-un) Placental mammal; mammal whose young complete their embryonic development within the uterus, joined to the mother by the placenta.

evaporative cooling The process in which the surface of an object becomes cooler during evaporation.

evo-devo Evolutionary developmental biology; the field of biology that combines evolutionary biology with developmental biology.

evolution Descent with modification; the idea that living species are descendants of ancestral species that were different from present-day ones; also, the genetic changes in a population from generation to generation.

evolutionary tree A branching diagram that reflects a hypothesis about evolutionary relationships among groups of organisms.

Excavata One of four monophyletic supergroups proposed in a current hypothesis of the evolutionary history of eukaryotes. The other three supergroups are SAR (Stramenopila, Alveolata, and Rhizaria), Unikonta, and Archaeplastida.

excretion (ek-skrē´-shun) The disposal of nitrogen-containing metabolic wastes.

exergonic reaction (ek´-ser-gon´-ik) An energy-releasing chemical reaction in which the reactants contain more potential energy than the products.

exocytosis (ek´-sō-sī-tō´-sis) The movement of materials out of a cell by the fusion of vesicles with the plasma membrane.

exon The part of a gene that becomes part of the final messenger RNA and is therefore expressed.

exoskeleton A hard external skeleton that protects an animal and provides points of attachment for muscles.

exotoxin A poisonous protein secreted by certain bacteria.

exponential growth model A mathematical description of idealized, unregulated population growth.

external fertilization The fusion of gametes that parents have discharged into the environment.

extinction The irrevocable loss of a species.

extirpation The loss of a single population of a species.

extracellular matrix (ECM) The meshwork surrounding animal cells; consists of glycoproteins and polysaccharides synthesized and secreted by cells.

extraembryonic membranes Four membranes (the yolk sac, amnion, chorion, and allantois) that form a life-support system for the developing embryo of a reptile, bird, or mammal.

extreme halophile A microorganism that lives in a highly saline environment, such as the Great Salt Lake or the Dead Sea.

extreme thermophile A microorganism that thrives in a hot environment (often 60–80°C).

eyecup The simplest type of photoreceptor, a cluster of photoreceptor cells shaded by a cuplike cluster of pigmented cells; detects light intensity and direction.

F

F factor A piece of DNA that can exist as a bacterial plasmid. The F factor carries genes for making sex pili and other structures needed for conjugation, as well as a site where DNA replication can start. F stands for fertility.

F_1 generation The offspring of two parental (P generation) individuals; F_1 stands for first filial.

F_2 generation The offspring of the F_1 generation; F_2 stands for second filial.

facilitated diffusion The passage of a substance through a specific transport protein across a biological membrane down its concentration gradient.

family In Linnaean classification, the taxonomic category above genus.

farsightedness An inability to focus on close objects; occurs when the eyeball is shorter than normal and the focal point of the lens is behind the retina; also called hyperopia.

fat A lipid composed of three fatty acids linked to one glycerol molecule; a triglyceride. Most fats function as energy-storage molecules.

feces The wastes of the digestive tract.

feedback inhibition A method of metabolic control in which a product of a metabolic pathway acts as an inhibitor of an enzyme within that pathway.

fertility rate In a human population, the average number of children produced by a woman over her lifetime.

fertilization The union of the nucleus of a sperm cell with the nucleus of an egg cell, producing a zygote.

fertilizer A compound given to plants to promote their growth.

fetus (fē´-tus) A developing human from the 9th week of gestation until birth. The fetus has all the major structures of an adult.

fiber (1) In animals, an elongate, supportive thread in the matrix of connective tissue; an extension of a neuron; a muscle cell. (2) In plants, a long, slender sclerenchyma cell that usually occurs in a bundle.

fibrin (fi-brin) The activated form of the blood-clotting protein fibrinogen, which aggregates into threads that form the fabric of a blood clot.

fibrinogen (fi´-brin´-uh-jen) The plasma protein that is activated to form a clot when a blood vessel is injured.

fibrous connective tissue A dense tissue with large numbers of collagenous fibers organized into parallel bundles. This is the dominant tissue in tendons and ligaments.

filter feeder An aquatic animal that strains small food particles from the water as it is pumped through a sieve-like structure; a type of suspension feeder.

filtrate Fluid extracted by the excretory system from the blood or body cavity. The excretory system produces urine from the filtrate after removing valuable solutes from it and concentrating it.

filtration In the vertebrate kidney, the extraction of water and small solutes, including metabolic wastes, from the blood by the nephrons.

fimbria (plural, **fimbriae**) One of the short, hairlike projections on some prokaryotic cells that help attach the cells to their substrate or to other cells.

first law of thermodynamics The principle of conservation of energy. Energy can be transferred and transformed, but it cannot be created or destroyed.

fission A means of asexual reproduction whereby a parent separates into two or more genetically identical individuals of about equal size.

fixed action pattern (FAP) A genetically programmed, virtually unchangeable behavioral sequence performed in response to a certain stimulus.

flagellum (fluh-jel´-um) (plural, **flagella**) A long cellular appendage specialized for locomotion. The flagella of prokaryotes and eukaryotes differ in both structure and function. Like cilia, eukaryotic flagella have a "9 + 2" arrangement of microtubules covered by the cell's plasma membrane.

flatworm A member of the phylum Platyhelminthes.

fluid feeder An animal that lives by sucking nutrient-rich fluids from another living organism.

fluid mosaic model The currently accepted model of cell membrane structure, depicting the membrane as a mosaic of diverse protein molecules embedded in a fluid bilayer of phospholipid molecules.

fluke One of a group of parasitic flatworms.

follicle (fol´-uh-kul) A cluster of cells that surround, protect, and nourish a developing egg cell in the ovary. Follicles secrete the hormone estrogen.

food chain A sequence of food transfers from producers through one to four levels of consumers in an ecosystem.

food web A network of interconnecting food chains.

foot In an invertebrate animal, a structure used for locomotion or attachment, such as the muscular organ extending from the ventral side of a mollusc.

foraging Behavior used in recognizing, searching for, capturing, and consuming food.

foraminiferan A protist that moves and feeds by means of threadlike pseudopodia and has porous shells composed of calcium carbonate. Forams belong to the Rhizaria clade of the SAR supergroup.

forebrain One of three ancestral and embryonic regions of the vertebrate brain; develops into the thalamus, hypothalamus, and cerebrum.

forensics The scientific analysis of evidence for crime scene and other legal proceedings. Also referred to as forensic science.

fossil A preserved remnant or impression of an organism.

fossil fuel An energy-containing deposit of organic material formed from the remains of ancient organisms.

fossil record The chronicle of evolution over millions of years of geologic time engraved in the order in which fossils appear in rock strata.

founder effect Genetic drift that occurs when a few individuals become isolated from a larger population and form a new population whose gene pool is not reflective of that of the original population.

fovea (fō´-vē-uh) An eye's center of focus and the place on the retina where photoreceptors are highly concentrated.

fragmentation A means of asexual reproduction whereby a single parent breaks into parts that regenerate into whole new individuals.

frameshift mutation A change in the genetic material that involves the insertion or deletion of one or more nucleotides in a gene, resulting in a change in the triplet grouping of nucleotides.

free-living flatworm A nonparasitic flatworm.

frequency-dependent selection Selection in which the fitness of a phenotype depends on how common the phenotype is in a population.

fruit A ripened, thickened ovary of a flower, which protects developing seeds and aids in their dispersal.

functional group A specific configuration of atoms commonly attached to the carbon skeletons of organic molecules and involved in chemical reactions.

Fungi (fun´-ji) The kingdom that contains the fungi.

G

gallbladder An organ that stores bile and releases it as needed into the small intestine.

gametangium (gam´-uh-tan´-jē-um) (plural, **gametangia**) A reproductive organ that houses and protects the gametes of a plant.

gamete (gam´-ēt) A sex cell; a haploid egg or sperm. The union of two gametes of opposite sex (fertilization) produces a zygote.

gametogenesis The creation of gametes within the gonads.

gametophyte (guh-mē´-tō-fit) The multicellular haploid form in the life cycle of organisms undergoing alternation of generations; mitotically produces haploid gametes that unite and grow into the sporophyte generation.

ganglion (gang´-glē-un) (plural, **ganglia**) A cluster of neuron cell bodies in a peripheral nervous system.

gas exchange The exchange of O_2 and CO_2 between an organism and its environment.

gastric juice The collection of fluids (mucus, enzymes, and acid) secreted by the stomach.

gastrin A digestive hormone that stimulates the secretion of gastric juice.

gastropod A member of the largest group of molluscs, including snails and slugs.

gastrovascular cavity A central compartment with a single opening, the mouth; functions in both digestion and nutrient distribution and may also function in circulation, body support, waste disposal, and gas exchange.

gastrula (gas´-trū-luh) The embryonic stage resulting from gastrulation in animal development. Most animals have a gastrula made up of three layers of cells: ectoderm, endoderm, and mesoderm.

gastrulation (gas´-trū-lā´-shun) The second major phase of embryonic development, which transforms the blastula into a gastrula. Gastrulation adds more cells to the embryo and sorts the cells into distinct cell layers.

gel electrophoresis (jel´ ē-lek´-trō-fōr-ē´-sis) A technique for separating and purifying macromolecules, either DNA or proteins. A mixture of the macromolecules is placed on a gel between a positively charged electrode and a negatively charged one. Negative charges on the molecules are attracted to the positive electrode, and the molecules migrate toward that electrode. The molecules separate in the gel according to their rates of migration, which is mostly determined by their size: Smaller molecules generally move faster through the gel, while larger molecules generally move more slowly.

gene A discrete unit of hereditary information consisting of a specific nucleotide sequence in DNA (or RNA, in some viruses). Most of the genes of a eukaryote are located in its chromosomal DNA; a few are carried by the DNA of mitochondria and chloroplasts.

gene cloning The production of multiple copies of a gene.

gene expression The process whereby genetic information flows from genes to proteins; the flow of genetic information from the genotype to the phenotype.

gene flow The transfer of alleles from one population to another as a result of the movement of individuals or their gametes.

gene pool All copies of every type of allele at every locus in all members of the population.

gene regulation The turning on and off of genes within a cell in response to environmental stimuli or other factors (such as developmental stage).

gene therapy A treatment for a disease in which the patient's defective gene is supplemented or altered.

genetic code The set of rules that dictates the amino acid translations of each mRNA nucleotide triplet.

genetic drift A change in the gene pool of a population due to chance. Effects of genetic drift are most pronounced in small populations.

genetic engineering The direct manipulation of genes for practical purposes.

genetic recombination The production, by crossing over and/or independent assortment of chromosomes during meiosis, of offspring with allele combinations different from those in the parents. The term may also be used more specifically to mean the production by crossing over of eukaryotic or prokaryotic chromosomes with gene combinations different from those in the original chromosomes.

genetically modified organism (GMO) An organism that has acquired one or more genes by artificial means. If the gene is from another species, the organism is also known as a transgenic organism.

genetics The scientific study of heredity. Modern genetics began with the work of Gregor Mendel in the 19th century.

genital herpes A sexually transmitted disease caused by the herpes simplex virus type 2.

genome The complete set of genetic material of an organism or virus.

genomic library (juh-nō´-mik) A collection of cloned DNA fragments that includes an organism's entire genome. Each segment is usually carried by a plasmid or phage.

genomics The study of complete sets of genes and their interactions.

genotype (jē´-nō-tīp) The genetic makeup of an organism.

genus (jē´-nus) (plural, **genera**) In classification, the taxonomic category above species; the first part of a species' binomial; for example, *Homo*.

geologic record A time scale established by geologists that divides Earth's history into four eons—Hadean, Archaean, Proterozoic, and Phanerozoic—and further subdivides it into eras, periods, and epochs.

germinate To start developing or growing.

gestation (jes-tā´-shun) Pregnancy; the state of carrying developing young within the female reproductive tract.

gibberellin (jib´-uh-rel´-in) One of a family of plant hormones that triggers the germination of seeds and interacts with auxins in regulating growth and fruit development.

gill An extension of the body surface of an aquatic animal, specialized for gas exchange and/or suspension feeding.

gizzard A pouch-like organ in a digestive tract where food is mechanically ground.

glans The rounded, highly sensitive head of the clitoris in females and penis in males.

glia A network of supporting cells that is essential for the structural integrity and for the normal functioning of the nervous system.

global climate change Increase in temperature and change in weather patterns all around the planet, due mostly to increasing atmospheric CO_2 levels from the burning of fossil fuels. The increase in temperature, called global warming, is a major aspect of global climate change.

glomeromycete (glō´-mer-ō-mī´-sēt) Member of a group of fungi characterized by a distinct branching form of mycorrhizae (symbiotic relationships with plant roots) called arbuscules.

glomerulus (glō-mer´-ū-lus) (plural, **glomeruli**) In the vertebrate kidney, the part of a nephron consisting of the capillaries that are surrounded by Bowman's capsule; together, a glomerulus and Bowman's capsule produce the filtrate from the blood.

glucagon (glū´-kuh-gon) A peptide hormone, secreted by the islets of Langerhaus in the pancreas, that raises the level of glucose in the blood. It is antagonistic with insulin.

glucocorticoid (glū´-kuh-kor´-tih-koyd) A corticosteroid hormone secreted by the adrenal cortex that increases the blood glucose level and helps maintain the body's response to long-term stress.

glucose A six-carbon monosaccharide that serves as a building block for many polysaccharides and whose oxidation in cellular respiration is a major source of ATP for cells.

glycogen (glī´-kō-jen) An extensively branched glucose storage polysaccharide found in liver and muscle cells; the animal equivalent of starch.

glycolysis (glī-kol´-uh-sis) A series of reactions that ultimately splits glucose into two molecules of pyruvate; the first stage of cellular respiration in all organisms; occurs in the cytosol.

glycoprotein (glī´-kō-prō´-tēn) A protein with one or more short chains of sugars attached to it.

goiter An enlargement of the thyroid gland resulting from a dietary iodine deficiency.

Golgi apparatus (gol´-jē) An organelle in eukaryotic cells consisting of stacks of membranous sacs that modify, store, and ship products of the endoplasmic reticulum.

gonad A sex organ in an animal; an ovary or testis.

Gram stain Microbiological technique to identify the cell wall composition of bacteria. Results categorize bacteria as gram-positive or gram-negative.

gram-positive bacteria Diverse group of bacteria with a cell wall that is structurally less complex and contains more peptidoglycan than that of gram-negative bacteria. Gram-positive bacteria are usually less toxic than gram-negative bacteria.

granum (gran´-um) (plural, **grana**) A stack of membrane-bounded thylakoids in a chloroplast. Grana are the sites where light energy is trapped by chlorophyll and converted to chemical energy during the light reactions of photosynthesis.

gravitropism (grav´-uh-trō´-pizm) A plant's directional growth in response to gravity.

gray matter Regions within the central nervous system composed mainly of nerve cell bodies and dendrites.

green alga A member of a group of photosynthetic protists that includes chlorophytes and charophyceans, the closest living relatives of land plants. Green algae include unicellular, colonial, and multicellular species and belong to the supergroup Archaeplastida.

greenhouse effect The warming of Earth due to the atmospheric accumulation of CO_2 and certain other gases, which absorb infrared radiation and reradiate some of it back toward Earth.

ground tissue system A tissue of mostly parenchyma cells that makes up the bulk of a young plant and is continuous throughout its body. The ground tissue system fills the space between the epidermis and the vascular tissue system.

growth factor A protein secreted by certain body cells that stimulates other cells to divide.

growth hormone (GH) A protein hormone secreted by the anterior pituitary that promotes development and growth and stimulates metabolism.

guanine (G) (gwa´-nēn) A double-ring nitrogenous base found in DNA and RNA.

guard cell A specialized epidermal cell in plants that regulates the size of a stoma, allowing gas exchange between the surrounding air and the photosynthetic cells in the leaf.

gymnosperm (jim´-nō-sperm) A naked-seed plant. Its seed is said to be naked because it is not enclosed in an ovary.

H

habitat A place where an organism lives; the environment in which an organism lives.

habituation Learning not to respond to a repeated stimulus that conveys little or no information.

hair cell A type of mechanoreceptor that detects sound waves and other forms of movement in air or water.

haploid In the life cycle of an organism that reproduces sexually, a cell containing a single set of chromosomes; an *n* cell.

Hardy-Weinberg principle The principle that frequencies of alleles and genotypes in a population remain constant from generation to generation, provided that only Mendelian segregation and recombination of alleles are at work.

heart A muscular pump that propels a circulatory fluid (blood) through vessels to the body.

heart attack The damage or death of cardiac muscle cells and the resulting failure of the heart to deliver enough blood to the body.

heart rate The frequency of heart contraction, usually expressed in number of beats per minute.

heartwood In the center of trees, the darkened, older layers of secondary xylem made up of cells that no longer transport water and are clogged with resins. *See also* sapwood.

heat Thermal energy in transfer from one body of matter to another.

helper T cell A type of lymphocyte that, when activated, secretes stimulatory signals that promote the response of B cells (humoral response) and cytotoxic T cells (cell-mediated response) to antigens.

hemoglobin (hē´-mō-glō-bin) An iron-containing protein in red blood cells that reversibly binds O_2.

hepatic portal vein A blood vessel that conveys nutrient-laden blood from capillaries surrounding the intestine directly to the liver.

herbivore An animal that mainly eats plants or algae. *See also* carnivore; omnivore.

herbivory Consumption of plant parts or algae by an animal.

heredity The transmission of traits (inherited features) from one generation to the next.

hermaphroditism (her-maf´-rō-dī-tizm) A condition in which an individual has both female and male gonads and functions as both a male and female in sexual reproduction by producing both sperm and eggs.

heterokaryotic stage (het´-er-ō-ker-ē-ot´-ik) A fungal life cycle stage that contains two genetically different haploid nuclei in the same cell.

heterotroph (het´-er-ō-trōf) An organism that obtains organic food molecules by eating other organisms or substances derived from them; a consumer or a decomposer in a food chain.

heterozygote advantage (het´-er-ō-zī´-gōt) Greater reproductive success of heterozygous individuals compared to homozygotes; tends to preserve variation in gene pools.

heterozygous (het´-er-ō-zī´-gus) Having two different alleles for a given gene.

high-density lipoprotein (HDL) A cholesterol-carrying particle in the blood, made up of thousands of cholesterol molecules and other lipids bound to a protein. HDL scavenges excess cholesterol.

hindbrain One of three ancestral and embryonic regions of the vertebrate brain; develops into the medulla oblongata, pons, and cerebellum.

hinge joint A joint that allows movement in only one plane. In humans, examples include the elbow and knee.

hippocampus (hip´-uh-kam´-pus) An integrative center of the cerebrum; functionally, the part of the limbic system that plays a central role in the formation of memories and their recall.

histamine (his´-tuh-mēn) A chemical alarm signal released by mast cells that causes blood vessels to dilate and become more permeable in inflammatory and allergic responses.

histone (his´-tōn) A small protein molecule associated with DNA and important in DNA packing in the eukaryotic chromosome.

Eukaryotic chromatin consists of roughly equal parts of DNA and histone protein.

HIV (human immunodeficiency virus) The retrovirus that attacks the human immune system and causes AIDS.

homeobox (hō´-mē-ō-boks´) A 180-nucleotide sequence within a homeotic gene and some other developmental genes.

homeostasis (hō´-mē-ō-stā´-sis) The steady state of body functioning; a state of equilibrium characterized by a dynamic interplay between outside forces that tend to change an organism's internal environment and the internal control mechanisms that oppose such changes.

homeotic gene (hō´-mē-ot´-ik) A master control gene that determines the identity of a body structure of a developing organism, presumably by controlling the developmental fate of groups of cells.

hominin (hah´-mi-nin) Member of a species on the human branch of the evolutionary tree; a species more closely related to humans than to chimpanzees.

homologous chromosomes (hō-mol´-uh-gus) The two chromosomes that make up a matched pair in a diploid cell. Homologous chromosomes are of the same length, centromere position, and staining pattern and possess genes for the same characters at corresponding loci. One homologous chromosome is inherited from the organism's father, the other from the mother.

homologous structures (hō-mol´-uh-gus) Structures in different species that are similar because of common ancestry.

homology (hō-mol´-uh-jē) Similarity in characters resulting from a shared ancestry.

homozygous (hō´-mō-zī´-gus) Having two identical alleles for a given gene.

horizontal gene transfer The transfer of genes from one genome to another through mechanisms such as transposable elements, plasmid exchange, viral activity, and perhaps fusions of different organisms.

hormone (1) In animals, a regulatory chemical that travels in the blood from its production site, usually an endocrine gland, to other sites, where target cells respond to the regulatory signal. (2) In plants, a chemical that is produced in one part of the plant and travels to another part, where it acts on target cells to change their functioning.

human chorionic gonadotropin (hCG) (kōr´-ē-on´-ik gō-na´-dō-trō´-pin) A hormone secreted by the chorion that maintains the production of estrogen and progesterone by the corpus luteum of the ovary during the first few months of pregnancy. hCG secreted in the urine is the target of many home pregnancy tests.

Human Genome Project (hGP) An international collaborative effort to map and sequence the DNA of the entire human genome. The project was begun in 1990 and completed in 2004.

humoral immune response The branch of adaptive immunity that involves the activation of B cells and that leads to the production of antibodies, which defend against bacteria and viruses in body fluids.

humus (hyū´-mus) Decomposing organic material found in topsoil.

Huntington's disease A human genetic disease caused by a single dominant allele; characterized by uncontrollable body movements and degeneration of the nervous system; usually fatal 10 to 20 years after the onset of symptoms.

hybrid An offspring of parents of two different species or of two different varieties of one species; an offspring of two parents that differ in one or more inherited traits; an individual that is heterozygous for one or more pairs of genes.

hybrid zone A geographic region in which members of different species meet and mate, producing at least some hybrid offspring.

hydrocarbon An organic compound composed only of the elements carbon and hydrogen.

hydrogen bond A type of weak chemical bond formed when the slightly positive hydrogen atom of a polar covalent bond in one molecule is attracted to the slightly negative atom of a polar covalent bond in another molecule (or in another region of the same molecule).

hydrolysis (hī-drol´-uh-sis) A chemical reaction that breaks bonds between two molecules by the addition of water; process by which polymers are broken down and an essential part of digestion.

hydrophilic (hī-drō-fil´-ik) "Water-loving"; pertaining to polar or charged molecules (or parts of molecules) that are soluble in water.

hydrophobic (hī-drō-fō´-bik) "Water-fearing"; pertaining to non-polar molecules (or parts of molecules) that do not dissolve in water.

hydrostatic skeleton A skeletal system composed of fluid held under pressure in a closed body compartment; the main skeleton of most cnidarians, flatworms, nematodes, and annelids.

hydroxyl group (hī-drok´-sil) A chemical group consisting of an oxygen atom bonded to a hydrogen atom.

hyperglycemia An abnormally high level of glucose in the blood that results when the pancreas does not secrete enough insulin or cells do not respond to insulin. Hyperglycemia is a characteristic of diabetes.

hypertension A disorder in which blood pressure remains abnormally high.

hypertonic Referring to a solution that, when surrounding a cell, will cause the cell to lose water.

hypha (hī´-fuh) (plural, **hyphae**) One of many filaments making up the body of a fungus.

hypoglycemia (hī-pō-glī-sē´-mē-uh) An abnormally low level of glucose in the blood that results when the pancreas secretes too much insulin into the blood.

hypothalamus (hī-pō-thal´-uh-mus) The master control center of the endocrine system, located in the ventral portion of the vertebrate forebrain. The hypothalamus functions in maintaining homeostasis, especially in coordinating the endocrine and nervous systems; secretes hormones of the posterior pituitary and releasing hormones that regulate the anterior pituitary.

hypothesis (hī-poth´-uh-sis) (plural, **hypotheses**) A testable explanation for a set of observations based on the available data and guided by inductive reasoning.

hypotonic Referring to a solution that, when surrounding a cell, will cause the cell to take up water.

I

immune system An animal body's system of defenses against agents that cause disease.

immunodeficiency disorder An immunological disorder in which the immune system lacks one or more components, making the body susceptible to infectious agents that would ordinarily not be pathogenic.

imperfect fungus A fungus with no known sexual stage.

impotence The inability to maintain an erection; also called erectile dysfunction.

imprinting Learning that is limited to a specific critical period in an animal's life and that is generally irreversible.

in vitro **fertilization (IVF)** (vē´-tro) Uniting sperm and egg in a laboratory container, followed by the placement of a resulting early embryo in the mother's uterus.

inclusive fitness An individual's success at perpetuating its genes by producing its own offspring and by helping close relatives to produce offspring.

incomplete dominance A type of inheritance in which the phenotype of a heterozygote (*Aa*) is intermediate between the phenotypes of the two types of homozygotes (*AA* and *aa*).

incomplete metamorphosis A type of development in certain insects in which development from larva to adult is achieved by multiple molts, but without forming a pupa.

indeterminate growth Growth that continues throughout life, as in most plants. *See also* determinate growth.

induced fit The change in shape of the active site of an enzyme, caused by entry of the substrate so that it binds the substrate snugly.

induction During embryonic development, the influence of one group of cells on an adjacent group of cells.

inferior vena cava (vē´-nuh kā´-vuh) A large vein that returns oxygen-poor blood to the heart from the lower, or posterior, part of the body. *See also* superior vena cava.

infertility The inability to conceive after one year of regular, unprotected intercourse.

inflammatory response An innate body defense in vertebrates caused by a release of histamine and other chemical alarm signals that trigger increased blood flow, a local increase in white blood cells, and fluid leakage from the blood. The resulting inflammatory response includes redness, heat, and swelling in the affected tissues.

ingestion The act of eating; the first main stage of food processing in animals.

ingroup In a cladistic study of evolutionary relationships, the group of taxa whose evolutionary relationships are being determined. *See also* outgroup.

inhibiting hormone A kind of hormone released from the hypothalamus that prompts the anterior pituitary to stop secreting hormone.

innate behavior Behavior that is under strong genetic control and is performed in virtually the same way by all members of a species.

innate immunity The kind of immunity that is present in an animal before exposure to pathogens and is effective from birth. Innate immune defenses include barriers, phagocytic cells, antimicrobial proteins, the inflammatory response, and natural killer cells.

inner ear One of three main regions of the vertebrate ear; includes the cochlea, organ of Corti, and semicircular canals.

insulin A protein hormone, secreted by the islets of Langerhans in the pancreas, that lowers the level of glucose in the blood. It is antagonistic with glucagon.

integration The analysis and interpretation of sensory signals within neural processing centers of the central nervous system.

integrin A transmembrane protein that interconnects the extracellular matrix and the cytoskeleton in animal cells.

integumentary system (in-teg´-yū-ment-ter-ē) The organ system consisting of the skin and its derivatives, such as hair and nails in mammals. The integumentary system helps protect the body from drying out, mechanical injury, and infection.

interferon (in´-ter-fer´-on) An innate defensive protein produced by virus-infected vertebrate cells and capable of helping other cells resist viruses.

intermediate One of the compounds that form between the initial reactant and the final product in a metabolic pathway, such as between glucose and pyruvate in glycolysis.

intermediate filament An intermediate-sized protein fiber that is one of the three main kinds of fibers making up the cytoskeleton of eukaryotic cells. Intermediate filaments are ropelike, made of fibrous proteins.

internal fertilization Reproduction in which sperm are typically deposited in or near the female reproductive tract and fertilization occurs within the tract.

interneuron (in´-ter-nūr´-on) A nerve cell, located entirely within the central nervous system, that integrates sensory signals and relays signals to other interneurons and to motor neurons.

internode The portion of a plant stem between two nodes.

interphase The period in the eukaryotic cell cycle when the cell is not actually dividing. Interphase constitutes the majority of the time spent in the cell cycle. *See also* mitotic phase (M phase).

interspecific competition Competition between individuals or populations of two or more species that require the same limited resource.

interspecific interactions Relationships between individuals of different species in a community.

interstitial fluid (in´-ter-stish´-ul) An aqueous solution that surrounds body cells and through which materials pass back and forth between the blood and the body tissues.

intertidal zone (in´-ter-tīd´-ul) A shallow zone where the waters of an estuary or ocean meet land.

intestine The region of a digestive tract located between the gizzard or stomach and the anus and where chemical digestion and nutrient absorption usually occur.

intraspecific competition Competition between members of a population for a limited resource.

intrauterine device (IUD) A T-shaped device that, when placed within the uterus, acts as female contraception.

intron (in´-tron) An internal, noncoding region of a gene that does not become part of the final messenger RNA molecule and is therefore not expressed.

invasive species A non-native species that spreads beyond its original point of introduction and causes environmental or economic damage.

inversion A change in a chromosome resulting from reattachment of a chromosome fragment to the original chromosome, but in the reverse direction. Mutagens and errors during meiosis can cause inversions.

invertebrate An animal that lacks a backbone.

ion (ī-on) An atom or group of atoms that has gained or lost one or more electrons, thus acquiring a charge.

ionic bond (ī-on´-ik) A chemical bond resulting from the attraction between oppositely charged ions.

iris The colored part of the vertebrate eye, formed by the anterior portion of the choroid.

isomers (ī´-sō-mers) Organic compounds with the same molecular formula but different structures and, therefore, different properties.

isotonic (ī-sō-ton´-ik) Referring to a solution that, when surrounding a cell, causes no net movement of water into or out of the cell.

isotope (ī´-sō-tōp) One of several atomic forms of an element, each with the same number of protons but a different number of neutrons.

K

karyotype (kār´-ē-ō-tīp) A display of micrographs of the metaphase chromosomes of a cell, arranged by size and centromere position. Karyotypes may be used to identify certain chromosomal abnormalities.

kelp Large, multicellular brown algae that form undersea "forests."

keystone species A species whose impact on the community is much larger than its biomass or abundance would indicate.

kilocalorie (kcal) A quantity of heat equal to 1,000 calories. Used to measure the energy content of food, it is usually called a "Calorie."

kin selection The natural selection that favors altruistic behavior by enhancing reproductive success of relatives.

kinesis (kuh-nē´-sis) (plural, **kineses**) Random movement in response to a stimulus.

kinetic energy (kuh-net´-ik) The energy associated with the motion of objects. Moving matter does work by imparting motion to other matter.

kingdom In classification, the broad taxonomic category above phylum.

K-selection The concept that in certain (K-selected) populations, life history is centered on producing relatively few offspring that have a good chance of survival.

L

labia majora (lā´-bē-uh muh-jor´-uh) A pair of outer thickened folds of skin that protect the female genital region.

labia minora (lā´-bē-uh mi-nor´-uh) A pair of inner folds of skin, bordering and protecting the female genital region.

labor The series of events that expel the infant from the uterus.

lactic acid fermentation Glycolysis followed by the reduction of pyruvate to lactate, regenerating NAD^+.

lancelet One of a group of small, bladelike, invertebrate chordates.

landscape Several different ecosystems linked by exchanges of energy, materials, and organisms.

landscape ecology The application of ecological principles to the study of the structure and dynamics of a collection of ecosystems; the scientific study of the biodiversity of interacting ecosystems.

large intestine The portion of the alimentary canal between the small intestine and the anus; functions mainly in water absorption and the formation of feces.

larva (lar´-vuh) (plural, **larvae**) A free-living, sexually immature form in some animal life cycles that may differ from the adult in morphology, nutrition, and habitat.

larynx (lār´-inks) The upper portion of the respiratory tract containing the vocal cords; also called the voice box.

lateral line system A row of sensory organs along each side of a fish's body that is sensitive to changes in water pressure. It enables a fish to detect minor vibrations in the water.

lateral meristem Plant tissue made up of undifferentiated cells that enable roots and shoots of woody plants to thicken. The vascular cambium and cork cambium are lateral meristems.

lateralization The phenomenon in which the two hemispheres of the brain become specialized for different functions during infant and child brain development.

law of independent assortment A general rule of inheritance (originally formulated by Gregor Mendel) that when gametes form during meiosis, each pair of alleles for a particular character segregates independently of other pairs; also known as Mendel's second law of inheritance.

law of segregation A general rule in inheritance (originally formulated by Gregor Mendel) that individuals have two alleles for each gene and that when gametes form by meiosis, the two alleles separate, each resulting gamete ending up with only one allele of each gene; also known as Mendel's first law of inheritance.

leaf The main site of photosynthesis in a plant; typically consists of a flattened blade and a stalk (petiole) that joins the leaf to the stem.

learning Modification of behavior as a result of specific experiences.

leech A member of one of the three large groups of annelids, known for its bloodsucking ability. *See also* annelid.

lens The structure in an eye that focuses light rays onto the retina.

leukemia (lū-kē´-mē-ah) A type of cancer of the blood-forming tissues, characterized by an excessive production of white blood cells and an abnormally high number of them in the blood; cancer of the bone marrow cells that produce leukocytes.

leukocyte (lū´-kō-sȳt´) A blood cell that functions in fighting infections; also called a white blood cell.

lichen (lī´-ken) A close association between a fungus and an alga or between a fungus and a cyanobacterium, some of which are known to be beneficial to both partners.

life cycle The entire sequence of stages in the life of an organism, from the adults of one generation to the adults of the next.

life history The traits that affect an organism's schedule of reproduction and death, including age at first reproduction, frequency of reproduction, number of offspring, and amount of parental care.

life table A listing of survivals and deaths in a population in a particular time period and predictions of how long, on average, an individual of a given age will live.

ligament A type of fibrous connective tissue that joins bones together at joints.

light microscope (LM) An optical instrument with lenses that refract (bend) visible light to magnify images and project them into a viewer's eye or onto photographic film.

light reactions The first of two stages in photosynthesis; the steps in which solar energy is absorbed and converted to the chemical energy of ATP and NADPH, releasing oxygen in the process.

lignin A chemical that hardens the cell walls of plants.

limbic system (lim´-bik) A functional unit of several integrating and relay centers located deep in the human forebrain; interacts with the cerebral cortex in creating emotions and storing memories.

limiting factor An environmental factor that restricts population growth.

linkage map A listing of the relative locations of genes along a chromosome, as determined by recombination frequencies.

linked genes Genes located near each other on the same chromosome that tend to be inherited together.

lipid An organic compound consisting mainly of carbon and hydrogen atoms linked by nonpolar covalent bonds, making the compound mostly hydrophobic. Lipids include fats, phospholipids, and steroids and are insoluble in water.

liver The largest organ in the vertebrate body. The liver performs diverse functions, such as producing bile, preparing nitrogenous wastes for disposal, and detoxifying poisonous chemicals in the blood.

lobe-fin A bony fish with strong, muscular fins supported by bones.

locomotion Active movement from place to place.

locus (plural, **loci**) The particular site where a gene is found on a chromosome. Homologous chromosomes have corresponding gene loci.

logistic growth model A mathematical description of idealized population growth that is restricted by limiting factors.

long-day plant A plant that flowers in late spring or early summer, when day length is long. Long-day plants actually flower in response to short nights.

long-term memory The ability to hold, associate, and recall information over one's lifetime.

loop of Henle (hen´-lē) In the vertebrate kidney, the portion of a nephron that helps concentrate the filtrate while conveying it between a proximal tubule and a distal tubule.

loose connective tissue The most widespread connective tissue in the vertebrate body. It binds epithelia to underlying tissues and functions as packing material, holding organs in place.

low-density lipoprotein (LDL) A cholesterol-carrying particle in the blood, made up of thousands of cholesterol molecules and other lipids bound to a protein. An LDL particle transports cholesterol from the liver for incorporation into cell membranes.

lung An infolded respiratory surface of terrestrial vertebrates that connects to the atmosphere by narrow tubes.

lymph A colorless fluid, derived from interstitial fluid, that circulates in the lymphatic system.

lymph node An organ of the immune system located along a lymph vessel. Lymph nodes filter lymph and contain cells that attack viruses and bacteria.

lymphatic system (lim-fat´-ik) The vertebrate organ system through which lymph circulates; includes lymph vessels, lymph nodes, and the spleen. The lymphatic system helps remove toxins and pathogens from the blood and interstitial fluid and returns fluid and solutes from the interstitial fluid to the circulatory system.

lymphocyte (lim´-fuh-sīt) A type of white blood cell that is chiefly responsible for the adaptive immune response and is found mostly in the lymphatic system. *See also* B cell; T cell.

lysogenic cycle (lī-sō-jen´-ik) A type of bacteriophage replication cycle in which the viral genome is incorporated into the bacterial host chromosome as a prophage. New phages are not produced, and the host cell is not killed or lysed unless the viral genome leaves the host chromosome.

lysosome (lī-sō-sōm) A digestive organelle in eukaryotic cells; contains hydrolytic enzymes that digest engulfed food or damaged organelles.

lytic cycle (lit´-ik) A type of viral replication cycle resulting in the release of new viruses by lysis (breaking open) of the host cell.

M

macroevolution Evolutionary change above the species level, encompassing the origin of new taxonomic groups, adaptive radiation, and mass extinction.

macromolecule A giant molecule formed by the joining of smaller molecules, usually by a dehydration reaction: a protein, carbohydrate, or nucleic acid.

macronutrient A chemical substance that an organism must obtain in relatively large amounts. *See also* micronutrient.

macrophage (mak´-rō-fāj) A large, amoeboid, phagocytic white blood cell that functions in innate immunity by destroying microbes and in adaptive immunity as an antigen-presenting cell.

major histocompatibility complex (MHC) molecule *See* self protein.

malignant tumor An abnormal tissue mass that can spread into neighboring tissue and to other parts of the body; a cancerous tumor.

malnutrition Health problems caused by a diet that contains insufficient calories or nutrients.

mammal Member of a clade of amniotes that possess mammary glands and hair.

mantle In a mollusc, the outgrowth of the body surface that drapes over the animal. The mantle produces the shell and forms the mantle cavity.

marsupial (mar-sū´-pē-ul) A pouched mammal, such as a kangaroo, opossum, or koala. Marsupials give birth to embryonic offspring that complete development while housed in a pouch and attached to nipples on the mother's abdomen.

mass number The sum of the number of protons and neutrons in an atom's nucleus.

matter Anything that occupies space and has mass.

mechanoreceptor (mek´-uh-nō-ri-sep´-ter) A sensory receptor that detects changes in the environment associated with pressure, touch, stretch, motion, or sound.

medulla oblongata (meh-duh´-luh ob´-long-got´-uh) Part of the vertebrate hindbrain, continuous with the spinal cord; passes data between the spinal cord and forebrain and controls autonomic, homeostatic functions, including breathing, heart rate, swallowing, and digestion.

medusa (med-ū´-suh) (plural, **medusae**) One of two types of cnidarian body forms; an umbrella-like body form.

meiosis (mī-ō´-sis) In a sexually reproducing organism, the division of a single diploid nucleus into four haploid daughter nuclei. Meiosis and cytokinesis produce haploid gametes from diploid cells in the reproductive organs of the parents.

membrane potential The charge difference between a cell's cytoplasm and extracellular fluid due to the differential distribution of ions.

memory The ability to store and retrieve information. *See also* long-term memory; short-term memory.

memory cell A clone of long-lived lymphocytes formed during the primary adaptive immune response. Memory cells remain in lymph nodes until activated by exposure to the same antigen that triggered their formation. When activated, a memory cell forms a large clone that mounts the secondary immune response.

meninges (muh-nin´-jēz) Layers of connective tissue that enwrap and protect the brain and spinal cord.

menstrual cycle (men´-strū-ul) The hormonally synchronized cyclic buildup and breakdown of the endometrium of some primates, including humans.

menstruation (men´-strū-ā´-shun) Uterine bleeding resulting from shedding of the endometrium during a menstrual cycle.

meristem (mer´-eh-stem) Plant tissue consisting of undifferentiated cells that divide and generate new cells and tissues.

mesoderm (mez´-ō-derm) The middle layer of the three embryonic cell layers in a gastrula. The mesoderm gives rise to muscles, bones, the dermis of the skin, and most other organs in the adult.

mesophyll (mes´-ō-fil) Leaf cells specialized for photosynthesis; a leaf's ground tissue system.

messenger RNA (mRNA) The type of ribonucleic acid that encodes genetic information from DNA and conveys it to ribosomes, where the information is translated into amino acid sequences.

metabolic pathway A series of chemical reactions that either builds a complex molecule or breaks down a complex molecule into simpler compounds.

metabolic rate The total amount of energy an animal uses in a unit of time.

metabolism The totality of an organism's chemical reactions.

metamorphosis (met´-uh-mōr´-fuh-sis) The transformation of a larva into an adult. *See also* complete metamorphosis; incomplete metamorphosis.

metaphase (met´-eh-fāz) The third stage of mitosis, during which all the cell's duplicated chromosomes are lined up at an imaginary plane equidistant between the poles of the mitotic spindle.

metastasis (muh-tas´-tuh-sis) The spread of cancer cells beyond their original site.

methanogen (meth-an´-ō-jen) An archaean that produces methane as a metabolic waste product.

methyl group A chemical group consisting of a carbon atom bonded to three hydrogen atoms.

microbiota The community of microorganisms that live in and on the body of an animal.

microevolution A change in a population's gene pool over generations.

microfilament The thinnest of the three main kinds of protein fibers making up the cytoskeleton of a eukaryotic cell; a solid, helical rod composed of the globular protein actin.

micronutrient An element that an organism needs in very small amounts and that functions as a component or cofactor of enzymes. *See also* macronutrient.

microRNA (miRNA) A small, single-stranded RNA molecule that associates with one or more proteins in a complex that can degrade or prevent translation of an mRNA with a complementary sequence.

microtubule The thickest of the three main kinds of fibers making up the cytoskeleton of a eukaryotic cell; a hollow tube made of globular proteins called tubulins; found in cilia and flagella.

microvillus (plural, **microvilli**) One of many microscopic projections on the epithelial cells in the lumen of the small intestine. Microvilli increase the surface area of the small intestine.

midbrain One of three ancestral and embryonic regions of the vertebrate brain; develops into sensory integrating and relay centers that send sensory information to the cerebrum.

middle ear One of three main regions of the vertebrate ear; a chamber containing three small bones (the hammer, anvil, and stirrup) that convey vibrations from the eardrum to the oval window.

migration The regular back-and-forth movement of animals between two geographic areas at particular times of the year.

millipede A terrestrial arthropod that has two pairs of short legs for each of its numerous body segments and that eats decaying plant matter.

mineral In nutrition, a simple inorganic nutrient that an organism requires in small amounts for proper body functioning.

mineralocorticoid (min´-er-uh-lō-kort´-uh-koyd) A corticosteroid hormone secreted by the adrenal cortex that helps maintain salt and water homeostasis and may increase blood pressure in response to long-term stress.

missense mutation A change in the nucleotide sequence of a gene that alters the amino acid sequence of the resulting polypeptide. In a missense mutation, a codon is changed from encoding one amino acid to encoding a different amino acid.

mitochondrial matrix (mī´-tō-kon´-drē-ul) The compartment of the mitochondrion enclosed by the inner membrane and containing enzymes and substrates for the citric acid cycle.

mitochondrion (mī´-tō-kon´-drē-on) (plural, **mitochondria**) An organelle in eukaryotic cells where cellular respiration occurs. Enclosed by two membranes, it is where most of the cell's ATP is made.

mitosis (mī-tō-sis) The division of a single nucleus into two genetically identical nuclei. Mitosis and cytokinesis make up the mitotic (M) phase of the cell cycle.

mitotic phase (M phase) The part of the cell cycle when the nucleus divides (via mitosis), its chromosomes are distributed to the daughter nuclei, and the cytoplasm divides (via cytokinesis), producing two daughter cells.

mitotic spindle A football-shaped structure formed of microtubules and associated proteins that is involved in the movement of chromosomes during mitosis and meiosis.

mixotroph A protist that is capable of both autotrophy and heterotrophy.

mold A rapidly growing fungus that reproduces asexually by producing spores.

molecular biology The study of biological structures, functions, and heredity at the molecular level.

molecular clock A method for estimating the time required for a given amount of evolutionary change, based on the observation that some regions of genomes evolve at constant rates.

molecular systematics A scientific discipline that uses nucleic acids or other molecules in different species to infer evolutionary relationships.

molecule Two or more atoms held together by covalent bonds.

mollusc (mol´-lusk) A soft-bodied animal characterized by a muscular foot, mantle, mantle cavity, and visceral mass. Molluscs include gastropods (snails and slugs), bivalves (clams, oysters, and scallops), and cephalopods (squids and octopuses).

molting The process of shedding an old exoskeleton or cuticle and secreting a new, larger one.

monoclonal antibody (mAb) (mon´-ō-klōn´-ul) An antibody secreted by a clone of cells and therefore specific for the one antigen that triggered the development of the clone.

monocot (mon´-ō-kot) A flowering plant whose embryos have a single seed leaf, or cotyledon.

monogamous Referring to a type of relationship in which a male and a female mate exclusively with each other, and both parents care for the offspring.

monohybrid cross An experimental mating of individuals that are heterozygous for the character being followed (or the self-pollination of a heterozygous plant).

monomer (mon´-uh-mer) The subunit that serves as a building block of a polymer.

monophyletic (mon´-ō-fī-let´-ik) Pertaining to a group of taxa that consists of a common ancestor and all its descendants, equivalent to a clade.

monosaccharide (mon´-ō-sak´-uh-rīd) The simplest carbohydrate; a simple sugar with a molecular formula that is generally some multiple of CH_2O. Monosaccharides are the monomers of disaccharides and polysaccharides.

monotreme (mon´-uh-trēm) An egg-laying mammal, such as the duck-billed platypus.

morning after pill (MAP) A birth control pill taken within three days of unprotected intercourse to prevent fertilization or implantation.

morphological species concept A definition of species in terms of measurable anatomical criteria.

motor neuron A nerve cell that conveys command signals from the central nervous system to effector cells, such as muscle cells or gland cells.

motor output The conduction of signals from a processing center in the central nervous system to effector cells.

motor system The component of the vertebrate peripheral nervous system that carries signals to and from skeletal muscles, mainly in response to external stimuli. Most actions of the motor system are voluntary.

motor unit A motor neuron and all the muscle fibers it controls.

movement corridor A series of small clumps or a narrow strip of quality habitat (usable by organisms) that connects otherwise isolated patches of quality habitat.

muscle fiber Muscle cell.

muscle tissue Tissue consisting of long muscle cells that can contract, either on its own or when stimulated by nerve impulses; the most abundant tissue in a typical animal. *See* skeletal muscle; cardiac muscle; smooth muscle.

muscular system The organ system that includes all the skeletal muscles in the body. (Cardiac muscle and smooth muscle are components of other organ systems.)

mutagen (myū´-tuh-jen) A chemical or physical agent that interacts with DNA and causes a mutation.

mutagenesis (myū´-tuh-jen´-uh-sis) The creation of a change in the nucleotide sequence of an organism's DNA.

mutation A change in the genetic information of a cell; the ultimate source of genetic diversity. A mutation also can occur in the DNA or RNA of a virus.

mutualism An interspecific relationship in which both partners benefit.

mycelium (mī-sē´-lē-um) (plural, **mycelia**) The densely branched network of hyphae in a fungus.

mycorrhiza (mī´-kō-rī´-zuh) (plural, **mycorrhizae**) A close association of plant roots and fungi that is beneficial to both partners.

myelin sheath (mī´-uh-lin) A series of cells, each wound around, and thus insulating, the axon of a nerve cell in vertebrates. Each pair of cells in the sheath is separated by a space called a node of Ranvier.

myofibril (mī´-ō-fī´-bril) A contractile strand in a muscle cell (fiber), made up of many sarcomeres. Longitudinal bundles of myofibrils make up a muscle fiber.

myosin A type of protein filament that interacts with actin filaments to cause cell contraction.

N

NAD+ Nicotinamide adenine dinucleotide; a coenzyme that can accept electrons during the redox reactions of cellular metabolism. It cycles between oxidized (NAD+) and reduced (NADH) states.

NADP+ Nicotinamide adenine dinucleotide phosphate, an electron acceptor that, as NADPH, temporarily stores energized electrons produced during the light reactions.

natural killer (NK) cell A cell type that provides an innate immune response by attacking cancer cells and infected body cells, especially those harboring viruses.

natural selection A process in which individuals with certain inherited traits are more likely to survive and reproduce than are individuals that do not have those traits.

nearsightedness An inability to focus on distant objects; occurs when the eyeball is longer than normal and the lens focuses distant objects in front of the retina; also called myopia.

negative feedback A primary mechanism of homeostasis, whereby a change in a physiological variable triggers a response that counteracts the initial change. Negative feedback is a common control mechanism in which a chemical reaction, metabolic pathway, or hormone-secreting gland is inhibited by the products of the reaction, pathway, or gland. As the concentration of the products builds up, the product molecules themselves inhibit the process that produced them.

negative pressure breathing A breathing system in which air is pulled into the lungs.

nematode (nem´-uh-tōd) A roundworm, characterized by a pseudocoelom, a cylindrical, wormlike body form, and a tough cuticle that is molted to permit growth.

nephron The tubular excretory unit and associated blood vessels of the vertebrate kidney; extracts filtrate from the blood and refines it into urine. The nephron is the functional unit of the urinary system.

nerve A cable-like bundle of neurons tightly wrapped in connective tissue.

nerve cord An elongated bundle of neurons, usually extending longitudinally from the brain or anterior ganglia. One or more nerve cords and the brain make up the central nervous system in many animals.

nerve net A weblike system of interconnected neurons, characteristic of radially symmetric animals such as a hydra.

nervous system The organ system that forms a communication and coordination network between all parts of an animal's body.

nervous tissue Tissue made up of neurons and supportive cells called glia.

neural tube (nyūr´-ul) An embryonic cylinder that develops from the ectoderm after gastrulation and gives rise to the brain and spinal cord.

neuron (nyūr´-on) A nerve cell; the fundamental structural and functional unit of the nervous system, specialized for carrying signals from one location in the body to another.

neurosecretory cell A nerve cell that synthesizes hormones and secretes them into the blood and also conducts nerve signals.

neurotransmitter A chemical messenger that carries information from a transmitting neuron to a receiving cell, either another neuron or an effector cell.

neutron A subatomic particle having no electrical charge, found in the nucleus of an atom.

neutrophil (nyū´-truh-fil) The most abundant type of white blood cell; functions in innate immunity as a type of phagocytic cell that tends to self-destruct as it destroys foreign invaders.

nitrogen fixation The conversion of atmospheric nitrogen (N_2) to nitrogen compounds (NH_4^+, NO_3^-) that plants can absorb and use.

node The point of attachment of a leaf on a stem.

node of Ranvier (ron´-vē-ā) An unmyelinated region on a myelinated axon of a nerve cell, where nerve signals are regenerated.

noncompetitive inhibitor A substance that reduces the activity of an enzyme without entering an active site. By binding elsewhere on the enzyme, a noncompetitive inhibitor changes the shape of the enzyme so that the active site no longer effectively catalyzes the conversion of substrate to product.

nondisjunction An accident of meiosis or mitosis in which a pair of homologous chromosomes or a pair of sister chromatids fail to separate at anaphase.

nonpolar covalent bond A type of covalent bond in which electrons are shared equally between two atoms of similar electronegativity.

nonself molecule A foreign antigen; a protein or other macromolecule that is not part of an organism's body. *See also* self protein.

nonsense mutation A change in the nucleotide sequence of a gene that converts an amino-acid-encoding codon to a stop codon. A nonsense mutation results in a shortened polypeptide.

norepinephrine (nor´-ep-uh-nef´-rin) An amine hormone (also called noradrenaline) secreted by the adrenal medulla that prepares body organs for action (fight or flight); also serves as a neurotransmitter.

notochord (nō´-tuh-kord) A flexible, cartilage-like, longitudinal rod located between the digestive tract and nerve cord in chordate animals; present only in embryos in many species.

nuclear envelope A double membrane that encloses the nucleus, perforated with pores that regulate traffic with the cytoplasm.

nuclear transplantation A technique in which the nucleus of one cell is placed into another cell that already has a nucleus or in which the nucleus has been previously destroyed.

nucleic acid (nū-klā´-ik) A polymer consisting of many nucleotide monomers; serves as a blueprint for proteins and, through the actions of proteins, for all cellular structures and activities. The two types of nucleic acids are DNA and RNA.

nucleic acid probe (nū-klā´-ik) In DNA technology, a radioactively or fluorescently labeled single-stranded nucleic acid molecule used to find a specific gene or other nucleotide sequence within a mass of DNA. The probe hydrogen-bonds to the complementary sequence in the targeted DNA.

nucleoid (nū´-klē-oyd) A non–membrane-bounded region in a prokaryotic cell where the DNA is concentrated.

nucleolus (nū-klē´-ō-lus) A structure within the nucleus where ribosomal RNA is made and assembled with proteins imported from the cytoplasm to make ribosomal subunits.

nucleosome (nū´-klē-ō-sōm) The bead-like unit of DNA packing in a eukaryotic cell; consists of DNA wound around a protein core made up of eight histone molecules.

nucleotide (nū´-klē-ō-tīd) A building block of nucleic acids, consisting of a five-carbon sugar covalently bonded to a nitrogenous base and one or more phosphate groups.

nucleus (plural, **nuclei**) (1) An atom's central core, containing protons and neutrons. (2) The organelle of a eukaryotic cell that contains the genetic material in the form of chromosomes, made of chromatin.

O

obesity The excessive accumulation of fat in the body.

ocean acidification Decreasing pH of ocean waters due to absorption of excess atmospheric CO_2 from the burning of fossil fuels.

ocean current One of the river-like flow patterns in the oceans.

omnivore An animal that eats animals as well as plants or algae.

oncogene (on´-kō-jēn) A cancer-causing gene; usually contributes to malignancy by abnormally enhancing the amount or activity of a growth factor made by the cell.

oogenesis (ō´-uh-jen´-uh-sis) The development of mature egg cells.

open circulatory system A circulatory system in which blood is pumped through open-ended vessels and bathes the tissues and organs directly. In an animal with an open circulatory system, blood and interstitial fluid are the same.

operator In prokaryotic DNA, a sequence of nucleotides near the start of an operon to which an active repressor protein can attach. The binding of a repressor prevents RNA polymerase from attaching to the promoter and transcribing the genes of the operon. The operator sequence thereby acts as a "genetic switch" that can turn all the genes in an operon on or off as a single functional unit.

operculum (ō-per´-kyuh-lum) (plural, **opercula**) A protective flap on each side of a fish's head that covers a chamber housing the gills. Movement of the operculum increases the flow of oxygen-bearing water over the gills.

operon (op´-er-on) A unit of genetic regulation common in prokaryotes; a cluster of genes with related functions, along with the promoter and operator that control their transcription.

opportunistic infection An infection that can be controlled by a normally functioning immune system but that causes illness in a person with an immunodeficiency.

opposable thumb An arrangement of the fingers such that the thumb can touch the fingertips of all four fingers.

optimal foraging theory The basis for analyzing behavior as a compromise between feeding costs and feeding benefits.

oral cavity The mouth of an animal.

oral contraceptive A chemical contraceptive that contains synthetic estrogen and/or progesterone (or a synthetic progesterone-like hormone called progestin) and prevents the release of eggs. Also called a birth control pill.

order In Linnaean classification, the taxonomic category above family.

organ A specialized structure composed of several different types of tissues that together perform specific functions.

organ of Corti (kor´-tē) The hearing organ in birds and mammals, located within the cochlea.

organ system A group of organs that work together in performing vital body functions.

organelle (ōr-guh-nel´) A membrane-enclosed structure with a specialized function within a cell.

organic compound A chemical compound containing the element carbon and usually the element hydrogen.

organic farming A set of agricultural principles that are intended to promote biological diversity and ecological sustainability. The use of the term *organic* on food labels is regulated by the U.S. Department of Agriculture.

organism An individual living thing, such as a bacterium, fungus, protist, plant, or animal.

orgasm A series of rhythmic, involuntary contractions of the reproductive structures.

osmoconformer (oz´-mō-con-form´-er) An organism whose body fluids have a solute concentration equal to that of its surroundings.

Osmoconformers do not have a net gain or loss of water by osmosis. Examples include most marine invertebrates.

osmoregulation The homeostatic maintenance of solute concentrations and water balance by a cell or organism.

osmoregulator An organism whose body fluids have a solute concentration different from that of its environment and that must use energy in controlling water loss or gain. Examples include most land-dwelling and freshwater animals.

osmosis (oz-mō´-sis) The diffusion of free water across a selectively permeable membrane.

osteoporosis (os´-tē-ō-puh-rō´-sis) A skeletal disorder characterized by thinning, porous, and easily broken bones.

outer ear One of three main regions of the ear in reptiles (including birds) and mammals; made up of the auditory canal and, in many birds and mammals, the pinna.

outgroup In a cladistic study, a taxon or group of taxa known to have diverged before the lineage that contains the group of species being studied. *See also* ingroup.

ovarian cycle (ō-vār´-ē-un) Hormonally synchronized cyclic events in the mammalian ovary, culminating in ovulation.

ovary (1) In animals, the female gonad, which produces egg cells and reproductive hormones. (2) In flowering plants, the basal portion of a carpel in which the egg-containing ovules develop.

oviduct (ō´-vuh-dukt) The tube that conveys egg cells away from an ovary; also called a fallopian tube. In humans, the oviduct is the normal site of fertilization.

ovulation (ah´-vyū-lā´-shun) The release of an egg cell from an ovarian follicle.

ovule (ō-vyūl) seed plants, a structure that develops within the female cone (in gymnosperms) or ovary (in angiosperms) that contains the female gametophyte.

ovum (plural, *ova*) A mature reproductive egg.

oxidation The loss of electrons from a substance involved in a redox reaction; always accompanies reduction.

oxidative phosphorylation (fos´-fōr-uh-lā´-shun) The production of ATP using energy derived from the redox reactions of an electron transport chain; the third major stage of cellular respiration.

ozone layer The layer of ozone (O_3) in the upper atmosphere that protects life on Earth from the harmful ultraviolet rays in sunlight.

P

P generation The parent individuals from which offspring are derived in studies of inheritance; P stands for parental.

P site One of two of a ribosome's binding sites for tRNA during translation. The P site holds the tRNA carrying the growing polypeptide chain. (P stands for peptidyl tRNA.)

paedomorphosis (pē´-duh-mōr´-fuh-sis) The retention in an adult of juvenile features of its evolutionary ancestors.

pain receptor A sensory receptor that detects pain.

paleoanthropology (pā´-lē-ō-an´-thruh-pol´-uh-jē) The study of human origins and evolution.

paleontologist (pa´-lē-on-tol´-uh-jist) A scientist who studies fossils.

pancreas (pan´-krē-us) A gland with dual functions: The digestive portion secretes digestive enzymes and an alkaline solution into the small intestine via a duct. The endocrine portion secretes the hormones insulin and glucagon into the blood.

Pangaea (pan-jē´-uh) The supercontinent that formed near the end of the Paleozoic era, when plate movements brought all the landmasses of Earth together.

parasite Organism that derives its nutrition from a living host, which is harmed by the interaction.

parasympathetic division The component of the autonomic nervous system that generally promotes body activities that gain and conserve energy, such as digestion and reduced heart rate. *See also* sympathetic division.

parenchyma cell (puh-ren´-kim-uh) In plants, a relatively unspecialized cell with a thin primary wall and no secondary wall;

functions in photosynthesis, food storage, and aerobic respiration and may differentiate into other cell types.

Parkinson's disease A motor disorder caused by a progressive brain disease and characterized by difficulty in initiating movements, slowness of movement, and rigidity.

parsimony (par´-suh-mō´-nē) In scientific studies, the search for the least complex explanation for an observed phenomenon.

partial pressure The pressure exerted by a particular gas in a mixture of gases; a measure of the relative amount of a gas.

passive immunity Temporary immunity obtained by acquiring ready-made antibodies, as occurs in the transfer of maternal antibodies to a fetus or nursing infant. Passive immunity lasts only a few weeks or months.

passive transport The diffusion of a substance across a biological membrane, with no expenditure of energy.

pathogen An agent, such as a virus, bacteria, or fungus, that causes disease.

pattern formation During embryonic development, the emergence of a body form with specialized organs and tissues in the right places.

PCR *See* polymerase chain reaction (PCR).

pedigree A family genetic tree representing the occurrence of heritable traits in parents and offspring across a number of generations. A pedigree can be used to determine genotypes of matings that have already occurred.

pelagic realm (puh-laj´-ik) The region of an ocean occupied by seawater.

penis The copulatory structure of male mammals.

peptide bond The covalent bond between two amino acid units in a polypeptide, formed by a dehydration reaction.

peptidoglycan (pep´-tid-ō-glī´-kan) A polymer of complex sugars cross-linked by short polypeptides; a material unique to bacterial cell walls.

per capita rate of increase The average contribution of each individual in a population to population growth.

perennial (puh-ren´-ē-ul) A plant that lives for many years.

peripheral nervous system (PNS) The network of nerves and ganglia carrying signals into and out of the central nervous system.

peristalsis (per´-uh-stal´-sis) Rhythmic waves of contraction of smooth muscles. Peristalsis propels food through a digestive tract and also enables many animals, such as earthworms, to crawl.

permafrost Continuously frozen ground found in the arctic tundra.

peroxisome An organelle containing enzymes that transfer hydrogen atoms from various substrates to oxygen, producing and then degrading hydrogen peroxide.

petal A modified leaf of a flowering plant. Petals are the often colorful parts of a flower that advertise it to pollinators.

pH scale A measure of the acidity of a solution, ranging in value from 0 (most acidic) to 14 (most basic). The letters pH stand for potential hydrogen and refer to the concentration of hydrogen ions (H^+).

phage (fāj) *See* bacteriophage.

phagocyte (fag´-ō-sīt´) A white blood cell (for example, a neutrophil or macrophage) that engulfs bacteria, foreign proteins, and the remains of dead body cells.

phagocytosis (fag´-ō-sī-tō´-sis) Cellular "eating"; a type of endocytosis in which a cell engulfs macromolecules, other cells, or particles into its cytoplasm.

pharyngeal slit (fā-rin´-jē-ul) A gill structure in the pharynx; found in chordate embryos and some adult chordates.

pharynx (fār´-inks) The organ in a digestive tract that receives food from the oral cavity; in terrestrial vertebrates, the region of the throat that is a common passageway for air and food.

phenotype (fē´-nō-tīp) The expressed traits of an organism.

phenotypic plasticity An individual's ability to change phenotype in response to local environmental conditions.

phloem (flō´-um) The portion of a plant's vascular tissue system that transports sugars and other organic nutrients from leaves or storage tissues to other parts of the plant.

phloem sap (flō´-um) The solution of sugars, other nutrients, and hormones conveyed throughout a plant via phloem tissue.

phosphate group (fos´-fāt) A chemical group consisting of a phosphorus atom bonded to four oxygen atoms.

phospholipid (fos´-fō-lip´-id) A lipid made up of glycerol joined to two fatty acids and a phosphate group, giving the molecule two nonpolar hydrophobic tails and a polar hydrophilic head. Phospholipids form bilayers that function as biological membranes.

phosphorylation (fos´-fōr-uh-lā´-shun) The transfer of a phosphate group, usually from ATP, to a molecule. Nearly all cellular work depends on ATP energizing other molecules by phosphorylation.

photic zone (fō´-tik) The region of an aquatic ecosystem into which light penetrates and where photosynthesis occurs.

photoautotroph An organism that obtains energy from sunlight and carbon from CO_2 by photosynthesis.

photoheterotroph An organism that obtains energy from sunlight and carbon from organic sources.

photon (fō´-ton) A fixed quantity of light energy. The shorter the wavelength of light, the greater the energy of a photon.

photoperiod The relative lengths of day and night; an environmental stimulus that plants use to detect the time of year.

photophosphorylation (fō´-tō-fos´-fōr-uh-lā´-shun) The production of ATP by chemiosmosis during the light reactions of photosynthesis.

photopsin (fō-top´-sin) One of a family of visual pigments in the cones of the vertebrate eye that absorb bright, colored light.

photoreceptor A type of electromagnetic sensory receptor that detects light.

photorespiration In a plant cell, a metabolic pathway that consumes oxygen, releases CO_2, and decreases photosynthetic output. Photorespiration generally occurs on hot, dry days, when stomata close, O_2 accumulates in the leaf, and rubisco fixes O_2 rather than CO_2. Photorespiration produces no sugar molecules or ATP.

photosynthesis (fō´-tō-sin´-thuh-sis) The process by which plants, algae, and some protists and prokaryotes convert light energy to chemical energy that is stored in sugars made from carbon dioxide and water.

photosystem A light-capturing unit of a chloroplast's thylakoid membrane, consisting of a reaction-center complex surrounded by numerous light-harvesting complexes.

phototropism (fō´-tō-trō´-pizm) The growth of a plant shoot toward light (positive phototropism) or away from light (negative phototropism).

phylogenetic species concept (fī´-lō-juh-net´-ik) A definition of species as the smallest group of individuals that shares a common ancestor, forming one branch on the tree of life.

phylogenetic tree (fī´-lō-juh-net´-ik) A branching diagram that represents a hypothesis about the evolutionary history of a group of organisms.

phylogeny (fī-loj´-uh-nē) The evolutionary history of a species or group of related species.

phylum (fī´-lum) (plural, **phyla**) In Linnaean classification, the taxonomic category above class.

physiology (fī´-zē-ol´-uh-ji) The study of the functions of an organism's structures.

phytochrome (fī´-tuh-krōm) A plant protein that has a light-absorbing component.

phytoplankton (fī´-tō-plank´-ton) Algae and photosynthetic bacteria that drift passively in aquatic environments.

pineal gland (pin´-ē-ul) An outgrowth of the vertebrate brain that secretes the hormone melatonin, which coordinates daily and seasonal body activities such as the sleep/wake circadian rhythm with environmental light conditions.

pinna (pin´-uh) The flap-like part of the outer ear, projecting from the body surface of many birds and mammals; collects sound waves and channels them to the auditory canal.

pistil Part of the reproductive organ of an angiosperm, a single carpel or a group of fused carpels.

pith Part of the ground tissue system of a dicot plant. Pith fills the center of a stem and may store food.

pituitary gland An endocrine gland at the base of the hypothalamus; consists of a posterior lobe, which stores and releases two hormones produced by the hypothalamus, and an anterior lobe, which produces and secretes many hormones that regulate diverse body functions.

pivot joint A joint that allows precise rotations in multiple planes. An example in humans is the joint that rotates the forearm at the elbow.

placenta (pluh-sen´-tuh) In most mammals, the organ that provides nutrients and oxygen to the embryo and helps dispose of its metabolic wastes; formed of the embryo's chorion and the mother's endometrial blood vessels.

placental mammal (pluh-sen´-tul) Mammal whose young complete their embryonic development in the uterus, nourished via the mother's blood vessels in the placenta; also called a eutherian.

plasma The liquid matrix of the blood in which the blood cells are suspended.

plasma cell An antibody-secreting B cell; the effector cell of the humoral immune response.

plasma membrane The membrane at the boundary of every cell that acts as a selective barrier to the passage of ions and molecules into and out of the cell; consists of a phospholipid bilayer with embedded proteins.

plasmid A small ring of independently replicating DNA separate from the main chromosome(s). Plasmids are found in prokaryotes and yeasts.

plasmodesma (plaz´-mō-dez´-muh) (plural, **plasmodesmata**) An open channel in a plant cell wall that connects the cytoplasm of adjacent cells.

plasmodial slime mold (plaz-mō´-dē-ul) A type of protist that has amoeboid cells, flagellated cells, and an amoeboid plasmodial feeding stage in its life cycle; a member of the amoebozoan clade.

plasmodium (1) A single mass of cytoplasm containing many nuclei. (2) The amoeboid feeding stage in the life cycle of a plasmodial slime mold.

plate tectonics (tek-tän´-iks) The theory that the continents are part of great plates of Earth's crust that float on the hot, underlying portion of the mantle. Movements in the mantle cause the continents to move slowly over time.

platelet A pinched-off cytoplasmic fragment of a bone marrow cell. Platelets circulate in the blood and are important in blood clotting.

pleiotropy (plī´-uh-trō-pē) The control of more than one phenotypic character by a single gene.

polar covalent bond A covalent bond between atoms that differ in electronegativity. The shared electrons are pulled closer to the more electronegative atom, making it slightly negative and the other atom slightly positive.

polar ice A terrestrial biome that includes regions of extremely cold temperature and low precipitation located at high latitudes north of the arctic tundra and in Antarctica.

polar molecule A molecule containing polar covalent bonds and having an unequal distribution of charges in different regions of the molecule.

pollen grain The structure that will produce the sperm in seed plants; the male gametophyte.

pollination In seed plants, the delivery by wind or animals of pollen from the pollen-producing parts of a plant to a female cone (in gymnosperms) or the stigma of a carpel (in angiosperms).

polychaete (pol´-ē-kēt) A member of the largest group of annelids. *See also* annelid.

polygamous Referring to a type of relationship in which an individual of one sex mates with more than one of the other sex.

polygenic inheritance (pol´-ē-jen´-ik) The additive effects of two or more gene loci on a single phenotypic character.

polymer (pol´-uh-mer) A large molecule consisting of many identical or similar monomers linked together by covalent bonds.

polymerase chain reaction (PCR) (puh-lim´-uh-rãs) A technique used to obtain many copies of a DNA molecule or a specific part of a DNA molecule. In the procedure, the starting DNA is mixed with a heat-resistant DNA polymerase, DNA nucleotides, and a few other ingredients. Specific nucleotide primers flanking the region to be copied ensure that it, and not other regions of the DNA, is replicated during the PCR procedure.

polynucleotide (pol´-ē-nū´-klē-ō-tīd) A polymer made up of many nucleotide monomers covalently bonded together.

polyp (pol´-ip) One of two types of cnidarian body forms; a columnar, hydra-like body.

polypeptide A polymer (chain) of amino acids linked by peptide bonds.

polyploid An organism that has more than two complete sets of chromosomes as a result of an accident of cell division.

polysaccharide (pol´-ē-sak´-uh-rīd) A carbohydrate polymer of many monosaccharides (sugars) linked by dehydration reactions.

pons (pahnz) Part of the vertebrate hindbrain that functions with the medulla oblongata in passing data between the spinal cord and forebrain and in controlling autonomic, homeostatic functions.

population A group of individuals belonging to one species and living in the same geographic area.

population density The number of individuals of a species per unit area or volume.

population ecology The study of how members of a population interact with their environment, focusing on factors that influence population density and growth.

population momentum In a population in which $r = 0$, the continuation of population growth as girls in the prereproductive age group reach their reproductive years.

positive feedback A type of control in which a change triggers mechanisms that amplify that change.

post-anal tail A tail posterior to the anus; found in chordate embryos and most adult chordates.

posterior Pertaining to the rear, or tail, of a bilaterally symmetric animal.

posterior pituitary An extension of the hypothalamus composed of nervous tissue that secretes hormones made in the hypothalamus; a temporary storage site for hypothalamic hormones.

postzygotic barrier A reproductive barrier that prevents hybrid zygotes produced by two different species from developing into viable, fertile adults. Includes reduced hybrid viability, reduced hybrid fertility, and hybrid breakdown.

potential energy The energy that matter possesses because of its location or spatial arrangement. Water behind a dam possesses potential energy, and so do chemical bonds.

predation An interaction between species in which one species, the predator, kills and eats the other, the prey.

prepuce (prē´-pyūs) A fold of skin covering the head of the clitoris or penis.

pressure flow mechanism The method by which phloem sap is transported through a plant from a sugar source, where sugars are produced, to a sugar sink, where sugars are used.

prevailing winds Winds that result from the combined effects of Earth's rotation and the rising and falling of air masses.

prezygotic barrier A reproductive barrier that impedes mating between species or hinders fertilization if mating between two species is attempted. Includes temporal, habitat, behavioral, mechanical, and gametic isolation.

primary consumer In the trophic structure of an ecosystem, an organism that eats plants or algae.

primary growth Growth in the length of a plant root or shoot, produced by an apical meristem.

primary immune response The initial adaptive immune response to an antigen, which appears after a lag of about 10 days.

primary production The amount of solar energy converted to chemical energy (in organic compounds) by autotrophs in an ecosystem during a given time period.

primary structure The first level of protein structure; the specific sequence of amino acids making up a polypeptide chain.

primary succession A type of ecological succession in which a biological community arises in an area without soil. *See also* secondary succession.

primers Short, artificially created, single-stranded DNA molecules that bind to each end of a target sequence during a PCR procedure.

prion An infectious form of protein that may multiply by converting related proteins to more prions. Prions cause several related diseases in different animals, including scrapie in sheep and mad cow disease.

problem solving Applying past experiences to overcome obstacles in novel situations.

producer An organism that makes organic food molecules from CO_2, H_2O, and other inorganic raw materials: a plant, alga, or autotrophic prokaryote.

product An ending material in a chemical reaction.

progestin (prŏ-jes´-tin) One of a family of steroid hormones, including progesterone, produced by the mammalian ovary. Progestins prepare the uterus for pregnancy.

programmed cell death The timely and tidy suicide (and disposal of the remains) of certain cells, triggered by certain genes; an essential process in normal development; also called apoptosis.

prokaryotic cell (prŏ-kār´-ē-ot´-ik) A type of cell lacking a membrane-enclosed nucleus and other membrane-enclosed organelles; found only in the domains Bacteria and Archaea.

prolactin (PRL) (prŏ-lak´-tin) A protein hormone secreted by the anterior pituitary that stimulates human mammary glands to produce and release milk and produces other responses in different animals.

prometaphase The second stage of mitosis, during which the nuclear envelope fragments and the spindle microtubules attach to the kinetochores of the sister chromatids.

promiscuous Referring to a type of relationship in which mating occurs with no strong pair-bonds or lasting relationships.

promoter A specific nucleotide sequence in DNA located near the start of a gene that is the binding site for RNA polymerase and the place where transcription begins.

prophage (prŏ´-fāj) Phage DNA that has inserted by genetic recombination into the DNA of a bacterial chromosome.

prophase The first stage of mitosis, during which the chromatin condenses to form structures (sister chromatids) visible with a light microscope and the mitotic spindle begins to form, but the nucleus is still intact.

prostate gland (pros´-tāt) A gland in human males that secretes a thin fluid that nourishes the sperm.

protein A functional biological molecule consisting of one or more polypeptides folded into a specific three-dimensional structure.

proteobacteria A clade of gram-negative bacteria that encompasses enormous diversity, including all four modes of nutrition.

proteomics The study of whole sets of proteins and their interactions.

protist A member of a diverse collection of eukaryotes. Most protists are unicellular, but some are colonial or multicellular.

proton A subatomic particle with a single positive electrical charge, found in the nucleus of an atom.

proto-oncogene (prŏ´-tŏ-on´-kŏ-jēn) A normal gene that, through mutation, can be converted to a cancer-causing gene.

protostome A mode of animal development in which the opening formed during gastrulation becomes the mouth. Animals with the protostome pattern of development include the flatworms, molluscs, annelids, nematodes, and arthropods.

protozoan (prŏ´-tŏ-zŏ´-un) (plural, **protozoans**) A protist that lives primarily by ingesting food; a heterotrophic, "animal-like" protist.

proximal tubule In the vertebrate kidney, the portion of a nephron immediately downstream from Bowman's capsule that conveys and helps refine filtrate.

proximate cause In animal behavior, a condition in an animal's internal or external environment that is the immediate reason or mechanism for a behavior.

proximate question In animal behavior, a question that concerns the immediate reason for a behavior.

pseudocoelom (sū´-dō-sē´-lōm) A body cavity that is not lined with mesoderm and is in direct contact with the wall of the digestive tract.

pseudopodium (sū´-dō-pō´-dē-um) (plural, **pseudopodia**) A temporary extension of an amoeboid cell. Pseudopodia function in moving cells and engulfing food.

pulmonary artery A large blood vessel that conveys blood from the heart to a lung.

pulmonary circuit The branch of the circulatory system that supplies the lungs. *See also* systemic circuit.

pulmonary vein A blood vessel that conveys blood from a lung to the heart.

pulse The rhythmic stretching of the arteries caused by the pressure of blood during contraction of ventricles in systole.

punctuated equilibria In the fossil record, long periods in which a species undergoes little or no morphological change (equilibria), interrupted (punctuated) by relatively brief periods of sudden change.

Punnett square A diagram used in the study of inheritance to show the results of random fertilization.

pupil The opening in the iris that admits light into the interior of the vertebrate eye. Muscles in the iris regulate the pupil's size.

Q

quaternary consumer (kwot´-er-ner-ē) An organism that eats tertiary consumers.

quaternary structure (kwot´-er-ner-ē) The fourth level of protein structure; the shape resulting from the association of two or more polypeptide subunits.

R

R plasmid A bacterial plasmid that carries genes for enzymes that destroy particular antibiotics, thus making the bacterium resistant to the antibiotics.

radial symmetry An arrangement of the body parts of an organism like pieces of a pie around an imaginary central axis. Any slice passing longitudinally through a radially symmetric organism's central axis divides the organism into mirror-image halves.

radioactive isotope An isotope whose nucleus decays spontaneously, giving off particles and energy.

radiolarian A protist that moves and feeds by means of threadlike pseudopodia and has a mineralized support structure composed of silica. Radiolarians belong to the Rhizaria clade of the SAR supergroup.

radiometric dating A method for determining the absolute ages of fossils and rocks, based on the half-life of radioactive isotopes.

radula (rad´-yū-luh) A toothed, rasping organ used to scrape up or shred food; found in many molluscs.

random dispersion pattern A pattern in which the individuals of a population are spaced in an unpredictable way.

ray-finned fish Bony fish; member of a clade of jawed vertebrates having fins supported by thin, flexible skeletal rays.

reabsorption In the vertebrate kidney, the reclaiming of water and valuable solutes from the filtrate.

reactant A starting material in a chemical reaction.

receptor potential The electrical signal produced by sensory transduction.

receptor-mediated endocytosis (en´-dō-sī-tō´-sis) The movement of specific molecules into a cell by the infolding of vesicles containing proteins with receptor sites specific to the molecules being taken in.

recessive allele An allele that has no noticeable effect on the phenotype of a gene when the individual is heterozygous for that gene.

recombinant DNA A DNA molecule that has been manipulated in the laboratory to carry nucleotide sequences derived from two sources, often different species.

recombination frequency With respect to two given genes, the number of recombinant progeny from a mating divided by the total number of progeny. Recombinant progeny carry combinations of alleles different from those in either of the parents as a result of crossing over during meiosis.

Recommended Dietary Allowance (RDA) A recommendation for daily nutrient intake established by a national scientific panel.

rectum The terminal portion of the large intestine where the feces are stored until they are eliminated.

red alga A member of a group of marine, mostly multicellular, autotrophic protists, which includes the reef-building coralline algae. Red algae belong to the supergroup Archaeplastida.

red blood cell *See* erythrocyte.

red bone marrow A specialized tissue that is found in the cavities at the ends of bones and that produces blood cells.

redox reaction Short for **red**uction-**ox**idation reaction; a chemical reaction in which electrons are lost from one substance (oxidation) and added to another (reduction).

reduction The gain of electrons by a substance involved in a redox reaction; always accompanies oxidation.

reflex An automatic reaction to a stimulus, mediated by the spinal cord or lower brain.

regeneration The regrowth of body parts from pieces of an organism.

regulatory gene A gene that codes for a protein, such as a repressor, that controls the transcription of another gene or group of genes.

relative fitness The contribution an individual makes to the gene pool of the next generation, relative to the contributions of other individuals in the population.

releasing hormone A kind of hormone secreted by the hypothalamus that promotes the release of hormones from the anterior pituitary.

renal cortex The outer portion of the vertebrate kidney, above the renal medulla.

renal medulla The inner portion of the vertebrate kidney, beneath the renal cortex.

repetitive DNA Nucleotide sequences that are present in many copies in the DNA of a genome. The repeated sequences may be long or short and may be located next to each other (tandomly) or dispersed in the DNA.

repressor A protein that blocks the transcription of a gene or operon.

reproduction The creation of new individuals from existing ones.

reproductive cloning Using a somatic cell from a multicellular organism to make one or more genetically identical individuals.

reproductive cycle A recurring sequence of events that produces eggs, makes them available for fertilization, and prepares the female body for pregnancy.

reproductive isolation The existence of biological factors (barriers) that impede members of two species from producing viable, fertile hybrids.

reproductive system The organ system responsible for reproduction.

reptile Member of the clade of amniotes that includes snakes, lizards, turtles, crocodilians, and birds, along with a number of extinct groups, such as dinosaurs.

respiratory system The organ system that functions in exchanging gases with the environment. It supplies the blood with O_2 and disposes of CO_2.

resting potential The voltage across the plasma membrane of a resting neuron. The resting potential in a vertebrate neuron is typically around -70 millivolts, with the inside of the cell negatively charged relative to the outside.

restoration ecology The use of ecological principles to develop ways to return degraded ecosystems to conditions as similar as possible to their natural, predegraded state.

restriction enzyme A bacterial enzyme that cuts up foreign DNA (at specific DNA sequences called *restriction sites*), thus protecting bacteria against intruding DNA from phages and other organisms. Restriction enzymes are used in DNA technology to cut DNA molecules in reproducible ways. The pieces of cut DNA are called restriction fragments.

restriction fragment length polymorphism (RFLP) (rif´-lip) Variation in the length of a restriction fragment. RFLPs are produced when homologous DNA sequences containing SNPs are cut up with restriction enzymes.

restriction fragments Molecules of DNA produced from a longer DNA molecule cut up by a restriction enzyme. Restriction fragments are used in genome mapping and other applications.

restriction site A specific sequence on a DNA strand that is recognized as a "cut site" by a restriction enzyme.

retina (ret´-uh-nuh) The light-sensitive layer in an eye, made up of photoreceptor cells and sensory neurons.

retrovirus An RNA virus that reproduces by means of a DNA molecule. It reverse-transcribes its RNA into DNA, inserts the DNA into a cellular chromosome, and then transcribes more copies of the RNA from the viral DNA. HIV and a number of cancer-causing viruses are retroviruses.

reverse transcriptase (tran-skrip´-tās) An enzyme encoded and used by retroviruses that catalyzes the synthesis of DNA on an RNA template.

RFLP *See* restriction fragment length polymorphism (RFLP).

Rhizaria A clade of the SAR supergroup of protists that includes foraminiferans and radiolarians.

rhizome (rī´-zōm) A horizontal stem of a plant that grows below the ground.

rhodopsin (ro-dop´-sin) A visual pigment that is located in the rods of the vertebrate eye and that absorbs dim light.

rhythm method A form of contraception that relies on refraining from sexual intercourse when conception is most likely to occur; also called natural family planning.

ribonucleic acid (RNA) (rī-bō-nū-klā´-ik) A type of nucleic acid consisting of nucleotide monomers with a ribose sugar and the nitrogenous bases adenine (A), cytosine (C), guanine (G), and uracil (U); usually single-stranded; functions in protein synthesis, gene regulation, and as the genome of some viruses.

ribosomal RNA (rRNA) (rī´-buh-sōm´-ul) The type of ribonucleic acid that, together with proteins, makes up ribosomes; the most abundant type of RNA in most cells.

ribosome (rī´-buh-sōm) A cell structure consisting of RNA and protein organized into two subunits and functioning as the site of protein synthesis in the cytoplasm. In eukaryotic cells, the ribosomal subunits are constructed in the nucleolus.

ribozyme (rī´-bō-zīm) An RNA molecule that functions as an enzyme.

RNA interference (RNAi) A biotechnology technique used to silence the expression of specific genes. Synthetic RNA molecules with sequences that correspond to particular genes trigger the breakdown of the gene's mRNA.

RNA polymerase (puh-lim´-uh-rās) A large molecular complex that links together the growing chain of RNA nucleotides during transcription, using a DNA strand as a template.

RNA splicing The removal of introns and joining of exons in eukaryotic RNA, forming an mRNA molecule with a continuous coding sequence; occurs before mRNA leaves the nucleus.

rod A photoreceptor cell in the vertebrate retina enabling vision in dim light.

root cap A cone of cells at the tip of a plant root that protects the root's apical meristem.

root hair An outgrowth of an epidermal cell on a root, which increases the root's absorptive surface area.

root system All of a plant's roots, which anchor it in the soil, absorb and transport minerals and water, and store food.

rough endoplasmic reticulum (reh-tik´-yuh-lum) That portion of the endoplasmic reticulum with ribosomes attached that make membrane proteins and secretory proteins.

r-selection The concept that in certain (*r*-selected) populations, a high reproductive rate is the chief determinant of life history.

rule of addition A rule stating that the probability that an event can occur in two or more alternative ways is the sum of the separate probabilities of the different ways.

rule of multiplication A rule stating that the probability of a compound event is the product of the separate probabilities of the independent events.

ruminant (rū´-min-ent) An animal, such as a cow or sheep, with multiple stomach compartments housing microorganisms that can digest cellulose.

S

SA (sinoatrial) node (sȳ´-nō´-ā´-trē-ul) The pacemaker of the heart, located in the wall of the right atrium, that sets the rate and timing at which all cardiac muscle cells contract.

sac fungus *See* ascomycete.

salivary glands Glands associated with the oral cavity that secrete substances to lubricate food and begin the process of chemical digestion.

salt A compound resulting from the formation of an ionic bond.

sapwood Light-colored, water-conducting secondary xylem in a tree. *See also* heartwood.

SAR (Stramenopila, Alveolata, and Rhizaria) One of four monophyletic supergroups proposed in a current hypothesis of the evolutionary history of eukaryotes. The other three supergroups are Excavata, Unikonta, and Archaeplastida.

sarcomere (sar´-kō-mēr) The fundamental unit of muscle contraction, composed of thin filaments of actin and thick filaments of myosin; in electron micrographs, the region between two narrow, dark lines, called Z lines, in a myofibril.

saturated fatty acid A fatty acid in which all carbons in the hydrocarbon tail are connected by single bonds and the maximum number of hydrogen atoms are attached to the carbon skeleton. Saturated fats and fatty acids solidify at room temperature.

savanna A biome dominated by grasses and scattered trees.

scanning electron microscope (SEM) A microscope that uses an electron beam to study the surface details of a cell or other specimens.

scavenger An animal that feeds on the carcasses of dead animals.

schizophrenia Severe mental disturbance characterized by psychotic episodes in which patients have a distorted perception of reality.

sclera (sklār´-uh) A layer of connective tissue forming the outer surface of the vertebrate eye. The cornea is the frontal part of the sclera.

sclereid (sklār´-ē-id) In plants, a very hard sclerenchyma cell found in nutshells and seed coats.

sclerenchyma cell (skluh-ren´-kē-muh) In plants, a supportive cell with rigid secondary walls hardened with lignin.

scrotum A pouch of skin outside the abdomen that houses a testis and functions in cooling sperm, keeping them viable.

search image The mechanism that enables an animal to find a particular kind of food efficiently.

second law of thermodynamics The principle stating that every energy conversion reduces the order of the universe, increasing its entropy. Ordered forms of energy are at least partly converted to heat.

secondary consumer An organism that eats primary consumers.

secondary growth An increase in a plant's diameter, involving cell division in the vascular cambium and cork cambium.

secondary immune response The adaptive immune response elicited when an animal encounters the same antigen at some later time. The secondary immune response is more rapid, of greater magnitude, and of longer duration than the primary immune response.

secondary phloem A type of phloem plant tissue produced by the vascular cambium during secondary growth.

secondary structure The second level of protein structure; the regular local patterns of coils or folds of a polypeptide chain.

secondary succession A type of ecological succession that occurs where a disturbance has destroyed an existing biological community but left the soil intact. *See also* primary succession.

secondary xylem A type of xylem plant tissue produced by the vascular cambium during secondary growth.

secretion (1) The discharge of molecules synthesized by a cell. (2) In the vertebrate kidney, the discharge of wastes from the blood into the filtrate from the nephron tubules.

seed A plant embryo packaged with a food supply within a protective covering.

seed coat A tough outer covering of a seed, formed from the tissue surrounding an ovule. The seed coat encloses and protects the embryo and its food supply.

seedless vascular plants The informal collective name for lycophytes (club mosses and their relatives) and monilophytes (ferns and their relatives).

segmentation Subdivision along the length of an animal body into a series of repeated parts called segments; allows for greater flexibility and mobility.

selective permeability (per´-mē-uh-bil´-uh-tē) A property of biological membranes that allows some substances to cross more easily than others and blocks the passage of other substances altogether.

self protein A protein on the surface of an antigen-presenting cell that can hold a foreign antigen and display it to T cells. Each individual has a unique set of self proteins that serve as molecular markers for the body. The technical name for self proteins is *major histocompatibility complex (MHC) proteins. See also* nonself molecule.

semen (sē´-mun) The sperm-containing fluid that is ejaculated by the male during orgasm.

semicircular canals Fluid-filled channels in the inner ear that detect changes in the head's rate of rotation or angular movement.

semiconservative model Type of DNA replication in which the replicated double helix consists of one old strand, derived from the old molecule, and one newly made strand.

seminal vesicle (sem´-uh-nul ves´-uh-kul) A gland in males that secretes a thick fluid that contains fructose, which provides most of the sperm's energy.

seminiferous tubule (sem´-uh-nif´-uh-rus) A coiled sperm-producing tube in a testis.

sensitive period A limited phase in an individual animal's development when learning of particular behaviors can take place.

sensory adaptation The tendency of sensory neurons to become less sensitive when they are stimulated repeatedly. For example, a prominent smell becomes unnoticeable over time.

sensory input The conduction of signals from sensory receptors to processing centers in the central nervous system.

sensory neuron A nerve cell that receives information from sensory receptors and conveys signals into the central nervous system.

sensory receptor A specialized cell or neuron that detects specific stimuli from an organism's external or internal environment and sends information to the central nervous system.

sensory transduction The conversion of a stimulus signal to an electrical signal by a sensory receptor.

sepal (sē´-pul) A modified leaf of a flowering plant. A circle of sepals encloses and protects the flower bud before it opens.

sessile An organism that is anchored to its substrate.

sex chromosome A chromosome that determines whether an individual is male or female.

sex-linked gene A gene located on a sex chromosome. In humans, the vast majority of sex-linked genes are located on the X chromosome.

sexual dimorphism (dī-mōr´-fizm) Marked differences between the secondary sex characteristics of males and females.

sexual reproduction The creation of genetically unique offspring by the fusion of two haploid sex cells (gametes), forming a diploid zygote.

sexual selection A form of natural selection in which individuals with certain inherited traits are more likely than other individuals to obtain mates.

sexually transmitted disease (STD) A contagious disease spread by sexual contact.

shared ancestral character A character shared by members of a particular clade that originated in an ancestor that is not a member of that clade.

shared derived character An evolutionary novelty that is unique to a particular clade.

shoot system All of a plant's stems, leaves, and reproductive structures.

short tandem repeat (STR) A series of short DNA sequences that are repeated many times in a row in the genome.

short-day plant A plant that flowers in late summer, fall, or winter, when day length is short. Short-day plants actually flower in response to long nights.

short-term memory The ability to hold information, anticipations, or goals for a time and then release them if they become irrelevant.

sickle-cell disease A genetic condition caused by a mutation in the gene for hemoglobin. The mutation causes the protein to crystallize, which deforms red blood cells into a curved shape. Such blood cells produce a cascade of symptoms that can be life-threatening.

sieve plate An end wall in a sieve-tube element that facilitates the flow of phloem sap.

sieve-tube element A food-conducting cell in a plant; also called a sieve-tube member. Chains of sieve-tube elements make up phloem tissue.

signal In behavioral ecology, a stimulus transmitted by one animal to another animal.

signal transduction pathway In cell biology, a series of molecular changes that converts a signal on a target cell's surface to a specific response inside the cell.

silent mutation A mutation in a gene that changes a codon to one that codes for the same amino acid as the original codon. The amino acid sequence of the resulting polypeptide is thus unchanged.

single circulation A circulatory system with a single pump and circuit, in which blood passes from the sites of gas exchange to the rest of the body before returning to the heart.

single nucleotide polymorphism (SNP) A one-nucleotide variation in DNA sequence found within the genomes of at least 1% of a population.

single-lens eye The camera-like eye found in some jellies, polychaetes, spiders, many molluscs, and vertebrates.

sister chromatid (krō´-muh-tid) One of the two identical parts of a duplicated chromosome in a eukaryotic cell. Prior to mitosis, sister chromatids remain attached to each another at the centromere.

skeletal muscle A type of striated muscle attached to the skeleton; generally responsible for voluntary movements of the body.

skeletal system The organ system that provides body support and protects body organs, such as the brain, heart, and lungs.

small intestine The longest section of the alimentary canal. It is the principal site of the enzymatic hydrolysis of food macromolecules and the absorption of nutrients.

smooth endoplasmic reticulum That portion of the endoplasmic reticulum that lacks ribosomes.

smooth muscle A type of muscle lacking striations; responsible for involuntary body activities.

SNP *See* single nucleotide polymorphism (SNP).

social behavior Any kind of interaction between two or more animals, usually of the same species.

social learning Learning by observing the behavior of other individuals.

sociobiology The study of the evolutionary basis of social behavior.

sodium-potassium (Na-K) pump A membrane protein that transports sodium ions out of, and potassium ions into, a cell against their concentration gradients. The process is powered by ATP.

solute (sol´-yūt) A substance that is dissolved in a solution.

solution A liquid that is a homogeneous mixture of two or more substances.

solvent The dissolving agent of a solution. Water is the most versatile solvent known.

somatic cell (sō-mat´-ik) Any cell in a multicellular organism except a sperm or egg cell or a cell that develops into a sperm or egg.

spatial learning Modification of behavior based on experience of the spatial structure of the environment.

speciation The evolution of a new species.

species A group whose members possess similar anatomical characteristics and have the ability to interbreed and produce viable, fertile offspring. *See also* biological species concept.

species diversity The variety of species that make up a community. Species diversity includes both species richness (the total number of different species) and the relative abundance of the different species in the community.

sperm A male gamete.

spermatogenesis (sper-mat´-ō-jen´-uh-sis) The formation of sperm cells.

spermicide A sperm-killing chemical (cream, jelly, or foam) that works with a barrier device as a method of contraception.

sphincter (sfink´-ter) A ringlike band of muscle fibers that regulates passage between some compartments of the alimentary canal.

spinal cord A bundle of nervous tissue that runs lengthwise inside the spine in vertebrates and integrates simple responses to certain stimuli.

spirochete (spī´-ruh-kēt) A member of a group of helical bacteria that spiral through the environment by means of rotating, internal filaments.

sponge An aquatic animal characterized by a highly porous body.

sporangium (spuh-ranj´-ē-um´) (plural, **sporangia**) A structure in fungi and plants in which meiosis occurs and haploid spores develop.

spore (1) In plants and algae, a haploid cell that can develop into a multicellular individual without fusing with another cell. (2) In prokaryotes, protists, and fungi, any of a variety of thick-walled life cycle stages capable of surviving unfavorable environmental conditions.

sporophyte (spōr´-uh-fit) The multicellular diploid form in the life cycle of organisms undergoing alternation of generations; results from a union of gametes and meiotically produces haploid spores that grow into the gametophyte generation.

stabilizing selection Natural selection that favors intermediate variants by acting against extreme phenotypes.

stamen (stā´-men) A pollen-producing male reproductive part of a flower, consisting an anther supported by a filament (stalk).

starch A storage polysaccharide in plants; a polymer of glucose.

start codon (kō´-don) On mRNA, the specific three-nucleotide sequence (AUG) to which an initiator tRNA molecule binds, starting translation of genetic information.

stem The part of a plant's shoot system that supports the leaves and reproductive structures.

stem cell An unspecialized cell that can divide to produce an identical daughter cell and a more specialized daughter cell, which undergoes differentiation.

steroid (ster´-oyd) A type of lipid whose carbon skeleton is in the form of four fused rings with various chemical groups attached. Examples are cholesterol, testosterone, and estrogen.

steroid hormone (ster´-oyd) A lipid made from cholesterol that acts as a regulatory chemical, entering a target cell and activating the transcription of specific genes.

stigma (stig´-muh) (plural, **stigmata**) The sticky tip of a flower's carpel, which traps pollen grains.

stimulus (plural, **stimuli**) (1) In the context of a nervous system, any factor that causes a nerve signal to be generated. (2) In behavioral biology, an environmental cue that triggers a specific response.

stoma (stō´-muh) (plural, **stomata**) A microscopic pore surrounded by guard cells in the epidermis of a leaf. When stomata are open, CO_2 enters a leaf, and H_2O and O_2 exit. A plant conserves water when its stomata are closed.

stomach An organ in a digestive tract that stores food and performs preliminary steps of digestion.

stop codon In mRNA, one of three triplets (UAG, UAA, UGA) that signal gene translation to stop.

STR *See* short tandem repeat (STR).

Stramenopila A clade of the SAR supergroup of protists that includes diatoms, brown algae, and water molds.

STR analysis Short tandem repeat analysis; a method of DNA profiling that compares the lengths of short tandem repeats (STRs) selected from specific sites within the genome.

stratum (plural, **strata**) Rock layer formed when a new layer of sediment covers an older one and compresses it.

stretch receptor A type of mechanoreceptor sensitive to changes in muscle length; detects the position of body parts.

stroke The death of nervous tissue in the brain, usually resulting from rupture or blockage of arteries in the head.

stroma (strō´-muh) The dense fluid within the chloroplast that surrounds the thylakoid membrane and is involved in the synthesis of organic molecules from carbon dioxide and water. Sugars are made in the stroma by the enzymes of the Calvin cycle.

stromatolite (strō-mat´-uh-līt) Layered rock that results from the activities of prokaryotes that bind thin films of sediment together.

substrate (1) A specific substance (reactant) on which an enzyme acts. Each enzyme recognizes only the specific substrate or substrates of the reaction it catalyzes. (2) A surface in or on which an organism lives.

substrate feeder An organism that lives in or on its food source, eating its way through the food.

substrate-level phosphorylation The formation of ATP by an enzyme directly transferring a phosphate group to ADP from an organic molecule (for example, one of the intermediates in glycolysis or the citric acid cycle).

sugar sink A plant organ that is a net consumer or storer of sugar. Growing roots, shoot tips, stems, and fruits are sugar sinks supplied by phloem.

sugar source A plant organ in which sugar is being produced by either photosynthesis or the breakdown of starch. Mature leaves are the primary sugar sources of plants.

sugar-phosphate backbone In a polynucleotide (DNA or RNA strand), the alternating chain of sugar and phosphate to which nitrogenous bases are attached.

superior vena cava (vē´-nuh kā´-vuh) A large vein that returns oxygen-poor blood to the heart from the upper body and head. *See also* inferior vena cava.

surface tension A measure of how difficult it is to stretch or break the surface of a liquid. Water has a high surface tension because of the hydrogen bonding of surface molecules.

surfactant A substance secreted by alveoli that decreases surface tension in the fluid that coats the alveoli.

survivorship curve A plot of the number of members of a cohort that are still alive at each age; one way to represent age-specific mortality.

suspension feeder An aquatic animal that collects small food particles from the water; includes filter feeders.

sustainability The goal of developing, managing, and conserving Earth's resources in ways that meet the needs of people today without compromising the ability of future generations to meet theirs.

sustainable agriculture Long-term productive farming methods that are environmentally safe.

sustainable resource management Management practices that allow use of a natural resource without damaging it.

swim bladder A gas-filled internal sac that helps bony fishes maintain buoyancy.

symbiosis (sim´-bē-ō-sis) A physically close association between organisms of two or more species.

sympathetic division A set of neurons in the autonomic nervous system that generally prepares the body for energy-consuming activities, such as fleeing or fighting. *See also* parasympathetic division.

sympatric speciation The formation of new species in populations that live in the same geographic area.

synapse (sin´-aps) A junction between two neurons, or between a neuron and an effector cell. Electrical or chemical signals are relayed from one cell to another at a synapse.

synaptic cleft (sin-ap´-tik) In a chemical synapse, a narrow gap separating the synaptic terminal of a transmitting neuron from a receiving neuron or an effector cell.

synaptic terminal (sin-ap´-tik) The tip of a transmitting neuron's axon, where signals are sent to another neuron or to an effector cell.

synaptic vesicle (sin-ap´-tik) A membrane-enclosed sac containing neurotransmitter molecules at the tip of the sending neuron's axon.

systematics A scientific discipline focused on classifying organisms and determining their evolutionary relationships.

systemic acquired resistance A defensive response in plants infected with a pathogenic microbe; helps protect healthy tissue from the microbe.

systemic circuit The branch of the circulatory system that supplies oxygen-rich blood to, and carries oxygen-poor blood away from, organs and tissues in the body. *See also* pulmonary circuit.

systems biology An approach to studying biology that aims to model the dynamic behavior of whole biological systems based on a study of the interactions among the system's parts.

systole (sis´-tō-lē) The contraction stage of the heart cycle, when the heart chambers actively pump blood. *See also* diastole.

T

T cell A type of lymphocyte that matures in the thymus; T cells include both effector cells for the cell-mediated immune response and helper cells required for both the humoral and cell-mediated adaptive responses.

taiga (tī´-guh) The northern coniferous forest, characterized by long, snowy winters and short, wet summers, extending across North America and Eurasia to the southern border of the arctic tundra; also found just below alpine tundra on mountainsides in temperate zones.

tapeworm A parasitic flatworm characterized by the absence of a digestive tract.

target cell A cell that responds to a regulatory signal, such as a hormone.

taxis (tak´-sis) (plural, **taxes**) Virtually automatic orientation toward or away from a stimulus.

taxon A named taxonomic unit at any given level of classification.

taxonomy The scientific discipline concerned with naming and classifying the diverse forms of life.

technology The application of scientific knowledge for a specific purpose, often involving industry or commerce but also including uses in basic research.

telomere (tel´-uh-mēr) The repetitive DNA at each end of a eukaryotic chromosome.

telophase The fifth and final stage of mitosis, during which daughter nuclei form at the two poles of a cell. Telophase usually occurs together with cytokinesis.

temperate broadleaf forest A biome located throughout midlatitude regions, where there is sufficient moisture to support the growth of large, broadleaf deciduous trees.

temperate grassland A grassland region maintained by seasonal drought, occasional fires, and grazing by large mammals.

temperate rain forest Coniferous forests of coastal North America (from Alaska to Oregon) supported by warm, moist air from the Pacific Ocean.

temperate zones Latitudes between the tropics and the Arctic Circle in the north and the Antarctic Circle in the south; regions with milder climates than the tropics or polar regions.

temperature A measure in degrees of the average thermal energy of the atoms and molecules in a body of matter.

tendon Fibrous connective tissue connecting a muscle to a bone.

tendril A modified leaf used by some plants to climb around a fixed structure.

terminal bud Embryonic tissue at the tip of a shoot, made up of developing leaves and a compact series of nodes and internodes.

terminator A special sequence of nucleotides in DNA that marks the end of a gene. It signals RNA polymerase to release the newly made RNA molecule and then to depart from the gene.

territory An area that one or more individuals defend and from which other members of the same species are usually excluded.

tertiary consumer (ter´-shē-ār-ē) An organism that eats secondary consumers.

tertiary structure (ter´-shē-ār-ē) The third level of protein structure; the overall three-dimensional shape of a polypeptide due to interactions of the R groups of the amino acids making up the chain.

testcross The mating between an individual of unknown genotype for a particular character and an individual that is homozygous recessive for that same character. The testcross can be used to determine the unknown genotype (homozygous dominant versus heterozygous).

testicle A testis and scrotum together.

testis (plural, **testes**) The male gonad in an animal. The testis produces sperm and, in many species, reproductive hormones.

testosterone (tes-tos´-tuh-rōn) An androgen hormone that stimulates an embryo to develop into a male and promotes male body features.

tetrapod A vertebrate with two pairs of limbs. Tetrapods include mammals, amphibians, and birds and other reptiles.

thalamus (thal´-uh-mus) An integrating and relay center of the vertebrate forebrain; sorts and relays selected information to specific areas in the cerebral cortex.

theory A widely accepted explanatory idea that is broader in scope than a hypothesis, generates new hypotheses, and is supported by a large body of evidence.

therapeutic cloning The cloning of human cells by nuclear transplantation for therapeutic purposes, such as the generation of embryonic stem cells. *See also* nuclear transplantation; reproductive cloning.

thermal energy Kinetic energy due to the random motion of atoms and molecules; energy in its most random form.

thermodynamics The study of energy transformation that occurs in a collection of matter. *See also* first law of thermodynamics; second law of thermodynamics.

thermoreceptor A sensory receptor that detects heat or cold.

thermoregulation The homeostatic maintenance of an organism's internal body temperature within a range that allows cells to function efficiently.

thick filament The thicker of the two protein filaments in muscle fibers, consisting of staggered arrays of myosin molecules.

thigmotropism (thig´-mō-trō´-pizm) A plant's directional growth movement in response to touch.

thin filament The thinner of the two protein filaments in muscle fibers, consisting of two strands of actin and two strands of regulatory protein coiled around each other.

three-domain system A system of taxonomic classification based on three basic groups: Bacteria, Archaea, and Eukarya.

thylakoid (thī´-luh-koyd) A flattened membranous sac inside a chloroplast. Thylakoid membranes contain chlorophyll and the molecular complexes of the light reactions of photosynthesis. A stack of thylakoids is called a granum.

thymine (T) (thī´-min) A single-ring nitrogenous base found in DNA.

thymus gland (thī´-mus) An endocrine gland in the neck region of mammals that is active in establishing the immune system; secretes several hormones that promote the development and differentiation of T cells.

thyroid gland (thī´-royd) An endocrine gland located in the neck that secretes thyroxine (T_4), triiodothyronine (T_3), and calcitonin.

thyroid-stimulating hormone (TSH) (thī´-royd) A protein hormone secreted by the anterior pituitary that stimulates the thyroid gland to secrete its hormones.

thyroxine (T₄) (thī-rok´-sin) An amine hormone secreted by the thyroid that stimulates metabolism in virtually all body tissues. Each molecule of this hormone contains four atoms of iodine.

tissue An integrated group of cells with a common function, structure, or both.

tonicity The ability of a solution surrounding a cell to cause that cell to gain or lose water.

topsoil The uppermost soil layer, consisting of a mixture of particles derived from rock, living organisms, and humus.

trace element An element that is essential for life but required in extremely minute amounts.

trachea (trā´-kē-uh) (plural, **tracheae**) The windpipe; the portion of the respiratory tube that passes from the larynx to the two bronchi.

tracheal system A system of branched, air-filled tubes in insects that extends throughout the body and carries oxygen directly to cells.

tracheid (trā´-kē-id) A tapered, porous, water-conducting and supportive cell in plants. Chains of tracheids or vessel elements make up the water-conducting, supportive tubes in xylem.

trade winds The movement of air in the tropics (those regions that lie between 23.5° north latitude and 23.5° south latitude).

trait A variant of a character found within a population, such as purple or white flowers in pea plants.

trans fat An unsaturated fat linked to health risks that is formed artificially during hydrogenation of vegetable oils.

transcription The synthesis of RNA on a DNA template.

transcription factor In the eukaryotic cell, a protein that functions in initiating or regulating transcription. Transcription factors bind to DNA or to other proteins that bind to DNA.

transduction (1) The transfer of bacterial genes from one bacterial cell to another by a phage. (2) *See* sensory transduction. (3) *See* signal transduction pathway.

transfer RNA (tRNA) A type of ribonucleic acid that functions as an interpreter in translation. Each tRNA molecule has a specific anticodon, picks up a specific amino acid, and conveys the amino acid to the appropriate codon on mRNA.

transformation The incorporation of new genes into a cell from DNA that the cell takes up from the surrounding environment.

transgenic organism An organism that contains genes from another species.

translation The synthesis of a polypeptide using the genetic information encoded in an mRNA molecule. There is a change of "language" from nucleotides to amino acids.

translocation (1) During protein synthesis, the movement of a tRNA molecule carrying a growing polypeptide chain from the A site to the P site on a ribosome. (The mRNA travels with it.) (2) A change in a chromosome resulting from a chromosomal fragment attaching to a nonhomologous chromosome; can occur as a result of an error in meiosis or from mutagenesis.

transmission electron microscope (TEM) A microscope that uses an electron beam to study the internal structure of thinly sectioned specimens.

transpiration The evaporative loss of water from a plant.

transport vesicle A small membranous sac in a eukaryotic cell's cytoplasm carrying molecules produced by the cell. The vesicle buds from the endoplasmic reticulum or Golgi and eventually fuses with another organelle or the plasma membrane, releasing its contents.

transposable element A transposable genetic element, or "jumping gene"; a segment of DNA that can move from one site to another within a cell and serve as an agent of genetic change.

TRH (TSH-releasing hormone) A peptide hormone that triggers the release of TSH (thyroid-stimulating hormone), which in turn stimulates the thyroid gland.

trial-and-error learning Type of associative learning in which an animal learns to associate one of its own behaviors with a positive or negative effect.

triiodothyronine (T₃) (trī-ī-ō-dō-thī´-rō-nīn) An amine hormone secreted by the thyroid gland that stimulates metabolism in virtually all body tissues. Each molecule of this hormone contains four atoms of iodine.

triplet code A set of three-nucleotide-long "words" that specify the amino acids for polypeptide chains. *See also* genetic code.

trisomy 21 A human genetic disorder resulting from the presence of an extra chromosome 21; characterized by heart and respiratory defects and varying degrees of mental retardation.

trophic structure The pattern of feeding relationships in a community.

trophoblast (trōf´-ō-blast) In mammalian development, the outer portion of a blastocyst. Cells of the trophoblast secrete enzymes that enable the blastocyst to implant in the endometrium of the mother's uterus.

tropical forest A terrestrial biome characterized by high levels of precipitation and warm temperatures year-round.

tropics Latitudes between 23.5° north and south.

tropism (trō´-pizm) A growth response that makes a plant grow toward or away from a stimulus.

true-breeding Referring to organisms for which sexual reproduction produces offspring with inherited traits identical to those of the parents. The organisms are homozygous for the characters under consideration.

tubal ligation A means of sterilization in which a segment of each of a woman's two oviducts (fallopian tubes) is removed. The ends of the tubes are then tied closed to prevent eggs from reaching the uterus (commonly referred to as having the "tubes tied").

tuber An enlargement at the end of a rhizome in which food is stored.

tumor An abnormal mass of rapidly growing cells that forms within otherwise normal tissue.

tumor-suppressor gene A gene whose product inhibits cell division, thereby preventing uncontrolled cell growth. A mutation that deactivates a tumor-suppressor gene may lead to cancer.

tundra A biome at the northernmost limits of plant growth and at high altitudes, characterized by dwarf woody shrubs, grasses, mosses, and lichens.

tunicate One of a group of invertebrate chordates, also known as sea squirts.

U

ultimate cause In animal behavior, the evolutionary reason for a behavior.

ultimate question In animal behavior, a question that addresses the evolutionary basis for behavior.

ultrasound imaging A technique for examining a fetus in the uterus. High-frequency sound waves echoing off the fetus are used to produce an image of the fetus.

uniform dispersion pattern A pattern in which the individuals of a population are evenly distributed over an area.

Unikonta One of four monophyletic supergroups proposed in a current hypothesis of the evolutionary history of eukaryotes. The other three supergroups are SAR (Stramenopila, Alveolata, and Rhizaria), Excavata, and Archaeplastida.

unsaturated fatty acid A fatty acid that has one or more double bonds between carbons in the hydrocarbon tail and thus lacks the maximum number of hydrogen atoms. Unsaturated fats and fatty acids do not solidify at room temperature.

uracil (U) (yū´-ruh-sil) A single-ring nitrogenous base found in RNA.

urea (yū-rē´-ah) A soluble form of nitrogenous waste excreted by mammals and most adult amphibians.

ureter (yū-rē´-ter or yū´-reh-ter) A duct that conveys urine from the kidney to the urinary bladder.

urethra (yū-rē´-thruh) A duct that conveys urine from the urinary bladder to the outside. In the male, the urethra also conveys semen out of the body during ejaculation.

uric acid (yū´-rik) An insoluble precipitate of nitrogenous waste excreted by land snails, insects, birds, and some reptiles.

urinary bladder The pouch where urine is stored prior to elimination.

urinary system The organ system that forms and excretes urine while regulating the amount of water and ions in the body fluids.

urine Concentrated filtrate produced by the kidneys and excreted by the bladder.

uterus (yū´-ter-us) In the reproductive system of a mammalian female, the organ where the development of young occurs; the womb.

V

vaccination (vak´-suh-nā´-shun) A procedure that presents the immune system with a harmless variant or derivative of a pathogen, thereby stimulating the adaptive immune system to mount a long-term defense against the pathogen.

vaccine (vak-sēn´) A harmless variant or derivative of a pathogen used to stimulate a host organism's immune system to mount a long-term adaptive response against the pathogen.

vacuole (vak´-ū-ōl) A membrane-enclosed sac that is part of the endomembrane system of a eukaryotic cell and has diverse functions in different kinds of cells.

vagina (vuh-jī´-nuh) Part of the female reproductive system between the uterus and the outside opening; the birth canal in mammals; also accommodates the male's penis and receives sperm during copulation.

vas deferens (vas def´-er-enz) (plural, **vasa deferentia**) Part of the male reproductive system that conveys sperm away from the testis; the sperm duct; in humans, the tube that conveys sperm between the epididymis and the common duct that leads to the urethra.

vascular bundle (vas´-kyū-ler) A strand of vascular tissues (both xylem and phloem) in a plant stem.

vascular cambium (vas´-kyū-ler kam´-bē-um) During secondary growth of a plant, the cylinder of meristematic cells, surrounding the xylem and pith, that produces secondary xylem and phloem.

vascular cylinder The central cylinder of vascular tissue in a plant root.

vascular plant A plant with xylem and phloem, including club mosses, ferns, gymnosperms, and angiosperms.

vascular tissue Plant tissue consisting of cells joined into tubes that transport water and nutrients throughout the plant body.

vascular tissue system A transport system formed by xylem and phloem throughout the plant. Xylem transports water and minerals, while phloem transports sugars and other organic nutrients.

vasectomy (vuh-sek´-tuh-mē) Surgical removal of a section of the two sperm ducts (vasa deferentia) to prevent sperm from reaching the urethra; a means of sterilization in males.

vector In molecular biology, a piece of DNA, usually a plasmid or a viral genome, that is used to move genes from one cell to another.

vein (1) In animals, a vessel that returns blood to the heart. (2) In plants, a vascular bundle in a leaf, composed of xylem and phloem.

ventilation The flow of air or water over a respiratory surface.

ventral Pertaining to the underside, or bottom, of a bilaterally symmetric animal.

ventricle (ven´-truh-kul) (1) A heart chamber that pumps blood out of the heart. (2) A space in the vertebrate brain filled with cerebrospinal fluid.

venule (ven´-yūl) A vessel that conveys blood between a capillary bed and a vein.

vertebra (ver´-tuh-bruh) (plural, **vertebrae**) One of a series of segmented skeletal units that enclose the nerve cord, making up the backbone of a vertebrate animal.

vertebral column Backbone, composed of a series of segmented units called vertebrae.

vertebrate (ver´-tuh-brāt) A chordate animal with a backbone, including lampreys, chondrichthyans, ray-finned fishes, lobe-finned fishes, amphibians, reptiles (including birds), and mammals.

vesicle (ves´-i-kul) A sac made of membrane in the cytoplasm of a eukaryotic cell.

vessel element A short, open-ended, water-conducting and supportive cell in plants. Chains of vessel elements or tracheids make up the water-conducting, supportive tubes in xylem.

vestigial structure A feature of an organism that is a historical remnant of a structure that served a function in the organism's ancestors.

villus (vil´-us) (plural, **villi**) (1) A finger-like projection of the inner surface of the small intestine. (2) A finger-like projection of the chorion of the mammalian placenta. Large numbers of villi increase the surface areas of these organs.

viroid (vī´-royd) A plant pathogen composed of molecules of naked, circular RNA several hundred nucleotides long.

virus A microscopic particle capable of infecting cells of living organisms and inserting its genetic material. Viruses are generally not considered to be alive because they do not display all of the characteristics associated with life.

visceral mass (vis´-uh-rul) One of the three main parts of a mollusc, containing most of the internal organs.

visual acuity The ability of the eyes to distinguish fine detail. Normal visual acuity in humans is usually reported as "20/20 vision."

vital capacity The maximum volume of air that a mammal can inhale and exhale with each breath.

vitamin An organic nutrient that an organism requires in small quantities. Many vitamins serve as coenzymes or parts of coenzymes.

vitreous humor (vit´-rē-us hyū´-mer) A jellylike substance filling the space behind the lens in the vertebrate eye; helps maintain the shape of the eye.

vocal cord A band of elastic tissue in the larynx. Air rushing past the tensed vocal cords makes them vibrate, producing sounds.

vulva The collective term for the external female genitalia.

W

water mold A fungus-like protist in the stramenopile clade of the SAR supergroup.

water vascular system In echinoderms, a radially arranged system of water-filled canals that branch into extensions called tube feet. The system provides movement and circulates water, facilitating gas exchange and waste disposal.

wavelength The distance between crests of adjacent waves, such as those of the electromagnetic spectrum.

westerlies Winds that blow from west to east.

wetland An ecosystem intermediate between an aquatic ecosystem and a terrestrial ecosystem, where soil is saturated with water permanently or periodically.

white blood cell See leukocyte.

white matter Regions within the central nervous system composed mainly of axons, with their whitish myelin sheaths.

whole-genome shotgun method A method for determining the DNA sequence of an entire genome. After a genome is cut into small fragments, each fragment is sequenced and then placed in the proper order.

wild-type trait The version of a character that most commonly occurs in nature.

wood Secondary xylem of a plant. See also heartwood; sapwood.

wood ray A column of parenchyma cells that radiates from the center of a log and transports water to its outer living tissues.

X

X chromosome inactivation In female mammals, the inactivation of one X chromosome in each somatic cell.

xylem (zī´-lum) The nonliving portion of a plant's vascular system that provides support and conveys xylem sap from the roots to the rest of the plant. Xylem is made up of vessel elements and/or tracheids, water-conducting cells. Primary xylem is derived from the procambium. Secondary xylem is derived from the vascular cambium in plants exhibiting secondary growth.

Y

yeast A single-celled fungus that inhabits liquid or moist habitats and reproduces asexually by simple cell division or by the pinching of small buds off a parent cell.

yellow bone marrow A tissue found within the central cavities of long bones, consisting mostly of stored fat.

yolk sac An extraembryonic membrane that develops from the endoderm. The yolk sac produces the embryo's first blood cells and germ cells and gives rise to the allantois.

Z

zoned reserve An extensive region of land that includes one or more areas that are undisturbed by humans. The undisturbed areas are surrounded by lands that have been altered by human activity.

zooplankton (zō´-ō-plank´-tun) Animals that drift in aquatic environments.

zygomycete (zī´-guh-mī-sēt) Member of a group of fungi characterized by a sturdy structure called a zygosporangium, in which meiosis produces haploid spores.

zygote (zī´-gōt) The diploid fertilized egg, which results from the union of a sperm cell nucleus and an egg cell nucleus.

Index

Page numbers with *f* indicate figure, *t* indicate table, and those in bold indicate page where listed as a key term.

Alligators, 3f, 397
Allopatric speciation, **282**, 286
α-actinin-3 protein, 616
Alpha animals, 716, 718
Alpha cells, 526f
Alpha-fetoprotein (AFP), 165
Alpha helix, protein, 45f
Alternation of generations, **336**, 343, **346f–347f**, 635
Alternative RNA splicing, 214–**215**
Altruism, 699, **717**
Alveolates, **332**–333
Alveoli, **459**
Alzheimer's disease, 21, 43, 248, **582**–583
Amazon rain forest, 354f
Ambulocetus, 259
American Cancer Society (ACS), 449
American pikas, 760–762
Amines, 35, 571
Amino acids, **44**. *See also* Polypeptides; Proteins
  abiotic synthesis of, 295
  adding of, to polypeptide chains during translation, 197
  in cellular respiration and biosynthesis, 102–103
  deficiencies of, 446
  essential, for animal and human diet, 443
  in food processing, 431
  genetic triplet code of codons for, 191–192
  in hormone signaling mechanisms, 519
  as neurotransmitters, 570–571
  proteins as polymers of, 36, 44
Amino group, **35**
Ammonia, 294–295, **509**, 754–755
Ammonifying bacteria, 655–656
Ammonites, 258
Ammonium, 754–755
Ammonium ions, 651, 655–656
Amnesia, 581
Amniocentesis, **164**
Amnion, 310, 397, 399, **554**–555
Amniotes, **390**, **397**, 399. *See also* Mammals; Reptiles
Amniotic eggs, **397**
Amniotic fluid, 463
Amoebas, **333**
Amoebic dysentery, 335
Amoebocytes, **370**
Amoeboid movement, 65
Amoebozoans, **335**
Amphetamines, 571, 577
Amphibians, **396**
  cardiovascular systems of, 469
  endangered species of, 763f
  endocrine disruptors and, 516–517, 520
  fungal diseases of, 356
  gas exchange by, 458
  prolactin in, 529
  waste disposal by, 509
Amplexus, 520
Amygdala, **581**
Amylase, 434
Amyloplasts, 622
Anabaena, 327
Anabolic steroids, **42**
Anabolism, 42
Anaerobes, 101
Anal cancer, 484
Analogies, **308**
Anaphase, **130**–131f, 140f
Anaphase I, 138f, 140f
Anaphase II, 139f
Anaphylactic shock, 501
Anatomy, **415**
Ancestral characters, 310–311
Anchorage dependence, **133**
Anchoring junctions, 68

Androgen insensitivity syndrome, 525
Androgens, **521**f, **525**, 539, 714
Anemia, 168, **480**
Angiosperms, **345**. *See also* Plant(s)
  in agriculture, 621
  annual, biennial, and perennial, and primary growth of, 630–631
  bodies of, 624–629
  flowers in life cycle of, 350–351
  fruits in seed dispersal by, 352
  as human food source, 352, 354
  monocots and eudicots of, 623
  pollination by animals in evolution of, 353
  reproduction of, 634–639. *See also* Plant reproduction
Angler fish, 687f
Animals. *See also* Invertebrates; Vertebrates
  adaptive radiations of, 286–287
  behavioral adaptations of. *See* Behavior
  birds, 8
  body plans of, 8, 368f–369. *See also* Animal bodies
  building phylogenetic trees for, 369
  cell cycle for, 130–132. *See also* Cell cycle; Cell division
  cells of, 56–57, 63–64, 67–69t. *See also* Eukaryotic cells
  cellular respiration by. *See* Cellular respiration
  characteristics of, 365
  circulatory systems of. *See* Circulatory systems
  cloning of, 208–209, 222–223
  as consumers in ecosystems, 5
  determinate growth of, 630
  discovery and naming of new species of, 408
  DNA profiling to determine origins of species of, 245
  effects of DDT on, 254, 263–265, 681
  effects of global climate change on, 768–769
  embryonic development of. *See* Animal embryonic development
  endocrine system of. *See* Endocrine system
  as eukaryotes, 7. *See also* Eukaryotes
  evolutionary diversification of, 367
  evolution of eyes among, 595. *See also* Vision
  external exchange and internal regulation in, 424–426
  fungal parasites of, 355, 361
  gas exchange mechanisms. *See* Gas exchange mechanisms
  genetically modified and transgenic, 230–231, 237, 239–240. *See also* Genetically modified organisms (GMOs); Transgenic organisms
  geographic distribution of, 301
  hibernating, 89
  homeotic genes and gene regulation in development of, 218
  hormonal regulation by. *See* Animal hormones; Hormonal regulation
  immune system of. *See* Immune system
  movement and locomotion as characteristic of, 604. *See also* Animal movement; Locomotion
  multiple functions of prolactin in, 529
  mutation rates of, 265
  nervous systems of. *See* Nervous systems
  nutrition for. *See* Animal nutrition
  organs and organ systems of, 419–423, 425, 426
  origin and macroevolution of, 297–299t
  osmoregulation by, 77, 508–513
  plant recruitment of predatory, 674
  pollination by, 351, 353, 635
  polysaccharides of, 39f
  prions as pathogens of, 203
  regeneration in, 221
  reproduction of. *See* Animal reproduction

  seed dispersal by, 352, 637
  senses of. *See* Senses
  sex determination of, 174–175
  sympatric speciation in, 284
  terrestrial, 689
  thermoregulation by, 504–507
  viral diseases of, 201
Animal bodies
  body plans for. *See* Body plans
  changes in, in macroevolution, 305
  circulatory systems of. *See* Circulatory systems
  elements in human, 18t
  embryonic development of. *See* Animal embryonic development
  energy requirements of, for diets, 442
  evolution of nervous systems and symmetry of, 573
  external exchange and internal regulation of, 424–426
  gas exchange in. *See* Gas exchange mechanisms
  hierarchical organization of, 415
  homeostatic regulation of, 425–426. *See also* Endocrine system; Hormonal regulation
  integumentary systems, 422–423
  organs and organ systems of, 419–423
  osmoregulation by, 508–513
  sexual dimorphism of, 271
  skeletal muscle of, 611–616
  skeletons of, 606–611
  somatic cells of, 136
  structure-function correlation in, 412–415
  thermoregulation by, 505–507
  tissues of, 414–418
Animal embryonic development. *See also* Animal reproduction; Human development
  cellular processes of embryo formation in, 552
  cleavage and blastula formation in, 548
  control of pattern formation in, by homeotic genes, 552–553
  fertilization and zygote formation as start of, 546–547
  gastrulation and embryo formation in, 549
  homeotic genes and gene regulation in, 218, 608–609
  organ formation in, 550–551
  vertebrate brains in, 576
  vertebrate embryonic development, laryngeal nerve, 414
Animal fats, 40–41
Animal hormones, **518**. *See also* Endocrine system; Hormonal regulation
  antagonistic, 526f
  DNA technology and therapeutic, 238
  endocrine disruptors as mimics of, 516–517, 520
  endocrine glands and, 521f
  evolution of multiple functions for prolactin, 529
  in hormonal regulation by endocrine and nervous systems, 518
  human behavior and, 719
  human female, 537
  human female reproductive cycles and, 542–543
  human male, 539
  oxytocin in social bonding, 530
  regulation of urinary system by, 513
  signaling mechanisms of water-soluble and lipid-soluble, 519
  similarity of plant hormones to, 660–661
Animalia kingdom, 7
Animal movement
  locomotion as, 604. *See also* Locomotion
  migratory. *See* Migration
  penguin huddling as thermoregulation, 504–505, 507
  as pump for open circulatory systems, 468
  and spatial learning, 706f

evolution of glycolysis in, 102
fermentation as anaerobic alternative to, 100–102
glycolysis and pyruvate synthesis in, 94–95f
human body energy needs and, 91
by mitochondria, 63–64, 69t
organic molecules as fuel for biosynthesis and, 102–103
photosynthesis and, 90, 110–111, 118
in plants, 644
pyruvate oxidation in, 96
redox reactions, electron transport chains, and, 92
stages of, 93–100
thermodynamics of, 80–81
Cellular slime molds, **335**
Cellulose, **39**, 57, 68, 118, 441
Cell walls, 55f, 57, **68–69**t, 321, 325, 628
Cenozoic era, 298–299t, 301f
Census of Marine Life, 408
Centers for Disease Control and Prevention (CDC), 517
Centipedes, **379**
Central canal, 574
Centralization, nervous system, 573–574
Central nervous system (CNS), **564**
evolution of, 573–574
peripheral nervous system (PNS) and, 564, 574
in sensory reception, 588–589, 600
in skeletal muscle contraction, 614–615
Central vacuole, **62**, 628
Centrifuge, 479
Centrioles, 65
Centromere, **128**
Centrosomes, 57, **65**, **131**
Cephalization, **573**
Cephalopods, **375**
Cereal grains, 637
Cerebellum, **577**
Cerebral cortex, **576–578**
Cerebral hemispheres, **577**
Cerebrospinal fluid, **574**
Cerebrum, 576–577t
Cervarix, 484–485, 496
Cervical cancer, 227, 484, 496, 532, 537, 544
Cervical vertebrae, 608
Cervix, **537**
Cetaceans, 259
Chaetae, 377
Chambered nautilus, 375
Champagne reefs, 29
Chance, natural selection and, 273
Channel proteins, 74f
Chaparral biomes, **692**
Chara, 342f, 343f
Characters, **154**. *See also* Phenotypes; Traits
alleles for, on homologous chromosomes, 157
chordate clades defined by derived, 390
constructing phylogenetic trees using shared, 310–311
effects of environment on, 170
as heritable features, 154
law of independent assortment on inheritance of two, 158–159
shared derived, 369
single, affected by multiple genes, 169
single genes affecting multiple phenotypic, 168
Chargaff, Erwin, 186
Chargaff's rules, 186
Charophytes, 337, 342
Chase, Martha, 182–183
Checkpoints, cell-cycle, 134–135
Cheddar Man, 245
Cheetahs, 683
Chelicerates, **378**–379
Chemical bonds, 3, **22–25**, 82

Chemical cycling, 5, **750**, 752–755
Chemical defenses
in animals, 742
in plants, 674, 742
Chemical digestion
in food processing, 431
in oral cavity, 434
in small intestines, 438–439
Chemical energy, 63–64, **80**, 111–115f, 118
Chemical fertilizers, 757
Chemical groups, 35
Chemical pesticides, 681
Chemical reactions, **25**
cell metabolism as exergonic and endergonic, 81–82
in cellular respiration, 92. *See also* Cellular respiration
chemical energy from, 80
life and, 16–17
making and breaking of chemical bonds by, 25
Chemicals
as abiotic factors affecting organisms, 682
abnormal behaviors caused by endocrine-disrupting, 714
bioremediation of toxic, 325
detection of, by chemoreceptors, 591, 599
as mutagens, 199
prokaryotic chemotrophs and, 323
soil pollution by, 653
synthetic, in agriculture, 669
Chemical signals. *See* Animal hormones; Hormonal regulation; Plant hormones
Chemical synapses, 569–571
Chemical work, cellular, 82. *See also* Work, cellular
Chemiosmosis, **93**
in cellular respiration, 93, 98–100
in light reactions of photosynthesis, 114–115f, 118
Chemistry
chemical bonds in, 22–25
elements, atoms, and compounds in, 18–21
elements in human body in, 18t
life and, 16–17
periodic table of elements in, 22t
water's properties in, 16–17, 26–29
Chemoautotrophs, 108, **323**
Chemoheterotrophs, **323**
Chemoreceptors, **591**, 599
Chemotherapy, 135
Chemotrophs, 323
Chernobyl nuclear reactor explosion, 21
Chest cavity, 458–459f
Chewing, 431, 434
Chiasmata, **142**–143
Chicken pox, 488
Chickens, 716
Chicxulub meteorite impact crater, 303
Chief cells, 436
Childbirth, 463, 522–523, 529, 558–559. *See also* Birth defects; Pregnancy
Chimpanzees, 247, 250, 304–305, 401f–402, 709, 718
China, 757
Chitin, **39**, **355**, 606
Chlamydia (STD), **544**
Chlamydias (bacteria), **327**
Chlamydomonas, 336
Chlorine, 120, 445
Chlorofluorocarbons (CFCs), 120
Chlorophyll, **109**, 112–115f
Chloroplasts, **64**
evolution of, by endosymbiosis, 64, 331
photosynthesis by, 57, 64, 69t, 90, 109, 114–115f, 118. *See also* Photosynthesis
in plant cells, 626, 628
Chloroquine, 254–255, 272

Choanocytes, **370**
Choanoflagellates, 337, 367, 370
Cholera, 324, 326
Cholesterol, **42**
in human health risks for cancer and cardiovascular disease, 449
in hypercholesterolemia, 162t, 166–167
receptor-mediated endocytosis and, 79
as steroid, 42
Chondrichthyans, **392**
Chordates, 369, 383–384, 390
Chorion, 397, 399, **555**
Chorionic villi, **555**
Chorionic villus sampling (CVS), 164f–**165**
Choroid, **596**
Chromatids. *See* Sister chromatids
Chromatin, **58**, **128**, 222–223
Chromosomal basis of inheritance
determination of sex by chromosomes in, 174–175
evolution of human males and Y chromosomes in, 177
explanation of G. Mendel's laws in, 170–171
inheritance of linked genes in, 172
linkage mapping of genes using crossover data in, 174
patterns of inheritance of sex-linked genes in, 176
production of new combinations of alleles by crossing over in, 172–173
sex-linked disorders of human males in, 177
Chromosomes, **55**, **126**. *See also* Gene(s)
alleles for characters on homologous, 157
alterations of number of, by nondisjunctions in meiosis, 144
in binary fission, 127
birth defects and cancer from alterations of structure of, 148
different versions of genes in homologous, 142
as DNA molecules of genes, 6
in Down syndrome, 146
in gene regulation, 212–213
inheritance of linked genes on, 172
karyotypes as photographic inventories of, 145
in meiosis. *See* Meiosis
mutations of, 264–265
in prokaryotic and eukaryotic cells, 55
sex. *See* Sex chromosomes
Chromosome theory of inheritance, **170–171**
Chronic bronchitis, 459
Chronic gastritis, 329
Chronic inflammation, 487
Chronic myelogenous leukemia (CML), 148
Chronic obstructive pulmonary diseases (COPD), 459
Chronic traumatic encephalopathy (CTE), **583**
Chronic wasting disease, 203
Chyme, **437**
Chymotrypsin, 438t–439
Chytrid fungi, 763
Chytrids, **356**
Cichlids, 284, 287–289
Cigarette smoking. *See* Smoking
Cilia, **66**
in hair cells, 590
microtubules and movement of, 65–67
protist, 330
in respiratory systems, 459
Ciliated epithelium, 416
Ciliates, **332**–333
Circadian rhythms, 521, **577**, **671–673**. *See also* Biological clocks
Circulatory systems, **374**, 420f, **468**
adaptations by, for thermoregulation, 506–507
arthropod, 378
earthworm, 376–377
evolution of vertebrate, 469

Crayfish, 379
C-reactive protein (CRP), 473
Creatine phosphate, 615
Creosote bushes, 639
Cretaceous mass extinction, 302–303
Creutzfeldt-Jakob disease, 203
Crick, Francis, 12, 186–187, 190
Cri du chat syndrome, 148
Cristae, **63**
Crocodiles, 311, 397
Crohn's disease, 500
Crop, digestive, **432**
Crops, agricultural. *See also* Agriculture
    angiosperms as, 352
    artificial selection of, 262
    first cultivation and domestication of, 620–622
    fungal parasites and pathogens of, 361
    genetically modified and transgenic, 230–231, 239–240, 654–655
    importance of plant diversity to, 354
    monocultures of, 639
    pesticide resistance and, 263
    phytoestrogens in, 660–661
    plant hormones and, 669
    polyploid speciation of, 285
    root crops, 625
    rotation of, 656
    threats to honeybees as pollinators of, 385
Cross-bridges, muscle contraction and, 613, 615–616
Crosses, genetic, **155**–159
Cross-fertilization, 155–159
Cross-fostering experiments, 702–703f
Crossing over, **142**
    bacterial DNA transfer in, 204–205
    genetic variation from, 142–143, 265
    linkage mapping of genes using data from, 174
    production of new combinations of alleles by, 172–173
Crust, 300
Crustaceans, **379**
C soil horizon, 652
Cuboidal epithelium, 416
Cubozoans, 371
Cultivation, plant, 620–622. *See also* Agriculture
Culture, science and, 10–11. *See also* Society
Cupula, 594
Currents
    freshwater, 688
    ocean, 685
Cuticle, nematode, **373**
Cuticle, plant, 342, **626**–627f
Cuttings, plant, 221, 639
Cuttlefish, 375, 712
Cuyahoga River fire, 678–679, 681
Cyanobacteria, 108, 323, **327**, 359, 756
Cycling, nutrient. *See* Chemical cycling
Cystic fibrosis, 162t–164, 239, 324
Cytochemistry, 66
Cytokinesis, **129**, 131f–132, 139f
Cytokinins, 664t, **666**
Cytoplasm, **55**, 194
Cytosine, 46–47, 184–**185**, 186–187, 191–192
Cytoskeletons, 50f–51f, 57, **65**–69
Cytosol, **55**, 57, 59, 60, 62, 68
Cytotoxic T cells, **497**–498

D

Darwin, Charles
    on elephant population growth, 726
    experiments of, on plant phototropism, 662–663
    mystery of speciation for, 278
    study of finches by, 286
    theory of, on evolution by natural selection, 8–9, 256–257, 262–263. *See also* Evolution; Natural selection
Darwin, Francis, 662–663
Data, types of scientific, 10
Dating
    by dendrochronology, 632–633f
    of evolutionary events by molecular clocks, 313
    radiometric, of plants, 622
    radiometric, of rocks and fossils, 298
Daughter cells, 126, 137, 140f
Daughter DNA strands, 189
Day length, plant flowering and, 672–673
Day-neutral plants, 672
DDT, 254–255, 263, 681, 695, 714, 765
Deadly nightshade, 738
Dead zone, Gulf of Mexico, 756
Deafness, 593
Death rates, 227, 724–729, 732–733
Decomposers, **744**
    in energy flow and chemical cycling, 5, 750, 753
    fungal, 7, 355, 356–357, 358–359
    prokaryotic, 324–325
    in trophic structures, 744–745f
Decomposition, **744**
Deductive reasoning, 10
Deep-sea hydrothermal vents, 295, 323, 682, 750
Deepwater Horizon oil spill, 324
Defecation, 441
Defensive cells, 490–491
Defensive proteins, 43
Defibrillators, 472
Deficiencies
    GMOs and human dietary, 239
    human dietary, 443–446
    human iodine, 19, 524
    human vitamin and mineral, 407, 598, 610
    plant nutrient, 651
Deforestation, 107, 354, 695, 757, 764
Dehydration
    diuretics and, 513
    plant terrestrial adaptations for preventing, 342
    skin and, 422
Dehydration reactions, **36**, 38, 40f
Dehydrogenase, 92
Deletions, chromosome, **148**
Delivery stage, childbirth, 558
Dementia, 583
Demographic transition, **732**–733
Denaturation, **43**
Dendrites, 418, **565**
Dendrochronology, 632–633f
Denitrifiers, 755
Density, cell division and cell, 133
Density, population, 724, 728–729
Density-dependent factors, population growth, **728**–729
Density-dependent inhibition, **133**
Density-independent factors, population growth, **728**–729
Dental plaque, 324
Deoxyribose, 46, 184–185
Dependent assortment, 158
Depression, psychological, 562–563, 571–572, 582
Depth perception, primate, 400f
Derived characters, 310–311, 369, 390
Dermal tissue system, **626**–627f, 631–632f
Dermis, 422
Descent with modification theory, C. Darwin's, 8–9, 257, 260, 273. *See also* Evolution
Desertification, **691**
Deserts, **691**
Design, experimental, 572
Desktop printing of transplant organs, 419
Detection, sensory receptor, 588–589
Determinate growth, **630**

Detoxification, 60, 63, 440
Detritivores, **744**
Detritus, **744**, 753
Deuterostomes, **368**f–369, 383
Development
    animal, 366, 524, 630. *See also* Animal embryonic development
    changes in, in macroevolution, 304–305
    human. *See* Human development
    plant embryonic, 636–638
    as property of life, 2
Development, sustainable, 777
Developmental biology, 218
Diabetes mellitus, 6, 38, 238, 500, **527**
Diadema antillarum, 747
Dialysis, kidney, **513**
Diaphragm (muscle), **458**–459f
Diaphragms, contraceptive, 545
Diarrhea, 441
Diastole, **471**
Diastolic blood pressure, 475
Diatomaceous earth, 332
Diatoms, **332**
Dicots, **623**
Dictyostelium, 335
Diet. *See also* Animal nutrition; Food; Human nutrition
    ecological cost of meat consumption in human, 752
    energy requirements of, for animals, 442
    essential nutrients as requirement for animal and human, 442–446
    evolution of vertebrate digestive systems as adaptations to, 441
    fats in human, 41
    human, and bone health, 610
    human, and cancer risk, 227
    human, and hypertension risk, 477
    human, and obesity, 428–429, 447–448
    human, and risk of cardiovascular disease and cancer, 449
Dietary fat, 38, 41
Dietary fiber, 39
Dietary health studies, 41
Differential interference contrast microscopy, 53
Differentiation, cell, **212**, 221
Differentiation zone, plant, 630–631
Diffusion, **75**
    in blood vessels, 474
    facilitated, across plasma membranes, 77
    gas exchange by, 454
    in osmoregulation, 508
    as passive transport across plasma membranes, 75
    in urinary system reabsorption, 511–512
Digestion, **431**
    in digestive systems, 420f, 424, 433–441. *See also* Human digestive system
    as food processing stage, 431
    fungal, 355
    lysosomes as cell compartments for, 62
    of polymers by hydrolysis, 36
    specialized compartments in animal, 432
Digestive systems, 420f, 424. *See also* Human digestive system
Digestive tracts, 373, 432
Digger wasps, 706f
Dihybrid crosses, **158**
Dilation, blood vessel, 506–507
Dilation stage, childbirth, 558
Dinoflagellates, **332**, 741
Dinosaurs
    in bird evolution, 259, 292–293, 398
    macroevolution of, 298–299t
    mass extinction of, 303–304
    in reptile evolution, 311, 397

Dioxin, 669, 714
Dipeptides, 44
Diphtheria, 200
Diploid cells, 137–140*f*, 272–273, 346*f*–347*f*
Direct inhibition hypothesis, 666
Directional selection, **270**
Disaccharides, **38**, 431
Discs, vertebral, 608
Diseases, animal
    endocrine disruptors and, 516–517, 520
    fungal, 356, 361
    prions and, 203
    viral, 201
Diseases, plant
    fungal, 357, 361
    nutrient deficiencies, 651
    plant defenses against, 674–675
    viral, 201, 230–231
    viroids and, 203
Diseases and disorders, human. *See also* Medicine
    from abnormal numbers of red blood cells in
        blood, 480
    from abnormal sex chromosome numbers, 147
    achondroplasia, 162*t*–163
    acid reflux, gastric ulcers, and digestive
        ailments, 437
    agricultural chemicals and, 669
    albinism, 162
    alkaptonuria, 190
    allergies, 501
    Alzheimer's disease, 248, 582–583
    amoebic dysentery, 335
    anabolic steroids and, 42
    appendicitis, 440
    atherosclerosis, 79, 166
    autism, 719
    autoimmune and immunodeficiency, 500–501
    autosomal dominant and recessive genetic,
        162–163
    bacterial pathogens and, 320–322, 326–329
    biofilms and, 324
    bipolar disorder, 582
    birth defects, 550–551, 555–556, 559
    bone injuries, 610
    brain injuries, 579, 583
    cancer. *See* Cancer
    cardiovascular disease. *See* Cardiovascular
        disease
    cholera, 324
    chronic gastritis and ulcers, 329
    cystic fibrosis (CF), 162*t*–163
    deafness, 593
    diabetes. *See* Diabetes mellitus
    dietary deficiencies, 443, 446
    DNA technology and, 236–238
    Down syndrome and trisomy 21, 146, 164–165
    drug-resistant microorganisms and, 254–255,
        272
    drugs for. *See* Drugs
    Duchenne muscular dystrophy, 177
    dwarfism, 238
    enzyme inhibitors and, 85
    epidemiology and, 448
    flatworm parasites and, 372
    fungal, 361
    gallstones, 438
    genetically modified and transgenic organisms
        and, 239–240
    genetic testing for, 164–165
    hemophilia, 177, 481
    high-fructose corn syrup and, 38
    human papillomavirus (HPV). *See* Human
        papillomavirus (HPV)
    Huntington's disease, 162*t*–164, 246
    hypercholesterolemia, 162*t*, 166–167
    inflammation and, 487
    iodine deficiencies, 19

kidney dialysis and kidney, 513
lactose intolerance, 32–33, 36, 47, 438
malaria, 168, 254–255, 263, 273, 333, 681
meningitis, 574
methicillin-resistant *Staphylococcus aureus*
    (MRSA), 272
misfolded proteins and, 43
motion sickness, 594
multiple sclerosis (MS), 565
mutations and, 199
neurological, 582–583
obesity, 428–429, 447–448
ozone layer depletion and, 120
Parkinson's disease, 248, 571, 577, 583
phenylketonuria (PKU), 162*t*, 165, 267
plague, 681
pituitary, 523
polycystic kidney disease, 67
potential of gene therapy for, 241
primary ciliary dyskinesia (PCD), 67
prions and, 203
protist pathogens and, 334–335
psychological, 562–563, 571–572
reproductive technologies and, 559
retinitis pigmentosa, 269
roundworm parasites and, 373
schizophrenia, 571, 582
severe combined immunodeficiency disease
    (SCID), 241
sex-linked, 177
sexually transmitted. *See* Sexually transmitted
    diseases (STDs)
sickle-cell disease, 162*t*, 164, 168, 199, 273
skurvy, 444
sleeping sickness, 335
smallpox, 238
stem cells and potential cures for blood cell,
    481
Tay-Sachs disease and lysosomal storage, 62,
    162*t*, 164
therapeutic cloning and, 223
thyroid, 524
typhus, 681
using RFLPs to detect genes for, 246
viral, 200–202
of vision, 596–598
Dispersal, seed, 343, 352, 637
Dispersion patterns, **724**–725
Disruptive selection, **270**
Distal tubules, **511**–512
Distance vision, 596*f*–597
Distribution function, eukaryotic cell, 61, 69
Disturbances, 689, **748**
Disulfide bridges, 45*f*
Diuresis and diuretics, 513
Diversification, crop, 354
Diversity, molecular, 34
Dizygotic twins, 548
DNA (deoxyribonucleic acid), **46**, **185**. *See also*
    Chromosomes; DNA sequences; DNA
    technology; Gene(s)
    animal behavior and, 702
    animal phylogenetic trees based on, 369
    bacterial transfer of, 204–205
    classification based on, 308–309
    discovery of double helix structure of, 186–187
    evidence for evolution in, 259–261
    experiments determining, as genetic material,
        182–183
    in gene expression, 190–199. *See also* Gene
        expression
    of *Homo* species, 405–406
    human behavior and, 719
    methylation of, 212–213, 222–223
    in mitochondria and chloroplasts, 63–64
    as molecule of inheritance, 3
    as nucleic acid, 46

as nucleotide polymer, 184–185
packing of, 212
phylogenetic species concept and, 279
phylogenetic trees based on, 312–314
as polymer of nucleotides, 36
in prokaryotic and eukaryotic cells, 4, 55, 58
proofreading of, 189
radiation and damage to, 21
replication of, 188–189, 224
sorting, by size using gel electrophoresis in
    DNA profiling, 243
triplet genetic code of, for amino acid
    sequences, 191–192
unity of life based on, 6
using restriction enzymes to cut and paste, in
    gene cloning, 234*f*
viral, 200–202. *See also* Viruses
DNA ligase, **189**, **232**–233*f*, 234*f*
DNA methylation, 212–213, 222–223
DNA microarrays, **219**
DNA polymerases, **189**
DNA probes, 236
DNA profiling, **242**–246
DNA replication, 128–136, 188–189, 224. *See also*
    Cell cycle
DNA sequences. *See also* DNA (deoxyribonucleic
    acid)
    amplifying, using PCR in DNA profiling,
        242–243
    of complete genomes, 6. *See also* Genomes;
        Genomics
    detecting differences in, using RFLPs in DNA
        profiling, 246
DNA technology, **232**
    DNA profiling, 242–246
    DNA transfer methods in, using bacteria,
        204–205
    gene cloning, 232–236
    gene therapy, 241
    genetic engineering and genetically modified
        organisms (GMOs), 230–231, 236–241
    genetic testing to predict athletic ability,
        602–603, 616
    genomics, 247–250
    proteomics, 249
    triplet genetic code in, 192
Dodd, Diane, 283
Dodder, 657
Dogs, 158–159, 527, 604*f*, 708
Doldrums, **684**
Dolly (cloned sheep), 222
Domains (taxonomic), 6–7, **309**, 325
Domestication, plant, 354, 620–622. *See also*
    Agriculture
Dominance hierarchies, **716**, 718
Dominant alleles, **156**, 166–167, 266–267
Dominant inherited human disorders, 162*t*–163
Dopamine, 571, 582–583
Dormancy, prokaryotic, 322
Dormancy, seed, 636, 638, 667
Dorsal, hollow nerve cords, **384**
Dorsal surfaces, 368*f*
Dorsal-ventral axis, 553
Dorudon, 259
Double-blind studies, 572
Double bonds, 23*f*, 34, 40
Double circulation, 469–470*f*
Double fertilization, 350–351, **635**
Double helix, DNA, 6, **46**–47, 184–185, **186**–187
Down, John Langdon, 146
Down syndrome, **146**, 164–165
Dragons, bearded, 397
Dramamine, 594
Dreaming, 580
Drip irrigation, 653
Drosophila melanogaster (fruit flies). *See* Fruit flies
Drought, 667–668

Energy, **80**
  in active transport of solutes across plasma
      membranes, 78–79
  algae as renewable source of, 334
  of cellular respiration. *See* Cellular respiration
  in cellular work, 80–82
  detection of mechanical, by mechanoreceptors,
      590–591*f*
  in ecosystems. *See* Energy flow
  eukaryotic cell processing of, 56–57, 63–64, 69
  fats as lipids for storing, 40
  processing of, as property of life, 2
  prokaryotic sources of, 323
  requirements of, for animal diets, 442
  sources of, as abiotic factor affecting organisms,
      682
  stimuli as, 588–589
Energy barriers, enzymatic lowering of, 83. *See
      also* Catalysis, enzymatic; Enzymes
Energy budgets, 750–751
Energy coupling, **81**
Energy flow, 5, **750**–752
Enhancers, **214**
Enteric division, autonomic nervous system, **575**
Entropy, **80**–81
Environmental issues
  acid precipitation, 755
  amphibian population decline, 396
  carcinogens, 227
  chemical pollutants causing abnormal animal
      behaviors, 714
  ecological footprints and resource
      consumption, 734–735
  global climate change. *See* Global climate
      change
  insights of ecology into human activities and,
      678–679, 681
  loss of biodiversity. *See* Biodiversity
  of marine biomes, 687
  mass extinctions of species, 303
  ocean acidification, 16, 28–29
  ozone layer depletion, 120
  pollution. *See* Pollution
  remediation of oil spills, 358
  safety of genetically modified organisms, 240
  sustainable resource management, 731
  of terrestrial biomes, 689
Environmental Protection Agency (EPA), 714
Environments. *See also* Aquatic biomes; Biomes;
      Biosphere; Terrestrial biomes
  allergies as hypersensitive reactions to antigens
      in, 501
  animal adaptations for exchange with, 424–425
  animal behavior and, 702–703
  animal homeostatic regulation of internal,
      425–426
  ecology as study of interactions of organisms
      with, 680. *See also* Ecology
  effects of, on human characters, 170
  extreme, of archaea, 326
  gills as adaptation for gas exchange in aquatic,
      455–456*f*
  human behavior and, 719
  lungs as adaptation for gas exchange in
      terrestrial, 455–456*f*
  natural selection and, 273
  prokaryotic adaptability to changes in, 322
  prokaryotic gene regulation in response to,
      210–211
  response to, as property of life, 2. *See also*
      Animal responses; Plant responses
  sex determination by, 175
Enzymes, **36**, **83**
  in catalysis of chemical reactions, 83–85
  in cellular respiration and biosynthesis,
      102–103
  cutting and pasting DNA using restriction, 234*f*

digestive, 433, 436–439
in DNA replication, 189
in fluid mosaic model, 74*f*
in formation of self-replicating RNA, 296
in gene regulation, 210–211
lysosomal, 62
as macromolecules, 36
one gene–one enzyme hypothesis and, 190
as proteins, 43
pseudogenes and, 261
ribosomes and synthesis of, 59
R plasmids, antibiotic resistance, and, 205
rubisco as, in Calvin cycle, 116, 118
smooth ER and detoxifying, 60
tRNA and, in transcription, 195
Eosinophils, 479
Ephedra, 738
Epidemics, 180–181, 202
Epidemiological studies, 448
Epidemiology, 448
Epidermis, 422, **626**–627*f*
Epididymis, **538**
Epigenetic inheritance, 212–**213**
Epiglottis, 434–**435**
Epileptic seizures, 579
Epinephrine (adrenaline), 472, 501, 518, **521***f*,
      528–529, 571
Epiphytes, 657
Epithelial tissue, **416**–417, 419, 422, 425
Epitopes, antigen, 491
EPO (erythropoietin), 237, **480**
Epstein-Barr virus, 498
Equations, photosynthesis and cellular
      respiration, 110
Equatorial tropical forests, 690
Equilibrium
  diffusion and, 75
  punctuated, 289
Equilibrium, Hardy-Weinberg, 266–267
Equilibrium receptors, 594
Equus genus, 307
Erectile dysfunction, 539, 559, 571
Erection, penile, 539, 559, 571
Ergots, 361
Erosion, soil, 653, 757
Erythrocytes (red blood cells), 76, 78, 216, 417,
      474, **479**–480. *See also* Sickle-cell disease
Erythropoietin (EPO), 237, **480**
Escherichia coli, 127, 182–183, 210–211, 232,
      236–237*t*, 247, 321, 326–327, 441
Esophagus, **432**, 434–435
Essential amino acids, **443**
Essential elements, human, 18
Essential elements, plant, **650**–651
Essential fatty acids, **443**
Essential minerals, 445*t*
Essential nutrients, 442–**443**, 444–445
Essential vitamins, 444*t*–445
Estradiol, 35*f*
Estrogens, **521***f*, **525**, 536, 542–543, 555, 558, 610,
      660–661
Estuaries, **687**
Ethanol, 101
Ethical issues
  regarding gene therapies, 241
  regarding genetic testing technologies, 165
  regarding genetically modified organisms,
      230–231, 240
  regarding human cloning, 223
  regarding human studies on genetically
      modified organisms, 239
  regarding synthetic chemicals in agriculture, 669
  regarding therapeutic cloning, 223
Ethyl alcohol, 101
Ethylene, 664*t*, **668**–669
Eudicots, **623**, 626–627*f*, 636, 638
Eukarya domain, **7**, 314, 325*t*. *See also* Eukaryotes

Eukaryotes. *See also* Animal(s); Fungi; Plant(s);
      Protists
  alternative RNA splicing in, 214–215
  cells of. *See* Eukaryotic cells
  differences between bacteria, archaea, and, 325*t*
  Eukarya domain of, 7, 314, 325
  evolution of multicellularity in, 337
  multiple gene regulation mechanisms in, 217*f*
  origin and macroevolution of, 297–299*t*
  protein regulation of transcription in, 214
Eukaryotic cells, **4**, **55**. *See also* Cell(s)
  animal, 56*f*, 63–64, 67–69*t*
  cell cycle of, 128–136. *See also* Cell cycle
  chloroplasts in, 64
  cytoskeletons and cell surfaces of, 65–69
  endomembrane system of, 59–63
  endosymbiosis in evolution of, 64
  energy processing of, 80–82
  enzyme functions of, 83–85
  functional groups of structures of, 56–57, 69
  mitochondria in, 63–64
  nuclei of, 58
  plant, 57*f*, 64, 68–69*t*
  plasma membranes of, 74*f*–79
  prokaryotic cells vs., 4, 55, 128
  regulation of gene expression in, 217*f*
  ribosomes of, 59
Eumetazoans, **369**, 370–371
Eustachian tube, **592**–593
Eusthenopteron, 394
Eutherians, **399**
Eutrophication, 756
Evaporation, 506, 695
Evaporative cooling, **26**, 507
Everolimus, 136
Evo-devo (evolutionary-developmental biology),
      304
Evolution, **8**, **257**. *See also* Evolution Connection
      modules
  adaptations of, as property of life, 2. *See also*
      Adaptations
  of altruism from inclusive fitness and kin
      selection, 717
  of animal nervous systems and body symmetry,
      573
  of animals, 367
  of carbon fixation methods in plants, 117
  of cell-signaling systems, 220–221
  as core theme of biology, 2, 6–9
  of drug resistance and pesticide resistance,
      254–255, 272
  in everyday life, 12
  of eyes among animals, 595
  factors of, in human obesity, 447
  fossils as evidence for, 258–259
  gene regulation of homeotic genes in arthropod
      body-plan, 382
  genomes as clues to human, 250
  genomics and study of, 247
  of gills as adaptation for gas exchange in
      aquatic environments, 455–456*f*
  of glycolysis, 102
  of homeotic genes as master control genes,
      552–553
  of hominins and humans, 403–407
  homologies as evidence for, 260–261
  of human lactose tolerance, 47
  imperfection in, 413–414
  in life histories of populations, 730–731
  limitations of natural selection in, 273
  of lungs as tetrapod terrestrial adaptation for
      gas exchange, 458
  macroevolution as history of life on Earth, 297.
      See also Macroevolution
  of mitochondria and chloroplasts by
      endosymbiosis, 64
  of multicellularity in eukaryotes, 337

Gastrovascular cavity, **371**, **432**, 468
Gastrula, 366, **549**
Gastrulation, 368*f*, **549**, 554
Gause, G. F., 741
Geese, 700–701, 704
Gel electrophoresis, **243**
Genbank, 248, 250
Gene(s), **6**, **46**. *See also* Chromosomes; DNA (deoxyribonucleic acid); Gene cloning
  alleles as alternative versions of, 156. *See also* Alleles
  in Alzheimer's disease, 583
  autosomal inherited human disorders from single, 162–163
  cancer and mutations of, 224–226
  control of embryonic pattern formation by homeotic, 552–553
  different versions of, in homologous chromosomes, 142
  DNA, RNA, protein synthesis, and, 46–47
  in evolution of mycorrhizae, 360
  expression of. *See* Gene expression
  in genetic history of crop domestication, 622
  in genome evolution, 312–313
  homologous, as evidence for evolution, 260–261
  human disorders of sex-linked, 177
  inheritance of linked, 172
  linkage mapping of, using crossover data, 174
  as G. Mendel's heritable factors, 154
  molecular clocks of, 313
  with multiple alleles, 167
  multiple phenotypic characters affected by single, 168
  mutations of, during protein synthesis, 199
  origin of first, 296
  patterns of inheritance of sex-linked, 176
  regulation of expression of. *See* Gene regulation
  role of developmental, in macroevolution, 305
  single characters affected by multiple, 169
  transfer of, using bacteria, 204–205
  tumor-suppressor, 225–226
  as units of inheritance, 6
Gene cloning, **232**
  cloned genes from, in genomic libraries, 235
  in pharmaceutical industry and medicine, 238
  recombinant plasmids in, 232–233
  using nucleic acid probes to identify cloned genes from, in genomic libraries, 236
  using restriction enzymes to cut and paste DNA in, 234*f*
  using reverse transcriptase to make genes for, 235
Gene expression, **210**
  flow of information from DNA to RNA to proteins in, 190, 198
  gene regulation of, 210–211. *See also* Gene regulation
  homeotic genes and, in animal development, 218
  messenger RNA in translation in, 196–197
  mutations in, 199
  phases of translation as protein synthesis in, 196–198
  ribosomal RNA in translation in, 196
  RNA splicing in, 194
  transcription as RNA synthesis in, 193*f*
  transfer RNA in translation in, 194–195
  triplet genetic code of codons for amino acid sequences in, 191–192
Gene flow, 267, **269**
Gene pools, **265**
Gene regulation, **210**. *See also* Gene expression
  alternative RNA splicing in, 214–215
  in animal development, 218
  in cancer, 224–227

changes in, in macroevolution, 305
chromosome structure and chemical modifications in, 212–213
cloning and, 208–209, 221–223
DNA microarray tests for gene transcriptions and, 219
in eukaryotes, 217*f*
evolution of cell-signaling systems for, 220–221
of homeotic genes in arthropod body-plan diversification, 382
of later stages of gene expression, 216
multiple mechanisms of eukaryotic, 217*f*
protein control of eukaryotic transcription in, 214
proteins and DNA in prokaryotic, 210–211
signal transduction pathways in, 220
small RNAs in, 215
Gene therapy, **241**
Genetically modified organisms (GMOs), 230–231, **239**. *See also* Transgenic organisms
  in agriculture, 230–231, 239–240, 654–655
  environmental safety and, 240
  health concerns about, 240
  labeling of in human food supply, 240
  in pharmaceutical industry and medicine, 237–238
  plants as, 639
Genetic code, 6, 191–**192**, 260
Genetic control function, eukaryotic cell, 56–58, 69
Genetic diversity, 639, 763. *See also* Genetic variation
Genetic drift, **268**–269
Genetic engineering, **232**. *See also* DNA technology; Gene cloning
  of crop plants and drugs, 12
  as DNA technology, 232
  of erythropoietin (EPO), 480
  gene therapy from, 241
  of genetically modified organisms (GMOs). *See* Genetically modified organisms (GMOs)
  genetic code in, 192
  of insulin, 6
  mass production of gene products with, 236–237
  in pharmaceutical industry and medicine, 238
  of transplant organs for humans, 419
Genetic markers, 242, 244, 246, 249
Genetic recombination, **143**
Genetics, **154**. *See also* Chromosomal basis of inheritance; DNA (deoxyribonucleic acid); Gene expression; Gene regulation; Gene(s); Genomics; Inheritance; Mendelian genetics
  ancient roots of, as study of hereditary inheritance, 154
  of animal behavior, 702
  cellular basis of. *See* Cell division
  of crop domestication, 622
  DNA technology in. *See* DNA technology; Genetic engineering
  in evolution of mycorrhizae, 360
  genetic diversity in, 763
  genetic testing in, 164–165, 602–603, 616
  of human behavior, 719
  of hypertension, 476
  molecular-based phylogenetic tree of animals in, 369
  molecular systematics in, 312–313
  of neurological disorders, 582–583
  of obesity, 447
Genetic variation. *See also* Genetic diversity
  from crossing over in meiosis, 142–143, 172–174
  from different versions of genes on homologous chromosomes, 142
  in microevolution of populations, 264–265

preservation of, by diploidy and balancing selection, 272–273
from random fertilization and independent orientation of chromosomes in meiosis, 141
Genital herpes, 532, **544**
Genital warts, 532, 544
Genomes, **6**
  clues to human evolution in, 250
  genomics and sequencing of, 6, 247, 249. *See also* Genomics
  Human Genome Project and composition of human, 248
  molecular systematics and evolution of, 312–313
  prokaryotic, 322, 325
  sequenced, 247*t*
  small RNAs in human, 215
Genomic libraries, **235**–236
Genomics, **247**
  clues to human evolution in, 250
  in genetic engineering, 12
  Human Genome Project in, 248
  proteomics and, 249
  sequencing and studying of genomes in, 6, 247, 249
Genotypes, **157**
  determining unknown, using testcrosses, 159
  human family pedigrees and, 161*f*
  phenotypes and, in gene expression of proteins, 190. *See also* Gene expression
  phenotypes vs., 157. *See also* Phenotypes
  in study of fast-twitch muscle fibers, 616
Genus (taxonomic), **308**–309
Geographic barriers, speciation and, 282–284
Geographic distribution of species, 301
Geologic record, **298**–299*t*
Geologic time, 297–299*t*
GERD (gastroesophageal reflux disease), 437
German measles, 555
Germination (germinate), 351, 356*f*, **634**, 638, 667
Gestation, 310, **554**–557*f*
Gestational diabetes, 527
Ghrelin, 328
Giant sequoia trees, 633*f*, 644
Giant squid, 375
Giant tortoises, 257
Giardia, 330, 334
Gibberellins, 664*t*, **666**–667, 669
Gibbons, 401*f*–402
Gigantism, 522
Gills, 378, 414, **455**–456*f*, 508
Gill slits, 392
Giraffes, 412–415
Gizzards, **432**
Glacier National Park, 774
Glaciers, 766
Glands, 421*f*, 433. *See also* Endocrine glands
Glans, **537**, 539
Glaucoma, 596
Glia, **565**
Global climate change, **119**
  as agent of natural selection, 769
  effects of, on biomes, ecosystems, communities, and populations, 768–769
  effects of, on photosynthesis and plants, 106–107, 119–120
  effects of, on terrestrial biomes, 689
  fossil fuels, carbon dioxide, and, 28
  fossil fuels and, 348
  human activities causing, 12, 767
  in mass extinctions, 302–303
  polar bears and, 27
  rapid warming and, 766
  as threat to biodiversity, 385, 760–761, 765–769
Global hectare (gha), 735
Global water cycle, 695

HMS *Beagle* sea voyage, 256–257
Hobbits (*Homo floresiensis*), 388–389, 406–407
Hodgkin's disease, 501
Hoekstra, Hopi, 11
Holdfast, 342
Homeoboxes, **553**
Homeostasis, **425**
  cardiovascular system in, 474
  endocrine system and, 421*f*
  hormonal regulation of. *See* Endocrine system;
    Hormonal regulation
  osmoregulation and, 508–513
  peripheral nervous system and, 575
  regulation of, 425–426
  thermoregulation and, 504–507
Homeotic genes, **218, 553**
  as animal master control genes, 218, 366
  arthropod, 382
  changes in, in macroevolution, 305
  control of embryonic pattern formation by,
    552–553
  in embryonic development of skeletons,
    608–609
  insect, 380
Home pregnancy tests, 496
Hominins, **403**
  australopiths, 404
  coexisting primate species in evolution of, 403
  hobbits as *Homo floresiensis* species of, 388–
    389, 406–407
  Homo species of, 405. *See also* Human(s)
  human skin colors as adaptations to sunlight,
    407
  origins in Africa and world-wide dispersement
    of *Homo sapiens* species of, 406
Homo erectus, 258, 403, 405–406
Homo floresiensis (hobbits), 388–389, 406–407
Homo habilis, 403, 405–406
Homologies, **260**–261, 388
Homologous chromosomes, **136**
  alleles for characters on, 157
  crossing over between, 142–143
  different versions of genes in, 142
  genetic variation from independent orientation
    of, 141
  independent orientation of, 265
  in meiosis, 136–137
Homologous genes, 260–261, 313
Homologous structures, **260**–261, 308–309
Homo sapiens (humans), 388–389, 403, 405–407.
    See also Human(s)
Homo species, 250, 403, 405–407
Homozygous genes, **156**
Homozygous traits, 161*f*
Honey, 37*f*
Honeybees, 385, 711
Hooke, Robert, 50–51
Hookworms, 373
Hopping, 604
Horizons, soil, 652
Horizontal gene transfer, **314**
Hormonal regulation
  of blood glucose levels by pancreas, 526*f*
  of development and metabolism by thyroid
    gland, 524
  diabetes as common disorder of, 527
  endocrine disruptors and, 516–517, 520
  endocrine system and nervous system in, 518,
    522–523. *See also* Endocrine system;
    Nervous systems
  of human female reproductive cycles, 542–543
  of labor in childbirth, 558
  multiple functions of single hormones in, 529
  promotions of social behaviors by oxytocin
    in, 530
  of responses to stress by adrenal glands,
    528–529

of sexual behavior and reproductive cycles by
    gonads, 525
  of urinary systems, 513
  water-soluble and lipid-soluble hormones in
    signaling mechanisms of, 519
Hormone cascade pathways, 523
Hormone-receptor complexes, 519
Hormones. *See* Animal hormones; Plant
    hormones
Hornworts, 344
Horses, 307
Horseshoe crabs, 378, 535
Hot spots, biodiversity, 772
Hoxc6 and *Hoxc8* genes, 609
Huddling, penguin, 504–505, 507
Human(s)
  ATP energy requirements of, 91. *See also*
    Cellular respiration
  basal metabolic rate for, 442
  bioengineering of transplant organs for, 419
  BPA exposure of, 517
  brown fat in, 88–89, 99
  cardiovascular system of. *See* Human
    cardiovascular system
  chordate features of, 384
  clues to evolution of, in genomes, 250
  communication signals of, 711
  cultivation and domestication of plants by,
    620–622
  developmental similarity of chimpanzees and,
    304–305
  development of. *See* Human development
  digestive system. *See* Human digestive system
  diseases and disorders of. *See* Diseases and
    disorders, human
  diversity of *Homo sapiens* species, 279*f*, 403
  ecosystem services as essential to well-being of,
    738–739, 757, 762, 777
  elements in bodies of, 18*t*. *See also* Animal
    bodies
  endocrine system of. *See* Endocrine system
  environmental impacts of, 12, 678–679, 681,
    687, 689, 764–767. *See also* Environmental
    issues; Global climate change
  ethical issues on cloning of, 223
  evolution of, 297, 388–389, 401*f*–407
  evolution of laryngeal nerves in, 414
  gas transport system of, 462–463
  genetic and environmental factors in behavior
    of, 719
  genome of, 6, 248–250
  hormonal regulation by. *See* Animal hormones;
    Hormonal regulation
  immune system of. *See* Immune system
  inherited genetic mutations of Tibetan,
    152–153
  invertebrate services to, 385
  life cycle of, 137*f*
  lymphatic system of, 478, 489–491
  microbiota communities and, 318–320
  molecular systematics and genomes of,
    312–313
  movement and locomotion by. *See* Animal
    movement; Locomotion
  nervous systems of. *See* Nervous systems
  nutrition for. *See* Human nutrition
  organs of, 419
  organ systems of, 420*f*–421*f*
  osmoregulation by urinary system of, 510–513
  pH of blood plasma of, 28
  plate tectonics as threat to, 302
  population of, 732–735
  practical uses of fungi by, 358–359
  promotion of social behaviors in, by oxytocin,
    527
  radioactive isotopes and, 21
  reproduction by. *See* Human reproduction

respiratory system. *See* Human respiratory
    system
  senses of. *See* Senses
  sex chromosomes and sex-linked genes of,
    174–177
  sixth mass extinction from activities of, 303
  skeletal muscle of, 611–616
  skeletons of, 607–611
  skin colors of, as adaptations to sunlight, 407
  small RNAs in genome of, 215
  soil conservation as essential to, 653
  thermoregulation by, 506–507
  tissues of, 416–418
  tracking traits of, through family pedigrees,
    161*f*, 177
Human cardiovascular system
  double circulation of pulmonary and systemic
    circuits of, 470*f*
  evolution of, 469
  gas transport by, 454, 462–463
  heart attacks in, 472–473
  heart contractions in, 471–472
  heart functions in, 466–469
  lymphatic system and, 489
  in regulation of breathing, 461
  structure and function of blood in, 479–481.
    See also Blood
  structure and function of blood vessels in,
    474–478. *See also* Blood vessels
Human chorionic gonadotropin (HCG), 496,
    543, **555**
Human development. *See also* Human
    reproduction
  childbirth in, 558–559
  pregnancy in, 554–557*f*
  reproductive technologies in, 558–559
Human digestive system. *See also* Human nutrition
  acid reflux, gastric ulcers, and ailments of, 437
  alimentary canal and accessory glands of, 433
  chemical digestion and nutrient absorption in
    small intestine of, 438–439
  Heimlich maneuver as response to choking
    in, 435
  mechanical and chemical digestion in oral
    cavity of, 434
  movement of food through esophagus to
    stomach by peristalsis after swallowing in,
    434–435
  processing and detoxification of intestinal
    blood by liver in, 440
  storage and breakdown of food in stomach of,
    436–437
  water reclamation and feces compaction by
    large intestine in, 440–441
Human evolution, 152–153, 177, 447
Human gas transport system, 454, 462–463. *See
    also* Human respiratory system
Human Genome Project, **248**–250
Human growth hormone, 238
Human nutrition. *See also* Diet; Food
  causes of dietary deficiencies in, 446
  dietary risk factors for cardiovascular disease
    and cancer in, 449
  digestive system in, 433–441. *See also* Human
    digestive system
  energy requirements of diets in, 442
  essential nutrients for, 443–446
  four stages of food processing in, 431
  genetically modified organisms as food and,
    239–240
  information on food labels for, 446
  nutritional modes and feeding mechanisms
    in, 430
  obesity, diets, and, 428–429, 447–448
  organic food for, 642–643, 654
  testing weight-loss claims of diets for, 448
  transgenic crops and, 654–655

Human papillomavirus (HPV), 484–485, 488, 496, 498, 532, 544
Human population
  age structures of, 733–734
  demographic transition of, 732–733
  ecological footprints of, as measures of resource consumption, 734–735
  in energy flow, 752
Human reproduction. *See also* Animal embryonic development; Animal reproduction
  cell division in, 126–127. *See also* Cell division
  childbirth in, 558–559
  contraception in, 545
  female reproductive system in, 536–537
  formation of sperm and eggs by meiosis in, 540–541
  hormonal regulation of female reproductive cycles in, 542–543
  male reproductive system in, 538–539
  population growth and, 732–734
  pregnancy in, 554–557*f*
  reproductive technologies in, 559
  sexually transmitted diseases (STDs) in, 532–533, 544–545
Human respiratory system
  automatic control of breathing in, 461
  as branching tubes conveying air to lungs, 458–459
  effects of cigarette smoking on, 452–453, 460, 463
  gas exchange by, 454
  gas transport system and, 462–463
  respiratory problems of, 459
  ventilation of lungs by negative pressure breathing in, 460–461
Hummingbirds, 280*f*
Humoral immune response, **490**–491, 497
Humpback whales, 259*f*, 430
Humulin, 238
Humus, **652**
Hunger, human deaths from, 654
Huntington's disease, 162*t*–**163**, 164, 246
Hybrid breakdown, 281*f*
Hybridization, 284–285, 287, 288–289
Hybrids, **155**, **279**, 281*f*, 288–289
Hybrid zones, **288**–289
Hydras, 371, 424, 432, 534, 573, 606
Hydrocarbons, **34**
Hydrochloric acid, 28, 436–437
Hydrogen
  in cellular respiration, 92
  molecules of, 23*f*
  in origin of life, 294–295
  water as compound of oxygen and, 18
Hydrogenated vegetable oils, 40–41, 449
Hydrogenation, 40–41
Hydrogen bonds, **24**–27, 39–41, 186–187
Hydrogen ions, 28
Hydrogen peroxide, 57, 63
Hydrolysis, **36**, 82
Hydrophilic molecules, **35**, 44*f*, 54
Hydrophobic molecules, **40**, 44*f*, 54
Hydroponic culture, 650
Hydrostatic skeletons, **606**
Hydrothermal vents, 295, 323, 682, 750
Hydroxide ions, 28
Hydroxyl group, **35**
Hypercholesterolemia, 162*t*, 166–167
Hyperglycemia, **527**
Hyperopia, 597
Hypertension, **476**–477
Hyperthyroidism, 524
Hypertonic cells, 508
Hypertonic solutions, **76**
Hyphae, **355**–356
Hypodermis, 422

Hypoglycemia, **527**
Hypothalamus, **521***f*, **522**–523, 525, 539, 542–543, 576–577, 580–581, 671
Hypotheses, **10**
  G. Mendel's, 156–157
  phylogenetic trees as, 311, 314
  in science, 10–11, 328–329
Hypothyroidism, 524
Hypotonic cells, 508
Hypotonic solutions, **76**
Hyracotherium, 307

I

Ibuprofen, 85, 487, 591
Ice, 27
Ice, polar, 694
Ichthyostega, 394–395
Identical twins, 548, 582, 719
Iguanas, 257
Imaging technologies, 580, 582
Imitation, social learning and, 708–709
Immigration, 724, 726
Immune system, **421***f*, **486**
  adaptive immunity in, 488–500. *See also* Adaptive immunity
  diabetes and, 527
  disorders of, 500–501
  functions of, 421*f*
  gene therapy for diseases of, 241
  immunoglobulins and leukocytes in, 479
  innate immunity in, 486–487
  innate vs. adaptive immunity in, 485
  stem cells in, 481
Immunodeficiency disorders, **500**–501
Immunofluorescence microscopy, 66
Immunoglobulins, 479
Imperfect fungi, **356**
Imperfection, evolution of, 413–414
Implants, penile, 559
Impotence, **559**
Imprinting, 703*t*, **704**–705
Inbreeding, 163
Incisors, 434
Inclusive fitness, **717**
Incomplete dominance, **166**–167
Incomplete metamorphosis, **380**
Incus, 592–593
Independent assortment, law of, **158**–160, 171
Independent orientation, chromosome, 141, 265
Indeterminate growth, **630**
India, 752
Indigo buntings, 707
Individual variation, 8–9, 262–265
Indoleacetic acid (IAA), 664. *See also* Auxins
Induced fit, **84**
Induction, **552**
Inductive reasoning, 10
Infant diarrhea, 239
Infants, passive immunity of, 488
Infections, 489, 499
Inferior vena cava, 470*f*
Infertility, 544, **559**
Inflammation, 85, 473, 476, 487–488, 494, 500
Inflammatory response, **487**, 529
Influenza viruses, 180–181, 202
Information processing, limbic system, 581
Ingestion, 7, **366**, 430–**431**
Ingredients, food, 446
Ingroups, **310**
Inhalation, 460–461
Inheritance
  artificial selection, natural selection, and, 262–263
  cell division and. *See* Cell division
  chromosomal basis of, 170–174

DNA as molecule of, 3, 6. *See also* Chromosomes; DNA (deoxyribonucleic acid); Gene(s)
  epigenetic, 212–213
  of genetic mutations by Tibetan people, 152–153
  genetics as study of, 154. *See also* Genetics
  of human disorders, 162–165, 177
  G. Mendel's laws on. *See* Mendelian genetics
  in microevolution of populations. *See* Microevolution
  obesity and, 447
Inhibiting hormones, **522**–523
Inhibition
  abscisic acid in, of plant processes, 667
  density-dependent, 133
  by enzymes, 85
  by nerve signals, 570
Initiation stage, transcription, 193*f*
Initiation stage, translation, 196–198, 216
Injuries
  bone, 610
  brain, 579, 583
Innate behaviors, **700**–701, 704
Innate immunity, **486**
  adaptive immunity vs., 485
  antigen-antibody complex in, 494–495*f*
  inflammatory response in, 487
  invertebrate and vertebrate, 486
Inner ear, **592**–594
Innocence Project, 245
Inorganic fertilizers, 651, 653
Inorganic nutrients, 644, 650–651, 682
Inquiry, scientific, 10. *See also* Science; Scientific Thinking modules
Insecticides, 654, 742
Insectivores, 744
Insects
  characteristics of, as most successful animals, 380–381
  compound eyes of, 595
  digestion of, by plants, 657
  diversity of, 364–365
  evolution of pesticide resistance in, 12, 254–255, 263
  fossils of, in amber, 258
  gas exchange by tracheal systems of, 455, 457
  limiting factors for population growth of, 728*f*–729
  nervous systems of, 573
  osmoregulation by, 508–509
  pollination by, 353, 635
  sex determination in, 175
Insoluble fiber, 39
Insulation, animal, 422, 506
Insulin, 6, 60, 216, 238, **521***f*, **526***f*–527
Integrated pest management (IPM), 731
Integration, **564**
Integrins, **67**
Integumentary systems, **420***f*, 422–423
Interaction theme, 5
Interbreeding, 279
Intercellular communication function, eukaryotic cell, 56–57, 69
Interferons, **486**
Intergovernmental Panel on Climate Change (IPCC), 766
Intermediate compounds, **94**–95*f*, 103
Intermediate filaments, **65**
Internal clocks, plant, 671–673. *See also* Biological clocks
Internal fertilization, **535**, 713
International Union for Conservation of Nature (IUCN), 763
Interneurons, **564**, 588–589*f*
Internodes, **624**

human brain in, 576–583. *See also* Brains, human

nerve signals and signal transmission in, 566–571. *See also* Nerve signals

neurons and functions of, 564–565

in regulation of breathing, 461

SSRIs in treatment of depression and physiology of human, 562–563, 571–572

vertebrate, as highly centralized, 574

vertebrate peripheral, 575

Nervous tissue, **418**

Nests, 311

Net primary production, 750–751

Networks, animal nervous tissue, 418

Neural plate and neural folds, 550

Neural tube defects, 165

Neural tubes, **550**–551, 576

Neurofibrillary tangles, 582

Neurological disorders, 582–583

Neurons, **418**, **564**. *See also* Nervous systems

communication of, at synapses, 569

as functional units of nervous systems, 565

in hormonal regulation, 518

nerve signals as charge differences across membranes of, 566

sensory receptors as specialized, 588–591

in skeletal muscle contraction, 614–615

Neuropeptides, 571

Neurophysiologists, 579

Neurosecretory cells, **518**

Neurospora crassa, 190

Neurosurgery, 579

Neurotransmitters, **569**, 572, 575, 582–583

as chemical signals, 569–571

in hormonal regulation, 518

serotonin as, 562–563, 571–572

Neutralization, humoral immune response, 494–495*f*

Neutral solutions, 28

Neutrons, **20**

Neutrophils, 479, **486**–487

Newborn screening, 165

Newborns, brown fat in human, 88–89

New England Journal of Medicine, 572

New World monkeys, 400*f*, 402

Niacin, 445

Nicotine, 62, 571, 738, 742

Night blindness, 598

Night-length, plant flowering and, 672

Nile perch, 288

Nirenberg, Marshall, 192

Nitrate ions, 651, 655

Nitric acid precipitation, 755

Nitric oxide, 571

Nitrifying bacteria, 655–656, 754–755

Nitrogen, 651, 653–656

Nitrogen cycle, 754–755

Nitrogen fixation, 327, **655**–656, **754**–755

Nitrogenous bases, 46–47, 184–187

Nitrogenous waste disposal, animal, 509. *See also* Urinary systems

Nitrogen oxides, 695, 755

Nitrogen pollution, 756

Nitrosomonas, 327

Nitrous oxide, 755, 766–767

Nobel Prizes, 78, 110, 120, 187, 215, 329, 437

Nodes, **624**

Nodes of Ranvier, **565**

Noncoding DNA, 194, 248

Noncompetitive inhibitors, **85**

Nondisjunctions, chromosome, **146**

Nongonococcol urethritis, 327

Non-native species, 749

Nonpolar covalent bonds, **23**

Non-protein-coding RNAs, 215

Nonself molecules, **497**

Nonsense mutations, **199**

Nonsteroid hormones, 519

Nonvascular plants, 344, 346*f*. *See also* Plant(s)

Norepinephrine (noradrenaline), **521***f*, **528**–529, 571, 575

Nori, 336

North American moles, 308

North American prairie, 692

North Star, migration by, 707

Norway rats, 702–703

Nostrils, 458

Notochords, **384**, **550**

Novel traits, macroevolution of, 306

N-P-K ratio, fertilizer, 651

Nuclear envelope, **58**

Nucleariids, 337

Nuclear transplantation, **222**–223

Nucleases, 438*t*–439

Nucleic acid probes, **236**

Nucleic acids, 46

DNA and RNA as, 46, 184–185

enzymatic digestion of, 438–439

in food processing, 431

as polymers of nucleotides, 46–47

in recent human evolution of lactose tolerance, 47

Nucleoid, **55**

Nucleolus, **58**

Nucleosomes, **212**

Nucleotides, **46**, **184**

DNA and RNA as polymers of, 184–185

in DNA structure, 6

in food processing, 431

molecular clocks and, 313

mutations and, 199

nucleic acids as polymers of, 36, 46–47

triplet genetic code of codons of, 191–192

Nucleotide substitution, insertion, and deletion mutations, 199

Nucleus, atomic, **20**

Nucleus, cell, **58**

as characteristic of eukaryotic cells, 4, 55, 56

DNA and RNA in, 46

as eukaryotic cell genetic control center, 58, 69*t*

Nurses' Health Study, 41

Nurture vs. nature issue, 719

Nuthatches, 709

Nutrient runoff, 756–757

Nutrients

as abiotic factors, 682, 688

chemical cycling of, in ecosystems, 5, 750, 752–755

degradation of aquatic ecosystems by inflow of, 756

Nutrients, animal

absorption of, 431, 439

essential, for animal and human diets, 442–446

in food chains and food webs, 744–745*f*

food labels for human, 446

Nutrients, plant

acquisition of, from air, water, and soil, 342–343*f*, 644

control of solute uptake of, by plasma membranes of root cells, 645

essential inorganic, in soil, 650. *See also* Soil

soil fertilizers to prevent deficiencies in, 651

from symbiotic relationships, 655–657

transport of sugars and, by phloem, 648–649

uptake of water and, in xylem vessels by transpiration, 646–647

Nutrition. *See* Animal nutrition; Human nutrition; Plant nutrition

Nutritional modes. *See also* Suspension feeders

animal, 366, 430

in Eukarya domain, 7

evolutionary adaptations of vertebrate digestive systems to, 441

fungal, 355

plant, 342–343*f*

prokaryotic, 323

protist, 330

Nutrition labels, 19*f*

O

Obesity, **447**

brown fat in adults and, 99*t*

dietary factors in, 428–429

evolutionary factors in, 447

Helicobacter pylori and, 328

high-fructose corn syrup and, 38

testing weight-loss claims of diets for, 448

Obesity epidemic, 38

Obligate anaerobes, 101

Observation

science and, 9, 41

social learning and, 708–709

Occipital lobe, cerebral cortex, 578

Ocean acidification, 16, **28**–29, 385

Ocean currents, **685**

Oceans

acidification of, 16, 28–29

rising temperature of, 766

search for new species in, 408

temperature moderation by, 26

Octopus, 374–375

Odor receptors, 599

Odors, 581, 708, 711, 715

Offspring, overproduction of, 8–9

Oil, 348. *See also* Fossil fuels

Oil glands, 422

Oil spills, 324–325, 358, 765

Okazaki fragments, 189

Old World monkeys, 400*f*, 402

Olfactory bulb, 581

Olfactory receptors, 599

Olfactory signals, 708, 711, 715

Omega-3 fatty acids, 239, 449

Ommatidia, 595

Omnivores, **430**, 441, 752

Oncogenes, **224**, 226

Oncologists, 136. *See also* Cancer

One gene–one enzyme hypothesis, 190

On the Origin of Species by Means of Natural Selection (book), 8, 256–257, 259, 264, 278

Oogenesis, **541**

Oparin, A. I., 295

Oparin–Haldane hypothesis, 295

Open circulatory systems, **376**–377, **468**

Open systems, organisms as, 424

Operation Migration, 705

Operators, **210**–211

Operculum, **393**

Operons, **210**–211

Opium poppies, 738

Opportunistic infections, **499**

Opposable thumbs, **400***f*

Optic nerves, 598

Optimal foraging theory, **710**

Oral cancer, 227

Oral cavity, **433**–434

Oral contraceptives, 545

Orange-crowned warblers, 741

Orangutans, 401*f*–402

Orbitals, electron, 22

Orchids, 657

Order, as property of life, 2

Orders (taxonomic), **309**

Organelles, 3, **56**

endomembrane system, 59–63, 69

functional groups of eukaryotic cell, 56–57, 69*t*

in life's hierarchy of organization, 3

lysosomal digestion of, 62

INDEX

regional climate and, 684–685
terrestrial biomes and, 689
Precipitation, humoral immune response,
494–495*f*
Predation, **740**
adaptations of prey species to, 742
associative learning and, 708
as biotic factor affecting organisms, 683
in boom-and-bust cycles of population growth,
729
camouflage coloration field study on, 11
foraging costs and, 710
in interspecific interactions, 740
in life histories, 730–731
as limiting factor for population growth, 728
natural selection and selective, 8–9
social learning and, 708–709
Predator species, 742
Predictions, scientific, 10–11
Pregnancy
aquaporins and fluid retention in, 73
contraception for preventing unwanted, 545
development of embryo and placenta in first
month of, 554–555
female reproductive system and, 537
fetal gas exchange with maternal blood during,
463
home pregnancy tests for, 496
trimesters of, 556*f*–557*f*
Prehensile tails, 400*f*
Premolars, 434
Pre-ovulatory phase, ovarian cycle, 542
Prepuce, **537**
Presbyopia, 597
Pressure, mechanoreceptors of, 590–591*f*
Pressure flow mechanism, **648**–649
Pressure waves, hearing and, 592–593
Prevailing winds, **685**
Prey size, 710
Prey species, 742
Prezygotic barriers, **280***f*–281*f*
Primary cell wall, 628–629*f*
Primary ciliary dyskinesia (PCD), 67
Primary cilium, 67
Primary consumers, **744**–745*f*, 752
Primary electron acceptors, 113, 114–115*f*
Primary growth, **630**–631
Primary immune response, **493**
Primary oocyte, 541
Primary phloem, 631
Primary production, **750**–751
Primary spermatocytes, 540
Primary structure, protein, 45*f*
Primary succession, **748**
Primary tissues, plant, 630
Primary xylem, 631
Primates, 400*f*–402, 408. *See also* Hominins;
Human(s)
Primers, **242**–243
Principles of Geology (book), 257
Printing of transplant organs, 419
Prions, 43, **203**
Probability, Mendelian genetics and rules of, 160
Probes, nucleic acid, 236
Problem solving, 703*t*, **709**
Processing, sensory receptor, 589
Producers, **744**
autotrophs as biosphere's, 108, 118
in energy flow and chemical cycling, 5,
750–753
plants as, 7
in trophic structure, 744–745*f*
Products, **25**
Professional journals, publication bias of, 572
Progesterone, 525, 542–543, 545, 555
Progestins, 521*f*, **525**
Programmed cell death, **552**

Projections, prokaryotic, 321
Prokaryotes
adaptability of, to environmental changes, 322
as anaerobes, 101
Archaea and Bacteria domains of, 7, 320, 325.
See also Archaea; Bacteria
biofilms as complex associations of protists,
fungi, and, 324
bioremediation using, 324–325
cells of. *See* Prokaryotic cells
diversity of, 320
diversity of bacteria as, 326–328
in endosymbiont theory, 64
eukaryotes vs., 325*t*
evolution of glycolysis in, 102
external features of, 320–321
extreme environments and habitats of archaea
as, 326
mutation rates of, 265
nutritional diversity of, 323
origin of, 297
pathogenic bacteria as, 328
regulation of gene expression in, 210–211
reproduction of, by binary fission, 127
in stomach microbiota affecting human health,
328–329
Prokaryotic cells, **4**, **55**, 128, 320–321
Prolactin (PRL), **522**–523, 529, 559
Prometaphase, **130**
Promiscuous mating, **713**
Promoters, **193**, **210**–211
Pronghorn antelope, 683
Propagation, vegetative, 638–639
Prophages, **200**
Prophase, **130**, 140*f*
Prophase I, 138*f*, 140*f*
Prophase II, 139*f*
Propionibacterium acnes, 423
Propylthiouracil, 599
Prospective studies, 41
Prostaglandins, 85, 558, 591
Prostate cancer, 227, 449, 538
Prostate gland, **538**
Protease inhibitors, 85
Protected areas, 771–772, 774–775
Protective coloration, 11, 381, 742. *See also*
Camouflage
Protein complexes, electron transport
chain, 98
Protein deficiencies, 446, 655
Proteins, **43**. *See also* Polypeptides
allergens as, 501
as amino acids linked by peptide bonds, 36, 44
antibodies as, 488. *See also* Antibodies
aquaporins as membrane, 72–73, 78
in cell movement, 65–67
in cellular respiration and biosynthesis,
102–103
contractile, 418
DNA and RNA in synthesis of, 6, 46–47
in energy coupling, 82
enzymatic digestion of, 438–439
enzymes as. *See* Enzymes
eukaryotic cell synthesis of, 58–61
in fast-twitch muscle fibers, 616
in food processing, 431
functional shape of, and structure of, 43–45*f*
gene regulation in activation and in breakdown
of, 216
growth factors as, 133–134
histones, 212–213
in hormone signaling mechanisms, 519
human dietary deficiencies of, 443, 446
in humoral immune response, 494–495*f*
in innate immunity, 486–487
mass producing, using recombinant DNA,
236–237

misfolded, 43
plasma, 479
plasma membranes as fluid mosaics of lipids
and, 74*f*
prions as infectious, 203
proteomics as study of sets of, 249
regulation of eukaryotic transcription
by, 214
self, 497, 500
signal transduction pathway interference by
faulty, in cancer, 226
in skeletal muscle, 612
structure, 45*f*
translation as synthesis of, in gene expression,
190–191, 194–198. *See also* Gene
expression
transport. *See* Transport proteins
transport of, across plasma membranes, 79
triplet genetic code for amino acid sequences
of, 191–192
Proteobacteria, **326**–327
Proteomics, **249**
Proterozoic eon, 297–299*t*
Protists, **330**
algae as renewable source of energy, 334
archaeplastids (Archaeplastida), 336
in biofilms, 324
diversity of, 330–331
endosymbiosis as key to diversity of, 327, 331,
336
as eukaryotes, 7
evolution of multicellularity in, 337
excavates (Excavata), 334–335
in human microbiota, 318–319
SAR supergroup of, 332–333
unikonts (Unikonta), 335
vacuoles of, 62
Protocells, 294–296
Protons, **20**
Proto-oncogenes, **224**, 226
Protostomes, **368***f*–369, 383
Protozoans, **330**
Proviruses, 203
Proximal-distal axis, 553
Proximal tubules, **511**–512
Proximate causes, **700**, 719
Proximate questions, **700**
Prozac, 572
Pseudogenes, 261
Pseudopodia, **333**
P site, **197**
Psychoactive drugs, 571
Psychological disorders, 562–563, 571–572,
582
Publication bias, 572
Public health science. *See also* Medicine
drug-resistant microorganisms as concern in,
272
Hardy-Weinberg equation in, 267
Puffballs, 357
Pulmocutaneous circuit, 469
Pulmonary arteries, **470***f*
Pulmonary circuit, **469**–470*f*
Pulmonary veins, **470***f*
Pulse, **475**
Pumps, active transport and, 78–79
Punctuated equilibrium, **289**
Pundamilia species, 287–289
Punnett, Reginald, 172
Punnett squares, 156*f*–**157**, 158*f*, 169, 172
Pupil, **595**–596
Purines, 185–186
Purple sulfur bacteria, 323
Pus, 487
Pyramid of production, 751–752
Pyrethrin, 742
Pyrimidines, 185–186

INDEX